D1179770

Ordered

DISCARDED

PRINCIPLES OF NEMATOLOGY

McGRAW-HILL PUBLICATIONS IN THE AGRICULTURAL SCIENCES

R. A. BRINK, *Consulting Editor*

ADRIANCE AND BRISON · Propagation of Horticultural Plants
AHLGREN · Forage Crops
ANDERSON · Diseases of Fruit Crops
BROWN AND WARE · Cotton
CARROLL AND KRIDER · Swine Production
CHRISTOPHER · Introductory Horticulture
CRUESS · Commercial Fruit and Vegetable Products
DICKSON · Diseases of Field Crops
ECKLES, COMBS, AND MACY · Milk and Milk Products
ELLIOTT · Plant Breeding and Cytogenetics
FERNALD AND SHEPARD · Applied Entomology
GARDNER, BRADFORD, AND HOOKER · The Fundamentals of Fruit Production
GUSTAFSON · Conservation of the Soil
GUSTAFSON · Soils and Soil Management
HAYES, IMMER, AND SMITH · Methods of Plant Breeding
HEALD · Manual of Plant Diseases
HEALD · Introduction to Plant Pathology
HERRINGTON · Milk and Milk Processing
HUTT · Genetics of the Fowl
JENNY · Factors of Soil Formation
JULL · Poultry Husbandry
KOHNKE AND BERTRAND · Soil Conservation
LAURIE AND RIES · Floriculture
LEACH · Insect Transmission of Plant Diseases
MAYNARD AND LOOSLI · Animal Nutrition
METCALF, FLINT, AND METCALF · Destructive and Useful Insects
NEVENS · Principles of Milk Production
PATERSON · Statistical Technique in Agricultural Research
PETERS AND GRUMMER · Livestock Production
RATHER AND HARRISON · Field Crops
RICE, ANDREWS, WARWICK, AND LEGATES · Breeding and Improvement of Farm Animals
ROADHOUSE AND HENDERSON · The Market-milk Industry
ROBBINS, CRAFTS, AND RAYNOR · Weed Control
STEINHAUS · Principles of Insect Pathology
THOMPSON · Soils and Soil Fertility
THOMPSON AND KELLY · Vegetable Crops
THORNE · Principles of Nematology
TRACY, ARMERDING, AND HANNAH · Dairy Plant Management
WALKER · Diseases of Vegetable Crops
WALKER · Plant Pathology
WILSON · Grain Crops
WOLFE AND KIPPS · Production of Field Crops

The late Leon J. Cole was Consulting Editor of this series from 1937 to 1948. There are also the related series of McGraw-Hill Publications in the Botanical Sciences, of which Edmund W. Sinnott is Consulting Editor, and in the Zoological Sciences, of which Edgar J. Boell is Consulting Editor. Titles in the Agricultural Sciences were published in these series in the period 1917 to 1937.

Nathan Augustus Cobb, 1859–1932

"We depend on the soil for our very existence, and it may seem that this fact should have caused us long ago to have made ourselves thoroughly acquainted with it and all its inhabitants. Yet the truth is otherwise. ⁻ . . . Relatively speaking, in a biological sense, this soil we daily tread under foot is almost a veritable *terra incognita.*" *Nematodes and Their Relationships,* Yearbook of the U.S. Department of Agriculture, 1914. (*Photograph courtesy of Freida Cobb Blanchard.*)

Principles of
NEMATOLOGY

GERALD THORNE

PROFESSOR OF PLANT PATHOLOGY AND ZOOLOGY
UNIVERSITY OF WISCONSIN
Formerly
SENIOR NEMATOLOGIST
DIVISION OF NEMATOLOGY
UNITED STATES DEPARTMENT OF AGRICULTURE

McGRAW-HILL BOOK COMPANY, INC.

New York   Toronto   London

1961

College of the Sequoias
Library

PRINCIPLES OF NEMATOLOGY

Copyright © 1961 by the McGraw-Hill Book Company, Inc. Printed in the United States of America. All rights reserved. This book, or parts thereof, may not be reproduced in any form without permission of the publishers. Library of Congress Catalog Card Number 60-53223

64527

To Zelda, my wife

Preface

This book has been designed as a text and guide for students and workers in nematology, plant pathology, zoology, agronomy, horticulture, soil science, and other branches of agriculture. Identification of ecto- and endoparasitic nematodes is emphasized by detailed descriptions of their morphology and symptoms of plant diseases incited by them. Pertinent available information on life history, hosts, distribution, and control of each species is presented. Descriptions and illustrations are included of about one hundred free-living species of nematodes which will most frequently be found associated with plant parasitic forms in soil and plant material.

Instructions for collecting specimens and preparing permanent microscopic slides are especially useful because each worker should assemble reference material from the geographical area in which he is working and keep it available for comparative purposes. Methods of recording and indexing specimens simplify the problem of locating each one in a minimum of time. Only by carefully studying and restudying the many species can one become proficient in identifying the closely related forms. Proper and efficient use of the microscope is stressed because identification work requires the most exacting adjustment of the highest powers.

Recommendations for control of plant parasitic species are based on the best practical information available, but in many instances our limited knowledge precludes specific instructions for crop rotations, nematicides, therapeutics, or resistant varieties. It is hoped that the many young nematologists now in the field will eventually solve at least part of the many baffling problems facing us.

The writer is indebted to the Nematology Division, U.S. Department of Agriculture, for the opportunity to work on nematological problems in many parts of the United States during the years 1918 to 1956. Mr. A. L. Taylor of that Division kindly loaned many illustrations from the works of Dr. N. A. Cobb and Dr. G. Steiner. Miss Edna M. Buhrer secured numerous references and notes necessary for completion of the manuscript. Mr. E. C. Jorgensen forwarded specimens from the Salt Lake City, Utah, collection from which morphological observations were completed.

Completion of this book was made possible through the cooperation of faculty members of the Department of Plant Pathology of the University of Wisconsin. Their generous aid and encouragement is gratefully acknowledged. Dr. H. M. Darling and Miss Ella Mae Noffsinger have contributed many suggestions on the manuscript and aided in proofreading. Mrs. Eleanor Elphick typed the text, and Mrs. Byrl Stelter the bibliography and figure legends.

Mrs. T. Goodey and Dr. J. B. Goodey graciously consented to the use of several illustrations from the works of Dr. T. Goodey. Dr. A. D. Baker of the Canadian Department of Agriculture cheerfully offered his preliminary check lists of species of Tylenchida, which were invaluable in organizing certain portions of the taxonomy.

Methuen and Company, E. J. Brill, Martinus Nijhoff, *The Journal of Parasitology,* Phytopathology, and the Helminthological Society of Washington generously approved reproducing many of the illustrations and portions of the descriptions.

Unfortunately, deletion of about 20 per cent of the original manuscript necessitated removal of considerable material contributed by R. C. Esser, H. J. Jensen, C. A. Loos, W. F. Mai, and other nematologists.

The writer assumes responsibility for all statements and for any errors which may be present.

Gerald Thorne

Contents

Abbreviations Used in the Illustrations

Ac, accessory
al, wing
amp, ampulla
amph, amphid
an, anus, anal
ann, annule
ant, anterior
ap, aperture
ar, area, field

Blb, bulb, bulbous
brs, bursa, bursal

Cav, cavity
cd, cdl, tail, caudal
ceph, cephalid
cerv, cervical
chrsm, chromosome
cir, cirrus, cirri
cl, cell, cellular
cntr, centrosome
col, collum, constriction
cop, copulatory
corp, body, thing, corpus
cph, cephalum, cephalic
crd, cardia, cardiac
crp, corpus, body, thing
cut, cuticle, cuticular

Dct, duct
deir, deirid
dir, deirid
div, division
dsc, disc, discoid
dsl, dorsal, dorsad
dxt, right, right-hand

Ex, excreta, excretory
exp, excretory pore
extr, exterior, outer

Fab, fb, framework
flx, flexure

Gl, gland, glandular
gnd, gonad
grn, granule, granular

Im, immature
inc, incisure
int, intestine, intestinal
intr, interior

Jnc, junction, junctional

Lat, lateral, laterad
lb, lip, labial
lp, labial papillae
lum, lumen

Maj, major, the larger
mb, vulvar membrane
md, middle, median
min, minor, the lesser
msc, muscle, muscular
mur, wall, mural

N, nerve
ncl, nucleus, nuclear
nr, nerve ring
nrv, nerve

Oe, esophagus, esophageal
oes, esophageal

xiii

on, onchium, tooth, spear

op, opening

or, mouth, oral

org?, organ in doubt, doubtful

os, ostium

ov, ovum, egg, ovary

ovr, ovary, ovarian

P, *por,* pore

pex, excretory pore

ph, pharnyx, pharyngeal

phas, phasmid

plr, polar

post, posterior

pp, ppl, papilla, papillate

prm, primary, first

Rct, rectum, rectal

red, reduction, reduced

rem, lost, discarded

ren, renette, ventral gland

res, resv, reservoir

rud, rudiment, rudimentary

Sal, saliva, salivary

secnd, second, secondary

set, seta, setaceous

snst, left, left-handed

som, soma, body, somatic

sp, spinneret, spear, spiculum, spicula

spm, sperm, spermatozoa

spmt, spermatocyte

spmtd, spermatid

spn, spinneret

sub, sub, nearly, almost

subm, submedian

Teg, shell, tegument

trm, end, blind end, terminal

tst, testes

Ut, uterus, uterine

Vag, vagina, vaginal

valv, valve, valvular

vlv, vulva

vnt, ventral, ventrad

Zy, zygote

Chapter 1

INTRODUCTION

Nematodes constitute one of the most important groups of organisms which inhabit the soil about the roots of plants and which frequently play a vital part in their growth and production. Rarely is any crop free from their attacks, whether in the field, the orchard, the home garden, or the greenhouse; yet we usually are unaware of their presence because of their microscopic size and protected position within the soil. These slender, active, wormlike creatures are found not only in the soil but also in fresh and salt water wherever organic matter exists, from the arctics to the tropics, and from the ocean depths to the tops of high mountains. So numerous are they that Cobb (1914a) remarked, ". . . if all the matter in the universe except the nematodes were swept away, our world would still be dimly recognizable . . . we would find its mountains, hills, valleys, rivers, lakes, and oceans represented by a film of nematodes."

Throughout the years these exceedingly interesting organisms have remained a little-known group in the biological complex, principally because of the technical difficulties encountered in isolating and preparing them for the detailed microscopic examination necessary in the process of identification. Not until the past three decades have they achieved even a small portion of the recognition they deserve among the problems confronting agriculture. Their relationship to the increased production demanded from our farms offers some of the most promising fields for research, because there is not a single problem in the field of nematology which has been adequately explored. This statement applies to agriculture throughout the world and especially to that of our own country, where farm acreage is rapidly diminishing through expansion of cities, industrial plants, highways, and other agencies.

Today (1961) nematology occupies just about the same position that entomology did in 1900 and plant pathology in 1920. If we are to make our proper contribution to the world food problem during the coming years, we must have as many trained nematologists as we have workers in entomology or plant pathology. Cooperating with plant breeders, they will develop higher-yielding and nematode resistant varieties of crop plants, while teamwork between chemists and nematologists will produce more efficient and less expensive nematicides. Engineers will develop more efficient machinery for the application of these nematicides, and farmers will learn that crop rotations, supplemented by soil fumigation, will produce higher yields than have ever been achieved previously.

Biochemists and nematologists must intensively explore the possibilities of systemic nematicides, which thus far have shown little promise. They must also cooperate in developing methods of synthetically producing plant diffusates which stimulate nematodes to emerge from their dormant stages.

All this work must be coordinated with studies on the host ranges of closely related species of certain groups like those found in *Meloidogyne, Heterodera,* and *Pratylenchus.* These must be accompanied by intensive studies in morphology, physiology, and life history. While engaged in this difficult but fascinating field, those trained in the skillful use of the microscope will find an almost never-ending challenge in the taxonomy of the many species encountered. The possibilities of biological controls by predators, sporozoan parasites, nemic-trapping fungi, and other natural enemies have scarcely been touched; yet they offer an almost endless array of interesting and worthwhile opportunities.

For convenience, we often anglicize the scientific names of many groups. Thus we have "tylenchs" for members of the Tylenchida, "rotylenchs" for *Rotylenchus,* "dorylaims" for Dorylaimoidea, "monochs" for Mononchidae, "cephalobs" for Cephalobidae, and similar names which are simpler to use. Common names have been suggested for many of the plant parasitic species, as will be noted when discussing them: sugar beet nematode, *Heterodera schachtii;* bulb or stem nematode, *Ditylenchus dipsaci;* pin nematodes, *Paratylenchus* spp.; ring nematodes, *Criconemoides* spp.; root lesion or meadow nematodes, *Pratylenchus* spp.; "burrowing" nematode, *Radopholus similis;* rice-root nematode, *Radopholus oryzae;* and many others.

HISTORICAL

Knowledge of animal parasitic nematodes probably is almost as ancient as the history of man.[1] Among the first zoological records are references to the dread Guinea worm, *Dracunculus medinensis,* which inhabits the human body, especially the arms and legs, and causes intense pain and inflammation. There are said to be Egyptian references to this and to the large roundworm, *Ascaris lumbricoides,* as early as 1553–1550 B.C. Some historians believe that the "fiery serpents" which attacked the Israelites, as recorded in Numbers 21: 6–9, were actually Guinea worms. Aristotle (384–322 B.C.) mentions animal parasitic nematodes as if they were well known at that time, and during the following centuries they were frequently recorded by various writers in medicine and zoology. Linnaeus

---

[1] A comprehensive history of nematology would require a large volume, and therefore this discussion is limited to only a few of the most important and interesting events which have led up to the present world-wide interest in the science. Generally only the achievements of nematologists engaged in the work prior to 1940 are reviewed. Unfortunately this excludes the numerous youthful workers who have entered the field in recent years.

(1758) recorded several genera under the group Vermes in his *Systema Natura*.

These animal parasitic forms are so large that they were easily seen by the ancients, but it was not until the nineteenth century that they were investigated extensively with the aid of microscopes. It was during this time that the particular branch of science under which they were studied became known as "helminthology."

Development of Nematology in Europe

We find that William Shakespeare unwittingly gave us what may be our first record of plant parasitic nematodes in 1594 when in *Love's Labour's Lost*, Act IV, Scene 3, he wrote the line, "Sowed cockle, reap'd no corn."

One hundred and forty-nine years after the Bard of Avon wrote these words, Turbevill Needham (1743), a Catholic clergyman, discovered the riddle of the "cockle" when he crushed one of the shrunken, blackened wheat grains, examined a portion of it under his primitive microscope, and described what he saw in these words:

> Upon opening lately the small black Grains of smutty Wheat, which they here distinguish from blighted Corn, the latter affording nothing but a black Dust, into which the whole Substance of the Ear is converted; I perceived a soft white fibrous Substance, a small Portion of which I placed upon my Object-plate: It seemed to consist wholly of longitudinal Fibres bundled together; and you will be surprised, perhaps, that I should say, without any least Sign of Life or Motion. I dropped a Globule of Water upon it, in order to try if the Parts, when separated, might be viewed more conveniently; when to my great Surprise these imaginary Fibres, as it were, separated from each other, took Life, moved irregularly, not with a progressive, but twisting Motion, and continued to do so for the Space of Nine or Ten Hours, when I threw them away. I am satisfied that they are a species of Aquatic Animals, and may be denominated Worms, Eels or Serpents, which they very much resemble.

Our first information on free-living nematodes dates from Borellus (1656), who first observed "Vinegar eels," which once were present in practically all vinegar. During the ensuing years, Power, Hooke, Leeuwenhoek, and other early microscopists also found this species, *Anguillula aceti, = Turbatrix aceti,* a most convenient subject for their adventures into the realm of microorganisms. The writer well remembers observing, as a boy, these vinegar eels in the family vinegar and learning that they imparted to it a very special and pleasing flavor.

After Needham demonstrated that *Vibrio tritici, = Anguina tritici,* was the causal agent of "cockles" in wheat, Linnaeus (1767), Scopoli (1777), Steinbuch (1799), and others recorded the same species and noted that it also attacked other cereals. No additional observations of plant parasitic nematodes were recorded until Kühn (1857) found *Anguillula dipsaci, = Ditylenchus dipsaci,* infesting the heads of teasel, *Dipsacus fullonum* L.

The tremendous economic potential of plant parasitic nematodes was first realized by workers in the beet sugar industry, which had produced the first commercial sugar in Germany in 1802. By 1860 there were 184 sugar factories in operation in Europe, and during the next decade the number was increased to 304 and sugar beet production had reached 3,364,760 short tons. Intensive production without adequate crop rotation furnished ideal conditions for the development of pests, and Schacht (1859) wrote of a serious disease caused by a nematode which for some years had inflicted losses in many fields of Germany. Schmidt (1871) named the pest *Heterodera schachtii*, and Strubell (1888) presented a detailed morphological study of the species which was so complete that little has since been added to it. Oddly enough, this fine piece of work was Strubell's only contribution to nematology.

Investigations on the control of the sugar beet nematode dominated the nematological scene in Europe from 1870 to 1910 as it made deeper inroads into beet sugar production. Julius Kühn was the outstanding leader in this campaign, with Liebscher, Molz, Muller, Chatin, and many others contributing their efforts to studies on host plants, life history, habits, distribution, etiology, and methods of control. Probably the first soil fumigation for nematode control was done by Kühn (1871) when he applied carbon disulfide in sugar beet nematode infested fields. He and his associates spent much of their time on futile efforts to use "trap crops," or *Fangpflanzen* as he called them, planting rape and other rapidly growing hosts in an attempt to induce the larval nematodes to hatch from the eggs and emerge from the brown cysts. Then by careful timing the plants were removed and destroyed before the life cycle of the nematode could be completed. But crop rotation proved to be the most practical and economical control, and the recommendations which Kühn and his associates formulated are to this day the principal methods followed throughout the industry both in Europe and in the United States.

As workers became more nematode conscious, other important plant parasites were described in rapid succession. Berkeley (1855) had observed "Vibrios" from galls on the roots of cucumbers in England. Greef (1872) found *Anguillula radicicola, = Ditylenchus radicicola,* producing galls on the roots of *Poa annua* and other grasses. The first specific mention of root-knot nematodes was that of Cornu (1879), who described *A. marioni, = Meloidogyne marioni,* the causal agent of galls on the roots of *Onobrychis sativa*. Goeldi (1887) published a description of *M. exigua,* which produced galls on the roots of coffee in Brazil. Numerous papers on various plant parasitic nematodes described their host ranges, life history, and taxonomy. An excellent summary of these works was made by Kati Marcinowski (1909) in her book *Parasitisch und Semiparasitisch an Pflanzen lebenden Nematoden,* which also included considerable original research of her own.

Meantime, free-living nematodes had been found in fresh and salt water by Müller (1786), Bory (1824), Dujardin (1845), Carter (1859),

Eberth (1863), and others, and from their studies came the first descriptions of the gross anatomy of these interesting little creatures.

Henry Charlton Bastian developed an interest in nematodes when he read the writings of Carter (1859), and as a result of his studies in certain limited areas of England he was able to describe 100 new species belonging to 30 genera, of which 23 were new. His "Monograph of the Anguillulidae" (1866) marked the beginning of the science of nematology. In it he presented for the first time a preview of the possibilities of intensive collecting in soil and plant tissues as well as in both fresh and salt water.

But it was Otto Bütschli (1873) who gave us our first detailed descriptions of the morphology of free-living nematodes and pointed out many of the characters which are used today in differentiating genera and species. For most of the species which he described he prepared excellent full-length detailed drawings which set a standard in the illustration of these minute animals. Perhaps the credit for founding the science of nematology should belong to him, rather than to Bastian.

J. G. deMan (1876) closely followed Bütschli with an excellent, well-illustrated paper and then (1884) produced his memorable taxonomic monograph, "Die einheimschen, frei in der reinen Erde und im süssen-Wasser lebenden Nematoden der Niederlandischen Fauna," which to this day remains one of the classic works which has been published on this subject.

DeMan was one of the most interesting personalities ever engaged in nematology. Born at Middelburg, Netherlands, he studied at the University of Leiden, where he received his doctorate in 1883, writing his dissertation on the "Comparative Mycological and Neurological Studies on Amphibians and Birds." For 10 years he worked with the Rijksmuseum, first as assistant, then as curator until 1889, when he resigned to continue his researches in private life. Financially independent, he was free to pursue any problem which attracted him, but most of his 168 publications were on the higher crustaceans and nematodes. In 1893 he moved to the island of Iserke and remained there until his death in 1930. His interest in nematodes never waned. The writer highly prizes several of his letters, written in perfect longhand which even to his last year remained steady and uniform. Often these were accompanied by his familiar line sketches, with which he was able to portray diagnostic features with a minimum of effort, yet illustrate the essential points with clarity.

Oerley (1881) made an excellent compilation of pertinent information on 202 species, representing 27 genera of free-living and plant parasitic nemas. Brief descriptions were included and numerous illustrations of fair quality. A comprehensive bibliography constituted an important part of this work and became a valuable source of reference for subsequent publications by other workers.

Heinrich Micoletzky in Austria entered the field of nematology with his first paper in 1914 and immediately began compiling the literature on soil and fresh-water nematodes, bringing together all the published

Henry Charlton Bastian, 1837–1915

(Photograph courtesy of The Royal Society.)

Otto Bütschli, 1848–1920

(Photograph from Biologische Grundprobleme und ihre Meister. Courtesy of H. Goffart.)

Johannes G. deMan, 1851–1930

Heinrich Micoletzky

Fig. 1-1

species in his "Die freilebende Erd-Nematoden" (1922). In this very ambitious piece of work he gave extensive keys to species and discussions on the various groups found in different habitats. Considering the tremendous financial and political handicaps under which he labored during and after the First World War, this was an outstanding accomplishment and it still remains the most valuable source of reference to papers published up to that time. But unfortunately he endeavored to condense the taxonomy rather than expand it. He lumped together all species which were in any way similar to each other and thus produced an impossible conglomeration of trinomial nomenclature which other workers refused to accept. He was especially irked by the many species described by Cobb without illustrations, as he had every right to be, and his footnotes frequently refer to them, "Leider ohne Abbildung!" His best publication probably is "Die freilebenden Süsswasser- und Moornematoden Dänemarks" (1925), in which he greatly improved the quality of his illustrations and included a good chapter on sporozoan parasites of nematodes.

An unusual and interesting series of papers by Gilbert Fuchs appeared between 1914 and 1938, opening up a hitherto little-known field of nematology dealing with nematode parasites and associates of bark beetles. Very little is known of Fuchs, but apparently he was a forest entomologist in Austria who chanced to discover nematodes associated with the insects under investigation. Numerous species of Tylenchoidea, Aphelenchoidea, and Rhabditoidea were described, including several new genera. At first glance the work appeared to be superficial, but after studying many of the groups which he presented, the writer found that he had been a very keen observer and that his simple line drawings were most accurate in depicting important diagnostic characters.

In 1934 I. N. Filipjev in Russia produced his book *Nematodes That Are of Importance for Agriculture,* and the following year J. H. Schuurmans Stekhoven, Jr., began collaborating with him to translate this work into English. The work proceeded until 1937, when Filipjev's letters ceased, and the remainder of the translation was made with the aid of F. Frechkob. The translation was published in 1941 under the title *A Manual of Agricultural Helminthology.* This is a most comprehensive compendium of nematological information and is especially valuable as a reference source for plant parasitic, free-living, and insect parasitic nematodes described up to that time. Just what happened to Filipjev has not been learned, but there was a rumor to the effect that he was lost during an expedition to the Arctic. However, in the several letters the writer received from him in 1936 and early 1937, he made no mention that such a trip was contemplated.

Between 1910 and 1940 there appeared numerous papers on soil and fresh-water nematodes by Ditlevsen, deConinck, Filipjev, Hofmänner, Menzel, Steiner, Stefanski, and many others, all of whom added new species and occasionally new genera. The wide distribution of many species was now evident, and reports of the fauna of various localities became largely a repetition of well-known species, with occasionally a few new ones added. W. Schneider (1939) made an especially notable compilation of species in his "Freilebende und pflanzenparasitische Nematoden."

Plant parasitic nematodes were also demanding widespread attention, and many research reports were published by Bovien, Carrol, Edwards, Franklin, Goffart, Korab, Ritzema Bos, van Slogteren, Staniland, Triffit, and numerous others. A summary of papers on nematode parasites of cultivated plants in Europe was presented by Goffart (1951) in "Nematoden der Kulturpflanzen Europas."

In England Tom Goodey published his first paper on nematodes in 1922, and from this beginning nematology prospered in that country under his able and enthusiastic leadership. During the early years of his career he was located at the London School of Tropical Medicine Laboratory in St. Albans, but in 1946 he became associated with the Rothamsted Experiment Station at Harpenden. Although his first interest was in protozoans, he quickly made the transition to nematodes, especially those attacking plants. Numerous papers appeared in rapid succession, culminating in his book *Plant Parasitic Nematodes and the Diseases They Cause* (1933). In this very important work he assembled pertinent information on all the known plant parasitic nematodes, including illustrations of typical symptoms and fair diagnostic drawings of the species involved. This book constituted a most important step in the direction of educating plant pathologists, horticulturists, agronomists, and other agricultural workers in the role of plant parasitic nematodes in crop production.

Following the publication of this book, Goodey began assembling a second, and in 1951 *Soil and Fresh Water Nematodes* appeared. This valuable volume included information on the genera of nematodes in these two groups, gave diagnoses and illustrations of the genotypes or a representative species, and listed the known species of each genus. Distribution, food habits, and ecological notes were included in most instances. Immediately following the completion of this book, he began developing plans for an international nematology course and symposia to be sponsored by the Food and Agriculture Organization of the United Nations. This successful enterprise was held at the Rothamsted Station, September 3 to 14, 1951, with forty-six persons in attendance. The majority of these were from nine European countries, with one each from Egypt, Indonesia, Israel, Uganda, South Africa, and the United States.

A man of many interests, Tom Goodey found time to participate in the activities of the community in which he lived, to sing in grand opera, and to be a leader in the Friends Meeting, of which he was a member. It was after a meeting that he was suddenly stricken with a heart attack which closed his illustrious career. Honors which came to him included the Order of the British Empire and Fellow of the Royal Society of London.

E. Van Slogteren   Hans Goffart

I. N. Filipjev   Hjalmar Ditlevsen

Fig. 1-2

Fig. 1-3. Food and Agricultural Organization International Nematology Course and Symposia. Rothamsted, England, September 3 to 14, 1951. (*Photograph courtesy of Rothamsted Experiment Station.*)

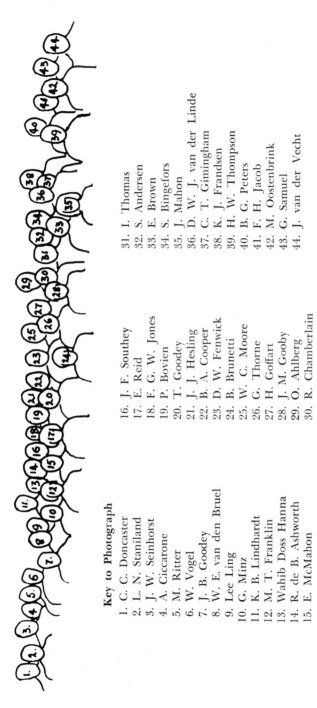

Key to Photograph

1. C. C. Doncaster
2. L. N. Staniland
3. J. W. Seinhorst
4. A. Ciccarone
5. M. Ritter
6. W. Vogel
7. J. B. Goodey
8. W. E. van den Bruel
9. Lee Ling
10. G. Minz
11. K. B. Lindhardt
12. M. T. Franklin
13. Wahib Doss Hanna
14. R. de B. Ashworth
15. E. McMahon

16. J. F. Southey
17. E. Reid
18. F. G. W. Jones
19. P. Bovien
20. T. Goodey
21. J. J. Hesling
22. B. A. Cooper
23. D. W. Fenwick
24. B. Brunetti
25. W. C. Moore
26. G. Thorne
27. H. Goffart
28. J. M. Gooby
29. O. Ahlberg
30. R. Chamberlain

31. I. Thomas
32. S. Andersen
33. E. Brown
34. S. Bingefors
35. J. Mahon
36. D. W. J. van der Linde
37. C. T. Gimingham
38. K. J. Frandsen
39. H. W. Thompson
40. B. G. Peters
41. F. H. Jacob
42. M. Oostenbrink
43. G. Samuel
44. J. van der Vecht

Not included in photograph: C. Ellenby, H. C. Gough, F. Kébreau, R. S. Pitcher, A. Savary, A. H. Strickland, T. E. T. Trought.

11

Tom Goodey, 1885–1953   Mary T. Franklin

Ernst A. Bessey, 1877–1957   D. G. Milbrath

Fig. 1-4

Development of Nematology in the United States

Joseph Leidy was a most versatile individual, combining the qualities of explorer and scientist in his never-ending search for items of interest, especially in the field of zoology. To him a thrilling adventure could be found either in the vast, unexplored West, where he discovered and named fossilized prehistoric monsters, or in the mud and slime of a slough near his home in Philadelphia. And it was during his explorations in this latter region that he observed slender, active organisms which he recognized as nematodes. As an ardent member and voluminous contributor to the Philadelphia Academy of Natural Sciences, he reported certain observations in 1851, a portion of which constitutes our first record of free-living nematodes in America:

5. *Anguillulula Longa* n.s.—Body cylindrical, translucent, and colorless. Mouth round, buccal capsule inverted, campanulate. Esophagus and intestine cylindrical, equal in diameter, the former $\frac{1}{25}$ inch long from anus.

Female 2 to 3 lines long; anteriorly $\frac{1}{33}$ inch broad, middle $\frac{1}{285}$ inch. Tail narrow, acute, $\frac{1}{111}$ to $\frac{1}{75}$ inch long from anus.

Male 1½ to 2 lines long; posteriorly dilated, obtusely rounded, curved, with three slight tubercular thickenings of the integument ventrally $\frac{1}{265}$ inch broad; at middle $\frac{1}{370}$ inch broad. Penus a curved spiculum $\frac{1}{280}$ inch long.

Hab.—Found in very great abundance, wriggling above the surface of soft mud, in stagnant ditches in the neighborhood of Philadelphia.

The three ventral tubercular structures of the male indicate that this species was a *Trilobus,* and it was from this information that Cobb (1914) redescribed and Chambers illustrated *T. longus* (Leidy) from specimens collected in the same general locality. The term "line" generally indicates $\frac{1}{12}$ inch, or about 2.0 mm. Perhaps Leidy used a different scale, for these would be nemas 3 to 6 mm long, too large for *Trilobus.*

In the same paper Leidy described *Anguillula Longicauda* n.s. and *Anguillula Fossolarius* n.s., neither of which is recognizable.

As might be expected, root-knot nematodes, *Meloidogyne* spp., were the first plant parasitic species observed in the United States, and these were recorded by May in 1888. Working independently, Atkinson in Alabama and Neal in Florida made extensive researches in the morphology, host ranges, and crop damage of these pests, and in 1889 both published the results of their investigations. Halstead in New Jersey (1891) and Stone and Smith in Massachusetts (1898) published additional observations, and from that time on numerous workers recorded the results of their research and observations.

An important event in the development of nematology occurred in 1907, when N. A. Cobb joined the U.S. Department of Agriculture. Cobb had secured his doctorate at Jena in 1889, after which he worked in Italy for a short time. Here he collected nematodes, some of which he mounted in balsam; so expertly were the slides made that the specimens are still in excellent condition. He then proceeded to Australia, but failing to find professional employment he sold watches until an opening was available in the New South Wales Department of Agriculture. His first paper on plant parasitic nematodes, "Tylenchus and Root Galls," appeared in the *Agricultural Gazette of New South Wales* (1890). Apparently, at that time he did not know that the names *Heterodera* and *Meloidogyne* had already been proposed for the gall-forming nematodes.

About 10 years later he became associated with the Experiment Station of the Hawaiian Sugar Planters Association, where he investigated the nematodes found in sugar cane fields. Here he began developing equipment for microscopy, fitting the windows with special shades and reflectors to control lighting while working over the microscope and making camera lucida drawings. Much of this equipment is still preserved at the station.

His first assignment in the U.S. Department of Agriculture was the standardization of cotton grades, which were published in 1907. About 1910 he succeeded in transferring his attention to nematodes. His first paper, "New Nematode Genera Found Inhabiting Fresh-water and Non-brackish Soils," was published in 1913. From that time on, a long series of important papers came from his versatile pen. Among his writings *Contributions to a Science of Nematology* is the most outstanding. It was Cobb who proposed that plant parasitic and free-living nematodes be removed from helminthology and be assigned to a new branch of science to be known as "nematology." He also proposed that "nema" be substituted for "nematode," and it is most unfortunate that this suggestion has not met with general acceptance. His ingenious nature was then directed to the development of equipment and techniques necessary to separate nematodes from soil and prepare them for microscopic study. His laboratory manual "Estimating the Nema Population of Soil" (1918) formed the basis for a large portion of the methods and apparatus used in nematology today.

Studies on the minute morphological details of plant parasitic nematodes occupied much of his time, with special reference to those organs which he named "amphids," "phasmids," and "deirids." To secure a better perspective on their morphology, he studied the large marine species, on which details were much more easily observed, and for this purpose he spent several summers at the Bureau of Fisheries Station at Woods Hole, Massachusetts. Those who were fortunate enough to be included on these expeditions will ever remember those halcyon days of nematology.

Cobb's interests were not confined to nematology and microscopy but extended to photography of birds and insects and the development of special equipment for photomicrography and other microscopic work, such as the installation of heavy pipes filled with concrete to reduce vibration during such work. Often these devices resulted in weird and complicated assemblies, for he seemed to lack the ability to simplify either apparatus or procedures. His laboratories were always a show place of revolving tables with several microscopes on each and special devices to perform laboratory techniques. Probably his most useful invention was the metal microscopic slide, which many of us prefer to the conventional glass type. Another important contribution was the use of a simple beam splitter and large mirror to replace the old-type camera lucida.

His genial and humorous nature will ever be remembered, especially by those who were present at a certain meeting of the Helminthological Society of Washington. He appeared with numerous boxes and cartons which contained "A Collection of Holes," which he had assembled during his travels, and on them he proceeded to deliver a solemn and profound dissertation which rocked the audience with laughter. This was probably a satire on certain members of the society who always had entirely too much to say about things of which they knew little or nothing. His sudden death at the age of seventy-three terminated all too soon an important period in the development of the science of nematology. No other individual has had a more profound and permanent influence on the profession than N. A. Cobb.

Associated with Cobb during those early eventful years was W. E. Chambers, artist and microscopist. From his gifted hands nematology received the finest illustrations of nematodes that have ever been made, and it is doubtful that they will ever again be equaled. Cobb's microscopic ability and unusual ingenuity, coupled with the artistry of Chambers, established a new era in nematology on which our present science is largely founded, not only in America but in all parts of the world.

Among the early contemporaries of Cobb in the U.S. Department of Agriculture we find Ernst A. Bessey, soon after the turn of the century, working on root-knot nematodes. His report (1911) included a review of the principal work done up to that time and included considerable original research. This paper still remains one of the outstanding contributions to our information on this group.

E. G. Titus observed sugar beet nematodes in a field near Lehi, Utah, in 1907 and reported his findings to the U.S. Department of Agriculture. A few years later Harry B. Shaw was assigned to make a survey of the distribution of the pest. His report (1915) included an excellent summary of the voluminous European literature and remains one of the outstanding publications on this subject. In 1918 Titus was responsible for initiating the sugar beet nematode project in the U.S. Department of Agriculture. The writer is deeply indebted to him for the opportunity to head the work which eventually developed into the first permanent nematology field station in the United States, located at Salt Lake City, Utah. Studies were extended to many phases of nematology, with special emphasis on assembling a taxonomic collection which eventually reached over thirty-six thousand indexed specimens representing upward of two thousand species. Based on this collection, monographs were compiled for over sixty genera, and numerous other papers were

W. E. Chambers   Jesse Roy Christie

(*Photograph courtesy of George F. Weber.*)

Edward Gaige Titus   Gerald Thorne

Fig. 1-5

issued. The collection attracted many visitors both from home and abroad who found it a valuable source of reference in studying rare and little-known genera and species. The specimens are still available to qualified and responsible persons engaged in assembling monographs on various groups. W. D. Courtney, C. W. McBeth, M. W. Allen, H. W. Reynolds, and other young nematologists of the Western states received much of their training at this station. Allen has carried on the tradition in the Nematology Department of the University of California, Berkeley, where he has trained several of the world's outstanding younger nematologists.

Other members of the U.S. Department of Agriculture who were associated with Cobb were J. R. Christie, G. Steiner, B. G. and M. B. Chitwood, A. L. Taylor, Helen Heinley Swanger, Edna M. Buhrer, Grace Sherman Cobb, Louise Crossman, Josephine Danforth, Florence E. Albin, Margaret N. Corder, Cevilla Brooks, and numerous others who aided with laboratory and office work for shorter periods of service.

A considerable number of other workers in the United States made valuable contributions on nematological problems during this time. Among them were L. P. Byars, D. G. Milbrath, G. H. Godfrey, R. W. Leukel, M. B. Linford, J. R. Watson, and A. G. Newhall.

Perhaps the most important index to species of nematodes is that of Stiles and Hassall, which was issued in 1920 under the title "Index Catalog of Medical and Veterinary Zoology. Roundworms." Fortunately, the authors included practically all the citations to plant-infesting and free-living nematodes that had been published up to that time. This compilation is a boon to anyone searching for references to early works on nematology.

Following Cobb in 1932, G. Steiner directed the work of what is now known as the Nematology Section of the U.S. Department of Agriculture. His first work on nematodes had been done in Switzerland, his native land, but in 1921 he came to Yale University for a year of study and accepted a position under Cobb in 1922. His work was divided between plant and insect parasitic nematodes and fresh-water and marine forms. His contributions cover a wide range of subjects and total about two hundred at the present time (1959). Working with Cobb, he collaborated on morphological and taxonomic problems which added many interesting items to our knowledge.

Funds for expanding research were increased about 1940, and several new projects were initiated in the Eastern and Southern states. Personnel of the Nematology Section increased until about thirty are now employed. Encouraged by this recognition of the importance of nematology, state experiment stations, plant inspection services, and industry have added nematologists to their staffs. There are now about one hundred workers engaged on a wide variety of nematological projects located throughout the country.

Many workers were trained in the Beltsville, Maryland, laboratories, and numerous visitors from home and abroad received instruction while

Gotthold Steiner   Albert L. Taylor

(Photograph courtesy of George F. Weber.)

George H. Godfrey   Benjamin G. Chitwood

(Photograph courtesy of George F. Weber.)

Fig. 1-6

Edna M. Buhrer   Grace S. Cobb

Wilbur D. Courtney   Walter Carter

Fig. 1-7

assigned there for various lengths of time. Two of the most important persons in this training program were Edna M. Buhrer and Grace S. Cobb.

At the time of his retirement in 1956, Steiner was presented with the Distinguished Service Medal of the U.S. Department of Agriculture and soon afterward accepted a position with the government of Puerto Rico.

A. L. Taylor succeeded Steiner after spending twenty years in the Nematology Section in field stations of the Southeastern states and as assistant in the Beltsville office and laboratory. His long and successful career in practical field nematology and administrative training augurs well for the future of nematology in this country.

One of the finest achievements of this period was that of working out the life histories and economic importance of two mermithid parasites of grasshoppers in the northeastern United States. This was done by J. R. Christie, working in collaboration with N. A. Cobb and G. Steiner. Their papers on *Mermis subnigrescens* and *Agamermis decaudata* will always remain as classics in this branch of nematology. As a perfectionist, Christie is without a peer among the nematologists of the world, and his papers, while not numerous, are all outstanding contributions to the science.

The story of nematology in America would not be complete without a tribute to A. D. Baker, Wm. Newton, R. J. Hastings, and J. E. Bosher of Canada. Working largely by themselves, in isolated stations, they have produced some of our best studies on stem, root lesion, potato rot, and other plant parasitic nematodes.

Among the outstanding works published during these years is *An Introduction to Nematology* by B. G. and M. B. Chitwood. This approaches the subject of nematology from a purely zoological standpoint and covers the entire Phylum Nemata. Detailed morphological studies of the supergeneric groups are presented, with a lavish use of figures illustrating the principal diagnostic characters of each. Discussions and comparisons are made largely on a family basis, with occasional figures setting forth the characters of genera or species representative of the higher groups. The work is especially valuable for the advanced student in nematology. However, the beginner will find much of interest in the historical and general discussions and in the great variety of morphological structures illustrated.

An excellent book, *Plant Nematodes, Their Bionomics and Control,* has recently been published by J. R. Christie (1959). Discussions are presented of all plant parasitic nematodes, either individually or in generic groups. Special attention is given to symptoms, life history, feeding habits, distribution, and control. Research workers in agriculture, teachers, students, plant inspectors, county agents, and other workers in agriculture will find a wealth of information presented in simple, direct language.

The most numerous of all nematodes are those inhabiting salt water; doubtless there are more marine species than all others combined.

Among them we find species possessing well-developed eye lenses, long sensory setae instead of the obscure papillae of soil-inhabiting forms, and elaborately developed "ambulatory setae" with which they travel in much the same manner as a measuring worm. Many are predators feeding on microorganisms, while others are saprophagous and devour the decaying remnants of all kinds of animal life which make up a considerable portion of the covering of the ocean floor. Obviously, these marine types comprise one of the basic groups of the lower forms of animal life, which contribute food for somewhat larger forms, which, in turn, become the food of fish, lobsters, crabs, and other economically important denizens of the ocean.

Extensive studies on the marine nematode fauna have been made by Allgen, deMan, deCononck, Schuurmans Stekhoven, Filipjev, Steiner, Kreis, and Cobb. Numerous genera and species have been added with almost every publication, but the vast majority have scarcely been touched. From a purely zoological and taxonomic standpoint, the marine nematode fauna offers the greatest unknown field in the phylum.

THE ROLE OF PLANT PARASITIC NEMATODES IN AGRICULTURE

Plant parasitic nematodes present some of the most difficult pest problems encountered in our agricultural economy. Each year these minute organisms exact an ever-increasing toll from almost every cultivated acre in the world: a bag of rice in Burma, a pound of tea in Ceylon, a ton of sugar beets in Germany, a bag of potatoes in England, a bale of cotton in Georgia, a bushel of corn in Iowa, a box of apples in New York, a sack of wheat in Kansas, or a crate of oranges in California. Perhaps the amount is relatively small in most instances, but the aggregate represents a staggering total which the farmers of the world can ill afford to lose and which the undernourished millions of the earth would welcome if made available to them.

This world-wide distribution of economically important plant parasites indicates that they have doubtless been an important factor in the economy of ancient civilizations. Perhaps they were at least partly responsible for the famines which decimated certain nations or forced them to migrate and conquer more fortunate peoples, as did the innumerable hordes of Attila, Genghis Khan, and other predatory leaders.

Plant parasitic nematodes doubtless played an important but unrecognized role in the early agriculture of America, where they probably were partly responsible for the rapid deterioration of soils in the colonies along the Atlantic coast. George Washington stated, "Our lands were originally very good, but use and misuse has made them otherwise." A. O. Cranven, about 1775, revealed something of the situation when he discussed soil exhaustion in Virginia and Maryland: "New land is taken up, tobacco grown for 3 or 4 years, and then Indian corn as long as any of it will come, and in the end when the soil is thoroughly impoverished they begin again with a new piece and go through the rotation." So serious did the situation become that in 1832 Thomas Marshall estimated that all the crops of Virginia were worth less than the agricultural exports of the state ninety years before.

Soil depletion and erosion have been blamed for this sorry state of affairs, and this explanation has been generally accepted by agricultural scientists. In 1931 and 1932 the writer visited some of the abandoned plantations of Virginia and collected soil from fields which were then overgrown with brush and forest. In almost every instance it was possible to recover plant parasitic nematodes belonging to the root-knot, root-lesion, spiral, ring, and other well-known groups. It appears quite evident that they must have been associated with the losses sustained by crops which were formerly grown on these fields. Perhaps they were just as important as erosion and soil depletion in forcing the owners to abandon the land many decades before. Probably most of the species were indigenous and had merely transferred to cultivated crops when their native hosts were destroyed.

As previously mentioned, the first plant parasitic nematode ever observed was the wheat gall nematode, *Anguina tritici,* which produced black, gall-like "cockles" in place of the normal grains of wheat, rye, and other cereals. This form is representative of a large number of species found in the seeds of grains and grasses throughout the world. The contaminated seeds provide an ideal means of distribution from country to country and from continent to continent. Species have been moved about in this manner until they are cosmopolitan in distribution.

The bulb and stem nematode, *Ditylenchus dipsaci,* is a complex group of populations which attack several hundred different plants varying from fuller's teasel, alfalfa, clover, and weeds to the bulbs of tulips, narcissi, hyacinths, onions, and garlic. Not only have severe losses been exacted from these crop plants, but also heavy expenditures have been necessary to enforce sanitation and quarantine measures enacted to prevent their distribution.

Between 1920 and 1930 the bulb and stem nematode gained international importance because of its possible distribution through narcissus, tulip, and other bulbs. The United States imposed rigorous quarantine measures against infested foreign bulbs, beginning a long series of regulatory acts designed to protect the agriculture of the country from the ravages of imported plant parasitic nematodes. Because of the high value of the bulb crops, millions of dollars were spent on control measures which varied from field sanitation to the construction of mammoth plants where bulbs were given hot-water treatment before entry into the country. These regulatory measures, with their wide publicity, resulted in a high degree of control and served as an important step in making certain parts of the country "nematode-conscious."

Members of the genera *Ditylenchus, Anguina* and *Aphelenchoides* are frequently found in the aerial parts of certain plants. Several lessknown groups like *Neotylenchus, Nothanguina,* and *Nothotylenchus* occasionally appear in similar roles. These invade the tissues and produce a wide variety of injuries which account for economically important losses of grass seeds, forage, and floral products.

Among the best-known plant parasitic species are the root-knot nematodes of the genus *Meloidogyne*, which often produce conspicuous gall-like swellings on the roots in which they live. Over one thousand hosts are recorded for this group, including practically all our field, truck, garden, orchard, ornamental, and greenhouse plants. The annual losses incurred by their depredations are almost incalculable.

Root-knot nematodes were once the principal cause of an embarrassing international situation. In 1909, the mayor of Tokyo, Japan, presented a collection of Japanese flowering cherries to the city of Washington, D.C. When they arrived in early 1910, plant quarantine officials found them infested with root-knot and other pests and ordered that they be destroyed. In December, 1911, a second lot was carefully selected and arrived in Washington on March 25, 1912. From these have been developed the extensive plantings which now attract hundreds of thousands of visitors each spring during the cherry blossom festival.

Condemnation of nursery stock and seedling plants because of root-knot nematode infestations probably accounts for more losses in this industry than all other diseases combined. Yet species of *Pratylenchus, Tylenchulus,* and other genera doubtless are just as important but have not been recognized because workers trained in nematology and capable of recognizing these other species have not been available. Dissemination of plant parasitic nematodes through nursery stock is demonstrated by the fact that almost every citrus grove in California and many of those in Florida and other states are infested with the citrus nematode, *T. semipenetrans.*

The insidious "slow decline," or "dieback," of walnut, cherry, prune, apple, citrus, and other orchard trees baffled investigators for many years. But this condition is almost invariably associated with large populations of *Pratylenchus, Xiphinema, Tylenchulus, Rotylenchulus, Meloidogyne, Criconemoides,* and other plant parasitic nemas. Often these species were indigenous and merely transferred from their native hosts to the orchards, which they found to be very satisfactory substitutes. Certain endoparasitic forms have been introduced through infested nursery stock, seedling plants, tubers, bulbs, soil, and other agencies.

Unexplained losses to crops following old, declining orchards have sometimes been attributed to toxic agents excreted by the tree roots. The problem can usually be solved by the nematologist, who knows that during the long life of these orchards certain plant parasitic nematodes have built up huge populations. There they enjoyed the undisturbed hospitality of choice cherry, prune, apple, or walnut roots, and when these were destroyed, they transferred their attentions to roots of following crops. Soil fumigants applied in the proper manner usually demonstrated that crop losses ended when nematodes were controlled.

Because of our limited information on certain nematodes, plant diseases have occasionally been attributed to fungi and bacteria and their true nature not recognized. A destructive "stubby root" of vegetables in Florida baffled research workers for many years until Christie and Perry (1951) determined that relatively small populations of *Trichodorus christiei* were the causal agents. This was the first time that this genus had been recognized as being of economic importance.

Many cherry plantings in Wisconsin, Michigan, Idaho, and other states have been severely damaged by root-lesion nematodes, *Pratylenchus* spp., which were introduced in seedlings from other states. Prunes in New York, apples in Colorado, walnuts in California, peaches in Georgia, grapes in Arizona, and raspberries in Utah are just a few of the hundreds of examples which have been revealed by nematologists. Obviously, plant inspection will eventually require the services of many workers trained in taxonomy, host relationship, and distribution of plant parasitic nematodes.

Winterkill of orchard trees, raspberries, strawberries, ornamentals, and other perennials frequently is associated with nematode infestations. Freezing is a dehydration process, and root systems damaged by nematodes are unable to provide the moisture necessary for survival of top growth during periods of extreme cold. Outstanding instances of winterkill were observed in Utah raspberry plantings, where, in the spring, areas infested with *Pratylenchus vulnus* were delineated by dead canes.

Alfalfa plants on root-knot infested soil often die during the winter because they have failed to establish their normal, deep-feeding taproots. One nematode gall on the young tap-root stops its growth, and the plant sends out several small laterals, which usually penetrate no farther than the plow sole. Infestations of *Trichodorus* in Wyoming alfalfa fields were responsible for similar damage.

Among the most interesting species of nematodes known are the predatory types, which aid in maintaining the balance of nature among the soil fauna. Chief among these are the mononchs, which occur in almost all soils and fresh water, and which prey on nematodes, rotifers, and other microorganisms. It is not unusual to find specimens of these voracious little monsters which contain the bodies of four or five other nematodes which they have swallowed. Sometimes they even devour their associate mononchs. If specimens of various species are placed in a hollow ground slide where they come into contact with each other, they sometimes engage in combats which leave torn carcasses scattered over the battlefield. It is never safe to leave live mononchs overnight in a mixed collection because by morning a good portion of the dorylaims, tylenchs, rhabditids, and other species will have been devoured.

Another group of predators, the nygolaims, sectonemas, and their dorylaim relatives, feed largely on small earthworms known as oligochaetes, and it is not at all uncommon to find setae of these worms in their intestinal tracts. Unfortunately, this particular type does not feed on other nematodes so far as is known. They would be ideal for attacking the females of sugar beet, root-knot, citrus, and reniform nematodes as they lie attached and unprotected on the roots. Perhaps the gelatinous matrix surrounding the bodies of sessile females acts as a repellent to predators.

Saprophagous nematodes inhabit decaying organic material, and frequently individuals of this group comprise the greater portion of populations in soil where the organic content is high. Rarely is a collection made which does not contain several species of rhabditids, cephalobs, diplogasters, and related forms. We know little of their role in soil biology, but no doubt they aid in breaking down organic matter and reducing it to plant food. Populations of these saprophagous species fluctuate rapidly, and as supplies of organic material are exhausted, they may almost disappear from a given area within two or three weeks.

Certain groups of nematodes inhabit bodies of insects and other invertebrates and play important roles in control of some species. Some of the most outstanding examples are members of the family Mermithidae, which parasitize grasshoppers. In the United States mermithids are very numerous in states east of the Mississippi River, especially in New England and the North Central states. In some parts of New Hampshire, Vermont, and neighboring states parasitism may reach 80 to 90 per cent, and grasshopper populations are very low. Distribution in the West appears to be limited by the 24-inch rainfall belt, which ends approximately along the Mississippi River. West of that river mermithids occur infrequently.

A treatise covering all these groups would present a problem beyond the abilities of any one person, and so we must confine our efforts to only a small segment of the total. The groups covered in this text should enable nematologists, plant pathologists, horticulturists, and zoologists to determine the identity of many species which they find and to learn something of the life history, economic importance, and control of each one.

The above examples include only a small portion of the important problems confronting us in the field of nematology. We know little or nothing of the feeding habits, hosts, and pathogenicity of hundreds of species of spear-bearing nemas of the genera *Tylenchus, Rotylenchus, Hoplolaimus, Aphelenchoides, Dorylaimus, Diphtherophora,* and their many relatives.

Association of nematodes with numerous plant diseases is well recognized, especially those involving root rots of various types. These associations may present widely varying symptoms because of the many factors involved. Vigor of host, species of nematode, and cultural and climatic conditions combine with certain fungi and bacteria in creating the disease complex. Discussions of these complexes are well set forth by Steiner (1953) and Holdeman (1954), as well as by numerous previous workers cited by these writers.

Soil fumigants have made it possible to demonstrate that elimination of plant parasitic nematodes often removes certain disease symptoms formerly attributed to fungi and bacteria. This statement does not imply that soil fumigation is a cure-all for nematodes and all associated soil organisms. But some of the remarkable accomplishments of fumigation have demonstrated that these associations are far more important than had previously been suspected.

Demands for "pathogenicity" demonstrations as proof of nematode injury have been met in practically every instance where favorable environmental conditions have been provided for the nemas. These demonstrations have been so successful that when failures are reported it can usually be suspected that proper ecological habitats have not been attained. So important are these factors that in one instance the breakdown of an air conditioner in a greenhouse for only two hot summer days was responsible for the loss of almost every colony of *Meloidogyne, Rotylenchus, Tylenchorhynchus,* and *Xiphinema* in several dozen experiments. One of the most common causes of failures in greenhouse experiments is inadequate irrigation, which may result in the lower half or more of the pots or boxes being too dry to permit nemic activity.

METHODS OF CONTROLLING NEMATODES

We must be realistic in planning control methods for plant parasitic nematodes and must recognize certain facts concerning their taxonomy, host plants, habitat, and life history. A frank evaluation of these facts generally results in the inevitable conclusion that we must learn to live with these nematodes. The possibilities of complete eradication are exceedingly remote except perhaps in a few isolated instances. Six principal avenues of approach are available, and each has its limitations:

1. Crop rotation. Some plant parasitic nematodes have distinct host preferences. When such nematodes are deprived of their favorite hosts for three or four years, their numbers decrease to a point where a profitable crop can be produced. This is the usual method of control for the sugar beet nematode, *Heterodera schachtii,* and the alfalfa stem nematode, *Ditylenchus dipsaci.* For other species like the root-knot nematodes, *Meloidogyne* spp., this method frequently is unsuccessful because the extensive host ranges cover most of our common crops and the weeds found growing among them. Recommendations for rotations to be followed in the control of the various species will be presented as each is discussed in following chapters. For certain well-known forms, information is extensive and recommendations are rather definite, but for many groups only limited data are available.

Taxonomy is a necessary adjunct in planning crop rotations because certain closely related species of *Meloidogyne, Pratylenchus, Ditylenchus,* and other genera have different host preferences. Unless proper identification is made, it will be difficult to select the proper crops. For many years the stem nematode, *D. dipsaci,* and the potato rot nematode, *D. destructor,* were thought to be a single species although host records were often conflicting. When diagnostic characters separating them were discovered, it was possible to determine which crops were best to use in rotations for the control of both species. The baffling complex of the root-knot nematodes, *Meloidogyne* spp., is gradually being solved by critical morphological studies. Eventually the various species will probably be definitely separated on certain diagnostic characters and their host ranges fixed. After this a certain degree of control by rotations will usually be possible.

2. Cultural methods. Time of planting and harvest sometimes can be combined with rotations and successful production maintained by avoiding periods of high nematode activity. An outstanding example of this method is utilized in the southern San Joaquin Valley of California, where the entire potato crop is planted early in the year and harvested in April and May as "new" potatoes. Thousands of carloads are produced each year without loss from nematode infestation because harvest occurs before the larvae enter the tubers. Fields allowed to remain until June generally produce nothing but culls because of the severe galling which appears by the time that the tubers have matured. In this area, the first generation of larvae attacks only the roots. Thousands of females can be found with only the anterior end buried in the tissues, while the protruding posterior part is enclosed in a gelatinous mass into which eggs are deposited. Larvae from these eggs have no opportunity to cause appreciable damage to the crop, which is dug soon after they hatch. Under these conditions there is only rarely a slight galling of the roots, and the plants make a "normal" growth.

Fallow. Hot, dry climates offer an opportunity to employ fallow in the rotation. This consists in plowing the soil two or three times, the nemas thus being turned up to the heat of the sun, where they perish from desiccation. Vegetable growers of the Imperial Valley of California have successfully used this method for the past three decades. It is also frequently used in the Rio Grande Valley of Texas and other parts of the arid Southwest as reported by G. H. Godfrey in 1943. After two months of this fallow treatment, carrots, lettuce, and other vegetables are produced without loss. Frequently carrots penetrate to the undisturbed subsoil, and small galls are produced on the terminal roots by *Meloidogyne* larvae working up from below.

3. Resistant plants. Early in the study of plant parasitic nematodes it was observed that some varieties of crops grew more vigorously than others on infested soil. This was especially true of certain varieties of cotton, cowpeas, tobacco, and beans produced on root-knot infested land, and these have become the leading varieties in many parts of the country. Shalil and Yunan peach root-stocks are very resistant to certain species of *Meloidogyne,* and native black walnut roots are apparently immune to the small but destructive *Cacopaurus pestis.* In Ceylon, Loos selected tea plants which are resistant to *Pratylenchus coffeae.* Only occasional specimens enter the roots, and these do not reproduce. Harvey Westover secured an alfalfa from Turkestan which is immune to stem nematode and is now known as Nemastan. From this variety, O. F. Smith selected superior plants and formed a synthetic known as Lahon-

tan which carries the immunity factor of Nemastan. Research of this type should be followed by nematologists with special training in plant breedings and genetics. Teamwork between nematologists and plant breeders may offer the best approach to certain unusually difficult problems.

Steiner (1941) observed that the larvae of *Meloidogyne* sp. entered roots of marigolds, *Tagetes* hybrids, but failed to develop. Following this lead, Oostenbrink, Kuiper, and s'Jacob (1957a) planted marigolds on soil infested with *Pratylenchus pratensis* and *P. penetrans* and found that populations were greatly reduced in one season. Occasional nemas entered the roots but failed to develop and reproduce.

Rohde and Jenkins (1958) discovered that asparagus juice was toxic to *Trichodorus christiei* and other nemas even in dilutions of 1 to 10. Populations did not feed on roots of mature asparagus, and their numbers rapidly declined.

Further investigations for plants with similar qualities are desirable and may lead to more effective control through crop rotations.

4. Soil fumigation. Historical. Soil fumigation originated in France in the early 1860s, when entomologists applied carbon disulfide for the control of *Phyloxera* on grapes. Various types of applicators were devised, embodying many of the mechanical principles found in machines today. After the efficacy of carbon disulfide was established for insects, Julius Kühn became interested in it as a possible nematicide. He first applied it in attempts to control sugar beet nematode in Germany in 1871, but results were not encouraging. In the United States, Ernst A. Bessey experimented with carbon disulfide for the control of root-knot nematodes in South Carolina in 1906–1907, but the method proved impractical. Formaldehyde, cyanide, quicklime, and numerous other chemicals were found to have nematicidal qualities, but all were too expensive to use even on high-priced specialty crops.

The nematicidal qualities of chloropicrin were discovered in 1919, when Mrs. J. D. Mathews conducted preliminary experiments in England. No further reports were made until Johnson and Godfrey carried out their investigations in California in 1927–1928, which they reported in 1932. Godfrey, Oliveira, and Hoshino (1934) established small field plots in Hawaii where they injected chloropicrin with a hand applicator known as the "Vermorel carbon disulfide injector." This machine placed the chemical 6 to 8 inches deep at rates of 150 to 170 pounds per acre. To contain the gas, plots were covered with impermeable paper with the edges buried in soil. Results indicated a kill of 99 to 100 per cent of the nematodes. The same year larger field plots were established, and these, too, showed a high degree of control.

Soon after the preliminary experiments in Hawaii, large quantities of chloropicrin were declared surplus by the United States Army, and many tons were purchased by the Hawaiian pineapple industry. Tractor-drawn applicators were developed, and field-scale fumigation became an established procedure until supplies of surplus chloropicrin were exhausted.

Commercial fumigation ceased for several years until Walter Carter, entomologist of the Hawaiian Pineapple Research Institute, reported (1943) that a dichloropropene-dichloropropane mixture produced by the Shell Chemical Corporation was a promising new soil fumigant when applied at the rate of 250 pounds per acre. Carter stated that not only were nematodes controlled but also the destructive larvae of a beetle, *Anamola orientalis*.

Following are the common and technical names of the more important soil fumigants, together with the names of the companies producing them and the usual method of application.

Chloropicrin (tear gas), trichloronitromethane. Larvacide Products, Inc. Used principally in greenhouse soils and in seedbeds. An excellent fungicide as well as nematicide, and also kills weed seeds.

D-D, 1,3-dichloropropene and 1,2-dichloropropane in about equal parts, together with small amounts of other chlorinated products. Developed by the Shell Chemical Company. Used as broadcast, row, and spot treatments.

EDB, ethylene dibromide = 1,2-dibromoethane. First used as a soil fumigant by The Dow Chemical Company and now usually sold by them as Dowfume W-85. Also sold by other companies under various trade names. Used as broadcast, row side dressing, and spot treatments.

Nemagon, 1,2-dibromo-3-chloropropane, originating with the Shell Chemical Company. Distributed as Fumazone by The Dow Chemical Company. Applied as broadcast, row, and spot treatments. Sometimes mixed with fertilizers in granular form. Also can be used about roots of certain living plants, especially orchard trees.

Methyl bromide, bromomethane. A common fumigant used in greenhouse soils and in seedbeds and for stored products. Soil must be in containers or under airtight covers. When mixed with 2 per cent chloropicrin, it is sold under various trade names and used as above.

This discovery of D-D, as it was named, marked the beginning of the present soil fumigation industry. Experimental plots were soon established throughout the United States by the Shell Chemical Corporation, cooperating with Federal, state, and private agencies. These early demonstrations were so successful that within five years many thousands of acres had been treated and soil fumigation had been accepted as a successful and profitable practice.

Preliminary experiments with ethylene dibromide were made in 1944 by J. F. Kagy and C. R. Youngson of The Dow Chemical Company, Seal Beach, California, and by J. R. Christie, Nematology Section, U.S. Department of Agriculture in Florida. Christie (1945) reported the favorable results of his experiments. The same year The Dow Chemical Company introduced the chemical as a successful soil fumigant and made field-scale demonstration plots near Ventura, California. EDB, as it became known, not only proved to be effective against nematodes (except cyst-forming species) but also gave remarkable control of wireworms. By 1954 about 72,000 acres had been fumigated with EDB in Ventura County alone, with an additional 24,000 acres in Orange County (Lane and Stone, 1954).

Limitations on the efficiency of soil fumigants were soon discovered. Light sandy loams, having a moisture-holding capacity (moisture equivalent) of 20 per cent or less, responded readily, and generally excellent crops followed fumigation. However, heavy clay loams and muck required two or three times the amount of fumigant used on sandy loams. Loose peat soils gave little or no response, even to excessive applications.

It is estimated that about 600,000 acres will be fumigated in 1959. This represents an investment of approximately $14,500,000, which will bring to the farmers at least four times that amount in increased crop returns.

It is fitting that a few words of commendation be given to the officials of the Shell Chemical Corporation and The Dow Chemical Company for their foresight in pioneering the field of soil fumigation. Their efficient, generous, cooperative, and persistent campaigns have carried the science of soil fumigation into almost every country. Those of us who had spent many years attempting to control nematodes by crop-rotation and cultural methods, often with futile, discouraging results, now realized the satisfaction of recommending D-D and EBD for the control of nematodes on certain moderate- and high-priced crops.

Land on which seedling plants or nursery stock are to be grown should be fumigated with at least twice the amount of chemical recommended for general crop production. These heavier applications approach eradication of plant-infesting nematodes and ensure approval of the plants by crop-pest inspectors. Because of the high value of nursery stock, the extra amount of fumigant required still represents an excellent investment. Applications should be made in the fall or at least two months prior to planting; otherwise phytotoxicity may occur. Young seedlings often are very susceptible to even small quantities of fumigants.

In warmer sections of the country, deep fallow with three plowings during the hot summer months, followed by fumigation, has enabled growers to produce hundreds of millions of seedling plants without a trace of root-knot nematodes where once the land was heavily infested.

Shallow-rooted crops tend to concentrate the nematodes near the surface, where they are more vulnerable to fumigation. Therefore, a more efficient kill can be made after peas, beans, grain, melons, and similar crops than can be secured after alfalfa, cotton, and other deep-rooted types.

How Soil Fumigants Kill Nematodes

The manner in which soil fumigants kill nematodes has not been determined. Chitwood (1938) demonstrated that the outer layer of the bulb and stem nematode, *Ditylenchus dipsaci,* is a very thin, thermolabile membrane, "possibly a wax or sterol," which acts as a barrier to the penetration of nematicides. Later (1952) he stated that the halogenated hydrocarbons are "contact killers"; these include our best fumigants, dichloropropane (D-D), ethylene dibromide (EDB), chlorobromopropane, methyl bromide, and similar compounds. Chitwood's premise is based on the fact that these chemicals dissolve waxes, sterols, and other lipide materials frequently found on, or in, the cuticle of nematodes.

It is true that if an application of one of these soil fumigants is made at a certain point and a soil sector removed three or four days later, the nematodes near the point of injection will be found twisted and distorted as if they had died in agony. But 6 or 8 inches distant from the point of injection they will be found relaxed as if they had been anaesthetized through some gentle action on the nerve centers.

Nematodes placed in low concentrations of nematicides and observed under the binoculars exhibit a gradual slowing down of activity until complete cessation of movement is reached with no indications of physical discomfort. Just how this is accomplished is problematical. The most logical theory is that the nematicide enters through the amphid apertures, which are the external outlets of the nervous system. Proceeding inward to the sensillae, the fumigant reaches the first elements of the nervous system in such minute quantities that a slow, narcotizing effect is produced, with death eventually following. When dichlorobromopropanes are applied at the rate of only 1 or 2 gallons per acre, there is a delayed action which may continue for a month or more before activity ceases and death occurs.

Active nematodes are always found in the film of moisture surrounding soil particles. To reach them, the gaseous nematicide must be absorbed by this film of water and then make contact with the nematodes. Our best nematicides have an exceedingly low rate of solubility in water, and only minute quantities can be absorbed. Therefore, it appears doubtful that nematicides ever become concentrated on the cuticle in quantities sufficient to dissolve the protecting lipide layer. Only in the vicinity of application is such a concentration possible, and this fact doubtless accounts for the distorted carcasses found in that area.

Oral ingestion may also occur, for nematodes, like other forms of animal life, probably drink a certain amount of water and may imbibe a lethal amount of fumigant. That soil moisture has an important influence on the toxicity of nematicides is indicated by the fact that fumigation of dry fields does not prove successful. However, it is obvious that dry, loose soil affords a much better opportunity for the diffusion of nematicides and their contact with nematodes. Under dry conditions nemas lie quiescent, and respiration is at a minimum, a condition which is not favorable to the action of fumigants. Therefore, it appears best to assume that nematodes are usually killed by a combination of penetration through the amphids and oral ingestion.

However, there are other organs through which fumigants may reach the vital organs of nematodes. Cephalic papillae are assumed to be sensory organs connected with the nervous system, and attack through them may occur. Many tylenchs possess prominent deirids which extend from the external surface to tissues connected with the nerve ring and ventral nerve commissure. Entrance through deirids would doubtless be very effective. All dorylaims have numerous porelike organs leading through the cuticle into the lateral fields, and penetration may take place through these channels.

It will generally be noted that dorylaims and other nemas with large amphid apertures are more easily killed than are those with minute, porelike apertures like tylenchs, rhabditids, and cephalobs. It should be noted that these last two groups, and others which normally live in decaying organic materials, are much less susceptible to nematicides, especially ethylene dibromide. It is also interesting to note that nematodes are able to detect the direction from which a nematicide is approaching. Large, active species like *Dorylaimus obscurus* are able to move away from it, except for those in the immediate vicinity of application (Thorne, 1951).

Unsegmented eggs and larval nematodes within eggs are much more difficult to kill than are those living free in soil. The eggs and larvae of cyst-forming *Heterodera* are especially difficult to kill because they have not only the eggshells to protect them but also the tough, almost impermeable wall of the brown cyst. The writer (1951) found that the killing range of *H. schachtii* larvae within the protected eggs was only about half the distance of larvae living free in the soil. Those that had hatched, but still remained within the cyst, had an intermediate killing range. Perry (1954) found that *Trichodorus christiei* rapidly increased to much greater populations after fumigation. Apparently the eggs with their unusually thick coverings escaped, while natural enemies were destroyed.

Larvae and eggs of endoparasitic species remaining within roots are very often safely protected from nematicides, and a satisfactory kill will not be secured unless fumigation is delayed until the roots have decayed. This poses a special problem in the control of root-knot nematodes when a fall application is desired in order to permit early spring planting. In such instances the roots of tomatoes, beans, potatoes, and other crops should be removed and burned when the field is plowed and prepared for fumigation. The longest possible time should elapse to give remaining roots an opportunity to decay before the chemical is applied.

The soil-fumigation industry is rapidly expanding, and interested companies are endeavoring to produce more efficient and less expensive chemicals. These are being carefully evaluated by industry and cooperating nematologists. As they are made available, every effort should be made to utilize them efficiently by following the recommendations as established for the crops and soil types of a particular locality.

Applicators for soil fumigants are of various types, ranging from hand injectors used in home gardens and small experimental plots to large multichisel machines capable of covering 20 or 30 acres per day. Larger units usually operate with the chemical under about 25 pounds' pressure to ensure uniform distribution through the tubes which lead down behind the chisels and place chemicals at the desired depth. Efficient applicators built on plows apply the fumigant in the bottom of the furrow, where it is immediately covered by the following furrow. Plow applicators are especially suitable for smaller farms since they are inexpensive and can be adapted to almost any type of tractor and plow. Thorough loosening of the soil as the furrow is turned ensures a maximum diffusion of fumigants.

Pressure on the flow of fumigants is maintained either by a gear pump attached to the tractor power drive or by a small pressure tank operated from a gasoline motor. Gravity systems are satisfactory, especially for plow applicators. Flow of fumigants is regulated by lengths of Saran or copper tubing leading from a tank in which a uniform pressure is maintained by a hydrostatic pump. However, satisfactory results may be secured without this pump attachment.

Chisels of large applicators should be spaced not more than 12 inches apart when full coverage is being made. On heavy clay loams and muck a 10-inch spacing is advisable. For heavy soils a broad "spear-point" type of chisel is preferable since it tends to loosen the soil and promote diffusion.

Instructions for Soil Fumigation

Soil fumigation is a technical process and must be carefully accomplished in accordance with the following instructions:

1. Fumigate when the soil moisture content is similar to that of a good seedbed. Dry, loose soil allows much of the gas to escape, while excessive moisture prevents diffusion.

2. Fumigate when soil temperatures are between 40 and 85°F at a depth of 6 inches.

3. Plow to a depth of 8 to 12 inches. Do not depend on disking. This rarely works the soil to a depth of more than 5 or 6 inches, leaving a solid subsoil through which the gas has difficulty in penetrating.

4. Soil should be in good tilth without large clods, straw, roots, corn stubble, or coarse manure, which will form pockets and permit fumigants to escape.

5. Apply fumigants, as recommended by the manufacturer, at a depth of not less than 8 inches.

6. Immediately after fumigation, work the surface down firmly with a drag, harrow leveler, packer, roller, or other suitable equipment. The all too common practice of dragging a piece of plank or iron behind the applicator rarely gives satisfactory sealing of the surface, and considerable fumigant may thus be lost.

7. Delay planting 7 to 15 days after fumigation to avoid injury to seed or young plants. If possible, fumigate in the fall, and plant the following spring.

8. Be certain that soil fertility is sufficient to ensure returns for the investment in fumigants.

9. Handle fumigants only in open air, and avoid breathing fumes. Be prepared to immediately wash fumigants from hands with kerosene. If fumigants accidentally reach the eyes, flush copiously with water. Remove clothing or shoes if they become wet with chemical; otherwise, severe burns may result.

Dichlorobromopropene fumigants may be applied at the rate of 1 to 2 gallons per acre in the row with cotton seed without deleterious results. They may also be used in similar low applications about fruit trees, grape vines, and other perennials without visible injury.

Should heavy rains fall immediately after fumigation, allow fumigants to remain 7 to 10 days, and chisel thoroughly to facilitate aeration before planting; otherwise, phytotoxic quantities of gas may remain and severely damage young seedlings.

5. Therapeutics. According to Goodey (1936a), British entomologists were the first to use warm water when they attempted to control fly larvae in narcissus bulbs. The method was first suggested by Saunders as recounted by Wilks (1902), but the recommended 115°F for 20 minutes was reported to have killed the bulbs. Fryer (1915) determined that 110°F for one hour was most efficient for control of bulb flies without damage to the bulbs. Barr, about 1905, was the first to experiment with warm water for control of the bulb nematode, *Ditylenchus dipsaci*. The method was further developed by Ramsbottom in England and van Slogteren in Holland. By 1920 it was used extensively by the narcissus bulb industry, as will be noted later.

Warm-water treatment of daffodil, lily, bulbous iris, and other bulbs has since been recognized as successful if carefully carried out. But the physical and mechanical difficulties encountered in maintaining the delicate balance between the thermal death point of nematodes and that of bulbs frequently nullified the results or injured the bulbs. Rate of nematode survival in bulbs usually is correlated with the amount of dead and decaying tissue around the nematode colonies. In recently infested solid bulbs, the nematodes rarely escape when given the prescribed treatment. However, many nemas survived when pockets of decayed tissues were present, and in badly decayed bulbs the rate of survival often was as high as 50 to 75 per cent.

Until the use of formaldehyde in the hot water, there was the additional hazard of spreading fungus and bacterial diseases during the treatment. But this chemical provided a satisfactory answer to the problem and also aided in killing the many nematodes which leave the bulbs and enter the water during treatment.

Similar methods for the treatment of nursery stock roots, young strawberry, and other plants have given a certain degree of control when they were properly prepared for the process. Here again the balance between the thermal death point of plants and nematodes is so close that it is difficult to accomplish eradication on a commercial scale.

Steam apparently was first used for nematode control by Stone and

Smith (1898) and has since remained the most practical method of denematizing greenhouses. So popular has the method become that many operators install steam-distributing systems when greenhouses are built. Tight-fitting pans are sometimes placed over the beds and steam injected under them. Extent of penetration may be determined by placing a few potatoes in the soil and applying steam until they are cooked.

6. Mulching. Watson (1937) demonstrated that heavy organic mulches reduced nematode damage under Florida conditions. Linford and Yap experimented with five nemic-trapping fungi in Hawaiian soils high in organic matter. Root-knot injury was reduced when *Dactylella ellipsospora* Grove was introduced. However, the other four species produced no appreciable differences in nematode populations.

Loos applied 20 to 30 tons of Guatemala grass, *Tripsicum laxum,* about tea severely infested with *Pratylenchus coffeae,* and results were most satisfactory. When the writer visited these demonstrations in 1952, the evidence in favor of mulching was outstanding.

The golden nematode of potatoes, *Heterodera rostochiensis,* typifies the almost insurmountable problems faced by nematologists in devising satisfactory control methods for any plant parasitic nematode. First observed in Germany in 1881, it was regarded as a form of the sugar beet nematode, *H. schachtii.* In 1914 it was definitely established that potatoes were the preferred host, and in 1923 Wollenweber described the nematode as a distinct species. It is now established in most of the potato-growing sections of Europe. In the Americas it is known in Mexico and Peru and on Long Island, New York. In spite of the fact that the concentrated efforts of scores of workers have been directed toward control methods, the problem today is still practically unsolved. Millions of dollars have been spent in research and regulatory activities. Yet crop rotations remain the only generally recognized methods of control, and in many instances these have been far from satisfactory. Soil fumigants give fair control on the lighter sandy soils, but the cost is almost prohibitive. Extensive studies on the biology of the pest have revealed little that was not learned by the first research workers. Successful avenues of attack have not been opened by the combined efforts of the many scientists who have been engaged on the project in both Europe and the United States.

EXPERIMENTAL TECHNIQUES

Nematologists have long been aware of the fact that nematodes often are a serious disturbing factor in field, plot, and greenhouse experiments. Unfortunately, many workers in plant breeding, soils, fungicides, insecticides, and fertilizer testing have been unaware of this, and frequently their results were completely confused by the presence of nematodes. Many experiment-station soils are infested with indigenous and introduced species to such an extent that data secured from them are of doubtful value, if not worthless (Thorne, 1948).

Plant parasitic nematodes are rarely, if ever, uniformly distributed throughout a field, and experiments are subject to error because of this "spotting factor" of nematode distribution. Randomized replicated plots are especially subject to error because one plot on a severely or slightly infested area may nullify the results of the entire experiment. This is especially true when differences as low as 5 or 10 per cent are of importance in determining the value of fertilizers, crop varieties, or agronomic practices.

Fertilizer experiments are especially susceptible to nematode interference because the success of such an experiment depends on the plant roots reaching and assimilating the fertilizer. When considerable portions of the roots are destroyed, much of the fertilizer remains out of their range and the results of such a situation are obvious. The same is true of field applications of commercial fertilizers, which often fail to produce the expected increases in yields because the depleted root systems fail to reach far enough to utilize them. Even in the rhizosphere a portion of the fertilizer may not be assimilated because of the damaged and unthrifty condition of the roots in which nematodes are feeding.

Evaluation of tests for resistance to fungus diseases, viruses, and rusts may easily be nullified by nematodes, since weakened plants are much more susceptible to injury than are healthy ones.

Often the only method of correcting this "spotting factor" of nematode distribution in experimental plots is to use long, replicated strip plantings, a procedure which makes it possible to locate the heavily populated areas and secure "paired samples" from the infested or noninfested spots. If data from nematicides or nematode resistant plants are desired, the samples should be selected from the obviously infested areas; only under these conditions can a fair evaluation of the nematicide or crop variety be accurately ascertained. But if the experiment deals with fertilizers or varieties being tested for yields, it will be advisable to select samples from the least infested and most "normal" growing areas.

Greenhouse experiments with nematodes present special problems in that many species do not thrive in captivity and refuse to cooperate when brought in from the field. This is especially true of root lesion, spiral, stylet, stem and bulb, dagger, and other forms, which frequently disappear soon after transfer into pots and flats in the greenhouse. Temperature probably is the principal factor influencing their survival; there is a great contrast between the constant temperature indoors and the night and day fluctuations in the field. Too frequently indoor temperatures range considerably above those in the field, especially in the summer, and it usually is during this period that the greatest mortality occurs. Wallace (1955) found that the larvae of *Heterodera schachtii* hatched in greater numbers under varying temperatures than when maintained at a constant level.

Humidity appears to play an important part in survival, as evidenced by the successful colonies maintained in the cool, moist climate of Berkeley, California, and similar locations, and in greenhouses, where both humidity and temperature are maintained at favorable levels. Many attempts made by the writer to establish colonies in the arid climate of Utah invariably ended in failure, even when 8-inch pots were used with moist peat moss packed between them to prevent excessive drying.

Size of pots appears to be an important item. Usually 6 inches or larger gives best results, probably because smaller sizes experience greater fluctuations in temperature and moisture. Frequently plant roots adjacent to pot walls are practically free of infestation, a fact which indicates that the nemas avoid the outer part of the soil mass, where temperatures and moisture are more erratic.

Nematodes for greenhouse studies should be segregated from soil by the usual sifting and gravity and Baermann-funnel methods. If they are held in refrigerated storage for more than a few hours, it is advisable to secure fresh water from a stream or spring, since chlorine in the usual tap water may be injurious. Dagger nematodes and other species often go into a form of shock when placed in tap or distilled water, but if unchlorinated water is used, they survive transfer in better condition, especially if clean sand crystals from a stream bed or field soil are included.

The first prerequisite for conducting greenhouse experiments with plant parasitic nematodes is to demonstrate that colonies can be maintained on the host plant from which they were collected. Until this fact is established and the techniques of rearing the nematodes are worked out, it will be a waste of time to set up a series of experiments to study the effects of nematode parasitism on various plants. Negative results mean nothing unless it has been demonstrated that favorable conditions have been provided for their survival and reproduction.

An air-conditioned greenhouse doubtless is more suitable for maintenance of nematode populations than the ordinary type, which generally is subject to considerable fluctuations in temperature. In fact, summer temperatures in the average greeenhouse are frequently so high over long periods that colonies disappear regardless of the care given them, and experiments can be successfully conducted only during the cooler months. In one instance, failure of an air-conditioning unit for two days resulted in the loss of almost every colony being maintained in the room.

An interesting point to be considered is the fact that many species of nematodes appear to have certain periods of reproduction. In temperate climates this period is usually during the spring months. In the winter nematodes do not reproduce even if favorable temperature and moisture conditions are provided. A similar situation seems to prevail in the tropics, as the writer noted in Indonesia: between September and March not a single gravid female of *Radopholus oryzae,* the rice-root nematode, was observed among the thousands collected. The same was true of root lesion, spiral, and many other forms.

However, it is not surprising that, even under the most careful regulation of temperature and moisture, colonies disappear for no apparent reason. *Pratylenchus* and *Tylenchorhynchus* are susceptible to certain sporozoan parasites like *Duboscquia penetrans,* and these may inadvertently be introduced among the nemas, with disastrous results. Van der Vecht and Bergman in Java found that one of their experiments with rice-root nematode, *Radopholus oryzae,* had failed to develop as expected. Examination of the soil revealed that a *Mononchus,* apparently *M. longicaudatus,* had accidentally been introduced, had increased to great numbers, and had reduced the population of root parasites.

Correct identification of the nemas with which one is working is a most important point before experiments are set up. The writer has known of at least two instances in which experiments ended in negative results because saprophagous *Rhabditis, Diplogaster,* and *Panagrolaimus* were incorrectly identified as root-knot nematode larvae.

Even experiments with root-knot species may end in failure if the proper host plants are not provided. We now know that at least eight species of *Meloidogyne* exist and that certain species have host preferences.

TRAINING SUGGESTIONS FOR NEMATOLOGISTS

The well-grounded nematologist must have a more versatile training than the plant pathologist, entomologist, or zoologist if he is to evaluate properly the many factors involved in the field problems which he will encounter. The time has arrived when "applied" nematology is especially important if we are to justify the expenditures being made by state, Federal, and private agencies. Such expenditure will be justified only if our workers are trained in all phases of agriculture and understand the many factors involved in the successful production of the crops with which they are working. It is especially important that, whenever possible, workers should be assigned to problems in those sections of the country where they have grown up and with whose general agricultural picture they are already acquainted. A farm background is invaluable; no amount of technical training can take its place.

If a program involving nematodes is to be carried to a successful conclusion, it must be "sold" to the farmers growing the crop and this job is an exceedingly difficult one unless the nematologist can talk the language of the farmer and intelligently discuss with him the problems of soil fertility, agronomic practices, crop rotation, production, harvesting, and even marketing. If the nematologist is not prepared to answer questions on these problems and offer intelligent suggestions, it will be difficult to convince the landowner that the advised program is practical. Even then it often is necessary first to convert some leading farmer and establish demonstration plots which can be visited by groups of farmers during the tours which are conducted by the extension service. In short, a nematologist must be a combination of research worker, farmer, and extension agent if he is to be successful in selling the gospel of nematology in the community in which he works.

The scholastic training mentioned in the following outline may not be feasible in its entirety for all students, because some may not have access to certain courses taught only at agricultural institutions. For those thus handicapped it is advisable that, once they are assigned to a problem, they immediately make contact with the state extension services, become acquainted with leading farmers of the community, and learn the basic production facts concerning the crops grown in that particular locality.

Nematology: The first and basic essential of nematology is to master the techniques of processing soil and plant material by means of the sifting and gravity and Baermann-funnel techniques. Then should follow isolating, killing, and fixing the specimens and preparing permanent microscopic slides for study and future reference. Accompanying these activities there should be intensive training in microscopy, with special emphasis on the use of oil-immersion objectives and camera lucida. Following this training should come a study of the taxonomy of plant parasitic species, both ecto- and endoparasitic, and of those other species most commonly found associated with plant parasites in soil and plant tissues. Advanced work should include the anatomy and taxonomy of all the Phylum Nemata, including marine and fresh-water forms, parasites and associates of insects, and those parasitic in the higher animals, including man.

Plant pathology: Basic courses in plant pathology should cover fungus and bacterial diseases and viruses, with special reference to those diseases and viruses attacking roots and producing various types of rots. Field and laboratory work should include studies of these diseases as possible associates of plant parasitic nematodes in producing these rots, since plants weakened by nematodes are more susceptible to infection by other organisms. Culture of nematodes on certain fungi should be part of laboratory studies, since it is sometimes possible to produce great numbers of certain plant parasitic nematodes for use in host studies. Studies of nematode-trapping fungi should be included, since they may be of economic importance under certain conditions.

Agronomy: Courses in agronomy should cover the growth and production of the basic crops, with special reference to fertilizers, cultural methods, and crop rotations, and with a study of root systems produced on different types of soil.

Horticulture: A general course in horticulture should cover the various orchard trees, small fruits, and berries. Studies should include the growth and extent of root systems. A prerequisite to this course is the ability to use a shovel efficiently.

Soils: The nematologist must have a basic knowledge of soil types, their moisture-holding capacity and structure, including subsoil, plow sole, and other features. These should be closely correlated with agronomic courses.

Entomology: A general course in entomology should cover those insect species which at some stage in their development inhabit the soil, e.g., wireworms, white grubs, and root maggots. Often of value is information on white centipedes, soil mites, tardigrads, and related organisms.

Zoology: Invertebrate zoology, parasitology including helminthology, and histological techniques provide valuable training and are necessary for anyone working with soil faunas. Investigations of natural enemies of nematodes like sporozoons, mites, collembolans, and tardigrads require extensive knowledge of soil microorganisms of all types.

Botany: A knowledge of plant anatomy, especially the anatomy of roots, will often be of value. This should be accompanied by course work in cytology to learn the techniques of staining, sectioning, and preparation of permanent microscopic slides. Taxonomy of plants may be of use in the selection and breeding of strains and varieties resistant to nematode attacks.

Genetics: Plant breeding for resistance and immunity to nematode attack will offer many opportunities to the geneticist who has a good working knowledge of plant parasitic nematodes. However, projects along these lines may best be carried out by teamwork between nematologists and geneticists.

Chapter 2

COLLECTING SOIL AND PLANT MATERIAL

Nematodes are so universally distributed that if plant life of any form grows in the soil it is almost certain to contain several species. Cultivated fields, with their high fertility and heavy plant covers, are especially favorable habitats for a wide range of species, and populations of several billions per acre are not unusual. A pound of soil from one of these fields generally contains ten to thirty species belonging to many and diverse genera, including endoparasites, ectoparasites, predators, saprophages, and other free-living forms. Forest soils contain a great variety of ectoparasitic tylenchs and dorylaims, as well as predaceous mononchs, saprophagous cephalobs, and rhabditids. Desert soils, too, have varied faunas, which are active only during brief periods when rainfall may occur and which remain quiescent during the remainder of the year. In the high mountains of western United States are found some of the most varied populations and the greatest numbers of free-living species per pound of soil. Interestingly enough, it is here that we frequently collect many of those species which deMan found along the humid coast of Holland. A few handfuls of soil in which lichens, moss, and other alpine plants grow on the top of Longs Peak, Colorado, elevation 14,255 feet, contained several hundred specimens including eighteen species, of which fifteen are known from Europe (Thorne, 1929).

When we investigate the wet soils of lakes and stream banks and the aquatic fauna of these bodies of water, we find a still different group, which generally are considerably larger than those from fields. Frequently, a large part of these will be types with filiform tails. By far the greatest variety of species found anywhere on the globe are those from marine waters, from the shallow coastal beaches to the greatest depths. Truly, there is an infinite variety which will provide endless interest for the student who ventures into this little-known world of nematology.

The geographical distribution of certain species is a most fascinating feature of nematology. A tiny predator, *Campydora demonstrans,* was described by Cobb (1920) from soil about citrus roots originating on the island of Corfu. The next time this interesting little species was collected, the writer (1939) found the nemas in soil from the summit of Mount Timpanogos in Utah at an elevation of 12,000 feet. One other collection was made from an alfalfa test plot near Salt Lake City, Utah.

Dorylaimus simplex is a widely distributed species which has appeared in collections from many parts of North America, Africa, Turkey, and Indonesia. *Mononchus papillatus* is another cosmopolitan species with widely varying habitats, from desert soils to swamps, and from sea level to high mountains. Such world-wide inhabitants must certainly be of very ancient origin. Of course, many plant parasitic and soil-inhabiting forms have been carried from country to country with plants, tubers, bulbs, and seeds, until it is impossible to determine their origin. After observing the global distribution of certain free-living species, there is little reason to doubt that plant parasitic types may also have been indigenous to more than one continent.

Naturally, we are generally most interested in those species which may be of economic importance. These we shall find in and about the roots of their host plants or in the stems, leaves, and seeds of the plants themselves. Nematodes are difficult subjects with which to work, and it is essential that all materials collected for identification should be given the best of care before arriving in the laboratory. Material in poor condition entails needless work and usually gives unsatisfactory results. The following procedures are suggested to ensure the arrival of specimens in the best possible condition:

Preparation of Collections for Transit

1. Stems and leaves should be packed in moist cotton, paper, or moss and placed in a neoprene bag or wrapped in wax paper. Keep as cool as possible.

2. Roots should be carefully lifted with a trowel, spade, or shovel, together with at least 2 or 3 pounds of the adhering soil, and placed in a neoprene bag. Do not pull up plants; most of the small roots will thus be lost, and with them a large portion of the nematodes.

3. Collect ample material whenever possible. This procedure will generally ensure a good number of specimens of the species present and will enable the operator to secure a more satisfactory evaluation of their relationship to the plant.

4. Give supporting data: subject, locality, date, collector, symptoms, extent of damage, distribution, and other data of importance or interest.

5. If material will be in transit for more than one week, it may be preserved in a solution composed of 1 part commercial formaldehyde and 7 parts of water. If this solution is used hot, about 130°F, it relaxes the nematodes and prevents distortion. After fixation and settling, excess liquid should be decanted to reduce weight and prevent damage in the event that the container is broken in transit.

6. If soil screens are available, follow instructions as outlined in soil-processing section, make a bulk sample of the screen residues, allow to settle for half an hour, and decant excess liquid. Add slowly an equal quantity of boiling water to relax the specimens, allow to settle for one hour, and decant again. To these residues add an equal amount of a solution composed of 1 part formaldehyde and 3 parts water. Allow to

settle for one hour, decant, and place in container together with the plant roots and ship. If a Baermann funnel is available, the residues may be concentrated still further before killing and fixing. This method is especially adapted for overseas and air shipment when weight is a factor to be considered.

Should soil screens not be available, cover the roots and soil well with water, mix thoroughly, and pour off the muddy liquid. Allow to settle one-half hour, and decant the excess liquid. Then kill with an equal amount of hot water, and fix as directed in the preceding paragraph. Include the plant roots.

7. If aquatic collections, or those from wet soil, are placed in sealed containers for as much as six or eight hours, especially during warm weather, the specimens may die and even decay before they reach the laboratory. Aeration of this type of material is essential. Tops should be removed from containers whenever possible. Always keep as cool as conditions permit.

8. Soil samples taken when dry should be transported in this condition. Before processing they should be moistened to "seedbed" condition and allowed to stand for a few days. This revives the nematodes from their quiescence, and frequently many of the free-living species will develop and begin to produce eggs. Collections made during the cold winter months should be brought into a warm laboratory for a few days before processing.

Generally, the sample should include soil in the root zone from near the surface to at least 1 foot in depth. For shrubs and trees it may be advisable to dig down to 3 or 4 feet and secure portions of the roots and soil. To secure a general survey of the fauna of a field or orchard, it is sometimes advisable to collect 25 to 50 pounds of soil from several locations, place it in a large container, cover well with water, mix, and dip out 2 or 3 quarts for processing. If specimens of particular interest are found, more of the material should be processed since it is always advisable to retain plenty of specimens for future study.

PROCESSING SOIL AND PLANT MATERIAL

The Cobb (1918) sifting and gravity method is usually most satisfactory for separating nemas from soil after it arrives in the laboratory. This method consists of a series of operations by which heavy particles are settled out and discarded. Lighter fractions containing the nematodes are passed through a series of screens which separate the nemas and small particles of light organic material from the muddy solution. The process is relatively simple, and those interested in nematology must become proficient in it before they can make real progress in the science.

The beginner should select 2 or 3 pounds of light sandy loam, together with the roots of plants growing in it. Lighter soils are much more easily processed than heavy clays, which require considerable patience and much more time. The most difficult types are those containing large amounts of organic matter like peat and muck, which neither settle nor sink. When techniques are once mastered, the average soil sample can be reduced to 8 or 10 syracuse watchglassfuls of clear residues in 5 to 10 minutes. Always use ample material so that you will not have to worry about losing a few nemas during the process.

A sink with ample working space beneath the spigot is essential. If hot and cold water are both available, the mixing-type water tap is preferable. If the mixing type is available, the cold side should be set permanently with a small stream and the hot side used for washing off screens after residues have been removed. Efficient use of this type of water tap will appreciably reduce the time required to process a sample. Heavy soil particles should be placed in a container; otherwise, clogging of the drain may occur.

Disposal facilities should be provided for all soil and plant residues which may carry plant parasitic nematodes or other pests and diseases. Arrangements should previously be made with plant quarantine officials relative to the introduction of such materials and disposal of residues.

Equipment: Soil processing is a relatively simple and inexpensive process except for the cost of fine-mesh metal-cloth screens. Screens made on pans with sloping sides are preferable to commercial types with straight sides. The following items are sufficient to equip a small laboratory:

Five 6-inch stainless steel or brass-cloth screens of 10, 25, 50, 100, and 200 meshes per inch. A 325 mesh is desirable if finances permit.
Three 10- or 12-inch tin, aluminum, or enameled pans.
Two 6- or 7-inch pans.
Two 2- or 3-gallon pans or pails.
Six 250-ml beakers or glasses of a similar size.
Two 100-ml beakers.
Four 50-ml beakers.
One syracuse watch glass.
One laboratory needle holder and a thick-walled piece of bamboo.
One box of smallest dental pulp files.

(See also list of equipment in Chapter 3 under Microscopic Techniques)

Mark the syracuse watch glass as shown in Fig. 2-1, and cut the pattern lightly into the glass with a diamond pencil. These sections are just wide enough to be covered by the low powers of the wide-field dissecting microscope when one is searching for nemas.

Split a small section from the tough layer of bamboo just beneath the hard outer surface, fit it into the needle holder, and bring to a fine point with a sharp knife or scalpel. Complete the sharpening under the low-power binocular until the point consists of only two or three fibers. This process is another one which must be mastered, for unless one has these finely pointed bamboo needles, it will be difficult to lift out and transfer specimens efficiently. The needles are especially essential in making face views and cross sections, as outlined later. Dental pulp files are excellent for picking out larger specimens and are especially good for beginners since they do not break as easily as do the bamboo points. Instead of bamboo, Reynolds (1950) found a cactus with very slender spines which made an excellent substitute, and Linford (1953) cut slender points on pieces of nylon rods.

Before proceeding with processing, it may be well to consider first what we can expect to collect on the different screens as the sample passes through them. One great advantage of using several screens lies in the fact that the nematodes are roughly divided into a series of sizes, and this feature frequently facilitates selecting specimens. As you examine the residues, note the characteristic movements of certain species. Some like *Bastiani* and *Prismatolaimus* will move frantically about, while most *Dorylaimus, Tylenchus,* and similar forms will move slowly, with a graceful, serpentine, gliding motion. When you see a nema with the head moving nervously as if searching for something, it is generally a *Mononchus, Nygolaimus,* or some other predator. Note that nemas lying in repose assume certain typical forms, spiral, straight, or ventrally arcuate curved tails; each form is often characteristic for a certain species or a genus of related species.

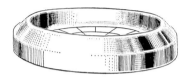

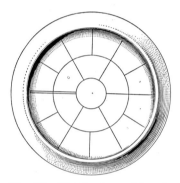

Fig. 2-1. Watch glass with subdivided bottom. This facilitates examination of screen residues for nemas. (*After Cobb.*)

The 10-mesh screen removes coarse organic material and contains nematodes only in those areas where large mermithid parasites of grasshoppers and other insects are found. These will readily be observed without the aid of a microscope after the residues are rinsed just before discarding. On this screen will be collected most of the roots broken off during digging. These, together with the main roots of the plants, should be reduced to pulp in the blendor. Or they may be shredded with a knife and allowed to soak overnight, releasing *Pratylenchus* and other nemas which may be in the tissues.

On the 25-mesh screen will be found certain *Dorylaimus, Sectonema, Mononchus,* and other large free-living species, sometimes in surprising numbers.

Nemas collected from the 50-mesh screen will include dorylaims, mononchs, and similar-sized forms 1.5 to 4 mm long. Unless the soil contains much organic matter, this screen can usually be eliminated.

The 100-mesh screen will hold most adult *Rhabditis, Panagrolaimus, Tylenchus, Rotylenchus, Ditylenchus,* and many other forms between 1 and 2 mm long and also the cysts and males of *Heterodera*.

Frequently, the greatest numbers will be found on the 200-mesh screen where the adults of many small species like *Tylenchus exiguus, Plectus parvus, Acrobeloides buetschli, Diploscapter coronata, Acrobeles ctenocephalus, Paratylenchus hamatus,* and others will collect. Here, too, will be found most of the larvae of *Heterodera, Meloidogyne, Pratylenchus,* and *Tylenchulus.* Many of these larvae and most of those of *Cacopaurus, Paratylenchus, Criconemoides,* and other minute forms less than 0.3 mm long may pass through and escape. A 325-mesh screen will collect most of these tiny individuals. A good substitute for this extra-fine screen can be made from a well-shrunk piece of fine-mesh millers' bolting silk held between two pans from which the bottoms have been cut, as described by Cobb (1918).

Cobb sifting and gravity methods: The following instructions for washing a soil sample may appear to be entirely too detailed, but the reader must remember that a few minutes of careful work with the screen will take the place of several hours spent at the dissecting microscope in searching through residues. Failure to use screens efficiently is responsible for the wide use of Baermann funnels, which generally give less satisfactory results. With these preliminary remarks, let's go into the laboratory, and get to work:

1. Place 1 to 3 pounds of the soil in a large pan or pail, cover well with water, and thoroughly break all lumps while working the mass into a thick, roily mixture. Allow to settle about 10 seconds.

2. Pour this muddy solution through the 10-mesh screen into one of the two large soil-washing pans. Add a pint or two of water to the heavy residues remaining, mix thoroughly, allow to settle a few seconds, and pour into the first lot through the same screen. Wash the residues from the screen into a pan, remove any plant roots which may contain endoparasitic nemas, and discard the remainder into a receptacle for final disposal. The heavy residues from the large pan or pail may also be discarded at this time. Thoroughly wash the screen before returning it to its place.

3. Pour the pan of muddy water through the 25-mesh screen, except the heavy portions which have settled to the bottom. Add about a half a pint of water to these residues, mix, allow to settle a few seconds, and pour into the first lot through the same screen. Discard the heavy portion remaining.

4. Dip the screen containing the residues into the pan of muddy water, lifting it up and down two or three times to rinse off adhering small particles.

5. Place the screen on edge in one of the 6-inch pans, and hold under the small stream from the water tap, turning the screen so that all residues are collected.

6. Pour the residues through the same screen again, in a small stream aimed into the lower edge of the screen, rather than all over it. Discard the heavier particles remaining in the pan after pouring.

7. Again, direct the stream of water on the back of the screen, and

wash the residues into one of the small pans, using just enough water to fill one of the 250-ml beakers into which it should be poured. Again discard heavy particles.

8. Repeat the process with the 50-, 100-, and 200-mesh screens, always discarding the heavy particles. If the residues are not clear after the first rinsing, give them a second, or even a third if necessary, before attempting to examine them under the dissecting microscope.

9. By the time the 200-mesh screening process is completed, the 25- and 50-mesh residues have settled. Carefully pick up the beaker of 25-mesh residues, and pour off the supernatant liquid with a rapid motion. This will carry away the floating organic matter and leave about 40 ml in the bottom. Pour this into a 50-ml beaker, allow to settle for a few minutes, and again decant, leaving one syracuse watchglassful for examination. Repeat the process with the 50-mesh residues.

After the 25- and 50-mesh residues have been examined, the 100-mesh residues will be settled. Decant in the same manner, leaving a 50-ml beakerful for examination. After settling for a few minutes, the residues will be ready for examination under the dissecting microscope. By settling and decanting, these residues can be reduced to three or four watchglassfuls. Repeat this process with the 200-mesh residues.

The time required for examination will, of course, vary with the number of nematodes in the sample. These must be carefully observed and selections made for processing into permanent slides. Generally, one or two hours will suffice for complete examination and selection of specimens. If only a routine check for a few species is necessary, the process may be completed in 10 to 15 minutes.

This process, if properly carried out, leaves the heavy particles behind, while extremely fine particles are finally passed through the finest screen and discarded. Only the nematodes and small pieces of organic matter are retained on the screens, and these should always be rinsed until clear to facilitate examination. Time should never be wasted on partly-cleared residues. It is much simpler to run them through the screen a second or third time and have well-cleared residues in which the nemas are easily observed.

Efficiency of the process will vary from 50 to 90 per cent, depending upon the skill of the operator, type of soil being processed, size of the nematodes present, and size of mesh in the final screen. The beginner should check discarded portions until the proper times for settling and pouring the various fractions have been determined. An experienced operator can demonstrate in half an hour the techniques which a beginner will spend weeks in learning if working alone.

During the screening process use the screens singly. Never superimpose them and attempt to work the sample through them simultaneously. Devices for holding the screens in different positions have been suggested, but none is as satisfactory as the method described above.

Frequently specimens float on the beakers of residues and are lost when the excess is decanted. To correct this situation, spray the surface with 70 per cent alcohol from an atomizer, and allow a few minutes for the nemas to settle.

Heterodera cysts usually float on the screen residues unless completely filled with eggs. Most cysts pass through the 50-mesh and collect on the 100-mesh screen, except for occasional oversize or very small specimens. Therefore, flotsam from the 100-mesh screen should be scraped onto a glass slide and examined for cysts under the dissecting microscope.

When processing light sandy soil low in organic content, it generally is possible to make a satisfactory extraction by using only the 10-, 50-, and 200-mesh screens.

Baermann funnel: This device (Baermann, 1917) is useful for certain purposes and by some workers is preferred to the sifting and gravity method. It is especially suited to collecting the minute larvae of *Paratylenchus, Tylenchulus, Cacopaurus,* and other small specimens provided that they are active. The apparatus consists of a 4- to 6-inch funnel with a piece of rubber tubing attached to the stem and closed by a Day-type clamp. The funnel is partly filled with water and the soil sample placed in a cloth bag and carefully lowered into the water and allowed to remain a few hours to several days. Very active nematodes soon work their way out of the bag and settle into the stem, but slow-moving or quiescent forms may remain for several days or may even fail to emerge. In this respect the apparatus is less satisfactory than sieves. A much longer time is required before the population of a sample can be determined.

Fig. 2-2. Baermann-funnel assembly with screen residues in the inverted beaker. Beaker on table shows how cloth is applied after screen residues have been condensed to about half beaker volume. Funnel assemblies are suitable only for very active nemas. (*Photograph by E. H. Herrling. Courtesy of Department of Plant Pathology, University of Wisconsin.*)

The funnel system is an excellent method of separating specimens from the screen residues and condensing them for examination, as described by Christie and Perry (1951). This method is also very satisfactory for separating specimens from plant material which has been reduced to pulp in the blendor. The material should remain in the funnel overnight or longer.

Van der Vecht and Bergman (1954) constructed a 4-foot funnel at the Bogor, Java, Experiment Station in which they collected rice-root nematodes, *Radopholus oryzae*. The roots were first washed until free of soil, then cut into small fragments and placed on a piece of bolting silk fastened over the top of the funnel and allowed to remain overnight. It was not unusual to collect over half a million nemas at one time, and the liter of water in which they were drawn off was milky white with their wriggling bodies. This inoculum was then placed in concrete tubs in which rice plants were growing.

V. G. Perry devised a variation of the funnel technique which is much superior to the usual method. The soil is washed by the usual sifting and gravity methods. The screenings are then reduced by settling and decanting until only about 100 ml remains, all the lots having been combined during the reduction process. The composited screenings are then placed in a 250-ml beaker, and a 6-inch-square piece of moderately close-mesh muslin is wetted and fastened over the top with a rubber band. Finally the beaker is inverted into a 6-inch funnel partly filled with water. The nematodes immediately begin working through the cloth and settle to the bottom of the tube, where many of them will be found within a few minutes. After standing overnight practically all of them will have emerged, even the slow-moving ring nemas. Should particles of trash from the residues come through with the nemas, the mesh is too coarse. On the other hand, if large specimens are held back, it is too fine.

The centrifuge has been employed by certain workers, with perhaps the most thorough process developed by Jensen and Caveness (1955). Recovery by this method is higher than that secured through the screens, but the sample is very small. Oostenbrink (1954) suggested certain variations in the technique of employing the centrifuge, and a few other workers have attempted to use it. However, none of these methods has any particular advantage.

Probably the most accurate apparatus for detailed census work is that devised by Seinhorst (1956). This consists of an assembly of flasks, tubes, and other glass apparatus through which a continuous flow of water is maintained at different speeds, depending on the sizes of the nematodes being collected. Suspensions must be passed through sieves of different meshes five to seven times, after which the nemas are collected in the usual manner. A soil sample cannot exceed 500 g, which is a very small portion of a field plot, and certainly most inadequate if one is interested in the population of an acre of land.

For muck and peat soils the writer prefers an adaptation of the Baermann principle. Wood frames from 2 to 3 inches high are fitted to shallow trays. The tray bottom is covered with 20-mesh brass screen on which large paper napkins or unbleached cotton cloth is laid. Soil is then placed in the frame, and borders of the napkin or cloth are folded in over it. Water is added outside the frame and allowed to rise until the soil is saturated. After 24 to 48 hours the frame is carefully lifted out, leaving the nemas in 1 or 2 liters of water and practically free of soil residues. The contents is poured into beakers, allowed to settle, decanted, and examined in the usual manner.

Extracting nemas from roots: *Pratylenchus, Radopholus,* and other endoparasitic nematodes are removed from root tissues by means of the Waring blendor, as reported by Taylor and Loegering (1953). The roots are cut into pieces 10 to 20 mm long, placed in the blendor, covered with water, and then processed for 20 to 60 seconds, or until the roots have been reduced to small fragments. The residues may then be washed through the screens and examined immediately or placed in a funnel and allowed to stand for 10 to 24 hours. Most of the nemas will have made their way down to the clamp and may be drawn off. However, the blending process leaves the nemas dazed and torpid, and sometimes many of them remain in the root residues for several days.

Incubation method: Young (1954) described a method which requires no special apparatus, yet gives an excellent recovery. The roots are washed, then placed in a covered jar lined with moist filter paper or cloth, and then a small quantity of water is added. As the nematodes emerge, they work their way down into the water, which is then poured off and examined. Young reported that from fourteen samples of roots he secured 3,761 specimens of *Radopholus similis,* while from a similar group processed in Baermann funnels only 805 were collected.

Estimating nematode populations: Frequently, it is desirable to secure some measure of the nematodes inhabiting a square rod, an acre, or some other desired unit. This is an exceedingly difficult problem, and one which is subject to great error because of the relatively infinitesimal quantity of soil which can be examined and the erratic distribution of nematode colonies.

Cobb (1918) recommended the use of 1/1,000,000-acre tubes to be driven into the soil, dug out, and processed in the laboratory. These tubes were extensively used by the writer (1927), but rarely was it possible to process more than four sets of samples, and more often only two were taken. Obviously, these were woefully inadequate, but they represented the maximum which one or two men could process in the limited time available. However, it is strongly recommended that everyone interested in nematodes should take samples in this manner. Digging and processing them will give important information on soil structure, as well as on distribution of plant parasitic and free-living species.

The maximum amount of soil in a sample will usually be 25 to 50 pounds. This should be made up of a large number of small samples taken either at random or from designated points throughout the area under study. Each minor sample should be a column of soil at least 1 foot deep, and 2 feet may be necessary, depending on soil structure and root distribution. Samples from orchard trees and deep-rooted perennials must sometimes be dug to a depth of several feet. Certain tubular sampling devices facilitate sampling on an extensive scale.

Processing of aliquots from large samples will be the second limiting factor. This will depend upon the time and labor available and will vary from a one-man laboratory to large-scale projects with twenty or thirty employees. Equipment will consist of a few hand screens and pans to batteries of Seinhorst apparatus and automatic machines similar to those designed for the Golden Nematode Project on Long Island, New York. Each worker must make the most efficient use of the time and equipment available and adjust the number and size of samples accordingly.

The spotting factor of nematode distribution presents a most difficult problem, especially in dealing with root parasitic types. These congregate about the roots of their hosts, producing a pattern of nematode distribution very similar in extent and depth to that of root distribution. Under these conditions one sample may include hundreds of certain species of plant parasitic nematodes, while another taken a few inches distant will have very few or none. An area so severely infested in one season that the host is killed will often have a relatively low population the following year. This is because the dying plants had a trap-crop effect and a large portion of the nematodes died with the plants. Centers of population shift about according to the growth of hosts; "islands" of good plants generally are found even in the most severely infested fields.

Orchard trees affected by nematode slow decline frequently have root systems so severely damaged that it is difficult to find sufficient rootlets for a satisfactory sample. Sometimes the nematodes have been reduced by starvation until populations are very low and only occasional tufts of small, stunted roots can be found. Soil from severely infested trees always contains quantities of root fragments which will be found clogging the screens when samples are processed.

Even free-living *Mononchus, Nygolaimus, Rhabditis, Panagrolaimus,* and other forms may be found in groups, where they are apparently attracted by their favorite foods. Saprophagous *Rhabditis* and *Panagrolaimus* are especially numerous in areas near the surface, where there is an abundance of decaying organic material. *Mononchus* are more generally distributed through the less compact top foot of soil. *Nygolaimus* usually are deeper down in the subsoil, where they find numerous small oligochaetes, which comprise most of their food.

Heavy clay soil with dense subsoil and plow sole tend to restrict root growth to the first 10 or 15 inches, and in this zone the greatest concentration of nematodes will be found. Light, deep sandy soils allow roots to penetrate down several feet. The greatest nematode colonies may be at depths of 4 or even 6 feet in the cotton and alfalfa fields of the southern San Joaquin Valley, California. Localized concentrations frequently are encountered in thin layers of clay loams which are interspersed with the sand. Higher fertility of the loam layers produces masses of rootlets on which the nematodes thrive.

To be realistic, it is evident that any estimates of nematode populations per acre are subject to great error. Data secured by any method of sampling are merely indicative of the numbers of nematodes which actually exist at the points at which samples were taken. These facts practically preclude the possibility of sampling entire fields, predicting populations, and advising owners on the advisability of planting certain

College of the Sequoias
Library

crops. Such data are not without value, for they do afford necessary information on depths at which nematode colonies are located. They may also explain certain difficulties encountered in securing favorable yields after fallow, crop rotations, or soil fumigation.

While making population studies, one should always make observations on the time and place of reproduction of the various species. Also of importance are notes on stages in the life cycle in which the nemas pass through the heat of summer, drought, cold of winter, or other soil and climatic conditions. Information of this type has great interest, because there is always a personal satisfaction in knowing something of the life habits of these tiny denizens of the soil. Unless one makes such studies, it is impossible to know what is transpiring in this hidden world of which we know so little and on which we are so dependent.

Chapter 3

MICROSCOPIC TECHNIQUES

Nematological work requires the most exacting microscopic techniques for the resolution of certain minute diagnostic morphological characters. Accurate identifications cannot be made by superficial, casual observation under the lower powers of magnification except for a few very common and well-known species. Usually the nematologist must work with the equipment available to him and adapt it to his needs.

Compound microscope: Any of the standard domestic or imported types are satisfactory if in good mechanical condition. Binoculars are preferable, but the writer used a monocular model from 1918 until 1956 and found it most satisfactory. A rotary substage is almost a necessity when making camera lucida drawings, because it usually is desirable to orient specimens for convenience when sketching is being done.

Objectives must be of good quality in the 4- and 10-mm types, since they will be used in making outline sketches for measuring nemas. Gross examinations and low-magnification drawings will also be made with them, and these require a high degree of accuracy.

An oil-immersion objective of the highest quality is absolutely essential when making species determinations. Preferably this should be a 1.5-mm, but a high-grade 2.0-mm is often satisfactory. An objective which will resolve the membranous fringes of the cephalic probolae of *Acrobeles complexus* and similar species is satisfactory. Many objectives fail to meet this requirement.

Oculars of the best quality should be used; otherwise, the best objectives will fail to give desired resolution. For general studies of gross body anatomy a 5× ocular is usually sufficient. However, when observing lateral fields, deirids, phasmids, and other cuticular structures, a 10× ocular generally must be used. Cephalic papillae of tylenchs, cirri of *Chambersiella*, probolae of *Acrobeles*, and similar minutiae can be seen only with a 10× ocular. For certain excessively fine structures 12.5×, 15×, and even 20× are sometimes useful.

The question of achromatic, apochromatic, and other lens types usually is a matter of availability. Choice of lens type is largely a matter of personal preference and salesmanship. Testing prior to purchase is always desirable.

Condensers: Modern microscopes usually are equipped with satisfactory condensers. However, adjustment is very important in studying nemas and often will vary from one part of the body to another. The delicate illumination used in observing the nerve ring will not be suitable for studying refractive spicula. Proficiency in the use of the condenser can be acquired only by careful testing and experience.

The most satisfactory condenser is an oil-immersion objective. This can be mounted in the condenser frame by inserting an adapter ring. If the full-length objective interferes with the mirror, the capsule may be cut to one-half its length. This oil-immersion condenser can be used only with the Cobb metal microscope slide, which permits it to be brought in focus on the nema, the resolution thus being increased. Many of the cephalic papillae and other minute characters illustrated by the writer could not have been seen with the ordinary condenser.

Microscope lamps: Any standard lamp with daylight-blue filter will give satisfactory illumination when properly regulated, focused, and aligned. Overillumination is the most common fault in nemic microscopy and is responsible for many failures in observation. Cephalic papillae, radial striae of the cuticle, cuticular markings, and similar obscure characters are often "washed out" by excessive light. Usually it is desirable to replace the bright, short-lived light globes with inexpensive 20- or 40-watt 110-volt G.E. projection globes with aluminized backs. These give a soft, mellow light which is ideal for viewing nemas and they eliminate eyestrain. Built-in substage lights are generally unsatisfactory.

Camera lucida: The average camera lucida is little more than a mechanical abortion. A far superior assembly can be made from a 5- or 10-mm-cube beam splitter mounted in a turret fitting the ocular. This is combined with a 5×7 first-surface magnesium mirror sliding on a fixed bracket. Position of the mirror can be varied to produce desired magnifications. This comparatively inexpensive assembly will easily produce magnifications of 2,000, 3,000, and even 4,000 diameters with a clear, distinct image. When working with a binocular compound microscope it is not necessary to insert the monocular tube when the camera lucida is used. Close the left eye while drawing, and should some portion of the object be indistinct, open the left eye, examine the dim portion, and then continue. If inclined oculars are used, merely rotate the mirror to the desired angle, and insert a false table top at the same angle. The convenience and superiority of this assembly are immediately evident once it has been used.

Eye shades: The eyes are the nematologist's most precious possession. Cloth shades are easily arranged about the oculars, allowing only the light transmitted through the lenses to reach the eyes. Elimination of side lights removes eyestrain; one can work 8 hours with less strain than would be experienced in 10 minutes without the shade.

Headrests: The tiring effect of continuous microscope work can be practically eliminated by a headrest. Cast in plaster of paris, it approximately fits the operator's forehead and is used with a thin gauze pad. Stability assured by the headrest is indispensable when making camera lucida drawings at high magnifications. The tubular supporting assembly allows for vertical and lateral adjustments.

Dissecting or stereo microscope: This microscope should be of the low-power wide-field binocular type. Proper magnification and working space beneath the objectives are two of the most important qualities. Select short 1×, 2×, and 3× objectives and paired oculars of 15× or 18×. This combination will give sufficient magnification for the experienced nematologist to recognize common genera of nematodes and determine if specimens are young or mature. The long objectives presently in vogue leave little working space, and picks used in trans-

Fig. 3-1. Camera lucida assembly. Note brass turret holding beam-splitter prism on right ocular. Drawing board is at right angles to inclined oculars. A glass plate is taped to board to ensure a smooth drawing surface. First surface magnesium mirror in frame is rotated on milled 2-inch pipe to same angle as ocular and drawing board. Microscope and lamp are set tightly in a ⅜-inch plyboard form to ensure alignment. This assembly gives magnifications up to 4,000 diameters. (*Photograph by E. H. Herrling. Courtesy of Department of Plant Pathology, University of Wisconsin.*)

ferring nematodes are frequently broken on them. An eye shade should, of course, be fitted on this instrument.

Hand rests: Throw away the contraptions furnished by manufacturers, and replace them with one long, solid piece of aluminum, brass, plastic, or other available material. A 3-inch-round hole beneath the oculars allows for transmitted light illuminations. The glass-plate substage is held in place by brackets fastened to the aluminum plate by small bolts. Glass substages rapidly become scratched when one is working with soil residues and plant material. Replace them with inexpensive pieces cut from scrap plate glass by your local glazier.

Illumination for low-power binoculars: Paired 16-inch fluorescent tubes should be hung at an angle which allows light to be picked up by the substage mirror while the upper end illuminates the material. This closely approximates daylight in quality and is most satisfactory for low-power binocular work.

Miscellaneous items: To remove immersion oil from the cover slip, take a small tuft of absorbent cotton, fold under the loose fibers, moisten

Fig. 3-2. Dissecting microscope equipped with aluminum-plate hand rest and eye shade. Similar shades should be fitted to all microscopes to prevent eye strain and increase efficiency. (*Photograph by E. H. Herrling. Courtesy of Department of Plant Pathology, University of Wisconsin.*)

with xylene or alcohol from a dropper, and remove the oil with two or three light, deft strokes. This method eliminates the smearing of slides and labels which usually accompanies the use of lens paper. Lightly pass the cotton tuft over the objective, and remove the oil from the lens.

Indistinct striae and other cuticular markings can often be resolved by moving the condenser slightly to one side, giving an oblique lighting to the contour of the nema. This method often is effective when the number of annules on the lips of *Pratylenchus, Tylenchus,* and other groups is being determined.

Illumination of camera lucida sketches: Proper balance of light on the drawing table with that transmitted through the beam splitter is essential for camera lucida drawings. A fluorescent lamp which can be adjusted to any position is very satisfactory. This, combined with adjustment of the condenser, will enable the operator to produce the proper light balance which gives the desired image on both the object and the pencil point.

Camera lucida sketches should be neatly arranged on three-ring binder paper cut from 14-pound rag stock. Sulfate papers become brittle after long usage. Transfer sketches to drawing board with carbon paper made by rubbing prussian blue powder into porous tissue. Blue coloring will not show in reproductions. "Scratchboard" is preferable for illustrations because corrections can be made in the event of errors. It also enables the artist to etch the lines representing muscles and other internal organs, a method that gives depth to the illustration. A steel scalpel with all the blade except the point wrapped with leather is the best etching tool. All the writer's illustrations have been prepared in this manner.

Always use standard magnifications for similar-sized nematodes, and anticipate the size of the plate on which they will be reproduced. Allow for a reduction to not less than one-half the original size, and make lines and stippling with this point in mind. If these are too fine, they may be lost in reproduction. Careful planning before sketching is the secret of well-balanced and neatly arranged plates.

If the worker wears reading glasses, they will be necessary for camera lucida work. If bifocals are worn, a pair should be purchased in which the bifocal sector occupies about three-fourths the lens. It is almost impossible to use the ordinary small bifocal sector with the camera lucida.

If eyestrain develops from excessive use of the microscope, take 5,000 or 10,000 units of vitamin A each day.

PREPARATION OF PERMANENT MICROSCOPIC SLIDES

Equipment and Supplies

Preparation dishes, 28 × 63 mm	Medicine droppers
Plant Industry type watch glasses	Dropper bottles
Vials, 14 × 46 mm with screw caps	Curved dissecting needle
Needle holder	Glycerin, cp
Bamboo points for needle holder	Desiccator, 6 or 8 in.
Assorted glass fibers	Calcium chloride, anhydrous
Clear plastic, 1 × 3 × $\frac{1}{4}$ in.	Drierite
Microculture slides	Copper sulfate
Microscope slides	Alcohol, 98%
Cover glasses No. 1	Formaldehyde
Smallest dental pulp files	Acetic acid

Preliminary Procedures

Charge the 6-inch desiccator with calcium chloride, and seal.

Place about 50 ml glycerin in wide-mouth bottle without cork, and store in disiccator as a supply for mounting media. Partly fill a Plant Industry type watch glass with glycerin for immediate use on slides. Use a 1-inch piece of small glass rod for placing drops on slides. Keep this watch glass and rod in desiccator.

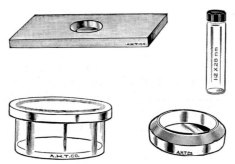

Fig. 3-3. Deep-well culture slide in which nemas are placed for killing and fixing; preparation dish; Plant Industry type watch glass; and vial used in evaporating nemas into glycerin. (*Courtesy of Arthur H. Thomas Company.*)

Mix $1\frac{1}{4}$ per cent glycerin in 20 per cent alcohol, and add 1 per cent saturated $CuSO_4$ solution to prevent fungus growth. Store in dropper bottle.

Prepare fixative composed of 100 parts distilled water, 20 parts 95 per cent alcohol, 16 parts 38 per cent formaldehyde, and 2 parts glacial acetic acid. Place part in dropper bottle, and store remainder.

Cut a channel in the plastic piece with routing tool or chisel, forming a shallow, elongated tray. Fill half full of glycerin. Place assorted tiny glass rods selected from glass wool, "angel's hair," and other sources in this tray, and store in desiccator. Excessively fine and very coarse rods may be pulled by hand from soft glass.

Grind a tiny, chisel-like point on the curved dissecting needle.

Drill 2.0-mm holes through vial tops.

Procedures: Let us assume that a soil sample has been processed as outlined and that the residues are well cleared and suitable for examination. Stir the contents of the beaker containing the residues of the 25-mesh screen, and pour a small quantity into the subdivided watch glass. Beginning at the double line, move the watch glass under the lower powers of the dissecting microscope, and search for nematodes. When they appear in the field, observe if they are young specimens or adults. This point can usually be determined by the presence of hyaline areas in the body adjacent to the vulva or extending back toward the anus of the male. Presence of eggs is an especially good indicator of fully matured females.

Killing and fixing: Pick the specimens into a deep-well microculture slide filled with water. When all residues have been examined and specimens selected, hold the slide over a small alcohol flame, and heat gradually until the nemas are relaxed. Check the progress of heating under the microscope to avoid overheating and cooking, which may ruin the specimens. Allow to cool, and, again working under the dissecting microscope, carefully draw off most of the water with a finely pointed dropper. Add fixative, slide square cover glass over opening, and fix for 48 hours.

Killing specimens in cold fixative causes twisting and distortion until observations and measurements made from them are of limited value. However, when one is working with species which relax in a straight position, a few specimens should be killed in cold fixative. These distorted specimens generally will be seen in a true lateral view, a result which has obvious merits. The lateral fields of tylenchs are often seen to best advantage in such specimens.

Fig. 3-4. Miniature desiccator assembly. Specimens are in the Plant Industry type watch glass, and the vial of desiccant is placed above them, and then the lid is sealed on. (*Photograph courtesy of J. L. Saunders, Department of Entomology, University of Wisconsin.*)

Desiccating specimens: Drop 1¼ per cent glycerin solution into a Plant Industry type watch glass, and pick the specimens from the fixative into it; place in a preparation dish, and fill level full. Fill a vial with calcium carbonate, Drierite, or other desiccant, insert into preparation dish, and let rest across edge of watch glass. Apply petroleum jelly to edge of preparation dish, and put cover in place, making certain that it is completely sealed.

Place preparation dish in warm spot, preferably in oven set at 90 to 95°F, or over a radiator. After four to six weeks the water will be absorbed by the desiccant and the specimens reduced to almost pure glycerin. Check this point by tipping the watch glass and observing flow of glycerin. If flow is very slow, transfer to 6-inch desiccator for 48 hours to ensure dehydration. When completely desiccated, the specimens are ready for mounting.

In humid climates it is possible to evaporate the specimens into almost pure glycerin by placing the Plant Industry type watch glass under a petri dish or similar vessel. This method dispenses with the preparation dish and desiccant and often produces satisfactory specimens. However, considerable experimenting may be necessary before the proper techniques are developed. Always complete desiccation over calcium chloride.

The following method will produce good specimens for permanent mounts in two to four hours: Relax the specimens, add fixative, and heat slightly. Transfer to a drop of fixative on a celluloid piece, cut in two with an eye knife, and transfer to a Plant Industry type watch glass filled with $1\frac{1}{4}$ per cent glycerin. Place in an oven or over a radiator, and evaporate rapidly. The specimens can then be mounted in desiccated glycerin. By cutting the nemas at different points and angles, the two parts of each specimen can then be identified and measurements made if necessary. If desired, heads and sections may be cut off in the usual manner and mounted in hard glycerin jelly.

Rapid methods of passing nemas into glycerin have been recommended by various workers and have certain merits if carefully carried out. One of the most successful is that of Baker (1953), which consists in relaxing and fixing in the usual manner. Specimens are then transferred to lactophenol in a hollow cavity slide and warmed to a temperature of about 65°C. Stain may be added during this process if desired. From lactophenol the nemas are passed through five solutions of different concentrations of glycerin, distilled water, lactic acid, phenol, and formol. In this manner the nemas reach pure glycerin in about one hour and can be mounted on permanent slides immediately. Instead of making an actual transfer from one solution to the next, the writer withdraws the solution with a finely pointed dropper and adds the next higher concentration of solution. If stain is used with lactophenol, always mount in acidified glycerin; otherwise bleaching will take place in a few months.

Franklin and Goodey (1949) first relaxed specimens by gentle heat, then fixed them overnight in 10 cc 40 per cent formaldehyde and 10 cc acetic acid. After fixation the specimens were placed in lactophenol solution with cotton blue stain and heated until the liquid fumed, then mounted in lactophenol.

An excellent summary of various techniques used on plant parasitic and soil-inhabiting nemas is that of J. B. Goodey (1957).

Preparing slides: It will be observed that specimens from a general collection are of various sizes and that often certain species have assumed characteristic forms when killed by gradual heat. Select those which are of about the same size and general appearance, dividing the collection into various groups. Four to ten specimens can usually be mounted on each slide, depending on the sizes. Place a small drop of glycerin on a slide, and transfer a group of specimens to it. Take a representative specimen from the group, place it among the glass rods, and select a rod which is slightly smaller in diameter Cut three pieces from the rod with the curved needle chisel, and transfer to the slide. Arrange specimens on slide with care, and see that they are at the bottom of the glycerin; then arrange the three glass rods a short distance from the specimens. Hold a cover glass in a pair of tweezers beside a finger of your other hand, and place it over a small alcohol flame until the finger gets hot. Quickly transfer it to the slide, hold one edge under the tip of the finger, lower it until it almost touches the glycerin drop, and release. If this procedure is properly carried out, the specimens will remain near the center of the cover glass. If specimens scatter, the cover glass was probably too cold. If air bubbles are trapped in the slide, the cover slip was dropped too far.

"Tack" the cover glass with three small drops of Zut or other ringing material, and allow to stand until set. With a small, stubby brush paint a ring about the cover glass, preferably working under the dissecting microscope to make certain that it is completely sealed. Or use thinner ringing material and apply on a ringing stand, using two or three thicknesses to ensure sealing. Estimating the proper size of the drop of glycerin is most important; only practice can make you proficient. If too much glycerin is used, tack the cover glass first, then slightly moisten a torn edge of filter paper between the lips, and remove the excess. Be sure that the cover glass is resting on the glass rods before ringing in; otherwise, the specimens will migrate to the side, where they cannot be examined. After considerable practice a skilled worker can mount 150 to 200 specimens on thirty to forty slides in a day.

Specimens mounted in desiccated glycerin should last indefinitely. Specimens in the writer's collection are still in perfect condition after 25 years. Of course, the most permanent slides are those mounted in balsam, but this is an extremely long and difficult process which is preferably carried out in the Cobb (1918) differentiators. This method necessitates staining in acid carmine or other stains. Balsam has the disadvantage of a refractive index similar to that of the spears of tylenchs and dorylaims. Frequently the details of spears, spicula, and other sclerotized organs are almost lost to visibility. Differentiators should have the constant attention of a trained assistant. The process requires two or three months.

The best pick holders are made from plant pathology loop holders. Remove the pin holding the fiber covering the upper part of the shaft, and discard the fiber. Replace it with a 6-inch piece of copper tubing which fits close to the chuck, and cut off the remainder of the shaft. Weight of the copper tubing gives stability to the hand when a face view of nemas is being made and other delicate operations are being performed.

Desiccants which have been used successfully are anhydrous calcium carbonate, Drierite, and sulfuric acid absorbed in Panacalite, an aluminum silicate product. Ten grams Panacalite with 10 cc 70 per cent H_2SO_4 makes an excellent desiccant when used in the vials with 2-mm holes in the caps. Other desiccants are always used in these vials, not placed loose in the preparation dishes.

Species file of camera lucida sketches: Pencil sketches of heads, tails, and other diagnostic features should be prepared for each species in your collection. These are best made on three-ring binder paper cut from 14-pound rag stock, which is strong and will not deteriorate over the years. It is also thin enough to allow tracings to be made from illustrations in publications not available in your library. A complete file of references is essential for efficient working conditions. Space for additional literature references should be provided on each sheet. Preparation of this file will require a considerable investment of time, but over the years it will repay well the hours spent.

Since most species will not be readily identified, it is necessary to use a numerical system and give a series of numbers to the species in each

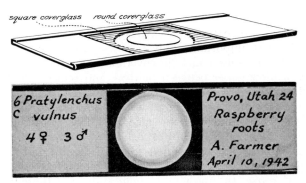

Fig. 3-5. Completed microscope slide. The number 6 shows that this is the sixth species of *Pratylenchus* added to the collection. Letter c indicates that this is the fourth slide of the species. Utah 24 is the number of the collection in that state. (*Photograph by E. H. Herrling. Courtesy of Department of Plant Pathology, University of Wisconsin.*)

genus: *Acrobeles* 1, 2, 3, 4, etc.; *Tylenchus* 1, 2, 3, 4, etc. These numbers should be placed on the three-ring binder sheets bearing the sketches of the respective species. Species names can be added after identification.

Labeling slides: The first step toward the proper indexing of specimens is that of numbering and naming the slides to correspond with the numbers carried on the above-described three-ring binder file. The system used by the writer begins with the species number followed by the generic name, placed in the upper left portion of the label, the remainder of the label being used for other pertinent data. If more than one slide of a species is made, the slides are numbered *Acrobeles* 1, *Acrobeles* 1a, 1b, etc.

Cross indexing of specimens: Because of the cost in time and materials, it is not feasible to mount only one specimen on each slide; therefore, specimens are grouped according to size. Frequently three or more species may be on one slide, necessitating a cross-index system. This is provided by preparing a 5×8 index card for each species on heavy rag paper, as shown in the following outline:

Species No.: *Dorylaimus 7 labiatus*

Slide No.	Locality	Date	Specimens
Dorylaimus 7	Ogden, Utah	Jan. 15, 1945	5f, 2m
Mononchus 4	Aberdeen, Idaho	July 3, 1947	2f
Nygolaimus 6a	Greeley, Colo.	July 9, 1949	1f, 1m
Dorylaimus 7a	Antigo, Wis.	Sept. 10, 1956	2f, 2m

With this record, information on each species is immediately available, and any specimen can be located in the generic file of slides in a few seconds. The Salt Lake City, Utah, collection of over 36,000 specimens was indexed in this manner. The many visitors who have worked with it can verify the accuracy and efficiency of this system. Other collections in California, Oregon, and Wisconsin now number more than 100,000 specimens, all indexed in this manner.

Recording collections: Set up another 5 × 8 file in which collections are indexed by states or countries: Utah 1, 2, 3, etc., England 1, 2, 3, etc. On this, record the following data and other pertinent facts:

Collection No.: Wisconsin 8   Locality: Antigo
Date: July 24, 1956   Collector: Lin Faulkner
Technique: FAA to glycerin in desiccator

Remarks: Soil and roots from clover field in which *Ditylenchus destructor* were very numerous in small lesions near crowns of plants. Many *Paratylenchus* spp. without males, and a few *Pratylenchus brachyurus*.

Slide Nos.:
Ditylenchus 1, 1a
Paratylenchus 3, 3a
Pratylenchus 4c
Panagrolaimus 1f
Mononchus 2k
Dorylaimus 7b

After all species in the collection have been identified, a complete list may be typed on the back of the card if desired, the record on the sample being thus completed. Common species which have been recognized, but of which no specimens were retained, should be included in this list.

Preparation of Face Views and Cross Sections of Nematodes

Satisfactory face views cannot be made from distorted, shrunken specimens, especially spear-bearing forms in which the spear is extruded. Careful relaxing by gradual heat is essential. After this step the specimens may be fixed and prepared for sectioning. Before beginning this very delicate process, there are a few items of equipment which are necessary if satisfactory slides are to be prepared.

A platform-type hand rest for the dissecting microscope is indispensable in performing these and other similar delicate operations.

Purchase a surgeon's eye knife with a very slender, pointed blade. If such a knife is not available, a narrow piece from the edge of a safety-razor blade makes a fair substitute when attached to a small handle by means of a piece of hard sealing wax. Or a steel needle can be ground to a fine edge and then honed under low magnification until very sharp. Never use any of these instruments on a glass slide, which is almost certain to turn the delicate edge.

A small piece of celluloid from an old photographic film provides an excellent surface on which the cutting may be done without injury to the edge of the knife blade.

A small brush of fine camel's hair is used to furnish "pointers" in locating the section on the slide.

Very finely pointed bamboo picks are needed for handling the minute pieces cut from the body. Prepare these by sharpening under the medium powers of the dissecting microscope.

A small alcohol lamp is used in heating slides and dissecting pins. Gas flames are usually too hot for the careful work required.

A supply of very hard glycerin jelly is required.

Cover glasses, preferably 10 mm round, 10 to 12 μ in thickness, are needed.

1. Kill, fix, and desiccate to pure glycerin as outlined under Microscopic Techniques.

2. Place a small piece of the hard glycerin jelly on a microscope slide, and carefully melt it over the alcohol flame. Spread the drop as thin as possible with a small bamboo point in the pick holder.

3. Select a slender hair from the brush, break off the tip with finely pointed tweezers, and place it in the drop of jelly with the point near the center of the drop, where it will become a pointer for the head or cross section.

4. Place the nematode in a drop of glycerin on the celluloid, and decapitate or cut the sections with the eye knife. This step is accomplished under the binocular with the hand held firmly on the special substage.

5. Pick up the head on a *very fine* bamboo point, and hold it in the hand while performing the next operation.

6. Place the slide under the binocular, heat a clean dissecting needle in the flame, and dip it into the jelly at the end of the camel's-hair pointer.

7. Insert the head into the melted spot, push it to the bottom of the drop, and lift the face to the perpendicular with the fine bamboo point and hold it in place until the jelly sets.

8. Apply one of the thin cover glasses to the drop of jelly, carefully centering it before it touches the drop.

9. Heat a dissecting needle, and carefully touch the cover glass above the head, melting the jelly until the glass rests near the face. Meantime,

make sure that the head remains upright. Don't use too much heat in this operation, or the entire drop of jelly will melt and the head will fall out of place.

10. Place two small drops of candle wax just under the edge of the cover glass on opposite sides, cementing it to the slide.

11. Examine the head under the higher powers; if not exactly perpendicular, it may be adjusted by pushing slightly on the edges of the cover glass.

When this process has been mastered after considerable practice, a face view or cross section can be mounted in 5 or 10 minutes.

Staining specimens in acid fuchsin or picric acid or by other means facilitates finding the minute portions cut off. Should a face view be desired immediately, place the specimen in a drop of fixative for five minutes. Then cut it in two, place in weak glycerin, and evaporate rapidly. Within an hour the head can be cut off and mounted.

Staining nematodes in root tissues: The most satisfactory and simple method of staining in root tissues is that of McBeth, Taylor, and Smith (1941), which consists of a modification of T. Goodey's (1937) method:

Phenol crystals............	20 g
Lactic acid..............	20 g
Glycerin................	40 g
Distilled water...........	20 ml
Acid fuchsin or cotton blue	5 ml (1 g in 100 ml water)

Bring the solution to a boil, immerse roots for about one minute, and clear in lactophenol solution until the desired intensity of stain is secured. Clearing may require a few hours up to several days. Transfer to glycerin for at least 48 hours; then mount in desiccated, acidified glycerin. Ring with Zut or other suitable compounds. Slides of stained specimens are almost essential for demonstration purposes when endoparasitic nematodes are being studied. Specimens in the writer's collection prepared by M. W. Allen in 1942 are still in excellent condition.

Roots of young plants or small roots of larger plants respond best to this technique. Hard, woody tree roots are more satisfactory if fixed, stained, and sectioned by standard methods.

Fleming medium and strong fixatives are sometimes recommended, but the process is slow and expensive. These fixatives produce a pale yellow to clear tissue in which the nemas are black and opaque and often unidentifiable.

Ectoparasitic nematodes can frequently be caught in the act of feeding by carefully lifting the plant roots and immediately plunging them into hot (130–150°F) 5 per cent formaldehyde or FAA solutions. The writer used this method to catch rice-root nematodes feeding on the cells about the bases of the root hairs. Material fixed in this manner may be transferred immediately to stain as outlined above.

Staining nematodes in leaves: Franklin (1949) used the above lactophenol method, boiling the leaves for three to five minutes and allowing them to remain until the stain cooled. They were then washed in water or 50 per cent alcohol, cleared in lactophenol or concentrated phenol to remove the chlorophyll, transferred to 50 and 70 per cent alcohol and isobutyl alcohol, and mounted in Euparal. The writer prefers to transfer from the lactophenol to desiccated, acidified glycerin for mounting.

Colbran (1953) determined the numbers of *Pratylenchus coffeae* in 40-g samples of soil by placing in each sample three flax seedlings with radicles ½ inch long. After four days the seedlings were removed, washed, and stained in lactophenol. They were then partly cleared and the nemas counted.

MORPHOLOGY OF NEMATODES

Typically, the plant parasitic and free-living soil and fresh-water nematodes are slender, active animals 0.2 to 10.0 mm in length, the majority of the species being less than 2.0 mm long. Usually, the body is somewhat cylindroid through at least part of its length, but occasionally it is fusiform. In a number of plant parasitic genera it may be pear, lemon, reniform, or irregularly saccate-shaped as in the females of *Meloidogyne, Heterodera, Nacobbus,* and *Rotylenchulus.* Anteriorly, the body may taper but little and may remain almost cylindroid to the lip region as in *Mononchus.* In genera like *Alaimus,* it may taper rapidly through the neck region to the narrow head, which may be only one-tenth as wide as the maximum body width. Posteriorly, the body may vary in form from the bluntly rounded terminus of *Hoplolaimus coronatus* to the elongate-filiform tail of *Prismatolaimus stenurus.* The body width may be less than 1 per cent of its length, as in *Ecphyadophora,* or as much as 15 per cent, as in *Criconema.*

The infinite numbers of forms among the nematodes are so variable in their respective characteristics that probably not one statement can be made concerning them that does not have exceptions. With our present rapidly expanding knowledge of the plant-infesting and soil-inhabiting groups, the exceptions are becoming more numerous. The problem of selecting diagnostic features by which nematodes may be distinguished is steadily becoming more complicated and difficult.

General body characteristics: The nematode body is not divided into definite parts, but there are certain subdivisions to which common names have been given for convenience. Beginning at the anterior end is the *head,* which is that portion containing the mouth and pharynx and bearing the cephalic papillae or setae. That portion between the head and the base of the esophagus is the *neck.* Beginning at the anus and extending to the terminus is the *tail.*

Longitudinally the body is divided into four regions: dorsal, right and left lateral, and ventral. For purposes of orientation, we generally determine the ventral region by the fact that the bodies of a majority of the species are naturally bent ventrally to some degree. But should the body be straight, the location of the anal opening is always a definite character on which we can depend, even in the larval stages. Mature females possess a vulva, a prominent organ, which also is always placed ventrally. Usually the vulva is near the middle of the body, although it may be far back near the anus as in *Criconema* or forward toward the base of the esophagus like that of *Tylencholaimellus*. If an excretory pore is present, it, too, is located ventrally, somewhere between the nerve ring and the base of the esophagus, except in rare instances as in *Tylenchulus*.

Cuticle: The protective covering of the nematode body is a tough, flexible layer which forms the exoskeleton and is known as the cuticle. This may be almost unmarked by striae as in many *Dorylaimus* or deeply incised into annules like those of *Criconemoides*. These striae divide the cuticle into segments, but they do not extend beyond the cuticle and therefore should not be confused with the true body-segment-forming annules of annelids. Longitudinal striae may also be present with the transverse, dividing the cuticle into several series of tiny segments as in *Tylenchus costatus*. *Dorylaimus stagnalis* and its relatives bear longitudinal *alae*, riblike structures extending from near the head to the tail region.

Frequently, the cuticle is marked by dots, dashes, circles, and sculpturing which often are of diagnostic value in the determination of genera and species. The segments of the cuticle of *Cruznema lambdiensis* are minutely sculptured, while those of certain *Diplogaster* are marked by dots and dashes. Many aquatic species, e.g., *Achromadora minima*, bear rows of circular, dotlike transverse markings. The annules of *Criconema* bear elaborately fringed processes, while on *Bunonema* and its relatives irregular tubercules break the uniform body contour. Marine species especially present an endless array of the most varied markings and sculpturing found in any group.

Nematodes usually undergo four moults during their development from egg to adult, and during each of these periods the cuticle is cast off, taking with it the cuticular portions of the pharynx, vagina, and rectum. With each moult the body becomes larger, and certain developments occur, especially in the reproductive system, which does not appear in its entirety until after the final moult. After feeding and reproduction begin, the body may increase considerably both in length and in diameter, especially in genera like *Rhabditis, Diplogaster,* and *Anguina*. This fact frequently is responsible for marked variations in measurements. On *Hemicycliophora* and *Hemicriconemoides* an extra cuticle forms after the last moult and remains an enveloping sheath about the body.

Lateral fields: Many members of the Adenophorea possess longitudinal cuticular structures known as lateral fields, overlying the lateral cords. These structures provide for free movement of the annules along the lateral lines as the nematode flexes in the dorsoventral plane. They also act as stabilizing braces which prevent the body from bending in the lateral plane. Perhaps they also provide a certain amount of "traction." Types of lateral fields vary with the many groups in which they appear, and general descriptions cannot adequately include all of them. Therefore, only those which will be encountered by the plant nematologist are discussed.

Among the Tylenchoidea, the lateral fields appear as four or more bright parallel lines which, when studied in cross section, are found to be infolded elements of the cuticle. They are now generally known as incisures, or involutures, but in the past they have been named wings, longitudinal alae, lateral alae, and lateral striae. Usually the incisures are separated by narrow refractive bands of cuticle. The full complement of incisures usually is present from a point about opposite the nerve ring to a short distance past the anus. Anteriorly, they decrease in numbers and usually disappear between the middle of the neck and the head. Posteriorly, they may continue to the terminus of blunt-tailed forms like *Rotylenchus* and *Belonolaimus* or may fade out near the middle of the tail of filiform types like *Tylenchus* and *Psilenchus*. These incisures are visible on larvae, males, and females of all species of Tylenchidae and Neotylenchidae except in certain senile females like those of *Anguina* and *Ditylenchus*. In these aberrant forms, development of the relatively huge gonads and the obese body place so much strain upon the incisures that the infolded cuticle flattens out and the lateral fields disappear. Larvae and males of Heteroderidae possess the usual incisures, and the females of *Meloidogyne* occasionally retain them, especially in the perineal region. The females of *Heterodera* retain neither incisures nor transverse striae, and the entire body becomes marked by an intricate series of rugose patterns which in some instances are of diagnostic value in species determination.

We find an interesting situation in the Criconematinae, in which the strongly annulated females do not possess lateral fields, while they are a prominent feature on the finely annulated males.

Among the Aphelenchoidea the lateral fields often are more like refractive cuticular bands, usually marked by four minute parallel lines, except on *Aphelenchus*, where as many as twelve lines may be present.

Among the Rhabditida we find no distinctive cuticular markings on the lateral cuticle of Rhabditidae and Diplogasteridae, except on certain *Diplogaster* species marked by punctate transverse striae. In these, there occasionally are lines of punctations overlying the lateral cords, which are somewhat larger or more refractive. However, the Cephalobidae usually bear prominent lateral lines, especially the genera *Eucephalobus, Chiloplacus,* and *Acrobeles,* on which the number of lines may be two, three, or four.

We are indebted to Chitwood for much of our most reliable information concerning the structure of the cuticle and the substances of which it is composed. The reader is referred to his papers for details of his extensive work and methods of analysis. Working with the large animal parasite, *Ascaris lumbricoides,* he determined (1936) that its cuticle is composed of at least five substances: albumins, a glucoprotein, a fibroid, a collagen, and a keratin. Subsequent studies by Chitwood and Chitwood (1937) demonstrated that the cuticle is divided into nine layers. Experiments with the plant parasite, *Ditylenchus dipsaci* (1938), determined that the impermeable characteristic of the cuticle is due to a very delicate thermolabile membrane, "possibly a wax or sterol," which disappears when specimens are heated to 65°C; after this heating the specimens are easily penetrated by stains. Under the thermolabile

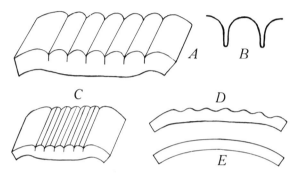

Fig. 3-6. *Ditylenchus destructor.* *A*—Cross section of lateral field showing six incisures. *B*—Diagrammatic section of two incisures showing how they are formed by infoldings of the cuticle. *C*—Cross section of specimen from sugar beet showing six incisures and also five similar appearing lines formed by the crest of the arches, making it appear as if eleven lines are present. *D*—Section of maturing female showing incisures almost outstretched. *E*—Section of female in which incisures have completely disappeared. (*After Thorne and Allen. Plant Pathology, Problems and Progress 1908–1958. Courtesy of Regents of the University of Wisconsin and the University of Wisconsin Press.*)

membrane lies a cortical layer which appears to be a keratoid. Beneath this is a fibroid matrix underlaid by collagenous layers.

The fibers of the outer cuticle lie just beneath the cortex and are easily visible on *Sectonema, Aporcelaimus,* and other large dorylaims. They are a striking feature of the insect parasitic Mermithidae. These fibers do not lie in bands but are interwoven like the threads of a piece of fabric. Apparently they originate in the cords, develop at oblique angles, and interlace where they meet and cross one another as they progress across the body to the adjacent cord.

Constituents of the cuticle vary greatly in their proportions or in their presence among the various genera. This is evidenced by their permeability to fixative and stains. It is a relatively simple matter to stain the body of a *Dorylaimus* but difficult to penetrate the cuticle of a *Criconemoides*. Distinct chemical variations of the cuticle are indicated by the tints of color and degree of penetration by the same stain: acid carmine stains *Dorylaimus* a deep pink or red, while *Tylenchus* in the same lot assumes a lavender tint. Variations in permeability are noted when desiccating specimens from weak to concentrated glycerin. The process requires 5 or 6 weeks for *Hexatylus viviparus*, but *D. obscurus* responds in 10 or 12 days.

Beneath the cuticle lies the hypodermis (subcuticle, epidermis). This thin layer becomes thickened to form the dorsal, the two lateral, and the ventral cords which extend throughout the length of the body. In these are series of nucleated cells which, in the lateral cords, may become a striking feature of the body, as in *Axonchium*, *Tylencholaimellus*, and *Discolaimus*. The nerve fibers lie in these cords, and with proper staining their nuclei are easily observed, especially in the ventral cord, where they are most numerous. In certain marine species there may be as many as eight cords.

The massive body muscles lie beneath the hypodermis and extend at a slightly oblique angle from the cords. They are easily observed on most specimens, especially those killed with cold fixative, which shrinks the tissues and causes the muscles to appear as minutely wrinkled bands. Chitwood (1950) illustrates the muscles as being composed of elongate, spindle-shaped cells attached to the hypodermis. Other body muscles control the movement of the lips, pharynx, esophagus, intestine, rectum, anus, vulva, and spicula. Most prominent of all are the copulatory muscles of male dorylaims, mononchs, and many other forms. In these groups these muscles form a series of broad, oblique bands extending from the tail forward to a point that is anterior to the copulatory supplements.

The space between the somatic muscles and the internal organs is known as the pseudocoel. In it are found numerous glands, cellular bodies, and granular material floating in the body fluid. The intestinal tract, gonads, and other organs are suspended from the body wall on muscles and fibers which allow them to move freely as the nema bends its body. To understand the great flexibility of the body and its contents, it is essential that the beginner study living specimens held under slight pressure of the cover glass. Unless one becomes acquainted with nemic anatomy in this manner, it may be difficult properly to interpret the same structures when they are observed after killing, fixing, and mounting on permanent slides.

External Structures of the Head

Typically, the nematode head is hexaradially symmetrical, with two subdorsal, two lateral, and two subventral sectors commonly known as lips. Heads closely approximating the symmetrical type are found in many Secernentea, especially in Tylenchidae like *Ditylenchus*, *Rotylenchus*, *Pratylenchus*, and *Anguina*. But in this same group we find the four-lipped head of *Tetylenchus* with amphid apertures close beside the oral opening. *Hexatylus* and *Neotylenchus* possess an extra pair of labial lobes which give their heads a somewhat octagonal appearance. Face views of other Tylenchida reveal many variations, a fact that indicates a long period of evolution during which the hexaradial type has been replaced by an extensive series of divergent forms.

Rhabditidae give us symmetrical hexaradial forms like *Pelodera* (*Pelodera*) *strongyloides,* three-lipped species like *Rhabditis terricola,* and numerous other variations. Perhaps the outstanding variant of this group is *Diploscapter coronata,* in which the lips are replaced by sclerotized fossores which move with an outward stroke.

Cephalobidae include such diverse types as *Panagrolaimus subelongatus, Cephalobus persegnis,* and *Eucephalobus oxyuroides* which possess the usual six lips arranged in a dorsal and two ventrosubmedian pairs. Frequently the two ventral lips are smaller than the others. In this family are *Chiloplacus symmetricus, Cervidellus cervus, Acrobeles complexus,* and many other species in which the lips bear simple to elaborate plates, furcate prongs (probolae), and membranes of almost every conceivable pattern. Most elaborate of all are the mandibles and cephalic cirri of *Chambersiella rodens,* beautifully illustrated by the artist in whose honor the genus was named.

Variations in lip regions of Adenophorea are even more abundant than those of Secernentea, because a large portion of the marine species are included in this class. Among them are found scores of different arrangements formed by elaborate series of setae and sclerotized labial and cephalic structures.

The hexaradiate symmetry is almost unbroken throughout the Dorylaimidae, Monchidae, Tripylidae, and numerous other families abundant in soil and fresh water. Usually, soil-inhabiting forms bear distinctly developed lips, but there are occasional genera like *Alaimus* and *Belondira* in which the lip regions are greatly reduced and the cephalic sectors so minute that they can be observed only by the most skillful use of the microscope. In moist soils we frequently encounter species of *Plectus, Monhystera, Prismatolaimus,* and other setae-bearing genera, all of which usually possess symmetrical hexaradiate lips.

Cephalic papillae and setae: These important sensory organs are present on all nematodes. Typically, they consist of an inner circlet of six, grouped about the oral opening, and a circlet of ten located on the outer contour of the lips. However, there are many variations from this arrangement. Plant parasitic and soil-inhabiting Tylenchida usually possess inconspicuous papillae visible only from a carefully prepared face view. In this order the numbers of visible papillae frequently are reduced: four (*Ditylenchus, Tetylenchus*), ten (*Anguina*), twelve (*Psilenchus*), and fourteen (*Rotylenchus, Pratylenchus*). Perhaps the use of superior optical equipment and differential strains will eventually reveal those which have thus far been overlooked.

Among Dorylaimidae, Mononchidae, and associated soil- and freshwater-inhabiting families, the full complement of sixteen cephalic papillae are almost always easily visible from a lateral view, and rarely must a face view be made to determine their presence. Most conspicuous of all the cephalic sensory organs are the setae of *Monhystera, Bastiana, Tripyla,* and similar genera. These setae vary from slender, filamentous (*B. exilis*) to strong, hornlike bristles (*T. arenicola*). Others are short and inconspicuous (*T. papillata, Plectus cirratus*).

Amphids: Among the most important diagnostic features of nematodes are the amphids. These are pairs of chemotaxic organs located laterally on the head or the anterior neck. They occur in a great variety of forms: minutely porelike (*Ditylenchus*), circular (*Monhystera*), hooked (*Plectus*), stirrup form (*Dorylaimus*), spiral (*Achromadora*), and many other types, all with numerous variations in form and size.

Actually, these varied forms are merely the cuticular manifestations of the entire amphidial system, and it is only as a matter of convenience that we use the term "amphid" to designate the first two of the five parts into which the system is divided: (1) the aperture, or opening, through the cuticle, which may vary from a minute pore (*Tylenchus*) to an elongated slit (*Dorylaimus*); (2) the amphidial chamber, which may encompass half the base of the lip region (*Axonchium*) or may be reduced to an almost invisible tube (*Alaimus, Tylenchus, Rhabditis*); (3) the amphidial *canal,* which leads back from the chamber to (4) the *sensillae,* a group of rodlike nerve structures lying in (5) a fusiform *pouch,* which surrounds the sensillae. From the sensillae, nerve fibers lead back into the lateral fields and connect with the nerve ring.

Amphid apertures of Class Secernentea are labial in position, while those of Adenophorea are postlabial. This constitutes a very definite morphological character by which the two classes may be separated

The amphid apertures of Secernentea usually are very small. In the Tylenchida they are located far forward on the front of the lips, where they can be observed only from a face view. Exceptions are the slit-like apertures of *Psilenchus* and *Macrotrophurus,* found well down on the outer contour of the lips. The elongated amphid apertures of *Heterodera* and *Meloidogyne* lie beneath the margin of the labial disc and lead to chambers in the lateral lips, forming what Cobb (1918) called the "cheeks" of *Meloidogyne.*

Amphid apertures of the family Rhabitididae are porelike and usually visible on the outer contours of the lateral lips. On Diplogasteridae, they vary from porelike to minute slits which frequently appear as ovate markings on fixed specimens.

Cephalobidae possess slitlike, ovate, or circular amphid apertures. On *Cephalobus, Eucephalobus, Panagrolaimus, Acrobeloides, Chiloplacus,* and related genera, the ovate apertures usually are easily seen on the outer contours of the lateral lips. But on *Acrobeles, Stegellata, Cervidellus,* and other genera, which bear both cephalic and labial probolae, the apertures generally are easily found near the middle of the lateral cephalic probolae.

Among the many Secernentea inhabiting soil and fresh water we find an almost unending series of intergrading amphidial aperture forms. Perhaps the most numerous of all groups are the many genera and hundreds of species of the Superfamily Dorylaimoidea. Among them the usual pattern is a very obscure, slitlike aperture located close under the base of the lateral lips, leading to a large stirrup-shaped chamber. Dorso-ventral views of *Axonchium, Belondira, Tylencholaimellus,* and related genera reveal such extreme development of the chambers that they appear almost to separate the lip region from the body.

The minute, porelike amphidial openings of *Alaimus* are located far back on the neck and are visible only under favorable circumstances. Oddly enough, species of *Amphidelus,* the genus most closely related to *Alaimus,* possess some of the most extraordinary developed amphidial openings and chambers.

Species of *Trichodorus* and *Diphtherophora* possess large, ovoid apertures located near the lip bases. From them elongated chambers lead almost directly to sensillae pouches.

Members of the genus *Plectus* bear hooked apertures well back on the neck, and in similar positions we find the circular amphids of *Monhystera.* The predatory Mononchidae have obscure slitlike or ovate apertures which frequently are located forward near the bases of the lips. Tripylidae often bear conspicuous stirrup-form organs located well back near the beginning of the neck. The spiral amphidial markings of *Achromadora* and *Cyatholaimus* are among the most conspicuous and striking of all.

Because of their infinite variety of form and variable positions, the amphids constitute some of the most valuable diagnostic characters used in taxonomy. This the reader will readily observe as we study the families, genera, and species presented here.

Deirids: Many genera of Tylenchoidea possess deirids. These are paired porelike organs opening in the center of the lateral field, usually in the vicinity of the nerve ring. From them slender connective tissues lead to the lateral cord near its junction with the hemizonid. They are best observed on species of *Tylenchus, Tetylenchus, Psilenchus, Deladenus, Thada,* and *Boleodorus.* Occasionally they may be dimly detected on *Tylenchorhynchus* and a few other genera. Their function is problematical. They are sometimes known as "cervical papillae."

Phasmids: Pairs of these organs are located in the lateral fields on the tails of Secernentea. From them, minute ducts lead in and forward to glands embedded in the lateral cords. They usually are easily observed on all genera except certain Tylenchoidea like *Ditylenchus, Anguina, Tylenchus,* and a few others. In these genera the phasmids are either absent or beyond the limits of visibility. They are especially well developed in Hoplolaiminae and Pratylenchinae and on the genera *Tetylenchus, Tylenchorhynchus, Psilenchus, Belonolaimus,* and *Dolichodorus.*

In a few exceptions, the phasmids are not located on the tails. Some species of *Hoplolaimus* possess very large, erratically arranged phasmids which may be found from the tail to a point almost opposite the base of the esophagus. *Hoplolaimus gracilidens* bears very small phasmids lying well anterior to the latitude of the anus. On *Rotylenchus* and *Helicotylenchus* the phasmids frequently are slightly anterior to the anal latitude. Doubtless other exceptions will be discovered in these groups.

Among the Rhabditoidea we find that Rhabditidae and Diplogasteridae possess very small porelike phasmids which occasionally are difficult to observe. However, there are very conspicuous phasmids on most Cephalobidae.

The functions of phasmids are not known, but observations made on living *Aphelenchus avenae*, held under slight pressure, revealed that it frequently was possible to see tiny jets of fluid shot from the phasmid into the water in which the nema was mounted. These minute droplets of fluid dissolved and disappeared almost instantly, and it appears logical that in this manner nematodes leave a scent trail by which other members of the species may follow them.

Bursae: The males of many Secernentea clasp the female during copulation with flaplike processes of the cuticle known as bursae. Usually, these flaps arise from the ventrosubmedian cuticle at a point about opposite the anterior end of the spicula and extend back past the cloacal opening until they again merge with the cuticle. On genera with short tails (*Rotylenchus, Pratylenchus*), the caudal bursae envelop the entire tail. Genera with elongated tails bear relatively short adanal bursae which extend approximately equal distances anterior and posterior to the cloacal opening.

Among the Tylenchoidea, bursae are found on all genera except those of Heteroderidae, Tylenchulidae, and certain members of the Criconematidae. The males of *Paratylenchus, Sphaeronema, Criconemoides,* and *Cacopaurus* are broadly flattened in the anal region, and the ventrally bent tails frequently are slightly cupped, giving the appearance of narrow, thick bursae. *Hemicycliophora* males possess broad flexible bursal flaps. Among the most interesting of all bursae are those of *H. penetrans,* which are kept folded over the protruding distal ends of the spicula as a protective covering as the nematode moves through the soil.

The tails of male *Tylenchorhynchus, Belonolaimus, Pratylenchus,* and similar genera are crescentic in cross section with rather thin borders which extend ventrally, forming caudal bursae. In this development, the lateral fields are shifted ventrad until the phasmids extend into the bursa, the impression being that a short bursal rib is present. For many years this effect was cited by certain workers as an indication that tylenchs were related to rhabditids. But a careful comparison with the bursal ribs of *Rhabditis* reveals that they are not homologous. In fact, the phasmids of *Rhabditis* lie in the lateral field entirely out of the bursal area.

Among the Aphelenchoidea, bursae are known only on *Aphelenchus,* and these are most unusual in that they possess true *Rhabditis*-like bursal ribs, the only instance known among the Tylenchida.

Perhaps the most unexpected bursae are those described by Allen (1957) on the males of certain species of *Trichodorus,* a group far removed from the Secernentea.

Digestive System

Stoma (mouth, pharynx, buccal capsule, etc.): The entrance to the digestive tract is perhaps the most variable morphological character of the Nemata. Frequently both major and minor taxonomic groups are determined by the form and armature of the mouth and its associated organs. Much confusion exists as to what actually constitutes the stoma in many forms, because the oral chamber is associated with an infinite variety of plates, denticles, teeth, spears, and other specialized organs.

The most detailed nomenclature of the mouth parts was suggested by Steiner (1933), who based his work principally on the mouth parts of the genus *Rhabditis*. He distinguished five segments, which were desig-

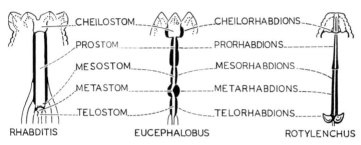

CHEILOSTOM	CHEILORHABDIONS	
PROSTOM	PRORHABDIONS	
MESOSTOM	MESORHABDIONS	
METASTOM	METARHABDIONS	
TELOSTOM	TELORHABDIONS	
RHABDITIS	EUCEPHALOBUS	ROTYLENCHUS

Fig. 3-7. Three types of rhabdion arrangement. Compare that of *Rhabditis* with Fig. 16-1.

nated as the cheilostom, protostom, mesostom, metastom, and telostom. The sclerotized or muscular linings of each were named cheilorhabdions, prorhabdions, mesorhabdions, metarhabdions, and telorhabdions. The five distinct segments are best seen in certain members of the Family Cephalobidae (*Cephalobus, Eucephalobus, Chiloplacus*) (Fig. 3-7). Accompanying the figures of *Eucephalobus* and *Rhabditis* is an illustration of the spear of *Rotylenchus* in which the presumed homologous parts are set forth as suggested by Chitwood and Chitwood (1937) and Chitwood and Wehr (1934). There has long been a theory that the spear of *Tylenchus* developed through a fusion of the rhabdions of a primitive rhabditid. Acceptance of this theory becomes difficult as one observes and works with the many species of each group. Perhaps the tylenchs and rhabditids had a common ancestry in remote antiquity, but if so, there is little, if any, semblance remaining between them at the present time.

The true stoma of *Eucephalobus* occupies only the cheilostom. The other four members form the pharynx, which, as in other forms of animal life, is that portion of the digestive tract connecting the mouth with the esophagus. Since it is frequently difficult to homologize the stomatal elements as they appear in various genera, it seems best to continue to follow the lead of Cobb and use the broad term "pharynx." This in-

cludes all the oral opening as far back as the beginning af the esophagus.
Thus we shall use the well-established terms "pharynx armed with a
protrusile spear" and "pharynx bearing a large dorsal tooth."

As nematologists, most of us are primarily interested in those species

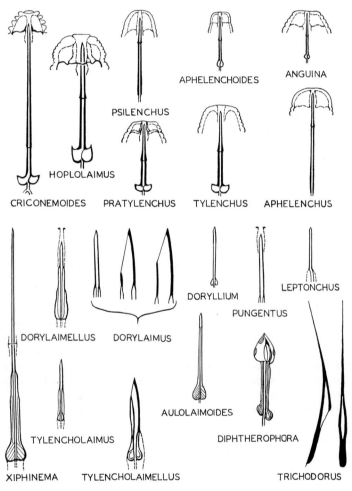

Fig. 3-8. Spear types of various Secernentea and Adenophorea.

which are ecto- or endoparasites of plants. These belong to either the
Order Tylenchida or the Superfamily Dorylaimoidea of the Order
Dorylaimida. All are equipped with protrusile spears, or stylets, with
which they puncture and feed upon the cells of their hosts. A spear is
similar to a minute hypodermic needle. Through it the nema may inject
esophageal gland secretions into plant cells or pump the cell contents
back through the spear into the digestive tract. Very frequently the

spear is of diagnostic value in identifying genera and species, and a detailed working knowledge of the many types is essential.

Frequently, the spear of a tylench is known as a "stomatostyl" because it develops in the pharynx along with other portions of the oral cavity. In contrast to this type of development, the spear of a dorylaim forms in a cell far back in the left submedial wall of the esophagus and moves forward to its place in the pharynx as each moult occurs. A spear developed in this manner is sometimes known as an "odontostyle."

IDENTIFYING NEMATODES

The beginner in nematology immediately encounters difficulties in determining the class to which many nematodes belong. Chitwood (1933) established two classes, Phasmidia and Aphasmidia, deriving the names from the presence or absence of the phasmids. After 25 years Dougherty determined that Phasmidia was preempted by a similar name which had previously been assigned to a group of insects of the Order Orthoptera. As a substitute he emended and validated the name Secernentea (v. Linstow, 1905) Dougherty 1958.

Chitwood (1958) emended and validated Adenophorea (v. Linstow, 1905). This supplants Aphasmidia, and we now have two new class names which will be used throughout this text.

Diagnostic characteristics will be the same as previously. The presence or absence of phasmids will continue to be one of the chief morphological characters. The uninitiated person will continue to be confused when he attempts to see phasmids on *Tylenchus, Ditylenchus, Anguina,* and other related genera on which they do not exist or are beyond the powers of resolution.

There is, however, one anatomical feature which immediately separates Secernentea from Adenophorea. In Secernentea the amphid apertures are always located anterior of the lip bases as in Tylenchoidea and Aphelenchoidea, while in Adenophorea the apertures are at the base of the lip region, as in Dorylaimoidea, or well behind the lips, as in Plectoidea and Tripyloidea.

Spears of all tylenchs have a ventrad oblique aperture, while in dorylaims the aperture invariably is dorsad. By this one character it is always possible to determine if a spear-bearing specimen belongs in Secernentea or Adenophorea.

Most tylench spears have rounded basal knobs which readily distinguish them. Dorylaims occasionally possess flangelike basal enlargements (*Xiphinema* and *Dorylaimellus*) or indistinct knobs (*Tylencholaimellus* and *Tylencholaimus*).

It is advisable to concentrate first on the study of generic characters and establish them firmly in mind before attempting to determine subfamilies, families, and other higher groups of classification. The first step in identification is carefully to study well-made illustrations, especially those by Chambers, which are labeled to show the various parts of nematode anatomy. Compare descriptions with the illustrations, and become thoroughly conversant with the terminology and the corresponding anatomical features portrayed. Examine illustrations in all available literature, and note the differences illustrated for various genera and species. Until you are well informed on the detailed anatomy of the common genera, it will be impossible to make progress in identification.

After diligently studying illustrations of the gross and detailed anatomy, select an adult specimen, preferably a female more than 1.0 mm long. First, use the low powers to secure a general view of the gross anatomy, observing the natural pose of the body, if it has been properly relaxed. Next note the tapering of the clearer anterior portion which marks the neck region. Determine the position of the vulva and anus and the shape of the posterior end. In specimens 2.0 mm long you will probably see the general structure of the gonads and eggs if they are present.

When this gross examination is completed, turn on the 4.0-mm objective, and examine the specimen again. Beginning at the anterior end, note the lip region, and determine if the lips are angular or rounded. Then examine the pharyngeal armature, and observe if the mouth is armed with a spear, teeth, or platelike rods or if it has no armature at all. Proceed to the esophagus, and determine if it contains valvular bulbs or is merely muscular. Compare with illustrations you have studied. The intestine is a simple tube composed of obscure cells filled with granules, and only in rare instances does it have diagnostic characteristics. As you follow along the intestine, you will soon encounter the gonads. Here you must determine if one or two ovaries are present and if they are outstretched as in tylenchs or reflexed as in dorylaims. If only one ovary is present, is it anterior or posterior to the vulva? Make similar observations on the testis, or testes, if the specimen is a male. If males are not found, examine the uteri for the presence of spermatozoa, and, if present, note if they are in a definitely setoff spermatheca. Continuing along the intestine, note if a prerectum lies between its terminus and the rectum. Observe the length and position of the rectum and location of the anal opening. Note the length and form of the tail, for this frequently is a valuable diagnostic character between species, and sometimes between genera.

Now return to the head, apply the oil-immersion objective, and using a 5× ocular repeat the study of the entire body. Note that you see only a thin field or portion of the head and that it is necessary to focus up and down a considerable distance to see all the head structures. Too often the novice expects to see lips, spear, amphids, and other structures all at the same time, an impossibility under the higher powers. Begin at the upper surface of the lips, and work down through the pharynx, comparing what you see with illustrations of similar species. Continue this process of careful study throughout the body until you are thoroughly familiar with the entire anatomy.

If the specimen is a tylench, it will test the quality of the microscope and your ability to observe if you correctly interpret the cephalic structures, deirids, phasmids, and the details of the cuticle and lateral fields. Each group will present special problems, which are usually just as difficult as those you find in the tylenchs. The workmanship of a true nematologist can be attained only by infinite patience and attention to the most minute details.

Measuring nematodes: The importance of measurements in describing nematodes has been recognized from the beginning. These were presented in actual figures until deMan (1884) introduced a system by which the three principal body proportions were designated by the Greek letters alpha, beta, and gamma. For convenience, the Greek letters have been replaced by a, b, and c. These body proportions are as follows:

 a = total length divided by the greatest width
 b = total length divided by the neck length
 c = total length divided by the tail length

These proportions are generally accepted by nematologists, and the beginner must immediately learn how to secure them from the specimen

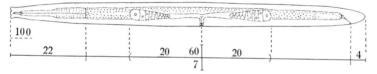

Fig. 3-9. Outline sketch of a small dorylaim with lines drawn for securing body proportions: Total length of body line = 100 mm; a = length/width = $\frac{100}{7}$ = 14; b = length/esophagus = $\frac{100}{22}$ = 4.5; c = length/tail = $\frac{100}{4}$ = 25; V = vulvar distance/100 = $\frac{60}{100}$ = 60%; ovary = $\frac{20}{100}$ = 20%. Completed measurements: ♀: 1.0 mm; a = 14; b = 4.5; c = 25; V = $^{20}60^{20}$. Reduced from original sketch made at 300 diameters.

under study. To them we add the position of the vulva and length of the testis, both expressed in per cent of the total body length.

The process of securing these measurements necessitates the use of a camera lucida, by means of which a line is drawn showing the length of the body in the position in which it is observed. Across the line are drawn three short lines marking the points where the esophagus joins the intestine and positions of the vulva and anus. Arcs are drawn to indicate the distances the ovaries extend from the vulva or the testes from the anal opening. Often the vulva marks the widest point of the body, and at this point the width should be very carefully recorded. But if the body is wider at another point, as in many monhystral species, this width should be used in computing the "a" proportion. To secure the most accurate measurements, a nematode 1.0 mm long should be drawn at a magnification of 250 diameters, giving a line 250 mm long. Unless the specimen lies in a spiral form, this cannot be drawn in one

field of the microscope. In this event the first portion should be drawn
to near the middle of the body and the remainder from there to the
tail. A specimen 2.0 mm long or over may be sketched at 125 diameters
with fair accuracy, while one 0.5 mm long should be sketched at 500
diameters. If a sketch is made at lower magnifications, the width measurement will be so small that the thickness of a fine pencil line may
make a considerable error in the "a" proportion. Rarely is it necessary
to carry the proportion figure to more than one decimal point. Measurements of that accuracy mark the limit of the camera lucida and the
human eye.

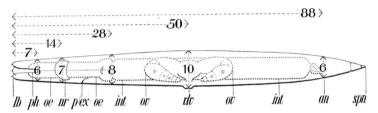

Fig. 3-10. Outline of a nematode illustrating the Cobb formula. The measurements 6, 7, 8, 10, and 6 indicate the body width at base of stoma, nerve ring,
base of esophagus, vulva, and anus, respectively. Longitudinal measurements 7,
14, 28, 50, and 88 show the distance from the anterior end to the points mentioned. To Cobb's sketch the ovary measurements 12 and 12 have been added.
All measurements are expressed as percentages of the total length. Assuming
the specimen to be 1.0 mm long, the formula is $\dfrac{7. \quad 14. \quad 28. \quad ^{12}50.^{12} \quad 88.}{6. \quad 7. \quad 8. \quad 10. \quad 6.}$ 1.0 mm.

The diagrammatic nematodes represent specimens which are straight,
but usually specimens are more or less arcuate or coiled. For curved
lines a map-measuring instrument is almost a necessity if they are to be
measured with reasonable accuracy. Slightly curved lines may be measured in segments with a small ruler if desired. Specimens killed by cold
fixative are practically worthless so far as measurements are concerned because of the shrinkage which takes place, especially in the neck. The
contorted bodies are exceedingly difficult to measure in any manner. Yet
we find published measurements of such specimens carried to the third
decimal place! The "a" measurements must be made on specimens which
are not flattened by the weight of the cover glass; otherwise, considerable
error may enter into calculations of this proportion. Literature is replete
with measurements and figures which obviously were made from flattened
specimens. Always use tiny glass-rod supports under a cover glass, as described under Microscopic Techniques.

The "nematode formula" of Cobb (1913a) was used extensively until
about 1940, when most workers discarded it because they found it both
cumbersome and impractical. This formula was based on a series of
percentages of the total length of the body. The numbers 6, 7, 8, 10,
and 6 are the transverse measurements indicating the body diameter at

the base of the pharynx (or spear), nerve ring, base of neck, vulva, and anus, respectively. Corresponding linear measurements are 7, 14, 28, 50, and 88. Theoretically this formula gives a mathematical outline of the nematode based on these ten measurements. To these measurements Cobb added a series of conventional signs and sketches indicating various characteristics of the nematode. These are well illustrated and explained in his "One Hundred New Nemas" (1920). But after attempting to translate these signs into words, the reader will doubtless realize that the system is idealistic rather than practical.

DESCRIBING A NEW SPECIES

Undescribed species are frequently discovered during routine examination of plant and soil material, and naturally the worker will desire to describe them. This situation involves a responsibility which few realize, for once you have presented a name for a species, it becomes part of the permanent scientific record and therefore it should be firmly established with a distinctive diagnosis which will enable other workers to identify it when they find similar specimens. Even today species are being inadequately described in too many instances. Such unsatisfactory descriptions are due to inadequate study of the literature, lack of specimens for comparative purposes, poor microscopic equipment, inadequate training, and, all too frequently, a desire to get into print and build up a bibliography.

The first step is to prepare permanently mounted specimens which will be deposited in some safe place where they will be protected and available for future reference. Entirely too often, descriptions are made from temporary slides which soon dry out, and specimens are thus lost to science. Often these mounts are made in drops of cold formalin solution or other media without first relaxing the specimens, the result being distorted, twisted wrecks. Such specimens are practically worthless as working material, because all measurements are far from correct and observations on morphology of doubtful accuracy. This word of caution is especially applicable to dorylaims and other forms in which cold fixatives cause spears to be extruded and the details of the pharynx and lip region are thus completely destroyed. Failure to use proper cover-glass supports results in flattened bodies, and these yield width measurements of no value.

Study descriptions and illustrations of related species made by previous workers, and observe the details described, comparing them with characters of the species under examination. If you do not see some of the minute papillae and other organs illustrated, get a better oil-immersion objective, or check the adjustment of light source and condenser. Degree of illumination is all-important in seeing many of these characters, which are just at the limits of visibility. Rarely will you be able to exhaust the information to be gathered from a specimen at the first examination: items overlooked one day may be resolved the next, or even a month or years later. Many of the finer details are not visible in a brightly lighted room without eye shades on the microscope.

After becoming familiar with the detailed morphology of the species, adjust the camera lucida, and make an outline sketch of the body from which the measurements are to be computed. When this is completed, make a few trial sketches of the head, tail, and other important diagnostic features. Determine how large the sketches should be drawn to make a convenient-sized plate of proper proportions for the publication in which the description will be printed. Plan for a reduction to one-half or one-third of the original diameter. To do this, lay out a sketch on tracing paper of a page two or three times the width and length of the publication selected. Trace your preliminary sketches in approximately the same position as you desire to have them in the completed illustration. This method is especially necessary if you plan to have a full-length drawing of the species accompanied by more highly enlarged diagnostic details.

Use labels indicating morphological characters very sparingly, if at all, and then use only neatly printed words or abbreviations symmetrically arranged. In like manner use only numbers and letters printed on gummed paper to designate the various parts of the illustration.

Begin the description with the measurements of both sexes, if you have found both males and females. Follow with a statement of the chief diagnostic characters and other pertinent morphological observations. This method will enable the reader to get the most important facts immediately and avoid the necessity of reading through two or three pages of discussion to locate pertinent points. End the description with a "diagnosis" in which you set forth the characters which justify establishing a new species. Compare them with those characters which have been used to diagnose related species. Information on biology, distribution, and other items of interest should follow.

A discussion of the importance of measurements in diagnosis may be pertinent at this time. Plant parasitic species frequently respond to the nutrition of different hosts and produce types which vary greatly in size and other characteristics. An outstanding example is found in host populations of *Ditylenchus destructor,* the potato rot nematode, in which not only a great difference in size may occur but also important differences in the gonads and esophageal gland region. Fortunately, such instances are not common, and most of the free-living and some plant parasitic forms retain a fairly uniform size without regard to the locality in which they are found, even on different continents. Variation in habitat may also involve difference in size. *Dorylaimus thermae* had a length of only 1.1 mm in the hot waters of Yellowstone Park, Wyoming, while in a cold alpine lake in Utah the length was 1.5 to 1.8 mm (Thorne and Swanger, 1936).

Nematology, like entomology, zoology, and other branches of biological science, will always have problems of variants within a species which have developed locally or over wide areas during long geographical separation. Such variants may retain enough of the original characteristics to be recognizable as members of the species or be sufficiently divergent to warrant the establishment of a new species. A decision on this point will depend largely on the personal judgment of the worker.

The International Rules of Zoological Nomenclature do not recognize as valid the naming of a species based on host plant only. At least an indication of the morphological characters by which it may be distinguished is required.

Suggestions on Nomenclature

Describe new species and genera only after a thorough search of the literature. This will avoid creation of synonyms and attendant embarrassment.

Do not make synonyms of species unless you have specimens on which to base your decision. That a species diagnosis is inadequate is no indication that it is a synonym of some other species. Creating a synonym means that you consider your judgment superior to that of the author. Beginners are especially prone to overlook and underevaluate details which experienced workers readily recognize. If you are monographing a genus or family, leave inadequately described species in a status of inquirendum. Present available information which will enable another worker to recognize the species should he be fortunate enough to collect specimens from which he can emend the original description.

Recognize the fact that minor variations occur in all species, especially among populations from different geographical areas. It will be an enlightening experience to visit a large entomological collection and observe the series of forms found in insect species. Or examine bird skins in an ornithological collection, and note the wide range in size and markings of certain species. Nematodes are just as subject to variation as are larger forms of animal life, and this fact must be recognized in developing the taxonomy.

Avoid establishing subgenera which necessitate the use of awkward trinomials. The same applies to subspecies and lower categories. Micoletzky (1922) attempted to establish species, varieties, forms, and subforms, which led to the creation of nomenclatorial abominations like *Aphelenchus parietinus tubifer parvus informis*.

Select short, easily pronounced names. A name does not have to be descriptive of the organism although it is desirable that it be so when feasible. It is far better to draw from four to six letters at random and arrange them into a pronounceable barbaric name than to create a jaw-breaking monstrosity. We now have trinomials with forty to fifty letters in fifteen to twenty syllables which are virtually unpronounceable.

Preparation of Illustrations

One carefully prepared illustration may often be worth more to your reader than a full page of descriptive text, and every effort should be made to attain accuracy in delineating diagnostic characters. Because of the minute sizes of many of the organs described, drawings must necessarily be somewhat schematic, especially those illustrating cephalic papillae, lateral pores, and structures like the cirri of *Chambersiella* and the probolae of *Acrobeles.* Study the works of the master artist Chambers, and note his techniques of producing intricate and lifelike illustrations by means of lines of varying weight, etching, and stippled shading of ova, glands, and other organs.

The best drawing material is "scratchboard," a lightweight cardboard with a fine surface of chalklike material, which permits etching to make corrections, shading, lacy muscle bands, and depth effects. Most important of all, it eliminates the hazard of accidentally spoiling a drawing after several days of labor have been expended on it. All the writer's illustrations have been prepared on this material, and each of the full-page plates represents 25 to 100 hours of work. Note how interior lines have been etched at short intervals to keep the internal organs "down in" the drawing. Had outlines of eggs not been etched, they would have resembled wieners lying on top of the nema, rather than eggs within the body. If scratchboard is not available, a good grade of drawing paper will produce acceptable results but figures should be simplified, with fewer lines and less stippling.

Drawing pens are an important item. Each artist has his preference, but for general use the writer finds the small "crow-quill" types very satisfactory and rarely uses any other. Occasionally long body lines are first run with a ruling pen and later shaded in certain areas by adding extra ink with the crow-quill. Black india ink and similar products are preferable since they produce a high contrast.

Curved rulers are almost a necessity in preparing full-length drawings. Types used by engineers and architects are very satisfactory for wide curves. For short sectors a large and a small "French curve" will be found very useful. To these should be added two or three homemade substitutes composed of 10- to 20-inch sections of assorted Saran tubing through which pieces of No. 8 or 10 galvanized wire have been inserted. Fasten the wire by turning a hook at each end. For very sharp curves like those in the illustration of *Axonchium amplicolle* (Fig. 17-3) the most satisfactory type is made from a piece of heavy insulated copper wire covered with thin plastic tubing.

Sketches are transferred from three-ring binder paper to scratchboard by means of a carbon paper made from rice or tissue paper. Model-airplane construction tissue is very satisfactory. The tissue is first laid on a piece of cardboard and the edges fastened with glue. Prussian blue powder is then thoroughly rubbed into the surface with a tuft of cotton. Excess powder is dusted off with a clean tuft of cotton and the edges cut loose from the board. The light blue lines disappear by the time they are inked over and do not interfere during reproduction as would commercial black carbon paper.

The most satisfactory tool for etching scratchboard is a strong steel scalpel with a sharp, pointed blade. Except for the point, the blade is covered with leather or tape to protect the fingers. With practice, this tool can be used to meet any etching requirement and is much superior to the usual commercial etching tools. For very exacting etching the writer frequently works under a low-power dissecting microscope or a large reading glass mounted on a short tripod.

Preparation of Full-length Illustrations

Illustrations of the female *Paratylenchus hamatus* (Fig. 13-16) and *Xiphinema index* (Fig. 17-6) will be used as examples in describing the procedure for making full-length drawings. The consecutive steps in the preparation of figures of this type are as follows:

1. Make camera lucida sketches on three-ring binder rag paper at the desired magnification, which should vary according to the size of the specimen. *Paratylenchus hamatus,* a very small species, was sketched at 2,000 diameters. *Xiphinema index,* a much larger species, was sketched at 500 diameters. Since the entire nema is not visible in the field of the microscope at these magnifications, it was necessary to draw *P. hamatus* in four sections and *X. index* in nine.

2. Beginning at the anterior end, measure the sketches, marking each 100 mm, as well as important body features like the base of the esophagus, ends of ovaries, vulva, and anus.

3. Prepare two pieces of No. 12 or 14 wire as long as the combined sketches. This was 700 mm for *Paratylenchus hamatus* and 1,800 mm for *Xiphinema index.* Sharpen both ends of one wire.

4. Make tracings of short sections of the body at the points marked on the sketches, showing the body width and other anatomical features at these points. Write the measurement on these tracings, cut out the pieces, clip off the corners, and thread them on the sharpened wire at the proper locations. Place weights on the wire to hold the paper pieces flat, and fasten them with a quick-drying cement like that used in model-airplane construction.

5. Bend the other wire into a position which appears to be suitable for the drawing and which will still leave in view the important body features. Then fit the wire bearing the paper pieces to this form, making any adjustments necessary. For simple postures like that of *Paratylenchus hamatus* the second piece of wire may not be necessary. For overlapping loops like those on *Xiphinema index,* the paper pieces often work loose while the posture is being determined unless experimental bending is done with the extra piece of wire.

6. Lay out a tentative plate with the proper proportions for the page on which it will be printed, using a lightweight tracing paper. Complete bending the wire form until it fits the plate, or alter the size and form of the plate until a satisfactory arrangement is made. Always leave space for diagnostic figures of the head, tails, and other necessary characters. A few small weights will aid in holding the wire form in place while adjustments are being made.

7. Mark the body widths at the points indicated. With these basic

points fill in the body contour lines, and outline the internal anatomy by freehand, tracings, or measurements with ruler and calipers. Large-scale drawings of the head, tail, and other desired features should now be arranged about the full-length sketch.

8. Prepare a piece of scratchboard of the proper size as determined in

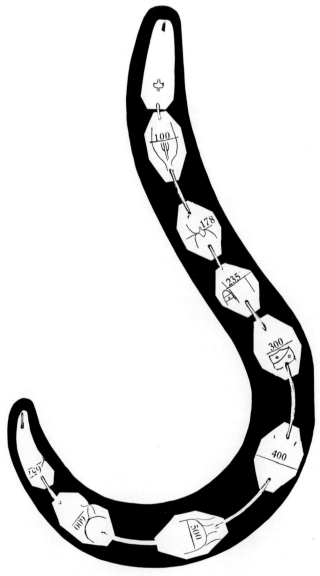

Fig. 3-11. Layout for drawing of *Paratylenchus hamatus.* Compare with Fig. 13-16.

step 7. Glue or cement it to a piece of heavy cardboard, place under pressure to prevent warping, and allow to dry overnight. This will add necessary "body" to the scratchboard and keep it flat.

9. Transfer the completed sketch to scratchboard with blue carbon paper. Keep all parts covered except those on which you are working, because the blue easily rubs off.

10. Work over the carbon tracing with a sharp, light blue pencil, filling in any portions not brought out distinctly by the carbon.

11. Complete the drawing in india ink with the aid of curved rulers and other techniques for drawing previously outlined.

Practice, combined with ingenuity, should enable the beginner to make a satisfactory illustration. After two or three trials it may be possible to eliminate the tracing-paper first copy and sketch the drawing directly on the scratchboard. Check frequently with calipers the widths of the body at various points to prevent unsymmetrical lines of the body contour.

After your first draft of the text and drawings is completed, submit it to an experienced nematologist for suggestions and criticisms. By doing this you may avoid embarrassing errors. A satisfactory illustration rarely is produced at the first trial. Several of the writer's early drawings were redone three to five times before Dr. Cobb approved them, and I now consider them very mediocre.

Chapter 4

CLASSIFICATION OF THE PHYLUM NEMATA

An outline of the entire classification of the Phylum Nemata would be too extensive to include in this text. However, a diagrammatic outline of the higher groups is presented that the reader may have some idea of the present organization. This includes animal and insect parasites as well as marine and fresh-water and soil-inhabiting groups, all of which are included in eleven orders. Many of the higher groups have been established on very limited knowledge of the great numbers of genera and species actually existing, and for this reason extensive revisions must be made as information increases. We boast that the nematodes approach the insects in numbers of species; yet we have only eleven orders, where there are about twenty-seven for the insects. Superfamilies like Plectoidea, Monhysteroidea, Enoploidea, Dorylaimoidea, Mermithoidea, and many others must eventually be given the rank of orders. But let these advances await the building of foundations of species and walls of genera before we attempt to erect a roof of families, superfamilies, and orders. A taxonomy developed in this logical manner will be far more stable than that built on examination of a small number of species.

Only representatives of those groups which the worker in agriculture will commonly encounter while working with plants and soil are included herein. Because of the many exceptions in morphology found in almost all groups, the few keys given may sometimes be found inadequate or misleading. The reader is urged to study carefully the many detailed illustrations and become well informed on generic and specific characters. This is more satisfactory than following long, tedious keys, which may sometimes terminate in the wrong group. Intimate acquaintance with the gross morphology and characteristic movements of genera and species is essential. This can be gained only by intensive observation and study of both living and permanently mounted specimens.

Class SECERNENTEA (von Linstow, 1905) Dougherty, 1958

Synonym: Subclass PHASMIDIA Chitwood and Chitwood, 1933

Order TYLENCHIDA Thorne, 1949

INTRODUCTION

Tylenchida includes the majority of the known ecto- and endoparasitic nematodes which attack plant life. Members of this order are encountered more frequently than those of any other group. It is therefore most fitting that we begin with them and become acquainted with their classification, morphology, habits, life histories, host preferences, and control.

The classification presented here is based on more than seven thousand specimens from twenty-eight states and twenty foreign countries. These represent over two hundred species from about forty genera. Two preliminary papers have already been published (Thorne, 1941, 1949). The best known genera were rediagnosed and illustrated in the 1949 paper and established a foundation on which several generic papers have since been published by other workers. But even these extensive collections probably represent not more than 20 per cent of the genera and 5 per cent of the species existing throughout the world. Future workers will find it necessary to establish additional higher categories of classification as our knowledge is advanced by more intensive and global collecting. Let us hope that this expansion will be achieved with specimens actually in hand and not on theory. The task will not be one for the overenthusiastic neophyte with just a few collections; rather it should be an extensive and intensive study by experienced nematologists with thousands of specimens on which to base extremely careful work.

Although the illustrations have been prepared very carefully, they are necessarily somewhat schematic. This is especially true of face views showing the arrangements of amphid apertures and cephalic papillae. Frequently the prominence of these minute organs is unavoidably exaggerated.

Critical morphological studies were made through a 1.5-mm oil-immersion objective and 5× and 10× oculars. All side lights were eliminated by means of a cloth screen fitted about the ocular. An observer working at an open table where side lights interfere with vision would find it impossible to see many of the details shown, especially in face views. With superior equipment and exceptionally good eyesight, someone may eventually see and illustrate the cephalic papillae, deirids, and phasmids which the writer was unable to find on certain species. Most observations were made on specimens mounted in glycerin or balsam.

The taxonomy of Tylenchoidea and Aphelenchoidea is included in considerable detail except for certain genera on which monographic studies have not been made. The most important known species of these genera are included. The Tylenchoidea parasites and associates of insects under the Family Allantonematidae Chitwood & Chitwood, 1937, have been omitted.

Order TYLENCHIDA

Diagnosis: Nemata, Secernentea. Stoma armed with a protrusile spear or stylet (except degenerate males of certain Criconematidae and Tylenchulidae). Spear aperture always ventrally located. Median esophageal bulb usually present, generally with a valvular apparatus (except Neotylenchidae). Basal portion of esophagus forming a bulb, without valvular apparatus, or lobelike.

Type superfamily: TYLENCHOIDEA Chitwood & Chitwood, 1937

General description: Cuticle marked by striae which usually are interrupted on the lateral fields by incisures or refractive bands. Deirids and phasmids frequently visible but often very difficult or impossible to see. Excretory tube and pore a conspicuous feature, usually located near region of nerve ring.

Hemizonid usually visible, located in vicinity of excretory pore. Lip region typically with two circlets of papillae, usually visible only from a face view. One circlet consisting of six is closely grouped about the vestibule; the other of eight is located farther out but still on the anterior contour of the lips. However, the numbers of these papillae may be reduced in certain species or beyond the limits of the microscope used. Amphid apertures usually porelike, located near apices of lips. Apertures of *Meloidogyne* and *Heterodera* slitlike, located just under margin of labial disc. Those of *Psilenchus* and *Macrotrophurus* are slitlike and located well down on the outer contour of the lips.

Esophagus consisting of a corpus which may or may not contain a median bulb with a sclerotized valvular apparatus, a narrow isthmus encircled by the nerve ring, and an enlarged basal portion containing the esophageal gland nuclei. This basal portion may consist of a true pyriform bulb, or the glands may form a lobe extending back over the anterior end of the intestine. If a basal bulb is present, there is also a valvular apparatus (cardia or esophagointestinal valve) connecting the lumen of the esophagus with the intestine. If the esophageal glands are lobelike, the junction of the lumen and the intestine is a minute, very obscure muscular apparatus. The duct of the "dorsal gland" may empty into the esophageal lumen near the base of the spear (Tylenchoidea) or into the median bulb (Aphelenchoidea). The two remaining glands enter into the submedian sectors of the median bulb. The arrangement of the three large esophageal gland nuclei is variable, even among individuals of the same species. In certain specimens, two very small additional gland nuclei are sometimes visible.

Intestinal cells generally are well filled with refractive granules which obscure details of the cell nuclei, except when stained and cleared. The intestine ends in a distinct rectum leading to a small, slitlike anus, except in certain Criconematidae in which the rectum and anus are very obscure, perhaps absent.

Ovaries one or two, reflexed, outstretched, or coiled (Heteroderidae and *Nacobbus*). Most frequently the ovary is made up of a single series of developing oögonia, but sometimes it consists of a compound series arranged about a rachis as in *Anguina*. Testis single except in certain aberrant *Meloidogyne*. Spicula simple, tapering, curved; resting on a plain troughlike gubernaculum. Bursa present in Tylenchoidea except in Heteroderidae, *Eutylenchus*, and certain Tylenchulidae and Criconematidae. Aphelenchoidea without bursa except in *Aphelenchus* and *Metaphelenchus*, in which *Rhabditis*-like bursal ribs occur.

Diagrammatic outline of higher groups of Nemata

	Order	Superfamily
	Tylenchida	Tylenchoidea * Aphelenchoidea *
	Rhabditida	Rhabditoidea * Drilonematoidea
	Strongylida	Strongyloidea Trichostrongyloidea Metastrongyloidea
Class SECERNENTEA (PHASMIDIA)	Ascaridida	Ascaridoidea Oxyuroidea Atractoidea Cosmocercoidea Subuluroidea
	Spirurida	Spiruroidea Acurioidea Thelazioidea Physalopteroidea Filarioidea
	Camallanida	Camallanoidea Dracunculoidea
	Dorylaimida	Dorylaimoidea * Mermithoidea Trichinelloidea
Class ADENOPHOREA (APHASMIDIA)	Chromodorida	Chromadoroidea Desmodoroidea Desmoscolecoidea
	Monhysterida	Monhysteroidea * Axonolaimoidea Plectoidea *
	Enoplida	Enoploidea Tripyloidea *
	Dioctophymatida	Dioctophymatoidea

Phylum NEMATA

* Groups of which representatives are included herein.
SOURCE: Outline courtesy of B. G. Chitwood, 1959.

Outline of the Superfamily Tylenchoidea

Families	Subfamilies	Genera
		Tylenchus
		Tylechorhynchus
		Tetylenchus
		Psilenchus
	Tylenchinae	Macrotrophurus
		Trophurus
		Ditylenchus
		Pseudhalenchus
		Anguina
		Paranguina
		Hoplolaimus
		Scutellonema
Tylenchidae	Hoplolaiminae	Rotylenchus
		Helicotylenchus
		Spyrotylenchus
		Pratylenchus
		Radopholus
	Pratylenchinae	Chitinotylenchus
		Nacobbus
		Rotylenchulus
	Genera of uncertain position	Atylenchus
		Eutylenchus
	Neotylenchinae	Neotylenchus
		Deladenus
		Nothotylenchus
		Boleodorus
	Nothotylenchinae	Thada
Neotylenchidae		Nothoanguina
		Halenchus
		Ecphyadophora
	Paurodontinae	Paurodontus
		Stictylus
	Hexatylinae	Hexatylus
		Heterodera
Heteroderidae		Meloidogyne
		Meloidodera
		Criconema
	Criconematinae	Criconemoides
		Hemicycliophora
		Hemicriconemoides
Criconematidae	Paratylenchinae	Paratylenchus
		Cacopaurus
	Dolichodorinae	Dolichodorus
		Belonolaimus
	Uncertain position	Macroposthonia
	Tylenchulinae	Tylenchulus
		Trophotylenchulus
Tylenchulidae	Sphaeronematinae	Sphaeronema
		Trophonema

TYLENCHOIDEA

Key to superfamilies of Tylenchida

1. Dorsal esophageal gland emptying into lumen of esophagus near base of spear; bursa, when present, not supported by ribs
   Tylenchoidea Chitwood & Chitwood, 1937
   Dorsal esophageal gland emptying into median bulb of esophagus; bursa absent except in *Aphelenchus* and *Metaphelenchus,* in which it is supported by ribs . . . . .Aphelenchoidea Fuchs, 1937

Key to families of Tylenchoidea

1. Median esophageal bulb greatly enlarged, isthmus and basal bulb reduced; cuticle often strongly annulated, sometimes bearing spines and plates
   Criconematidae Thorne, 1943
   Median bulb small to moderate or lacking; cuticle with only fine or moderately coarse annules, never with spines and plates 2
2. Females sessile, obligate parasites, living within or attached to plant roots; males usually without bursae 3
   Females free-living, ectoparasitic or migratory parasites in roots except *Nacobbus* and *Rotylenchulus;* males with bursae 4
3. Females cyst-forming or pyriform-saccate, often producing galls; males cylindroid with short, nonbursate tails . . . . .Heteroderidae Skarbilovich, 1947 *
   Females saccate, males with conoid elongate tails, with or without bursae
   Tylenchulidae Raski, 1957
4. Valvular median esophageal bulb present . . . . .Tylenchidae Oerley, 1880
   Valvular median esophageal bulb absent . . . . . . .Neotylenchidae Thorne, 1949

Family TYLENCHIDAE Oerley, 1880

Diagnosis: Tylenchoidea. Both sexes typical active nematodes except females of *Nacobbus* and *Rotylenchulus.* Median bulb of esophagus well developed with sclerotized valvular apparatus. Basal portion of esophagus ending in a pyriform bulb or extended in lobes over anterior end of intestine. Ovaries one or two. Tails hemispheroid to elongate-filiform. Bursa adanal in filiform types, caudal in blunt-tailed forms.

Type subfamily: TYLENCHINAE deMan, 1876
Tylenchidae is composed of an exceedingly variable group of genera. In many instances they are obviously distantly related, and their taxonomy is sometimes based on convenience rather than on morphological characters. Subfamily groups are of questionable value. At least eight of the genera are of uncertain position because common diagnostic morphological characters are not present among them. Perhaps *Rotylenchulus* and certain other genera should also remain in the category of uncertain position.

* Thorne (1949) established the Family Heteroderidae, not knowing that Skarbilovich had already done the same.

Key to subfamilies and genera of Tylenchidae

1. Basal portion of esophagus lobelike, extending back over anterior end of intestine, spears strongly developed................................. 2
   Basal portion of esophagus bulblike, except in *Pseudhalenchus* and certain *Ditylenchus* species, and in these the spears are very small
   Tylenchinae and genera of doubtful position 10
2. Lip region convex-conoid, ⅕ to ⅓ as wide as spear length, tails usually shorter than anal body diameter.....................Hoplolaiminae 3
   Lip region low, flattened, ½ to ⅗ as wide as spear length, tails conoid to blunt terminus.......................................Pratylenchinae 6
3. Spear knobs with forward-pointing processes, phasmids very large, erratically located...*Hoplolaimus*
   Spear knobs rounded or cupped, phasmids in tail region.............. 4
4. Body straight or nearly so when relaxed, phasmids well developed, larger than usual...*Scutellonema*
   Body arcuate when relaxed, phasmids small, normal................... 5
5. One or more annules of lip region tiled, males present in all species, spermagonium not present.......................................*Rotylenchus*
   Annules of lip region not tiled, males unknown, spermagonium present
   Helicotylenchus
6. Female a typical active nema...................................... 7
   Female greatly enlarged, saccate................................. 9
7. Two ovaries present.....................................*Radopholus*
   One ovary present.. 8
8. Spear knobs rounded or cupped.........................*Pratylenchus*
   Spear knobs furcate.................................*Chitinotylenchus*
9. Female with elongated posterior end, one ovary...............*Nacobbus*
   Female reniform, two ovaries...........................*Tylenchulus*
10. Head not armed with setae.. 11
    Head armed with setae... 18
11. Spear 90 to 120 μ long...............................*Macrotrophurus*
    Spear less than 30 μ long.. 12
12. Ovary one... 13
    Ovaries two... 16
13. Female obese, gonad cells arranged about a rachis..............*Anguina*
    Female not obese, cells not arranged about a rachis.................. 14
14. Female tails rounded, usually clavate.......................*Trophurus*
    Female tails elongate-conoid to filiform.......................... 15
15. Tails elongated filiform, bursa short, adanal.................*Tylenchus*
    Tails conoid, bursa enveloping ⅓ or more of tail.............*Ditylenchus*
16. Distance from anterior end to median bulb greater than from bulb to intestine ....*Psilenchus*
    Distance from anterior end to median bulb less than from bulb to intestine 17
17. Female tails blunt, rounded.......................*Tylenchorhynchus*
    Female tails acute or subacute...........................*Tetylenchus*
18. Cuticle with transverse striae only.......................*Eutylenchus*
    Cuticle with longitudinal and transverse striae...............*Atylenchus*

Chapter 5

TYLENCHINAE

Genus *Tylenchus* Bastian, 1865

Bastian's original description of *Tylenchus* was meager, and his figures left much to be desired. He stated that members of the genus possessed only one ovary. However, Bütschli (1873) and deMan (1880, 1884) placed species with two ovaries in the genus, and for 60 years it was a "dumping ground" for tylenchs of various forms. About 130 species are listed in Baker's check list (1958, unpublished). Of these, about 100 species have been transferred to other genera. Filipjev (1934, 1936) was the first to bring order into their taxonomy when he established the genera *Rotylenchus, Pratylenchus, Tetylenchus,* and *Ditylenchus* to receive certain groups of related species.

Andrassy (1954) recognized twenty species, for which he proposed four subgenera: *Tylenchus, Aglenchus, Filenchus,* and *Lelenchus.* Chief diagnostic characters are, body length, annulation of cuticle, development of spear, form of median esophageal bulb, and tail length. Among a small number of species, these characters may be sufficiently constant to indicate subgenera. However, in a large collection, specimens with overlapping characters indicate that these groups are not always valid. The few species of representative *Tylenchus* included herein do not carry the proposed subgeneric names.

Diagnosis: Tylenchinae. Tails elongate-conoid to filiform. Lip region striated. Vulva well behind middle of body. Anterior ovary outstretched. Posterior uterine branch short, rudimentary. Bursa short, adanal. Developing oöcytes and spermatocytes largely arranged in single file. Deirids usually prominent, located near the latitude of excretory pore. Phasmids not observed. Cuticle striated, lateral fields marked by incisures. No sclerotized cephalic framework present. Spear well developed with strong basal knobs. Median esophageal bulb variable in form with refractive valvular apparatus. Isthmus long, slender, ending in a somewhat pyriform basal bulb containing three large nuclei. Cardia present.

Type species: *Tylenchus davaini* Bastian, 1865
Synonym: *Anguillulina davaini* (Bastian) Goodey, 1932

Morphology: ♀: 1.0–1.3 mm; $a = 25$–35; $b = 6$–7.5; $c = 5.5$–7.2; $V = {}^{36}65^{2}$
♂: 0.9–1.1 mm; $a = 37$; $b = 5.5$; $c = 6$; $T = 46$

Tails elongated, filiform, ventrally bent. Cuticle strongly striated. Lateral fields with crenate borders. Deirids prominent, located near latitude of ex-

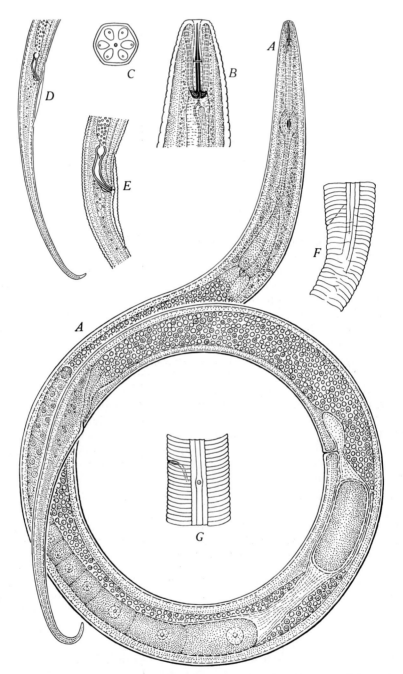

Fig. 5-1. *Tylenchus davaini.* *A*—Female. *B, C*—Head in lateral and face views. *D, E*—Male tail. *F*—Anal region of female tail; note terminus of lateral field. *G*—Region of excretory pore; note deirid in lateral field. (*After Thorne. Courtesy of Helminthological Society of Washington.*)

cretory pore. Phasmids not observed. Lip region striated, set off by a slight narrowing of body contour. Spear strongly knobbed. From a face view the head appears to be slightly flattened. Amphids located near margin of lateral lips. A single papilla present on each submedian lip. Median esophageal bulb ovate with refractive valve. Isthmus slender, ending in a somewhat pyriform bulb which contains three large gland nuclei. Cardia conoid. Anterior cells of intestine hyaline, remainder packed with coarse, dark granules. Anterior ovary outstretched, with oöcytes usually arranged in single file. Posterior uterine branch rudimentary, shorter than body diameter. Spicula of usual tylenchoid type. Gubernaculum thickened near middle. Bursa crenate, about three times as long as anal body diameter. Testis single, outstretched, with spermatocytes arranged in single file.

Tylenchus davaini is one of two known tylenchs which possess arcuate, ventrally bent tails. The other species is *Boleodorus thylactus,* a much smaller form. Because of this character, the two species can usually be identified under the dissecting microscope.

Biology: Members of the genus *Tylenchus* frequently are among the most numerous nemas found in soil from the rhizospheres of plants. However, they have not been observed as either ecto- or endoparasites, except *T. costatus.* Their small, strong spears indicate that they probably feed on either root hairs or fungus mycelia.

Distribution: The above descriptions were based on specimens collected in Ogden Canyon, Utah. Later T. Goodey secured specimens from the type locality in England which proved to be practically identical to those from Utah. The species is generally distributed in mountain and valley soils of the western United States and probably is cosmopolitan.

Tylenchus filiformis Bütschli, 1873

Morphology: ♀: 0.5 mm; a = 35; b = 5.3; c = 3.5; V = $^{20}59$
Body cylindroid from median bulb to vulva, then tapering uniformly to the acute terminus. Tail twice as long as vulva-anus distance, a very important character in identification. Striae coarser than in other *Tylenchus,* averaging 1.5 μ at mid-body. Lateral field with four incisures, crenate along its borders. Spear 12 to 14 μ long, with small rounded knobs. Median esophageal bulb ovate. Nerve ring near middle of slender isthmus. Basal esophageal bulb elongate-pyriform. Cardia discoid. Intestine with scattered refractive granules. Uterus of immature females unusually short, the oöcytes in tandem except for a short region of multiplication. Males unknown and no spermatheca observed in uterus.

Habitat and distribution: Described by Bütschli from Germany. The above description based on specimens collected by Allen in Holland.

Tylenchus filiformis is one of the most frequently mentioned tylenchs. Doubtless the many records include *T. exiguus* and several other small, slender species which somewhat resemble *T. filiformis.* However, *T. filiformis* is distinctive because of its coarse striae and tail length.

Tylenchus exiguus deMan, 1876

Morphology: ♀ : 0.5–0.65 mm; a = 26–30; b = 6–7; c = 3.8–5; V = ^{40}55–65
♂ : 4.5–6 mm; a = 28; b = 4.7; c = 4.4; T = 45

Female slender, spindle-shaped, tapering anteriorly to the narrow head and posteriorly to the uniformly conoid filiform tail. Vulva-anus distance about equal to tail length. Lateral field marked by four incisures. Amphid aperture

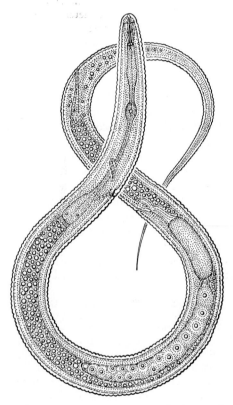

Fig. 5-2. *Tylenchus filiformis*. Note strong annulation and tail about twice as long as vulva-anus distance.

porelike, slightly below apex of lateral lip. Spear 12 to 14 μ long with well-developed knobs. Median esophageal bulb fusiform. Isthmus slender with nerve ring near middle. Basal bulb of esophagus elongate-pyriform with three prominent nuclei. Intestine packed with large refractive granules. Eggs thick-shelled, about three times as wide as long. Uterus made up of about four rows of cells. Spermatheca a prominent feature of the reproductive system. Ovary outstretched, the oöcytes in single file except for a short region of multiplication. Posterior uterine branch shorter than vulva body width.

Male more slender than female, and body more cylindroid. Spicula distally arcuate, resting on a strongly thickened gubernaculum. Bursa about three times as long as anal body diameter, with crenate border.

DeMan illustrated *Tylenchus exiguus* as a small, spindle-shaped nema with vulva-anus distance about equal to tail length. Unfortunately he later made it a synonym of *T. filiformis* Bütschli. Specimens from Seinhorst in the Netherlands closely resemble deMan's description. The fine

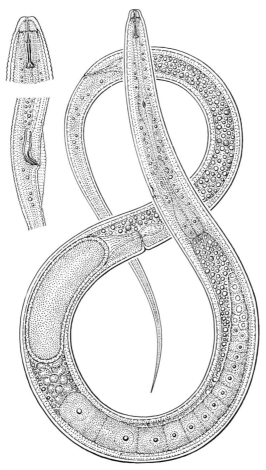

Fig. 5-3. *Tylenchus exiguus.* Note approximately equal length of vulva-anus distance and tail length.

striae and more robust body immediately distinguish *T. exiguus* from *T. filiformis.*

Habitat and distribution: Soil about plant roots in cultivated and virgin soil, Netherlands, Ireland, Indonesia, and many points in the United States. Nothing is known of its feeding habits.

Tylenchus costatus deMan, 1921

Synonym: *Tylenchus cancellatus* Cobb, 1925

Morphology: ♀: 0.5 mm; a = 24–30; b = 4.7; c = 6; V = $^{34}65$
Body marked by coarse transverse striae which are divided into tiny blocks by
deep longitudinal lines. Near the head these lines number 16 but increase to
18 near middle of neck and continue in this number to near the vulva region.

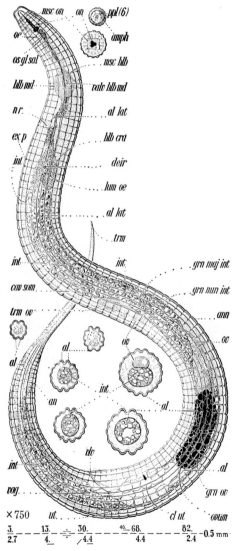

Fig. 5-4. *Tylenchus costatus.* (*After Cobb.*)

Then they decrease to 14, 10, 8 and finally disappear near middle of tail. Terminal third of tail bears no transverse striae. Spear 14 μ long with well-developed knobs. Median bulb of esophagus spheroid. Basal esophageal bulb broadly pyriform. Cardia discoid. Hemizonid adjacent to excretory pore. Deirids distinct. Vulva with thick lateral membranes. Uterus composed of six or eight rows of cells. Ovary short with oöcytes arranged in single file. Vulva-anus distance of Cobb's specimen illustrated as two-thirds the tail length. DeMan's figure shows this distance as slightly more than tail length.

When *Tylenchus costatus* is moving, the tail is held perfectly straight, a fact which makes it possible to recognize the species under the dissecting microscope.

Habitat and distribution: Described by deMan from wet soil on stream bank near Breda, Netherlands. Seinhorst sent the writer specimens from a pasture near Goree, Netherlands. Cobb's specimens were found infesting roots of peony, *Paeonia officinalis,* on which they caused gall-like swellings. Cobb failed to record the source of his material.

Genus *Tylenchorhynchus* Cobb, 1913a

Synonym: *Bitylenchus* Filipjev, 1934

Diagnosis: Tylenchinae. Lip region set off by constriction or continuous with head contour. Lateral fields marked by four, five, or six incisures. Phasmids conspicuous, located well behind anal region. Deirids generally not visible. Spear usually strong with large basal knobs. Basal bulb of esophagus well developed, connected with the intestine by a distinct cardia. Vulva near middle of body. Ovaries two, outstretched. Female tail conoid, blunt, usually two or more times as long as anal body diameter. Male tail slightly arcuate, enveloped by bursa. Spicula and gubernaculum tylenchoid.

Type species: *Tylenchorhynchus cylindricus* Cobb, 1913a

Members of the genus *Tylenchorhynchus* are sometimes known as "stylet" nematodes, a name proposed by Steiner (1949). In recent years the name "stunt" has become more popular. Pathogenicity tests have demonstrated that certain species are important plant parasites. Additional research will doubtless show that, under favorable ecological conditions, all species may be of some economic importance. The group is widely distributed wherever plant life is found. Almost any collection of soil will usually contain one to four species.

The many scattered references were assembled by Allen (1955) in a generic monograph which added twenty-two new species to the twelve already described. Since the appearance of this paper numerous other species have been added by various workers, and the total now (1959) is near fifty. A large portion of this section on *Tylenchorhynchus* is based on material from Allen's paper.

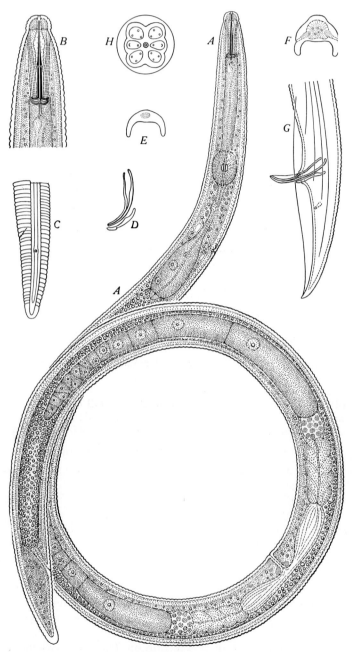

Fig. 5-5. *Tylenchorhynchus cylindricus.* *A*—Female. *B, C*—Head and tail in detail. *D*—Spicula and gubernaculum. *E*—Cross section through male tail, showing form of bursa. *F*—Cross section showing position of phasmids. *G*—Male tail. Originally published as *Tylenchorhynchus dubius.* (*After Thorne. Courtesy of Helminthological Society of Washington.*)

Tylenchorhynchus cylindricus Cobb, 1913a

Synonym: *Tylenchorhynchus dubius* Thorne, 1949

Morphology: ♀: 0.7–1.0 mm; a = 28–35; b = 4.2–6.0; c = 13–22; V = $^{28}54$–64^{31}

♂: 0.67–1.0 mm; a = 30–40; b = 4.4–5.8; c = 14–16; T = 64

Cuticle coarsely striated. Lateral field with four incisures. Lip region hemispheroid, set off by constriction, bearing five annules. Phasmids prominent. Deirids not observed. A face view shows the amphid aperture as located on the apex of the lateral lip. Number of labial papillae not determined. Spears 22 to 28 μ long with prominent, cupped knobs. Spear length usually about three times width of lip region. Median bulb slightly ovoid, basal bulb elongate-pyriform. Cardia well defined. Ovaries outstretched. A spermatheca present in each uterus. Hemizonid adjacent to excretory pore. Testis outstretched. Spicula tylenchoid. Gubernaculum troughlike, with a slight distal expansion. Bursa enveloping tail.

Filipjev (1936) made *Tylenchorhynchus cylindricus* a synonym of *T. dubius,* a European species. The writer (1949) accepted Filipjev's designation, emended the generic and specific descriptions, and illustrated them in the accompanying figure, which is now published under the correct name, *T. cylindricus.* This identification was verified by Allen (1955) by comparing specimens of *T. dubius* from Europe with those collected by the writer in Utah.

Hosts and distribution: *Tylenchorhynchus cylindricus* is indigenous to the arid soils of the Western states, where it frequently is found associated with roots of desert plants. Reynolds and Evans (1953) reported that *T. dubius, = T. cylindricus,* caused appreciable stunting of Hopi M cotton in both greenhouse and field tests near Sacaton, Arizona. Tepary bean, *Phaseolus acutifolius* A. Gray var. *latifolius,* was also stunted.

Near Benmore, Utah, extensive plantings of crested wheat grass, *Agropyron cristatum* (L.) Gaertn, were observed in a severe state of decline in 1953. These plantings had been established by the Intermountain Range Experiment Station of the U.S. Forest Service. An investigation of the problem was conducted by D. S. Havertz under a cooperative project between the Experiment Station and the University of Utah. Havertz's report (1957 unpublished thesis) recorded demonstrations of pathogenicity under greenhouse conditions. The indigenous nemas had transferred to the introduced grass and increased to great numbers. Typical injury was evident in dying centers of grass clumps, and this effect was followed by the outer portions breaking up into small, unthrifty bunches, a condition known as "birdnesting."

Tylenchorhynchus dubius (Bütschli, 1873) Filipjev, 1936

Synonym: *Anguillulina dubia* (Bütschli) Goodey, 1932b

Morphology: ♀: 0.62–0.78 mm; a = 30–35; b = 5–6; c = 13–16; V = 54–67

♂: 0.65–0.71 mm; a = 33–37; b = 5.0–5.6; c = 12–15

Body cylindroid except at extremities. Lateral field with four incisures. Cuticle finely striated. Lip region hemispheroid, bearing six annules, set off by constriction. Labial framework inconspicuous. Spear 19 μ long with well-developed, rounded knobs. Cardia hemispherical, inconspicuous. Spermatheca present in uterus. Tail subcylindrical. Terminus blunt, annulated. Postanal intestinal sac present, extending more than half the tail length. Bursa enveloping tail. Spicula tylenchoid. Gubernaculum a thin, flat trough with proximal end slightly curved.

Tylenchorhynchus dubius is distinguished by the setoff lip region, four lines in lateral field, postanal intestinal sac, and striae extending around terminus.

Habitat: A common species in the Netherlands, especially in pastures. Also recorded by T. Goodey from Winches Farm, St. Albans, England.

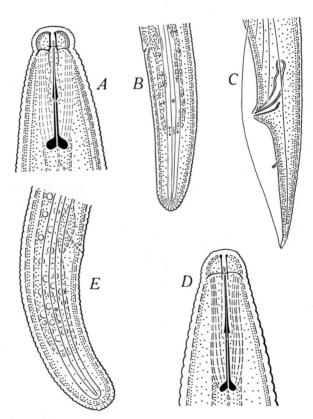

Fig. 5-6. *A–C—Tylenchorhynchus dubius. D, E—Tylenchorhynchus maximus.* (*After Allen. Courtesy of Helminthological Society of Washington.*)

Tylenchorhynchus maximus Allen, 1955

Morphology: ♀: 1.0–1.4 mm; a = 37–47; b = 5.4–8.1; c = 16–20;
V = $^{25-31}47-54^{21-26}$

Body cylindrical, forming an open spiral when relaxed. Lateral field marked by four incisures, sometimes aerolated by extensions of the coarse annules. Lip region rounded, bearing seven annules, set off by only a slight depression in the neck contour. Labial framework indistinct. Spear frail, about 23 µ long, with slender shaft and small rounded knobs. Esophagus typical of the genus. Cardia conoid, large. Gonads outstretched. Spermatheca or spermatozoa not observed. Male unknown. Tail cylindroid with annules extending around the blunt terminus. Phasmids conspicuous, slightly posterior to middle of tail. Postanal intestinal sac extending more than halfway into tail.

Tylenchorhynchus maximus is distinctive because of its large size, continuous lip region, frail spear, postanal intestinal sac, and cylindrical tail (Fig. 5-6).

Habitat and distribution: A widely distributed species of the United States. Reported from soil about the roots of various plants from New York, Michigan, Utah, and California. Common in pastures and lawns in Wisconsin. Specimens frequently are severely parasitized by *Duboscquia penetrans*.

Tobacco stunt nematode, *Tylenchorhynchus claytoni* Steiner, 1937

Morphology: ♀: 0.64–0.73 mm; a = 24; b = 5–6; c = 18–19;
V = $^{28-30}55-57^{20-25}$

♂: 0.57 mm; a = 26; b = 5.8; c = 14.6; T = 55–68

Body rather straight when relaxed. Cuticle marked by coarse striae which are divided into segments by longitudinal striae. These number about 20 near mid-body plus 4 deep incisures on each lateral field, making a total of 28. Lip region set off by constriction, bearing three annules. Cephalic sclerotization obscure. Spear slender with broad, cupped knobs. Median esophageal bulb ovate, basal bulb elongate-conoid. Hemizonid just anterior to excretory pore, about two annules wide. Ovaries outstretched, the oöcytes arranged in single file. Uterus with spermatheca. Female tail with 8 to 16 striae. Phasmids varying in position near middle of tail to near region of the anus. Male wth arcuate spicula and slender gubernaculum. Bursa unusually long, rising about one tail length anterior to anus and enveloping tail to its terminus.

Host and distribution: Steiner first reported *Tylenchorhynchus claytoni* as a rare parasite of tobacco roots, in which he found 23 specimens. Later investigations by other workers have demonstrated that it is a very widespread and serious parasite of tobacco. Graham (1954) found that 67 per cent of 175 collections of tobacco field soil in the vicinity of Florence, South Carolina, were infested and plants stunted. Pathogenicity demonstrations were secured by placing as few as 100 nemas about roots of tobacco plants. Lesions were not produced, but roots were shriveled and reduced in length. Mountain (1954) recorded *T. claytoni* as a frequent parasite of wheat and oats but did not find it attacking tobacco. Nelson (1956) demonstrated that *T. claytoni* was the causal agent of reduced corn growth in North Carolina. Numerous tests with corn varieties, inbreds and hybrids, revealed that in the roots of nine inbreds, nemas failed to reproduce and cause appreciable damage. In

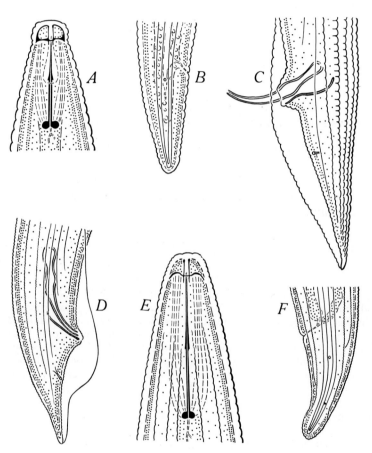

Fig. 5-7. *A–C. Tylenchorhynchus claytoni. D–F. Tylenchorhynchus lamelliferus. (After Allen. Courtesy of Helminthological Society of Washington.)*

Wisconsin, azaleas introduced from Southeastern states have been found severely damaged and sometimes killed by this nema.

Tylenchorhynchus lamelliferus (deMan, 1880) Filipjev, 1936

Synonym: *Anguillulina lamellifera* (deMan) Goodey, 1932b

Morphology: ♀: 0.86–1.0 mm; a = 25–31; b = 4.3–6.8; c = 16–24;
V = $^{27}46$–53^{27}
♂: 0.85–1.3 mm; a = 27–35; b = 5.1–6.4; c = 18–22

Body cylindroid, tapering rapidly at extremities, assuming an open C position when relaxed. Cuticle with fine transverse striae and 16 longitudinal striae. These are reduced to 14 in the neck region, and on the tail they coalesce until their identity is indefinite. Four incisures mark the lateral field. Phasmids near middle of conoid, slightly blunt tails. Annulation extending around terminus. Labial framework slightly sclerotized. Spear 24 μ long, slender, with small, rounded knobs. Esophagus, digestive system, and gonads typical of the genus. Spermatheca present (Fig. 5-7).

Habitat: *Tylenchorhynchus lamelliferus* is known only from the Netherlands, where it has been collected from soil in many places.

Genus *Tetylenchus* Filipjev, 1936

Diagnosis: Tylenchidae without sclerotized cephalic framework. Cuticle finely striated. Ovaries two, outstretched. Spear of moderate size, with or without basal knobs. Tails of both sexes tapering to an acute or subacute terminus. Deirids and phasmids present, generally easily visible. Bursa subcaudal, extending almost to terminus. Distance from anterior end to valve of median bulb shorter than that from valve to base of esophagus. Esophagus with elongate-ovate median bulb; unusually long, slender isthmus, and elongate-pyriform basal bulb containing the usual three large gland nuclei. Hemizonid anteriorly adjacent to excretory pore. Cardia usually discoid. Spicula tylenchoid; gubernaculum a simple, troughlike plate.

Type species: *Tetylenchus tenuis* (Micoletzky, 1922) Filipjev, 1936
Synonyms: *Tylenchus tenuis* Micoletzky; *Anguillulina tenuis* (Micoletzky) Goodey, 1932b
Tetylenchus slightly resembles *Tylenchorhynchus,* from which it is distinguished by the more acute tails, four lips, discoid cardia, absence of sclerotized labial framework, and location of the amphid apertures. Since the type species was inadequately described, a representative species, *T. joctus,* is presented in detail. The seven species described represent divergent forms, and the group may eventually merit a subfamily or family rank.

Tetylenchus joctus Thorne, 1949

Morphology: ♀: 0.7 mm; a = 30; b = 4.5; c = 9.4; V = $^{31}55^{28}$
           ♂: 0.6 mm; a = 30; b = 4.5; c = 9.0; T = 70
Cuticle finely striated. Lateral fields marked by six minute incisures. Deirids about opposite base of esophagus. Phasmids of both sexes slightly posterior to middle of tail. Lip region set off by a slight narrowing of the body contour, marked by six fine striae. There is no sclerotized cephalic framework. Spear about 15 μ long, its protrudor muscles attached to refractive elements at the side of the head. From a face view the lip region is seen to be slightly hexagonal with only four lips. Amphid apertures minute, located close to the oral opening. Four prominent submedian papillae present on the outer contour of the lips; if other papillae were present, they were beyond the limits of visibility.

Vulva a transverse slit. Anterior ovary extending almost to base of esophagus, posterior reaching almost to rectum. The specimens were not yet gravid, but had they been fully developed and producing eggs, the ovaries doubtless would

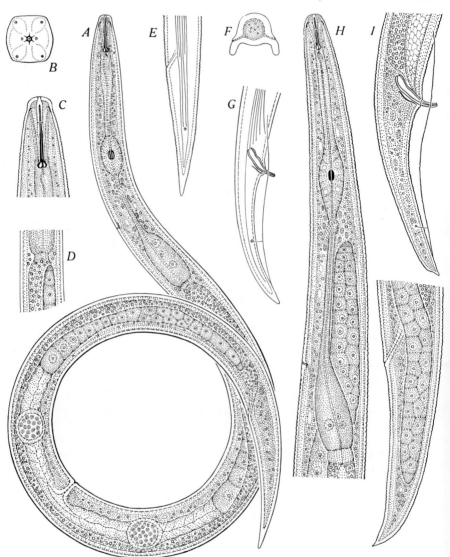

Fig. 5-8. *A–G. Tetylenchus joctus. A*—Female. *B*—Face view. *C*—Head. *D*—Cardiac region. *E*—Female tail. *F*—Cross section through male phasmids. *G*—Male tail. *H–J. Tetylenchus productus. (After Thorne. Courtesy of Helminthological Society of Washington.)*

have been even longer. Conspicuous features of the uteri were the spherical spermatheca. Oöcytes arranged in single file except the usual short region of multiplication. Spicula tylenchoid, with thin, troughlike gubernaculum. Bursa subcaudal, an accentuated stria extending from the phasmid to the border of the bursa.

Hosts and distribution: *Tetylenchus joctus* was first collected by Jocelyn Tyler from soil about the roots of grass and weeds near Wrangell, Alaska. In 1958, Martin T. Hutchinson of the New Jersey Experiment Station found this species associated with a severe decline of blueberries. Tests for pathogenicity have verified his observations that they are the causal agent. It is interesting to note that a random collection in Alaska should include a species of economic importance in New Jersey.

Tetylenchus productus Thorne, 1949

Morphology: ♀: 1.2 mm; a = 25; b = 7.1; c = 17; V = $^{45}5_{34}2$

                  ♂: 1.0 mm; a = 33; b = 7.1; c = 14; T = 72

Body tapering both ways from near the middle. Head rounded, the lips not set off in any manner. Terminus acute, sometimes slightly mucronate. Lateral fields marked by six incisures. Deirids about opposite base of esophagus. Hemizonid just anterior to excretory pore. Phasmids of female slightly posterior to middle of tail; on male about two-thirds the distance from anus to terminus. Lip region without sclerotized framework. From a face view the vestibule is seen to be slightly sclerotized with six minute radiating elements. Amphid apertures very minute, located close to oral opening. Four submedian cephalic papillae were easily seen, but others were either absent or beyond limits of visibility. Spear about 12 μ long, slender, with small basal knobs. Esophagus as illustrated. Cardiac valvular apparatus about one-third width of body. Ovaries a conspicuous feature of the body, the anterior one frequently extending well past the base of the esophagus, while the posterior one may reach far into the tail. Adjacent to the cap cell the ovary appears to be made up of about four lines of developing oöcytes (Fig. 5-8).

Habitat: A single collection from hillside soil near mouth of Ogden Canyon, Utah.

Genus *Psilenchus* deMan, 1921

Diagnosis: Tylenchidae. Striae present on both cuticle and subcuticle. Amphid apertures elongated, slitlike, conspicuous; located well below the anterior contour of the lip region. Spear elongated, slender, with or without basal knobs. Deirids prominent, opposite nerve ring. Hemizonid just anterior to excretory pore. Phasmids situated two to five body widths posterior to anal region. Lateral fields with incisures or, rarely, consisting of plain refractive bands. Tails of both sexes elongated, filiform; frequently clavate. Distance from anterior end of body to center of median esophageal bulb greater than that from center of bulb to base of esophagus, except in *P. magnidens,* in which these measurements are about equal. Ovaries one or two, outstretched; the developing oöcytes arranged in single file. Testis single with spermatocytes in single file. Spicula tapering, arcuate, cephalated. Gubernaculum thin, troughlike, slightly curved.

Type species: *Psilenchus hilarulus* deMan, 1921

Members of this genus are immediately distinguished by the elongated, slitlike amphid apertures, slender, frequently clavate tails of both sexes, and prominent deirids and phasmids. Distance from anterior end to valve of median bulb greater than from valve to base of esophagus. This one character often is diagnostic of the genus even under the dissecting microscope. Although only seven species of *Psilenchus* are known, they indicate a large group of variable forms which eventually may represent a higher taxonomic category.

Psilenchus hilarulus deMan, 1921

Morphology: ♀: 1.1–1.5 mm; a = 33–38; b = 6.5–7.1; c = 8.0–8.5;
V = $^{32}47^{32}$

♂: 1.0–1.2 mm; a = 32–36; b = 6.0–6.8; c = 6.0-6-6; T = 42

Cuticle marked by striae which average about 1 μ apart near the head, slightly less on the body proper, and generally much finer on the tail. Occasionally specimens occur on which the caudal striae are variable in width and sometimes extend completely to the terminus, as described by deMan. Lateral fields marked by four incisures except near the head and on the tail, where they are reduced to two. Deirids prominent, opposite nerve ring. Phasmids easily seen, two or three body widths posterior to anus. Tails elongate, tapering to the terminus, which varies from cylindrical to clavate. Amphid apertures elongate, slitlike, located well below contour of lips. From a face view the lateral sectors of the head are observed to be widened to make room for the broad, pouchlike amphidial chambers. Three papillae observed on each of the four submedian head sectors, but none seen on the lateral ones. Spear slender, devoid of basal knobs. Dorsal esophageal gland opening into lumen of the esophagus at base of the spear. Median bulb ovate with conspicuous valvular apparatus; posterior bulb pyriform with the usual three gland nuclei. Excretory pore opposite nerve ring. Cardia conoid, submerged in the anterior end of the intestine.

Ovaries paired, outstretched. An elongated spermatheca present in each uterus. Spicula curved, tapering, cephalated, resting on a thin, troughlike gubernaculum. Bursa crenate, rising near a point about opposite proximal ends of spicula and extending past anus a distance equal to about twice anal body diameter. Male phasmids located near posterior ends of bursa.

This species is readily distinguished among the didelphic forms by the unstriated lip region, slender, knobless spear, and location of the amphid apertures.

Habitat and distribution: Soil about roots of plants, bank of River Mark near Breda, Netherlands. A rather common species in cultivated and virgin soil from the western and north central United States. Nothing is known of its feeding habits.

Psilenchus aberrans Thorne, 1949

Morphology: ♀: 0.66 mm; a = 36; b = 6.0; c = 7.6; V = $^{4}26^{6}$
♂: 0.61 mm; a = 32; b = 6.4; c = 7.1; T = 43

Body assuming an open C form when killed by gradual heat. Cuticle marked by striae which become excessively fine near the terminus and finally disappear entirely. Lateral fields about one-third as wide as body with two fine, but distinct, incisures visible the larger part of their length. Excretory pore and deirids about opposite nerve ring. Phasmids two or three body diameters posterior to anus. Lip region unstriated. Amphid apertures almost half as wide as head, located near base of lip region. Spear slender, with very narrow lumen; slightly

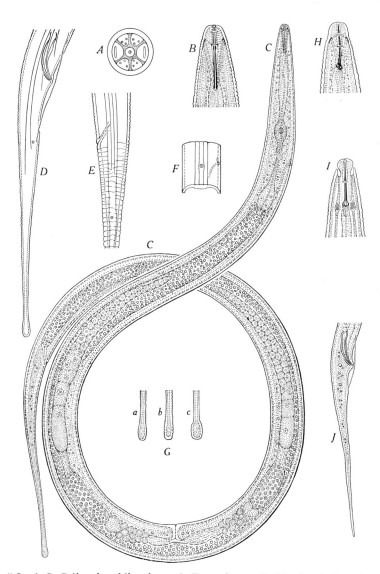

Fig. 5-9. *A–G. Psilenchus hilarulus. A*—Face view. *B*—Head. *C*—Female. *D*—Male tail. *E*—Anal region of female. *F*—Deirid region. *G*—Variations in female terminus. *H–J. Psilenchus aberrans.* (*After Thorne. Courtesy of Helminthological Society of Washington.*)

bent ventrally in its posterior third. Dorsal knob of spear larger than the submedian and extending somewhat farther back. Median esophageal bulb ovate
with obscure valve, posterior bulb elongate-pyriform. Cardia discoid to hemispherical. Ovary outstretched. Posterior uterine branch less than half as long
as body width. Spicula arcuate, cephalated, resting on a thin, flat, slightly
curved gubernaculum. Bursa as illustrated. Terminus minutely rounded
(Fig. 5-9).

Psilenchus aberrans is distinctive because of the slightly curved, asym-
metrically knobbed spear, open C form of body when killed by gradual
heat, and vulva-anus distance greater than tail length.

Habitat: Sugar beet fields near Fort Collins and Wellington, Colorado,
and alfalfa field near Murray, Utah.

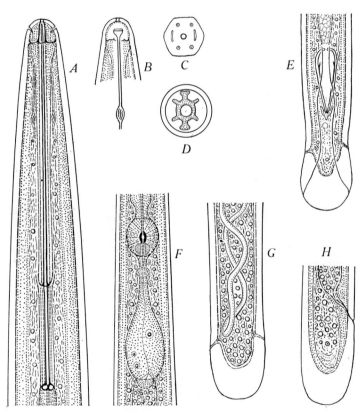

Fig. 5-10. *Macrotrophurus arbusticola. A*—Anterior end. *B*—Lip and amphid
region. *C*—Face view. *D*—Pattern of basal cephalic framework. *E*—Male tail,
ventral view. *F*—Esophagus, ventral view. *G*—Posterior portion of female,
showing lateral canals, dorsal view. *H*—Female tail. (*Specimens courtesy of
M. Oostenbrink.*)

Genus *Macrotrophurus* Loof, 1958

Diagnosis: Body cylindroid, tapering rapidly to a very narrow lip region. Amphid apertures elongate slits with pocketlike inner connections. Lateral cephalic sectors larger than submedian. Labial papillae very obscure from face view, but probably arranged like those of *Psilenchus*. Spear unusually long, varying from 90 to 120 μ, with very small knobs. Isthmus short, only slightly longer than neck width. Distance from anterior end to valve of median bulb much greater than from valve to base of esophagus. Cardia present. Ovaries two, outstretched. Cuticle very thick on tails of both sexes. Bursa caudal.

Type species: *Macrotrophurus arbusticola* Loof, 1958

Morphology: ♀: 1.2–2.1 mm; a = 38–48; b = 6.3–10.2; c = 28–42;
$$V = {}^{22-32}48{}^{22-27}$$
♂: 1.0–1.7 mm; a = 40–58; b = 6.7; c = 20–28

Characters of the genus. Striae visible anteriorly but not extending over lip region. Lateral fields two-fifths as wide as body, marked by four faint incisures. Phasmids slightly anterior to middle of tails. Cephalic framework lightly sclerotized, best seen from face view. Lateral cephalic sectors larger than submedian, similar to those of *Psilenchus hilarulus*. Cephalic papillae almost beyond limits of visibility, apparently arranged like those of *Psilenchus*. Spear unusually long, that of female 92 to 119 μ, of male 90 to 110 μ. Shaft of spear occupying only two-fifths of length, knobs very small. Esophageal lumen convoluted in anterior portion of esophagus. Nerve ring slightly anterior to middle of isthmus. Hemizonid adjacent to excretory pore. Female tail packed with coarse, granular material. A postrectal intestinal sac may be present. Male tail arcuate near terminus, crescentic in cross section, with phasmids reaching to base of bursa. Bursa enveloping tail.

Habitat: Clay soil about roots of pear and poplar, Opheusden, Netherlands, and tree nurseries near Zurich, Switzerland.

Genus *Trophurus* Loof, 1956

Synonym: *Clavaurotylenchus* Caveness, 1958

Diagnosis: Lip region smooth, pointed, with amphid apertures at apices of lateral lips. One papilla easily visible on each submedian lip. Labial framework lightly sclerotized, with lateral sectors much wider than submedian. Caudal cuticle abnormally thickened. Vulva near mid-body. Anterior ovary outstretched. Posterior uterine branch rudimentary, shorter than body width. Intestine sometimes, perhaps always, forming a postanal blind sac. Male tail flattened, arcuate, enveloped by bursa.

Type species: *Trophurus imperalis* Loof, 1956

Trophurus minnesotensis (Caveness, 1958) Caveness 1959

Synonym: *Clavaurotylenchus minnesotensis* Caveness, 1958

Morphology: ♀: 0.75 mm; a = 31; b = 5.7; c = 18; V = ${}^{29}58$
♂: 0.7 mm; a = 35; b = 5.6; c = 35; T = 38

Characters of the genus. Cuticle with easily visible striae, except on anterior end and terminus. Lateral field marked by four incisures. Spear very slender, 14 μ long, with small, sloping knobs. Distance from anterior end to valve of median bulb slightly greater than from valve to base of esophagus. Nerve ring adjacent to median bulb. Isthmus more than two body widths long. Excretory pore just behind nerve ring. Hemizonid about one body width be-

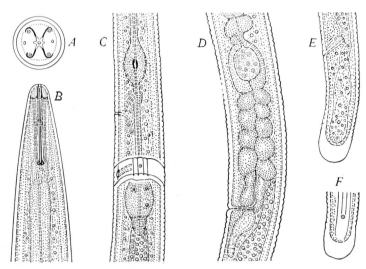

Fig. 5-11. *Trophurus minnesotensis. A*—Face view. *B*—Anterior end. *C*—Base of neck region. *D*—Vulvar region. *E, F*—Female tail. (*Specimens courtesy of F. Caveness.*)

hind pore, extending up to the lateral fields in the region of the prominent deirid. Ovary with oöcytes in single file except for a short region of reproduction. Spermatheca spheroid, containing many spermatozoa. Posterior uterine branch ending in two or three rudimentary cells. Phasmids posterior to middle of tail. Male tail with broad bursa and conspicuous phasmids. Spicula plain, arcuate, cephalated. Gubernaculum troughlike.

Habitat: Soil about sugar beets, Minnesota and North Dakota.

Chapter 6

Genus *Ditylenchus* Filipjev, 1934

Diagnosis: Tylenchinae. Lip region without obvious annules. Lateral fields marked by four or six incisures. Deirids very small but usually visible. Phasmids rarely visible even from a dorsoventral view. Tails elongate-conoid to acute or subacute terminus. Bursa enveloping one-fourth to three-fourths of tail. Ovary single, outstretched, rarely with one or two flexures. Gonad cells in one or two lines. Rudimentary postuterine branch present.

Type species: *Ditylenchus dipsaci* (Kühn, 1857) Filipjev, 1936

Members of the genus *Ditylenchus* are immediately distinguished from those of *Tylenchus,* a somewhat similar group, by the following characters: absence of obvious labial striae; presence of a sclerotized labial framework; less strongly developed spear; generally shorter, more conoid tails; and longer bursae.

Ditylenchus includes about thirty named species, several of them important obligate plant parasites. Others live in soil where they probably feed either on root-hairs of higher plants or on mycelia of fungi. About one-third of the species described inhabit tunnels of wood-boring beetles.

Bulb and stem nematode, *Ditylenchus dipsaci* (Kühn) Filipjev

Synonyms: *Anguillula dipsaci* Kühn, 1857; *Anguillulina dipsaci* (Kühn) Gerv. et v. Ben., 1859; *Tylenchus dipsaci* (Kühn) Bastian, 1865; *Anguillula devastatrix* Kühn, 1868; *Anguillula secale* Nitschke, 1868; *Anguillula putrefaciens* Kühn, 1877; *Tylenchus havensteini* Kühn, 1881; *Tylenchus hyacinthi* Prillieux, 1881; *Tylenchus alii* Beijerinck, 1883; *Tylenchus devastatrix* Ritzema Bos, 1888; *Ditylenchus phloxidis* Kirianova, 1951; *Ditylenchus fragariae* Kirianova, 1951; *Anguillulina dipsaci* var. *dipsaci* Steiner and Scott, 1935; *Anguillulina dipsaci* var. *communis* Steiner and Scott, 1935

The extensive synonymy is due to the fact that certain populations of *Ditylenchus dipsaci* have decided host preferences. Therefore, various workers assigned specific names to populations found only in certain plants, but they failed to present diagnostic morphological characters. The taxonomic status of certain populations still remains a controversial subject.

Historical: The first record of *Ditylenchus dipsaci* is that of Schwertz (1855), who recorded certain diseased conditions of rye, oats, clover, and other crops but did not observe the nematodes. Schwertz described the characteristic thickened bases of leaf sheaths and stems of rye, accompanied by wavy leaf growth and general stunting of the plant, and named the condition *Stock*. The causal agent was not discovered, however, until Kamrodt (1867) found nemas associated with plants exhibiting similar symptoms. Meantime Kühn (1857) had discovered *D. dipsaci* in teasel, *Dipsacus fullonum* L., and recognized those in rye as being similar in form. He then produced *Stock* in rye by placing diseased teasel heads under rows of rye plants. When Kühn discovered that alfalfa, clover, oats, rye, and other crop plants were attacked, he attempted to discard the name *dipsaci* and substitute *devastatrix*. This change was, of course, untenable under the rules of zoological nomenclature.

Bastian (1865) recognized the pest as belonging with a group of nemas for which he established the genus *Tylenchus*. It was under the name of *T. dipsaci* that it was known between 1880 and 1926 in the voluminous literature centered around the narcissus bulb industry. Baylis and Daubney (1926) revived the old name *Anguillulina dipsaci* (Kühn) Gerv. et v. Ben., and this was generally accepted until Filipjev (1936) designated it as the type species of his genus *Ditylenchus*. Earlier (1934) he had proposed *Ditylenchus*, using the first two letters of *dipsaci* and *Tylenchus* to form the generic name, but had failed to use the combination, *Ditylenchus dipsaci*.

Ritzema Bos (1888–1892) clarified a portion of the nomenclature by making transfers between certain of the thirty-eight known hosts. In this manner he demonstrated that the so-called species *hyacinthi, havensteini,* and *alii* were actually *dipsaci*. But he synonymized them with *Tylenchus devastatrix,* the accepted name at that time.

Morphology: ♀: 1.0–1.3 mm; a = 36–40; b = 6.5–7.1; c = 14–18;
$$V = {}^{60-70}80^7$$

♂: 1.0–1.3 mm; a = 37–41; b = 6.5–7.3; c = 11–15; T = 65–72

Body marked by transverse striae, about 1 μ apart, which are easily visible under the oil immersion at any point on the body. Lateral field marked by four incisures. Deirids usually visible near base of neck. Hemizonid adjacent to excretory pore, about six annules wide. Phasmids rarely visible and then only from a dorsal or ventral view on favorable specimens. Amphid apertures on apices of lateral lips, where they appear as minute refractive dots which can be seen only from a face view. Spear with strongly developed knobs from which protrudor muscles lead to the well-sclerotized cephalic framework. Basal esophageal bulb with the usual three prominent, and two inconspicuous, gland nuclei. Intestine connected to esophageal lumen by a very small valvular apparatus.

Ovary outstretched, sometimes reaching to median esophageal bulb, but more often near basal bulb, rarely with one or two flexures. Oöcytes lie largely in tandem and develop into eggs which are two to three times as long as the body diameter. Rudimentary posterior uterine branch present, extending about half-way back to anus. Vulva-anus distance equal to 1¾ to 2¼ times tail length. Terminus always acute.

Testis outstretched, with spermatocytes arranged in single file except for a short region of multiplication. From a perfectly lateral view the spicula exhibit a sclerotized pattern that apparently is characteristic of the species, but the

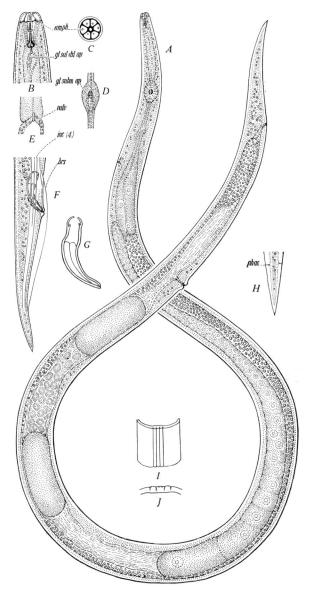

Fig. 6-1. *Ditylenchus dipsaci.* *A*—Female. *B, C*—Head in lateral and face views. *D*—Median bulb. *E*—Cardiac region. *F*—Male tail. *G*—Spiculum. *H*—Dorsal view of tail, showing phasmids (greatly exaggerated). *I*—Lateral field with typical four incisures. *J*—Aberrant lateral field with two small additional incisures. (*After Thorne. Courtesy of Helminthological Society of Washington.*)

proper angle of observation is so difficult to obtain that the pattern is rarely of taxonomic value. Bursa rising opposite proximal ends of spicula and extending about three-fourths the length of the tail. Lateral incisures ending in a pattern as illustrated.

Type host: *Dipsacus fullonum* L., fuller's teasel

The above description and measurements are of specimens collected from teasel, *Dipsacus fullonum,* the type host near Molalla, Oregon. The reader must keep in mind that specimens living on other hosts may be either smaller or larger than these, and gonad development will vary considerably depending on the suitability of the host. But the form of the head, four lateral incisures, esophagus with its nerve ring near the middle of the isthmus, pyriform basal bulb, form of the spicula, and acute tails of both sexes—all will be found to remain constant to a remarkable degree.

Biology: Nematodes in all stages of development are usually found throughout the growing season of the host, the number of generations varying with the succulence of the host tissues, favorable temperatures, moisture, and agronomic practices. Activity in narcissus bulbs may extend throughout the year since the nemas are active during the growing season and through harvest and storage. In alfalfa and clover activity may not exceed two or three months, depending on how early the crop is cut and on moisture. Conditions are far less favorable for nemic development under the arid climate of the western United States than in the humid areas of Europe.

Eggs: Eggs may vary from 70 to 100 μ in length and from 30 to 40 μ in width. Under favorable growing conditions eggs usually are found in all stages of segmentation, and the first larval moult probably occurs before hatching. Nothing is known of the ability of eggs to survive in field soil. When infested alfalfa is plowed under and nonhost crops grown for several years, it is difficult to find nemas in the soil. However, there is a rapid build-up within two years when alfalfa is again planted, and the areas of infestation usually correspond to those in the crop which was plowed under. This circumstantial evidence indicates that unsegmented eggs, or larvae lying dormant in eggs, do not hatch until stimulated by alfalfa diffusates.

Second-stage larvae: Young nemas emerging from eggs are usually about 0.3 mm long. These rapidly pass through the second and third moults, after which the genital primordia become visible near the middle of the body. This form is known as the preadult, or infective, larva. It is at this stage in the life history that the nemas have the remarkable ability to withstand adverse conditions of freezing and drying over long periods of time while waiting for the advent of favorable growing conditions for the host. During this preadult period they lie quiescent in fragments of plant tissue, in plant crowns, stems, leaves, and seeds, and in soil. These preadults gather about the basal plates of dried narcissus bulbs, forming cottony masses known as nematode "wool." In the field they become active under favorable moisture and temperature conditions. After entering a host they pass through the final moult and become adult males or females. Linford (1937b) has observed *Ditylenchus dipsaci* feeding on fungus hyphae, and there is a possibility that they secure food from this source when host plants are not present. Survival in the field for more than one season is doubtful because stored food supplies in the intestinal granules are eventually used. "Exhausted" larvae are sometimes found wandering in soil where hosts are not present. When stored in a laboratory, especially in a dry climate, they may survive for 20 years or more.

Larvae attacking the buds of alfalfa and other aboveground parts of plants must have a film of moisture in which to travel. Otherwise they are unable to move from the soil to the desired position in the plant crown, where the young leaves and shoots are developing. Entrance usually occurs through the stomata, although the larvae may enter at the base of stems or in leaf axils. Quanjer (1927) observed that the cells beneath the stomatal aperture began to enlarge before the larvae actually entered, a condition indicating that salivary secretions had been injected preparatory to the invasion. Swelling of these cells expanded the stoma until entrance was a simple matter. After the stoma was entered, the cortical cells were penetrated and points of infestation soon developed swellings or gall-like growths. Stunting, malformation, and sometimes death of the plant followed, depending on the severity of infestation and the ability of the host to withstand or tolerate the nemas. Often the nemas migrate from dying plants to others nearby or remain free in the soil. For this reason dead plants sometimes do not contain sufficient nemas to permit identification.

Seinhorst (1956) found that distribution and population density of stem nematodes in the Netherlands was definitely related to soil type. On heavy clay soils the populations are maintained at such a high level that onion bloat is always a menace to the crop. On light soils there is damage only when onions are grown more than once in three or four years. Seasonal variations in numbers are definitely correlated with soil type. Even when susceptible crops produce an increase in numbers, there is a much more rapid decline on sandy than on clay types. However, Seinhorst failed to secure any information as to the factor or factors which are responsible for the variations in mortality.

Perhaps no other plant parasitic nematode is more adaptable to climatic conditions than *Ditylenchus dipsaci*. It is found from the cool, moist areas of northern Europe to the irrigated lands of the western United States, and from the hot desert soils of southern California to the cold, high valleys of the Rocky Mountains. Wherever a host plant will grow, some population of this persistent species appears to thrive. The nemas were not injured when infested alfalfa crowns were exposed throughout the winter in the mountains of Utah where night temperatures ranged from 5 to 20° below zero for a period of four months. Collections have remained quiescent in the Salt Lake City, Utah, Laboratory of the Division of Nematology, U.S. Department of Agriculture, for

periods of 20 to 30 years. Bosher and McKeen (1954) found that preadults in narcissus "wool" survived −80°C for a period of 20 minutes.
Ditylenchus dipsaci has become one of the most cosmopolitan plant
parasitic nematodes. Bulbs, phlox, strawberry, and other perennials have
been among the most important distributing agents. Seeds of alfalfa,
clover, onions, and other plants have been among the common carriers.
There is also the possibility that indigenous colonies have been present
in many parts of the world and may have transferred to cultivated crops
when they were introduced.

Among the more comprehensive host lists are those of Steiner and
Buhrer (1932), T. Goodey (1933), and Filipjev and Stekhoven (1941).
Those of Goodey and Filipjev and Stekhoven include extensive discussions on bionomics and control and therefore are of outstanding value as
sources of information. However, all three lists doubtless include the
hosts of *Ditylenchus destructor* and perhaps other species.

Present records indicate that upward of four hundred plant species
belonging to more than forty families are attacked by *Ditylenchus dipsaci*
to some degree. Among the outstanding examples of polyphagous populations we have Quanjer's (1927) account of a race which attacked potatoes and transferred to fifty-two other plant species, twenty-eight of
which were not previously recorded. However, there is reasonable doubt
about the identity of the form investigated because it produced symptoms on potato tubers similar to those caused by *D. destructor,* the potato rot nematode.

Cobb, Steiner, and Blanton (1934) reported a polyphagous population
derived from narcissi on Long Island, New York. In this instance, thirty-
two plant species, largely weeds, were collected from an infested field,
and, of these, twenty-nine were found harboring the nemas. Among
them, twenty-one were new host records for *D. dipsaci,* and six others
had not previously been observed in the United States. Although the
tissues of all twenty-nine species were invaded, it was not determined
if the nemas were definitely established and reproducing. Oddly enough,
red clover was one of the plants which was not infested.

In contrast to these polyphagous populations we find that nemas
attacking teasel, daffodils, alfalfa, clover, phlox, onions, and certain
other plants are usually so restricted in their tastes that they do not
readily transfer from their favorite hosts. There may be a remote possibility that, with superior microscopic equipment and more critical evaluation of minute characters, some of these host races may be returned
to specific rank, as suggested by Steiner (1953a). At present it appears
more logical to regard them as merely biological strains or populations
without variety or specific standing.

Because of the polyphagous nature of certain populations, each colony
should be studied in relation to the plants with which it is associated
and under the conditions in which it is living. The possibility of mixed
populations should not be overlooked when conducting host tests.

Like many other species, *Ditylenchus dipsaci* frequently refuses to cooperate when brought into the greenhouse or placed in small, isolated plots. Because of this fact, negative experimental results may be of questionable value.

The wide and variable host range of bulb and stem nematodes necessitates limiting our discussion to only a few of the more important crops attacked. Hosts covered in the following sections are representative, and information on biology and control of the pest will usually be applicable to other plant species.

TEASEL

This interesting crop is grown on a limited acreage both in Europe and in the United States. It is of great importance to the textile industry, and Courtney (1952) gave a good account of its production and use.

Teasel is a biennial plant which produces a main stem 4 to 7 feet tall. There are many branches, each of which bears a spiny bur at its terminal. Each spine of the bur ends in a tiny hook. When mature, the burs are harvested, graded according to size, and shipped to the textile mills. There they are threaded on rods attached to revolving drums which pull the spines across the new-woven fabric and lift the nap from the hard, shiny surface.

Biology: Nemas enter the seedling teasel plants during moist periods. If high populations are present, death of the host may follow in a short time, while slight or moderately infested plants will live through the first season. When growth begins the second year, the nemas congregate about the center of the crown where they reproduce rapidly. They then enter the growing point, and are carried up on the stem as it develops, finally arriving at the termini of the many branches where the young burs are formed. The woody vascular tissues of the burs are attacked, producing a dwarfed "puffball" type of deformity. At maturity these puffballs are filled with thousands of preadult nemas congregated in shiny, white masses about the pith. Many attach themselves to the seed pedicels and are distributed in that manner. Those remaining in the puffballs lie dormant for long periods of time under laboratory conditions. Fielding (1951) reported many alive after 23 years. However, under moist field conditions it is doubtful that they survive more than 1 year.

Control: *Crop rotation.* Courtney records that infested fields were plowed and disked in the fall until all growing plants were destroyed. The following spring annual crops were planted, and these were either harvested or plowed under as cover crops. After three years the fields were relatively free of infestation, provided that all old teasel residues were completely destroyed and other host plants eliminated.

Hot water. Infested seed was successfully treated by immersing in water at 122°F (50°C) for one hour or 120°F (48.8°C) for two hours. Vitality of the seed was reduced until it was necessary to plant twice the usual quantity of seed. Addition of a wetting agent, Vatsol O.S., had no apparent effect on the success of the treatment. However, Courtney re-

Fig. 6-2. Teasel heads.   Left normal, right infested with *Ditylenchus dipsaci*. (*After Courtney.   Courtesy of Washington Academy of Sciences.*)

ported that plants from treated seed were more vigorous and produced higher-quality heads with superior stiffness of spines.

Hosts: Kühn succeeded in producing *Stock* in rye by placing infested teasel heads under the rows, and Courtney found that both spring and winter wheat, oats, rye, and the weeds *Collomia grandifloria* Dougl. and *Plantago lanceolata* L. all became infested with the teasel population. When the writer visited the Gregory teasel-packing plant at Molalla, Oregon, in 1928, thousands of infested teasel heads had been discarded and the soil where they lay was teeming with millions of nemas. Yet four well-known hosts in Oregon, red clover, dandelion, *Taraxacum officinale* L., plantain, *Plantago lanceolata*, and hawksbeard, *Crepis capillaris*, were all growing thriftily among the nemas without a trace of infestation. A few nemas were occasionally found about the crowns of plants or in leaf axils, but they were merely vagrants and had not become established and reproduced. Similar observations have been made on fields after daffodils had been harvested and on alfalfa and clover fields which had been plowed under. However, these instances well illustrate the vagaries of host observations, because Courtney, using inoculum from the Gregory site, was able to establish the nemas on *P. lanceolata*.

NARCISSI

Historical: The general distribution of *Ditylenchus dipsaci* throughout the bulb-producing areas of both Europe and the United States by 1922 indicated that the pest had long been present. The first record is that of Welsford (1917), who stated that it had been observed in England by J. W. Barr as early as 1905.

Discovery of *Ditylenchus dipsaci* in bulbs imported from the Netherlands prompted the first regulatory measures against nematodes by the United States. Between 1920 and 1930 this nematode was responsible for considerable friction between the two countries as shipments of bulbs were refused admittance or were condemned by inspectors after delivery. There was much concern over the possibility that the pest might transfer to alfalfa, clover, oats, and other crops; yet surveys by Godfrey (1923, 1924) revealed that it was already present in alfalfa and clover throughout the irrigated areas of the Western states. He also found that both cultivated and wild strawberries, dandelions, and hawksbeard were infested at various points along the Pacific coast and that the nemas were being widely distributed by the seeds of these two Compositae. But rarely, if ever, was it demonstrated that transfers to other crops actually occurred with populations from narcissi, alfalfa, clover, and teasel.

Biology: Leaves of severely infested bulbs bear small, elongate swellings known as "spikkles" which can be detected by stripping the leaf between the finger and thumb. In advanced stages these swellings may become yellow or brown in the center and occasionally break down into small dead spots. After the bulbs have matured and the leaves are dead, the nemas will still be found lying quiescent in the tissues. Entrance to the leaves is made as they emerge from the bulb, probably through the stomata. Part of the nemas go down into scales from which the leaves originate. When colonies are established, they form brown spots in the bulb scales which gradually spread until the entire scale is involved. In advanced stages brown rings will be seen when the bulb is

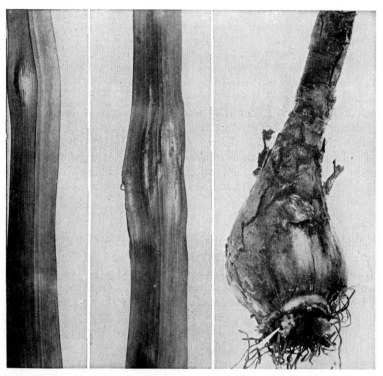

Fig. 6-3. *Ditylenchus dipsaci* infestation of narcissi. Left, two sections of leaves with characteristic spikkles. Right, bulb with masses of nematode "wool" on basal plate, as indicated by arrow. (*Courtesy of W. D. Courtney, Nematology Section, U.S. Department of Agriculture.*)

cut in two. Leaves and flower stems produced from partially infested bulbs are stunted and deformed and bear the familiar spikkles. Under severe infestation the bulb may be "blind" and may fail to produce flowers.

Reproduction continues during storage, and bulbs may completely break down and decay before planting time arrives. Badly decayed bulbs are not a desired habitat for the nemas, and the preadults frequently migrate down around the basal plate and emerge from the scales to form masses of "wool." In this form they are spread in crates and bags, on tools and machinery, and even on the shoes of workmen.

When diseased bulbs are planted, many of the nemas migrate out into the soil and move along the row to other bulbs. Sometimes four or five bulbs will be attacked on each side of the infested individual. In these instances many bulbs contain only a few nemas and exhibit none of the symptoms of infestation, either on the foliage or in the bulbs. At harvest they may easily be overlooked during inspection.

Control: *Hot water.* This method was first used by J. W. Barr in England about 1905, when he discovered that nematodes were the causal agents of a certain type of decay in narcissus bulbs. Ramsbottom (1918) further developed the method and recommended three hours' immersion at 110°F (43.3°C). Meantime, van Slogteren in the Netherlands had been working on a similar project and (1920) published instructions similar to those of Ramsbottom. During the following years van Slogteren became an outstanding leader in eliminating the bulb nematode from the fields of the Netherlands. Complete eradication was not achieved, and even today vigilant inspections are made of practically all plantings.

But in the United States hot water failed to give the desired control in many instances, and after further research Chitwood, Hassis, and Blanton (1941) demonstrated that by adding 1 pint of commercial formaldehyde USP to each 200 gallons of water, a superior control was effected. The efficacy was further increased by extending the period of treatment to $3\frac{1}{2}$ and 4 hours. To prepare bulbs for the hot-water bath, Courtney (1953) recommended a 2-hour presoak in water at 75°F, with a wetting agent such as Vatsol O.S. added at the rate of 1 pint to each 100 gallons of water.

Bulbs with visible signs of decay should be removed before treatment, because pockets of decayed tissue deep in the bulb act as insulation and nemas within them escape. Unpublished experiments conducted in 1929 by M. B. McKay and the writer demonstrated that the numbers surviving were in proportion to the amount of decayed scales. Complete kill was made in bulbs with only slight infestations, but in those which were badly decayed as high as 80 to 90 per cent of the nemas escaped.

Soil fumigation. Infested fields may be successfully fumigated, since the nemas live only in the top cultivated portion of the soil, where they are more vulnerable to fumigants. Prior to fumigation the field should be planted for at least two years in row or cover crops to facilitate finding and removing all volunteer bulbs remaining after harvest. Approved soil fumigants should then be applied in the quantities recommended by the producer, using an efficient applicator operated by a trained man. The method developed in Idaho and recommended for the eradication of the potato rot nematode, *Ditylenchus destructor,* should be especially effective for *D. dipsaci* also (Dallimore, 1955). This will cost $60 to $100 per acre, depending on the moisture-holding capacity of the soil.

Crop rotation. Courtney recommends that rotations cover a period of six years between bulb crops, with the first three years in row or cover crops while volunteer bulbs are being removed. Grain, hay, or row crops may be grown during the last three years. Elimination of possible weed hosts is an important part of any rotation.

Sanitation. Sanitary measures in fields and storage facilities are most important. If only occasional infested plants occur, applications of soil fumigants sufficient to kill the bulbs should be applied. These should include at least three bulbs on each side of the ones infested. Leaves and stems should be gathered and burned in the field. During storage every precaution should be exercised to prevent possible dissemination of infestation through nematode wool, soil, and fragments of infested tissues.

HYACINTHS

Prillieux (1881) reported *maladie vermiculaire des jacinthes* and described leaf lesions and other symptoms on *Hyacinthus orientalis.* He named the nematodes *Tylenchus hyacinthi* but stated that they were similar to *T. dipsaci.* While this is our first published record of the pest, Goodey (1933) states that "there is good reason for thinking that the disease was known to the Dutch bulb-growers in the latter half of the eighteenth century," where it was known as *ring ziek* and *oud ziek.* Ritzema Bos (1888–1892) made extensive studies on the effects of the nemas on both the bulbs and their foliage, which rather closely resemble the symptoms outlined for narcissi.

Control: The work of van Slogteren (1920) demonstrated that the usual hot-water treatment of 110° for three hours was a satisfactory method of control.

TULIPS

Tulips generally are not infested by *Ditylenchus dipsaci,* but Goodey (1943) reported finding the nemas in Lincolnshire, and a survey by George and Southey (1956) revealed that they were rather widely distributed. Symptoms and control are similar to those for daffodils and hyacinths.

OATS

During the period 1885 to 1900 a serious disease of oats was found in several countries of Europe which became known as *Stockkrankheit des Hafers* in Germany, *maladie vermiculaire de l'avoine* in France, and *tulip root* and *segging* in England. In the United States C. E. Scott found fields infested near Watsonville, California, in 1923 (personal communication), where it is still seen occasionally. Several workers in Europe investigated the pest, and Robertson (1928) reviewed the former work and added considerable information from his own research.

Control: Goodey (1937a) tested twenty-five varieties of oats and found two, Grey Winter and S-81, which were very resistant. Only a few nemas entered the crowns, and these did not reproduce. Other resistant varieties recently reported (Anonymous, 1954) are S-172, S-231, and a spring variety, Milford (S-225). Rotations with nonhost crops for three or four years should effectively reduce populations to a point where one crop of oats can be produced.

RYE

Rye was among the first crops reported to be infested by *Ditylenchus dipsaci*. Apparently infestations occur frequently in Europe. The only record of its presence in the United States is that of Bessey (1914), who found a field near Edgerton, Kansas, in which large areas were severely damaged. Many plants were killed, and others showed characteristic dwarfing.

Control: A few varieties of rye have been found in Europe which have resistance to stem nemas. The variety Ottersum is the most outstanding according to Bingefors (1957). Crop rotations based on host studies of local populations should give satisfactory control.

ONIONS

Historical: Onion *bloat,* or *Kroefziekte* as the Dutch know it, was first investigated in Holland by Beijerinck (1883) although he mentions that Kühn in Germany had observed the disease about five years previously. Chatin (1884) in France named it *maladie vermiculaire de l'oignon.* Ritzema Bos (1888–1892) made more detailed studies of the symptoms and pathology and found that the nemas were frequently carried in seeds. In the United States Godfrey and Scott (1935) reported what probably is the same biological strain infesting garlic in California. Chitwood, Newhall, and Clement (1940) gave a thorough description of the disease as found in onions in New York. Newhall (1943) followed with an excellent account of the pathogenesis in very young seedlings.

Biology: The manner in which the pest overwinters in the field has not been determined, but doubtless preadults lie dormant in dried foliage or discarded onions or live free in the soil. There is also the undetermined possibility of eggs remaining in the field after plant tissues have decayed.

Newhall (1943) demonstrated that the nemas had entered germinating seed six days after sowing and were attacking the cortical and parenchyma tissues. At this time they had entered in several places from near the root cap of the hypocotyl to points still within the seed. In one instance nemas were found within the seed four days after sowing when the sprout was only 2 mm long, having penetrated the hypocotyl just before it emerged. Cells about the heads of the invading nemas appeared to have lost all, or a portion, of their contents, indicating that the walls had been punctured and the contents sucked out during feeding, as observed by Linford (1937b).

Infested seedlings become twisted and deformed and frequently die in severely infested areas of the field. During growth the infested plants become irregular in form, and their leaves are short and thickened and frequently bear brown or yellowish spots similar to the spikkles produced in the leaves of narcissi. As the season advances, the foliage falls down and a softening of the bulb begins at the neck and gradually proceeds downward, the scales being soft and a pale gray color. In dry seasons the bulbs become desiccated and very light in weight. If moisture is present, a soft rot completes the process of destruction and is accompanied by a most offensive odor, which was responsible for Kühn bestowing the name *Anguillula putrefaciens* on the pest.

Lightly infested onions may unwittingly be used for seed production. Goodey (1943) determined that the nemas congregated in the growing point of the seed stalk and were lifted up with it until they were able to invade the inflorescence as it developed, part of them eventually becoming established in the seeds. He also found that particles of infested stems and seed heads remained in the seed after the cleaning process. Later (1945) he discussed the manner in which the nemas revived after the seed was soaked for several hours. Using the Fenwick (1943) culture cells, he examined 1,000 individual seeds and found that 17 carried nematodes varying in number from 1 to 47, with a total of 126. Unfortunately, Goodey did not record the stage in which the nemas were found, but probably they were preadults.

Control: Newhall and Chitwood (1940) successfully used steam and also chloropicrin, 350 pounds per acre, but both were too expensive for large-scale application. Applications of 40 to 50 gallons of D-D per acre should give good results on muck lands and 20 to 25 gallons on sandy loams. Ethylene dibromide fumigants should never be used, because this chemical is very toxic to onions, even two or three years after application.

Crop rotation. Nonhost crops for three or four years give control if clean culture is practiced and weeds eliminated, but much depends on the host preference of the particular population present.

Goodey (1945) determined that seed can be successfully disinfested by fumigating with 40 ounces of methyl bromide per 1,000 cubic feet for 24 hours. This application also killed nemas in pieces of stems. There were no deleterious effects on seed vitality.

Host range: Reports of various workers indicate that the onion race of *Ditylenchus dipsaci* infests rye, hyacinth, narcissus, teasel, and parsnip. But, as previously mentioned, each population may have different tastes. The local host range should be investigated before making recommendations for crop rotations.

Godfrey and Scott (1935) in California observed that the garlic population severely damaged salsify and parsley in the field and celery in the greenhouse. Garlic is propagated by planting "cloves," small sections of bulbs, and this fact accounts for the wide distribution of the pest. Uninfested stock is difficult to find. Six years in nonhost crops apparently disinfested the field.

ALFALFA (LUCERNE)

Historical: *Ditylenchus dipsaci* has doubtless accompanied alfalfa seed to practically every place on the earth where this popular forage crop has been introduced. This is indicated by the fact that whenever the pest has been discovered in a country it is usually already widely distributed. Kühn (1881) first recognized alfalfa as a host, and when his work revealed that the population appeared to be adapted to this crop only, he

Fig. 6-4. Young alfalfa stems infested with *Ditylenchus dipsaci.* (*After Thorne. Courtesy of Department of Entomology, Colorado State University.*)

went so far as to give it the specific name *Tylenchus havensteinii,* in honor of one of his coworkers. Ritzema Bos (1889–1892) investigated the alfalfa population and decided that it was merely a biological race of *T. devastatrix,* as the species was then known. Various workers in Europe occasionally mentioned it during the next 30 years, but it attracted little attention. Godfrey (1923) reported it from several points in the western United States. Other observers soon recorded it from widely separated areas of the country, especially in the irrigated areas of the Western states. Edwards (1932) discussed its presence in New South

Wales, and Goodey (1933) stated that it was known to be in South Africa. Burkhart (1937) found it widely distributed in Argentina and notes that Lorenzetti had seen it as early as 1913.

Wherever *Ditylenchus dipsaci* is found on alfalfa, it does not readily transfer to other hosts of the *dipsaci* complex. This fact suggests that all the existing populations have been distributed throughout the world in seed which once came from one certain infested locality. Since alfalfa is a plant native to southwest Asia, it would appear logical to find this nematode associated with it in its original habitat. However, we have no records of its presence there, although this lack of information may be due to the fact that those acquainted with the pest have had no opportunity to make observations in that region. However, the finding in Turkestan of an alfalfa immune to stem nematode suggests that in some part of that country there is, or was, a heavy concentration of the pest. This variety, known as Nemastan, will be discussed later under Control.

Biology: Nemas enter the young, succulent tissues of buds. Here they congregate under the developing leaflets and penetrate the young stem. Usually the base of an infested stem becomes enlarged, discolored, and marked by fine transverse ridges or wrinkles, a very characteristic symptom of early stages of infestation. The rapidly increasing nemas work their way up inside the stems, and occasionally enlarged nodes are produced several inches aboveground. Necrosis follows invasion, extending up into the stems and down into the large branches of the crown. Infested stems are easily broken off. Many saprophagous nemas like *Panagrolaimus subelongatus, Chiloplacus symmetricus, Rhabditis* spp., and similar forms accompany necrosis. A split stem may reveal hundreds of *Ditylenchus* in all stages of development, from eggs to adults. A considerable portion of these are removed with the hay and pass into commercial channels for wide distribution. Seed crops go through threshing and cleaning processes, but fragments of stems always remain and often find their way to other fields.

Distribution: Dissemination of stem nematode through seed is well illustrated by the following data secured from an infested field of Grimm alfalfa in eastern Utah:

Type of seed or screenings	Nematodes per pound
Recleaned seed ready for market	236
Thresher-run seed before cleaning	1,088
Fine seed passing through screens	1,134
Recleaned screenings	1,170
Fine screenings	16,629
Blowings from cleaning plant	4,398

Probably the average seed from infested fields is similar to the recleaned seed listed above. The numbers of nemas remaining would probably require several years to build up populations to a point where they would be noticed. But even today, economy-minded farmers sometimes plant thresher-run, fine seed and recleaned screenings, with attendant disastrous results.

Once nemas are introduced, they are spread rapidly by machinery moving hay during harvest. Floodwater from rains and irrigation water are especially effective means of distribution. Quiescent preadults in plant crowns, eggs, larvae, and some adults are readily carried in this manner. In 100 gallons of waste water from an infested field in Utah, there were 11,910 *Ditylenchus dipsaci*. Most of these were preadults. This waste water was flowing into a large canal which distributed the nemas over several thousand acres farther down the valley. Infestations may be introduced by feeding hay to livestock. Pieces of stems and buds often carry nemas and are accidentally scattered in manure from feeding lots. However, nemas cannot live through heating in manure piles or through silage fermentation.

Overwintering takes place in soil and litter about alfalfa crowns, where preadult nemas congregate after the hay is cut. In cool, moist climates nemas leaving the stubble of the first crop will move directly into the buds of the second, and even the third, crop. In dry climates there usually is only a spring invasion, with occasionally a small one in the autumn. A film of moisture is essential for the nemas to travel in as they work their way up into the buds, and this is not present under arid conditions. During a cool, moist spring in the irrigated Western states, infestation may reach 100 per cent of the buds, and no green growth will be visible over entire fields. A dry, windy spring prevents the nemas from reaching the developing buds, and not a trace of infestation will be found in fields known to be generally infested. Destruction of a crop usually is a severe blow to the vigor of the plants. Often they are attacked by bacterial wilt and other fungi, the result being a stand reduced to a point where it must be plowed.

Control: *Crop rotation.* Stem nematode can be successfully controlled by growing nonhost crops for two years or more. Sugar beets, grain, corn, potatoes, tomatoes, and other common crops are suitable. However, when alfalfa is planted again, the nemas usually appear in the second or third year, and by the end of the fourth year only a poor stand remains. In areas where polyphagous populations exist, more care must be exercised in selecting crops to meet the circumstances existing.

Resistant varieties. One of the most remarkable examples of nematode resistance is the alfalfa variety Nemastan, which originated in the district of Goek-Tere (Ash-Khabad), Turkestan. According to H. O. Graumann (1958, personal communication) 31 kg was sent in 1931 to Dr. R. O. Westover, Forage Crops Division, U.S. Department of Agriculture, by Dr. Belof via Moscow and Hamburg. Westover gave it the number Turkestan 19304 and on November 2, 1931, sent 4 pounds of this seed to R. J. Evans, Utah Agricultural College, Logan, Utah. Evans planted a portion of it in an experimental field near Midvale, Utah, in

1932. By chance this series of plantings was made on a field severely infested with stem nematode. By 1934, the plots of Turkestan 19304 were notable in that they maintained a perfect stand, while all other varieties were practically killed out by nematodes and bacterial wilt. Evans also established a small planting near Collinston, Utah, for seed-production purposes.

Demonstration plots were maintained by the Nematology Section, U.S. Department of Agriculture, from 1935 to 1954 near Salt Lake City.

Fig. 6-5. One of the original plots of Nemastan established by R. J. Evans. Foreground, Utah Common. Left, Turkistan 86696. Rear, Turkistan, 19300. Right, Ladak.

The name Nemastan was selected from among suggestions made by various workers in 1945. O. F. Smith of the Forage Crops Division, U.S. Department of Agriculture, became interested in the variety in 1938. Smith began a series of selections from the heterogeneous plants of which the variety was composed. This work produced the synthetic variety known as Lahontan which has become very popular in the western United States. It not only is resistant to stem nematode and bacterial wilt but also has considerable resistance to the alfalfa spotted aphid, *Therioaphis maculata* (Buckton).

The factor or factors responsible for resistance in Nemastan are unknown. That they may be of a chemical nature is indicated by the fact that under usual farm conditions there is poor seed production, while isolated plantings produce fair yields. O. F. Smith (personal communication) observed that when rows of Nemastan were placed between rows of Ranger, Grimm, and other common varieties, the pollinating wild bees avoided Nemastan. This preference suggested that for some reason the flowers of Nemastan were not attractive. However, Lahontan produces satisfactory seed crops and retains most of the parental resistance.

Serial sections of buds from susceptible Utah Common and Nemastan were compared for possible differences in cell-wall thickness or other structural characteristics, but none was found. Seinhorst (1956) indicates that the ability of the nemas to break down middle lamellae of cells is an important factor in alfalfa resistance. Therefore, resistance may be due to the chemical composition of the lamellae.

Certain populations of stem nematodes may differ in their ability to attack resistant varieties. Smith (1951) found a population near Orland, California, which attacked a clone known to be resistant to nemas from six other localities. Allison (1956) in North Carolina found that Lahontan was only moderately resistant to the population in that area. This emphasizes the necessity for evaluating plants on the basis of local nematode host preference. It is interesting to note that Reynolds (1955) found Nemastan more susceptible to *Meloidogyne incognita acrita* and *M. arenaria* than any other variety tested.

Burkhart (1937) took resistant alfalfa plants from infested fields and endeavored to produce a superior strain by selection and crossing. Of 76 plants from five crosses, 61 were resistant. Among 149 plants from four crosses between resistant and susceptible plants, 89 were resistant. Variations in the number of resistant progeny from these four crosses ranged between 47 and 65 per cent. In no instance did Burkhart secure complete resistance. He concluded that while resistance was dominant, it depended on a number of genes in different combinations. These produced variations not only in the number of resistant plants but also in the degree of resistance in individuals.

RED CLOVER

Symptoms: Evidence of infestation in red clover includes deformed buds, stunted shoots with swollen bases, and stems with galls. Seed heads are sometimes entered, and nemas consequently remain within the seeds. Loss of foliage frequently causes death of plants. Dwarfed or dying spots in fields usually are the first symptoms observed. Cool, moist climates like those of northern Europe, the British Isles, and the Pacific Northwest are most favorable for nematode development in this crop. Nemas also thrive in irrigated areas of the western United States.

Resistant varieties: Bingefors (1957) presents extensive data on selecting and breeding. His work is largely based on experiments with Ultuna, a very susceptible variety, and Merkur, a highly resistant type developed from field selections by Sylvén (1936). Under laboratory conditions Ultuna produced less than 1 per cent of resistant plants, while Merkur produced 80 to 90 per cent. By selecting the best plants from a highly infested field of Ultuna he produced in two years a progeny with a resistance index of 68. In the same experiment Ultuna gave an index of 19 and Merkur 92. Crosses between these two varieties produced a high percentage of resistant plants, but there were wide variations between the progeny of the various crosses, none of which produced more than 95 per cent resistant and some as low as 30 per cent. Several genes appear to be involved in the inheritance of resistance.

Resistance factors: Bingefors did not determine why certain plants are resistant, although he is inclined to agree with Seinhorst (1956) that the ability of the nemas to break down the middle lamellae of cells is a vital point in establishing colonies and building up lethal populations. Differences in the chemical composition of the middle lamellae may account for resistance, and these differences are being investigated by Bingefors.

Host-induced variations in nemic morphology: Morphology of nemas from the clover varieties Ultuna and Merkur is of special interest. Beginning with a population which averaged 868 μ in length, there was a marked increase in size of the nemas infesting Ultuna until, and at the end of 80 days, they averaged 1,270 μ. Those from Merkur averaged only 708 μ. In Ultuna there was no decrease in the number of infested plants, and the rate of nematode reproduction was more rapid. In Merkur there was a steady decrease in the number of infested plants and in the number of nematodes, and egg production was at a low ebb. In another instance nemas from red clover averaged 1,079 μ long, while members of the same population living in Alsike clover had an average length of only 869 μ.

STRAWBERRY

Historical: Ritzema Bos (1891) was the first to recognize infestations of *Ditylenchus dipsaci* in strawberries, but since that time references to the pest in Europe are infrequent. In the coastal regions of Washington and Oregon, Byars (1920) reported it in several localities, and McKay (1921) recorded it in his surveys and research in Oregon. This work was continued in the following three years in cooperative research on the presence of the nemas in wild strawberries and other hosts (Godfrey and McKay, 1924). An interesting observation made during the phase of this work indicated that the pest may have been brought into the United States in soil used as ship's ballast, since nemas are numerous in the vicinities of old ballast piles along the seashore.

Biology: Cool, moist climatic conditions are especially favorable for the development of nematodes in strawberries, and the Pacific coast from Monterey, California, to Canada offers ideal conditions. With abundant moisture they readily make their way from the crowns of the plants into the young leaves and stems, where all stages from eggs to adults can usually be found. Gall-like swellings develop at the base of the leaves and stems and up into the petioles, fruiting branches, and leaves. Frequently yellow, brown, or red spots are present on the distorted, swollen, and twisted foliage, all of which are usually inhabited by large numbers of nematodes. Foliage and fruit production become so reduced that entire plantings may be lost. Transmission to young plants may be either from nemas migrating from dying plants or from small numbers carried in the stolons (runners) to the young plants as they are formed.

Byars failed to find any indication that the population from strawberry and that on clover were the same; yet Courtney (1936) found a field in which strawberries were severely injured when planted in a field in which red clover had previously been infested. Investigations revealed there was little doubt that the clover nemas had transferred to strawberries.

Control: Crop rotations are practical provided that the population is not too polyphagous and that paying, nonhost crops are available. Careful investigation must be made of the local host range before making recommendations.

Soil fumigation. Applications of nematicides on sandy or light loam soils should be effective if carried out as recommended for *Ditylenchus destructor.* Prior to fumigation all plant residues on the field should be destroyed by burning or by plowing under some weeks previous to fumigation to ensure complete decay before the chemical is applied.

Clean, uninfested nursery stock should always be planted; otherwise the expense of crop rotations and soil fumigation will be lost. Certain nurseries are now featuring strawberry plants produced on fumigated fields, an excellent testimony to the value of nematicides.

PHLOX

Historical: Injury to phlox is one of the most spectacular effects produced by *Ditylenchus dipsaci.* These vigorously growing plants provide a favorable habitat for the nemas, yet generally make considerable growth in spite of the infestation until outstanding symptoms are evident. Nypels (1898) was the first to record infestations, but it was Ritzema Bos (1899) who identified the species as one he had found in other plants with which he was working. After several years' work in England, Wilson (1930) published a rather detailed account of the disease. In America, Weiss (1923) and Steiner and Dodge (1929) recorded additional information, the latter paper containing excellent photographs of typical forms of injury.

Symptoms: Terminal portions of growing young stems often are formed into elongate swellings in which the nemas are congregated. On these swollen portions a group of closely arranged leaves frequently forms a bunchy rosette. Taller stems may be spindly with elongated nodes and may bear deformed and contorted leaves with irregular edges, or some of the leaves may be elongated, narrow, and twisted. Tissues of both stems and leaves are brittle. In advanced stages wilting and browning of the leaves are followed by death of the stems. Severely infested plants may produce only a large number of short, deformed stems, giving a witches'-broom effect. Many of the basal buds developing from the crown fail to produce stems. Occasionally stems may split as the invaded tissues disintegrate.

Biology: According to Wilson the nemas enter by penetrating the epidermis of the underground portions of stems and young shoots and travel up the stems through the cortical layer. Deformation of the tissues appears to be due to the toxic effect of the salivary gland secretions

Fig. 6-6. Phlox infested with *Ditylenchus dipsaci*. (*Courtesy of Nematology Department, Rothamsted Experiment Station.*)

as they are injected during feeding, rather than to mechanical injury. Although the flowers are sometimes entered by the nemas, none were found in the seeds. As the plants decline, many nemas return to the soil through the layer of pith surrounding the vascular zone. Sometimes many are trapped there and lie quiescent until favorable growing conditions return. Wilson (1930) found that when these quiescent nemas were stored for five years and then placed in water, 8 per cent of the larval forms became active within 24 hours. In his host-transfer work the preadult stage gave best results. Reinfestation occurred most frequently in wet loam soils.

Infested plants were fed to rabbits, but there was no indication that nemas survived passing through the digestive tract, although fragments were found in the faeces.

Control: Since the root system is not invaded by the nemas, root cuttings may be used to produce clean stock, which should be planted on uninfested land. Goodey (1933) states that the varieties Antoinin Mercie and Widar are only lightly infested and make satisfactory growth in the presence of the nemas.

Infested plants should be burned and the soil denematized by growing nonhost plants or by the use of nematicides.

Hosts: In addition to three species of phlox, Goodey lists eleven species of plants belonging to the genera *Dianthus, Oenothera, Solidago, Campanula, Gila, Collomia,* and *Primula;* these figures indicate a rather wide host range of the phlox race.

Morphological studies fail to reveal diagnostic characters which justify recognition of the name *Ditylenchus phloxidis* proposed by Kirianova (1951). The minor host-induced variations found are no more important than those common to populations from various other hosts.

POTATOES

Ditylenchus attacking potatoes present a rather complicated problem because at least two species and two or three strains are involved in the complex. Kühn (1888) described tuber damage by a progressive dry rot which was not associated with visible symptoms on the stems and foliage. This rot doubtless was the same as that produced by *D. destructor* which will be discussed in detail later in this chapter. In the same year Ritzema Bos (1888) recorded an entirely different type of infestation in which not only the tubers were attacked but also the stems and leaves, resulting in stunted, malformed top growth which was easily observed in the field. Similar symptoms have been reported by various workers in Europe, both on the Continent and in the British Isles.

Quanjer (1927) made extensive investigations on a polyphagous population of what he presumed to be *Ditylenchus dipsaci.* He found that they attacked not only potatoes but also fifty-two other plants, twenty-eight of which were new host records. This population produced typical tuber symptoms and characteristic swelling and crinkling of stems and leaves. Quanjer probably was working with a group similar to that reported by Ritzema Bos. It is possible that he had a mixture of *D. destructor* and *D. dipsaci* with perhaps one or more strains of each species.

The combined evidence indicates that certain populations or strains of *Ditylenchus dipsaci* are serious parasites of potatoes and that these are able to perpetuate themselves on a wide variety of hosts. Intensive research must be made on each group before recommendations can be made for crop rotations designed to reduce their numbers to a point where a satisfactory crop of potatoes can be produced. The problem has certain interesting aspects similar to those involved with *D. destructor.*

Natural Enemies

While studying *Ditylenchus dipsaci* infesting *Calceolaria integrifolia* T. Goodey (1938) observed a fungus, *Arthrobotrys oligospora* Fres., in the lesions formed by the nemas, and large numbers were entangled in the hyphae. In some instances rings and loops held them firmly, and later their dead bodies were filled with hyphae. Drechsler (1941) had previously observed this fungus attacking nemas of other species.

J. B. Goodey (1951a) also reports *Ditylenchus dipsaci,* from the same plant species, which were parasitized by a fungus which he named *Verticillium sphaerosporum* This fungus produces spores which cling to the body of the nemas when they come in contact. Each spore produces a hypha which penetrates the cuticle and develops until the body cavity is filled with hyphae. Certain forms of the hyphae puncture the cuticle and emerge to produce flask-shaped phialides which bear sessile, spherical bodies 2 to 3 μ in diameter.

Potato rot nematode, *Ditylenchus destructor* Thorne, 1945

Historical: As previously mentioned, Kühn (1888) was the first to observe and describe the progressive dry rot of potato tubers which is typical of that produced by *Ditylenchus destructor.* The following year, Atkinson (1889) in Alabama illustrated a nematode found in potatoes which appears to be very similar, if not identical, to *D. destructor.* During the ensuing years this type of injury was reported by various workers in Europe. The general distribution of the pest on that continent is indicated by the fact that between 1930 and 1940 the Plant Protection Branch of the U.S. Department of Agriculture intercepted *"Ditylenchus dipsaci"* 227 times in ship's stores coming from twenty foreign countries (McCubbin et al., 1946). Obviously a large portion, if not all, of these must have been *D. destructor.* In the writer's collection are specimens from ship's stores collected at the port of Boston in 1932.

In America, Blodgett (1943) discovered an infestation near Aberdeen, Idaho, which proved to be the same species as that from Boston, and from this material a new species was described as *Ditylenchus destructor.* Baker (1946) discovered the pest in six fields on Prince Edward Island, Canada, in the vicinities of York and Montague. No additional infestations were reported until 1953, when it was found by Darling (1957) in potatoes from several fields near Antigo, Wisconsin. Circumstantial evidence indicates that the pest had been present in all three localities for many years. In western Canada, Bosher (1953) collected infested tubers in a potato field which had followed bulbous iris and definitely identified the nemas as *D. destructor.* Since infested bulbous iris have been reported from various points in the United States and Canada, there appears to be little doubt that incipient infestations exist in many localities.

Morphology: ♀: 0.8–1.4 mm; a = 33–35; b = 8–10; c = 15–20;
V = $^{65}78$–83^{10}
♂: 0.8–1.3 mm; a = 34–40; b = 7–8; c = 12–16; T = 73–80

Cuticle near head marked by transverse striae about 1 μ apart, while on the remainder of the body the striae are obscure unless the specimens are shrunken by cold fixative. Lateral fields with six incisures (Fig. 3-5), which are reduced to two on the neck and tail. Deirids usually visible near base of neck. Hemizonid slightly anterior to excretory pore. Phasmids not observed. Cephalic papillae and amphids visible only from a face view, arranged in a manner similar to those figured for *Ditylenchus dipsaci*. Labial framework well sclerotized. Spear typical of the genus, with rounded knobs. Basal bulb of esophagus with three large and two small gland nuclei, generally extended in a lobe reaching back over the dorsal side of the intestine. This lobe may be either shorter or longer than that illustrated. Anterior end of intestine extending into base of esophagus, where it connects with the lumen by an obscure valvular apparatus. Intestine densely granular, ending in a distinct rectum and anus.

Anterior ovary outstretched to near base of esophagus, the developing oöcytes often arranged in two lines, changing to tandem near the middle of the ovary. Eggs average slightly longer than body diameter and are about one-half as wide as long. Posterior uterine branch rudimentary, not observed to function as a spermatheca. Spermatozoa usually well up in the uterus. Lips of vulva thick, elevated. Vulva-anus distance 1¾ to 2½ times tail length.

Testis outstretched to near base of esophagus with spermatogonia arranged mostly in single line until near the middle of the body, where they become primary spermatocytes from which the spermatozoa are produced. Spicula with a distinctive sclerotized pattern as illustrated. Bursa extending from a point about opposite the proximal ends of the spicula to about two-thirds the tail length. Lateral incisures usually reduced to four near the tail, forming a pattern similar to that figured for *Ditylenchus dipsaci*.

Type host: *Solanum tuberosum,* potato
Type locality: Fields near Aberdeen, Idaho

Populations of *Ditylenchus destructor* from different fields and from widely separated infestations sometimes exhibit striking morphological variations from the type. A. D. Baker presented the writer with a collection from a certain field on Prince Edward Island in which most of the specimens were over 1.4 mm in length, with one reaching 2.0 mm. Baker also reported specimens with acute termini instead of minutely rounded. In both Idaho and Wisconsin, specimens with cylindroid or slightly clavate tails have been observed. Occasionally males have only four instead of six incisures in the lateral fields.

Host-induced variants frequently are encountered which differ from the type in body length, body proportions, reduced gonads, and development of the esophageal gland lobes. These will be discussed in more detail later.

Indigenous *Ditylenchus,* morphologically very similar to *D. destructor,* are found in many localities in the United States in both virgin and

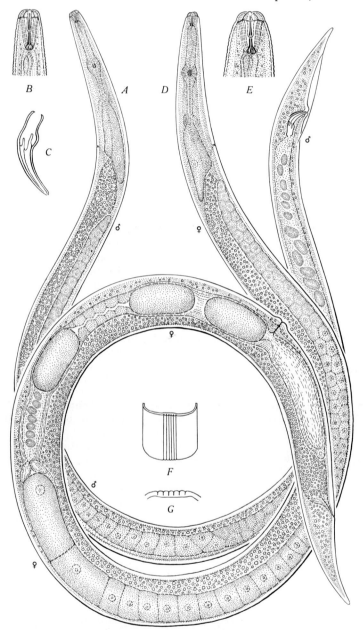

Fig. 6-7. *Ditylenchus destructor.* *A–C*—Male, head and spiculum. *D, E*—Female and head. *F, G*—Lateral field showing six incisures. (*After Thorne. Courtesy of Helminthological Society of Washington.*)

cultivated soils. Frequently they are associated with pasture and golf-green turf, alfalfa crowns, strawberry, and other plants. Smart (1959) established a colony originating in *St. Augustine* grass, *Stenotaphrum secundatum* (Walt.) Kuntze, in Arkansas. Nemas from this colony readily produced typical *D. destructor* symptoms on potato tubers in the greenhouse. Similar symptoms were produced by a colony from dahlia tubers discovered in Oregon by H. J. Jensen. A third colony secured from decaying roots on a gladiolus corm of unknown origin also produced typical symptoms on potato tubers. Morphologically, all three of these populations were very similar to *D. destructor*, to which they doubtless belong. These demonstrations indicate that indigenous populations may become parasitic in potato tubers under suitable ecological conditions.

The cuticle of *Ditylenchus destructor* is more impermeable to glycerin than that of any other species in the genus. Difficulty may be encountered in preparing satisfactory permanent microscopic preparations unless extreme care is exercised during the evaporation process.

Biology: The ability readily to attack and reproduce on a wide variety of plants belonging to many families is an outstanding characteristic of *Ditylenchus destructor;* generally there is little indication of host preference. Frequently these transfers are accompanied by conspicuous changes in morphology which constitute some of our most interesting examples of host-induced variations among the plant parasitic nematodes. Specimens from potatoes produced near Aberdeen, Idaho, were transferred to sugar beets; after the colony had been established, it was found that the nemas were only one-half to two-thirds as long as their progenitors, while those transferred to sweet potatoes became considerably larger than the original population. In the potato population the basal bulb of the esophagus usually is extended in a dorsal lobe reaching back over the anterior end of the intestine, but when the population is transferred to sugar beet or bulbous iris, the glandular extension usually develops on the ventral side of the body. Females from sugar beet and iris have only a limited number of developing oöcytes in their ovaries, compared with scores which are present in specimens from potatoes and sweet potatoes. In fact, the appearance of the specimens from sugar beets was so profoundly altered that had they been found in the field, and without knowledge of their origin, it would have been logical to describe them as a new species because of their smaller size, reduced gonads, and ventral esophageal lobes.

J. B. Goodey (1952a) studied populations from eleven hosts, made statistical analysis of the body and gonad lengths, and determined that there was a significant difference in body length at the 1 per cent level and in mean lengths at the 5 per cent level. Oddly enough he found that when the nemas were transferred from potato to iris the females became longer, while in the Idaho population the reverse was true. Potato to mint transfer made little difference, but *Tropaeolum polyphyllum* increased the length from 1.0 to 1.9 mm. The smallest females were 0.67

mm long in a transfer from hop to mint, while the smallest from Idaho was 0.6 mm long from a potato to sugar beet transfer. These data emphasize the necessity of using extreme care in diagnosing any species on the basis of length alone or on certain other characters such as development of the gonads and esophageal glands.

Two important biological differences distinguish *Ditylenchus destructor* from *D. dipsaci*. As J. B. Goodey (1951) noted, *D. destructor* does not produce wool on bulbs, tubers, or roots which it inhabits. Nor is there a great build-up of preadult nemas designed to carry the species over from one season to the next.

Extensive soil sampling in known infested fields has failed to reveal immature forms of *Ditylenchus destructor* overwintering in Idaho and Wisconsin, and this fact indicates that the nemas are carried through this unfavorable part of the year as eggs. There are no unusual numbers of preadults among the comparatively small populations remaining when the tuber is finally destroyed and becomes only a mummified shell. The nemas also fail to survive if wet rots invade the lesions and rapidly destroy the tuber, as often happens. Survival in soil appears to be extremely limited when infested tubers are disked or plowed into experimental plots: within a month very few can be found. In fact, plots in Idaho heavily inoculated in this manner were less infested than those to which diseased tubers were not added. There is no apparent explanation for this phenomenon.

Inoculation under laboratory conditions is a relatively simple matter, for the nemas are readily transferred from potatoes to sweet potatoes, turnips, carrots, onions, and beets by the tube method. Sections of ½-inch thin brass tubing about ¾ inch long are sharpened with a round file and dipped in alcohol. A spot on the tuber is then sterilized, the tube inserted about ¼ inch, and the skin inside the tube punctured in several places with a needle. Distilled water is placed in the tube and the nemas picked directly into it after being washed through three or four changes of distilled water. The water is soon absorbed by the tuber, carrying the nemas with it, after which the tube is removed and the hole covered with tape. Place the tubers on a shallow layer of moist soil in a tightly covered box, and move to a cool room or basement. A colony of fifty nemas of each sex will increase to several thousand in 4 to 6 weeks.

Baker (1948) successfully used the flap, plug, and pad methods. The flap was made by a diagonal cut with a cork borer, the lip of tissue lifted slightly, a small cavity excavated, and the nemas inserted, the flap then being covered by Scotch tape. In the plug method a cork borer was driven entirely through the potato, the core removed from the tube, a small section cut from it, and both portions replaced with a colony of nemas in the opening left where the section was removed. Criopodist pads were prepared by placing a small piece of filter paper in the open ring of the pad, a few drops of water containing the nemas were then added, and the pad was applied to the surface of the tuber and covered with tape. Colonies were readily established by the flap and core methods, but the pad attempts were successful only when placed over an eye.

Only a few of the more important hosts of *Ditylenchus destructor* will be discussed herein, illustrating some of the varied types of injury inflicted on certain plant species. Suffice it to say that this species probably is even more polyphagous than *D. dipsaci*, but only in recent years has this fact been recognized.

POTATOES

Symptoms: The first evidence of infestation can be observed only by peeling the tuber and examining the tissues for tiny white, chalky spots which mark the location of one or more nemas. In the field these initial lesions have been observed early in August in both Idaho and Wisconsin. According to Baker (1948) the nemas are unable to penetrate the skin of the tuber except in the region of the eyes, while Quanjer (1927) reported that they entered through the lenticles, especially in the vicinity of an eyebrow.

As the colony increases in numbers and invades larger portions of the tissue, secondary organisms usually enter and the combined attack produces a lesion which appears as a light brown welt under the unbroken skin. When opened, these present a gray to brown decaying area, with a somewhat granular and honeycombed appearance, in which a great number of nemas will be found. As the lesions spread through the tubers, a drying and shrinking of the skin occur and frequently cracks appear. Occasionally the entrance to a colony is marked by only a small pit.

Baker noted that a rather distinct area existed between the decayed portion and the uninvaded tissues which he termed the "feeding front," and in this recently invaded portion the nemas are found in abundance in all stages from eggs to adults. Baker suggested that in this area the nemas may be feeding on fungus mycelia as well as on potato tissue, and, considering the many thousands which are crowded into such a limited space, this possibly is true in certain instances. However, the bulk of the population will be found well in advance of the fungus-invaded portion, while numerous small groups penetrate even farther into the tuber to establish new colonies which produce the shiny, white spots so characteristic of this parasite.

Control: The polyphagous habits of *Ditylenchus destructor* practically eliminate any prospects of employing crop rotations as control methods. Experiments at the Aberdeen, Idaho, Branch Experiment Station indicated a very marked reduction in populations after two or three years of beans, corn, and fallow kept free of weeds, but occasional infested tubers appeared when potatoes were again planted. Potatoes following four to six years of alfalfa were among the most severely infested fields observed in that area, while grain and pasture were in much the same category.

Soil fumigation. Nematicides have proved very satisfactory when properly applied with an efficient applicator driven by an experienced operator. Experiments initiated in 1944 indicated that ethylene dibromide mixtures were especially efficacious against *Ditylenchus destructor.* Extensive soil examinations had revealed that the nemas live only in

Fig. 6-8. Idaho Russett potato tubers infested with *Ditylenchus destructor.* (*After Thorne. Courtesy of Helminthological Society of Washington.*)

the cultivated portion of the soil and therefore are much more vulnerable to fumigation than other species. Special equipment was designed to kill those nemas in the top 2 or 3 inches of soil, where lethal concentrations are not built up (Dallimore, 1955).

Eradication was accomplished by applying 90 pounds of actual ethylene dibromide per acre at a depth of 8 inches with a chisel-type applicator set on 12-inch spaces. The field was plowed five or six days later with a scraper attachment on the tool bar which pushed the top 3 inches of soil into the bottom of the furrow. There it came in contact with the fumigant and was immediately covered by the following furrow. The field was worked down and sealed with harrow sections attached to the plow shanks as illustrated by Dallimore (1955). Similar efficient results have been secured in Wisconsin by following this method.

When infested tubers were made into silage, all the nemas were killed by the fermentation process within five days.

Resistant varieties. All available varieties of potatoes have been tested for resistance to potato rot nematode, but all were found to be susceptible. Possibilities of breeding for resistance appear remote.

BULBOUS IRIS

Historical: When we consider the ease with which *Ditylenchus destructor* transfers from potatoes to bulbous iris or from iris to potatoes,

Fig. 6-9. Wedgewood iris infested with *Ditylenchus destructor.* *(After Gould. Courtesy of Washington State Extension Service.)*

it appears safe to assume that early records of *D. dipsaci* were doubtless based on *D. destructor.* Ritzema Bos was the first to observe infested iris in 1924, as recorded in his short note (1926). Steiner and Buhrer (1933) examined thirty-eight lots of infested bulbous iris collected between the fall of 1928 and July, 1932. Of these, twenty-three were of foreign origin (Canada, England, France, and the Netherlands), while fifteen were domestic-grown (Florida, North Carolina, South Carolina, Oregon, Virginia, Washington, and Wisconsin). Included were twenty-two varieties of Spanish (*Iris xiphium*), Dutch (*I. xiphium hybridum*), English (*I. xiphoides*), and Moroccan (*I. tingitana*). During the following 20 years several workers in Europe and Canada reported infestations. J. B. Goodey (1951) gave the first comprehensive discussion of the pest after it was given the specific name of *D. destructor;* the reader is referred to his paper for detailed information. Sher (1954) recorded infested iris from Hawaii.

Symptoms: Gould (1950) gives a summary of characteristics which indicate the presence of *Ditylenchus destructor* in bulbous iris. "Bulb husk sometimes shredded at base; basal plate and outer fleshy scale separated by a dark, sunken crevice; yellowish, gray or black streaks in fleshy scales, usually beginning at base and most numerous in outer scales; such streaks sometimes fusing and rotting the entire scale and bulb; basal plate honeycombed and grayish in color when basal plate is removed; sunken spots with dark margins sometimes present near tip of bulb." Leaves are stunted or lacking under severe infestations, but spikkles are not formed. Stems may have light gray or yellow areas where attached to bulb.

Symptoms may vary with varieties, but the gray discoloration of the basal plate is most consistent, especially in English iris. Dark lesions extending upward from the decaying basal plate usually are the most conspicuous markings in advanced infestations.

Control: Hot-water–formaldehyde solution for three hours at 110 to 111°F is effective. Bulbs should immediately be spread out in thin layers to cool and dry in a well-ventilated place.

Time of digging and curing before treatment varies with the locality; experienced operators should be contacted for detailed information, or damage to bulbs may result.

Crop rotation may not be effective because of the wide host range of *Ditylenchus destructor*. If fields become infested, they should first be planted to row crops while volunteer bulbs are being located and removed, then fumigated with ethylene dibromide as outlined for potato fields.

Sanitation both in the field and in packing houses is an important feature of any control program.

TULIPS

Ditylenchus destructor, as well as *D. dipsaci,* readily attacks tulips. In the Aberdeen, Idaho, plots, C. E. Dallimore found it a simple matter to infest tulips with populations of *D. destructor* from potatoes.

Symptoms: Similar to those described for bulbous iris. Nemas from lesions resemble those from potato populations.

SUGAR BEETS

Historical: As early as 1896, Vanha and Stoklasa observed *Rübenfaule* on sugar beets and from the lesions isolated a *Tylenchus* species. Ritzema Bos (1908) described a similar injury on mangels which he attributed to *Tylenchus dipsaci,* and during the following 40 years numerous references occur to injury of this type on sugar beets. These references are listed in detail by Dallimore and Thorne (1951).

Symptoms: Nemas enter the beets near the crown, and the first evidence of their presence is the appearance of small, discolored areas beneath the cortex which rapidly develop until the entire upper portion of the beet may be involved. Frequently the areas branch downward, forming elongated dark welts. Eventually these become rugose brown lesions in which cracks appear as the tissues shrink, exposing the dry, honeycombed infested areas, in which only the vascular bundles remain intact. In the final stages the nemas are followed by secondary bacteria and fungi until the beet is destroyed.

Control: Crop rotations are very apt to prove ineffective. Fumigation with ethylene dibromide as recommended for potatoes should give satisfactory control. However, under the arid conditions of Idaho actual injury to the beet crop is negligible. In Europe the problem apparently does not assume serious proportions, or it would be more in evidence in the literature.

RED CLOVER

Rugose, honeycombed lesions just below the crown contain considerable numbers of *Ditylenchus destructor* in all stages from eggs to adults. Usually little, if any, injury is evident on the growing plants.

MINT

Visible injury to the plants is not evident, but examination of the rhizomes growing in infested soil will frequently reveal elongated brown to black lesions in which the nemas are living. Specimens from mint and other plants with hard, woody tissues usually are smaller and have underdeveloped gonads compared with those from potatoes.

Miscellaneous hosts of *Ditylenchus destructor*

Divergent host tastes of this species are well illustrated in the variety of plants reported above and the following additional hosts reported by other workers: Thorne (1945) found the nemas living in the crowns of dandelions, *Taraxacum officinale*. Goodey and Goodey (1949) added sow thistle, *Sonchus arvensis*. Henderson (1951) in Canada reported that Baker had observed goldenrod, *Solidago graminifolia,* and added toad flax, *Linaria vulgaris,* plantain, *Plantago major, Sisyrinchium angustifolium,* vetch, *Vicia sativa,* and carrot, *Daucus carota.* J. B. Goodey (1952a) determined that hop, *Humulus lupulus,* lilac, *Syringia vulgaris, Tigridia pavonia, Tropaeolum polyphyllum,* and *Stachys palustris* were all hosts. Most of these plants had already been reported by various workers as hosts of *Ditylenchus dipsaci,* and doubtless many more records are in the same category. In view of these findings the suggested common name "potato rot nematode" is far from appropriate, as are so many common names in nematology and other branches of science.

Association of *Ditylenchus destructor* with fungi

As early as 1947 Baker (personal communication) indicated that *Ditylenchus destructor* colonies feed on fungi. After developing methods of producing the nemas on fungus plates, Baker, Brown, and James (1954) reported that they readily fed and reproduced on three species of *Fu-*

sarium, a *Mucor,* and *Trichoderma viridis.* Other fungi were included in subsequent experiments, and during the work these investigators noted that striking reduction in length of nemas occurred when fungus cultures became overgrown or contaminated or during drying under cold room conditions. Then they found that these miniature forms returned to normal lengths after a few generations on fresh fungus plates.

Darling, Faulkner, and Wallendal (1957) produced colonies of *Ditylenchus destructor* on thirty-seven species, representing fifteen genera of fungi. Many of the colonies were established from single fertilized females.

An unidentified species of *Ditylenchus* closely resembling *D. destructor* was reported by Lambert, Steiner, and Drechsler (1949) as the causal agent of *Cephalothecium* disease in mushroom beds in eastern Pennsylvania. Symptoms usually appeared in areas 3 to 6 feet in diameter where the mushroom mycelia had been destroyed. From these centers the disease spread outward with a definite "front" along which the nemas were abundant. As the hyphae were destroyed, surface-living predaceous fungi moved in and trapped and destroyed many of the nemas.

That mushroom mycelia may provide suitable food for the growth of identified colonies of *Ditylenchus destructor* was demonstrated by Seinhorst and Bels (1951) when they transferred nemas from mycelia to potatoes and produced typical tuber symptoms. Cairns (1953) worked extensively with a mushroom population and found it a simple matter to maintain colonies. He called attention to the possibilities of using such colonies in teaching nematology and invertebrate zoology, as well as in testing nematicides and other experimental work. Although the population with which Cairns worked was morphologically practically identical to *D. destructor,* he failed to succeed in transferring them to potatoes.

This ability to feed on the mycelia of fungi makes production of colonies of *Ditylenchus destructor* from single fertilized females much simpler than is possible by inoculating potato tubers or other hosts. Such pure colonies were first produced by Baker and his associates and were found more suitable for technical studies than are those from mass infestations. Colonies in petri dishes allow detailed observations on egg production, development of larvae, copulation, and other life-history studies. However, such data are of limited value in estimating nemic activities under actual field conditions with variable moisture and temperature, presence or absence of suitable hosts, and other soil factors. Although it is plausible to expect *D. destructor* to live on soil fungi in the absence of suitable higher plants, this has not been demonstrated.

Ditylenchus triformis Hirschmann and Sasser, 1955

This species is of special interest since it represents the only instance of intersexes in Tylenchida, except the males of *Meloidogyne javanica* reported by Chitwood (1949).

Morphology: ♀: 0.6–0.8 mm; a = 34–42; b = 5.2–7.3; c = 9.6–12; V = 75–82
    ♂: 0.6–0.7 mm; a = 33–43; b = 5.7; c = 9–11
    Intersexes: 0.5–0.8 mm; a = 34–44; b = 5–6; c = 9–12

Lateral field marked by six incisures. Base of esophagus extending slightly over anterior end of intestine. Gonads outstretched, their cells arranged in single file. Posterior uterine branch extending one-fourth to one-third the distance to anus. Tail elongate-conoid, with posterior third tapering very gradually. Terminus bluntly conical.

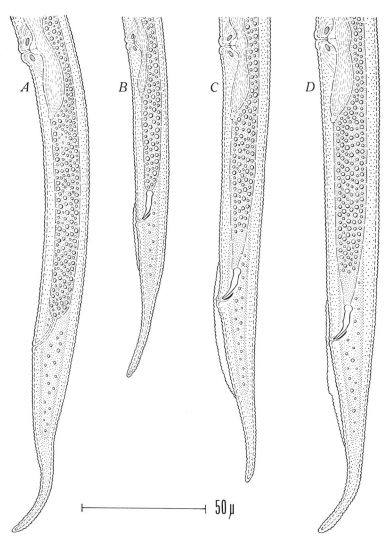

Fig. 6-10. *Ditylenchus triformis.* *A*—Posterior portion of normal female. *B–D*—Intersexes. (*Courtesy of Hedwig Hirschmann.*)

Ditylenchus triformis appears to be most closely related to *D. destructor,* from which it differs in the coarser striae, presence of intersexes, and somewhat longer, cylindroid tail. However, occasional colonies of *D. destructor* have similar elongated tails. *Ditylenchus triformis* also resembles the nema illustrated by Atkinson (1889) from potato in Alabama.

Host and distribution: Found in soil about the roots of gladioli near Wilmington, North Carolina. Inoculations failed to demonstrate that the species was a parasite of gladiolus roots. Some reproduction was secured on fungus cultures (*Fusarium, Trichoderma, Rhizopus* spp.) but only small numbers were produced. A *Fusarium* culture was inoculated with five females, five males, and two intersexes and kept at room temperature for 43 days. At the end of the experiment nineteen adults and thirty-nine larvae were recovered, but no intersexes.

The authors include a résumé of the more important records of intersexual nemas previously recorded for other genera.

Ditylenchus radicicolus (Greeff, 1872) Filipjev, 1936

Synonyms: *Anguillula radicicola* Greeff, 1872; *Tylenchus radicicola* (Greeff) Oerley, 1880; *Tylenchus hordei* Schøyen, 1885; *Anguillulina radicicola* (Greeff) Goodey, 1932

Historical: Greeff (1872) reported in Germany that as early as 1864 he had observed galls on the roots of annual meadow grass, *Poa annua,* and couch grass, *Agropyron repens,* from which he secured large numbers of nemas which he described as a new species. Trail (1881) next reported the species from Scotland, and then Schøyen (1885) in Denmark found it attacking barley and described it as *Tylenchus hordei,* apparently not being informed of Greeff's previous work. Goodey (1925) presented a discussion of the species, which he followed up (1932a) with a detailed account of the life history, biology, and pathology, basing his work on specimens from roots of barley, annual meadow grass, and sea lyme-grass (European dune wild rye grass), *Elymus arenarius.* Meantime, Kemner (1930) had reviewed several obscure references published in Sweden and Finland and demonstrated that nemas from barley roots produced the characteristic symptoms on *E. arenarius.* This species probably is an *Anguina,* not a *Ditylenchus.*

All known hosts are members of the Family Graminae.

Morphology: ♀: 1.2–3.2 mm; a = 24; b = 9–13; c = 19; V = 77

♂: 1.2–2.0 mm; a = 24–30; b = 6–9; c = 15–18

Body rather obese, tapering both ways from near its middle. Terminus pointed. Cuticle finely striated. Lip region set off by constriction. Stylet 12 to 16 μ long. Basal esophageal bulb more broadly pyriform than is usual in *Ditylenchus.* Excretory pore near base of esophagus. Developing oöcytes in two lines. Anterior portion of the ovary usually with two flexures, often reaching past the esophagus base. Spermatheca elongated; eggs 38 to 40 μ wide and 70 to 150 μ long, several often being present in the uterus at one time. Posterior uterine branch extending two-thirds the distance back to rectum. Vulva with rounded, rather prominent labia.

Testis reaching into esophageal region, often reflexed twice. Spicula cephalated, curved, similar to those of *Ditylenchus dipsaci*. Bursa rising well anterior to spicula and extending three-fourths the tail length, its borders slightly crenate.

The principal diagnostic characters of *Ditylenchus radicicolus* appear to be its greater length, more obese body of female, and smaller eggs, with several often present in the uterus at one time. However, host association doubtless is the principal characteristic by which it may be identified.

First-stage larvae were reported by Kemner as 0.3 to 0.36 mm long, while Goodey found them to be 0.45 to 0.5 mm, a difference indicating the usual variations found in different populations. Second-stage larvae measured 0.58 mm, third-stage 0.79 mm, and after the final moult the young females were 1.0 to 1.5 mm, compared with 1.0 to 1.3 mm for the males.

Biology: Goodey (1932a) determined that the first-stage larval forms enter the roots and rapidly pass through the moults to become adults in 18 to 21 days. After 10 to 12 days egg production begins, the life cycle requiring from 56 to 64 days. Probably only one generation develops within a gall, and after it disintegrates, the young larvae are free to move to other roots. Manner of survival between crops is not known.

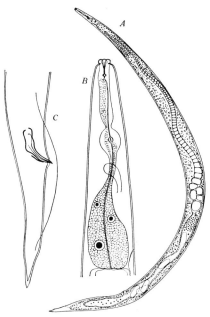

Fig. 6-11. *Ditylenchus radicicolus,* female, anterior portion of female and male tail. (*After Goodey. Courtesy of Methuen & Co., Ltd.*)

Symptoms: Schøyen states that very young barley plants may be killed under severe attack, or if they survive, they remain stunted and deformed, with yellow foliage. Even *Elymus arenarius* may be stunted if the roots are heavily galled. At the points where galls are formed, the roots often twist and turn backward. These galls may vary from 0.5 to 6.0 mm in length and width, are firm in texture, and bear no root-hairs.

A cross section of a gall shows that the epidermal cells are larger than normal and that those of the cortex are increased to ten to twelve layers, ranging from comparatively small cells near the center to greatly enlarged ones near the epidermis. The cortical cells are granular in appearance, and each contains a conspicuous nucleus in which there may be one or more nucleoli. The parasites congregate in these cortical cells

College of the Sequoias
Library

and often break down their walls until large chambers are formed. Increased development of the central cylinder also occurs, accompanied by an increase in size and numbers of cells. Goodey suggests that the nemas may not actually break down the walls of the cortical cells but "feed on nutrient substances exmosed from these cells which may be

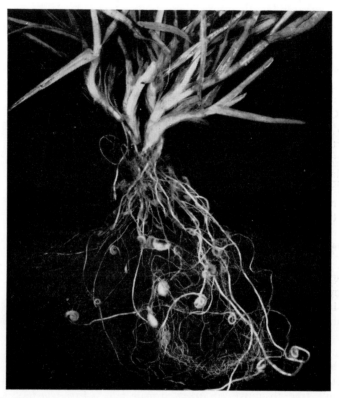

Fig. 6-12. Galls on wheat roots produced by *Ditylenchus radicicolus*. Slightly less than actual size. (*After Goodey. Courtesy of Nematology Department, Rothamsted Experiment Station.*)

considered as analogous to the giant cells produced in roots attacked by *Heterodera* species."

Hosts: Barley and rye are naturally infested, and experimentally wheat and oats have also proved susceptible to some degree. Among the several grasses known to be infested the most important are timothy and Kentucky blue.

Distribution: Sweden, Norway, Denmark, Finland, Germany, Scotland, and England, occurring from well within the Arctic Circle to as far south as Bonn, Germany. The writer received specimens from A. D. Baker which were collected near Radison, Saskatchewan, Canada, by T. C. Vanderpool, but it is not known elsewhere in the Americas.

Control: Crop rotations consisting of legumes, root crops, and vegetables should prove satisfactory, but definite information is not available.

Rice stem nematode, *Ditylenchus angustus* (Butler, 1913) Filipjev, 1936

Synonyms: *Tylenchus angustus* Butler, 1913; *Anguillulina angusta* (Butler) Goodey, 1932b

The rice stem nematode, causal agent of "ufra" disease, was first reported by Butler (1913), who later (1919) gave an extensive discussion of the pest, its habits, distribution, and control to which little has since been added. As early as 1916 about 6 million acres of the rice-producing region north of the Bay of Bengal and east of the Ganges River were infested to some degree. In many instances so little grain was produced that harvest was not attempted. Probably no other disease presents a greater menace to the rice crop of India in this region.

Areas in which the fields are submerged are most susceptible. The amount of water standing on the paddy may vary from a few inches deep to as much as 12 feet, and all traffic in the fields is carried on by boats. The principal crop is *aman,* which is sown between March and May and harvested in November and December. Lesser crops are the *boro,* planted in November to January and harvested in April to May, and the *aus,* sown between March and May and harvested between July and September. Hundreds of varieties of rice are grown in the region, and all appear to be susceptible hosts. Certain varieties adapted to deep water may have stems up to 20 feet in length, and reports indicate that they sometimes grow as much as 9 inches in 24 hours. Regions in which the plants are grown in seedbeds and transplanted into the fields are not known to be infested.

Morphology: ♀: 0.7–1.23 mm; a = 58; b = 7–8; c = 17–20; V = 80
♂: 0.6–1.0 mm; a = 36–47; b = 6–7; c = 18–23

Morphology in many respects similar to that of *Ditylenchus dipsaci,* but more slender. Lip region low, flattened. Spear 10 μ long. Esophagus with tapering basal bulb elongated until it is about three times as long as the neck width. Ovary outstretched, extending almost to base of esophagus, with oöcytes arranged in a single row. Posterior uterine branch reaching about two-thirds distance to anus. Tail tapering sharply to a pointed tip. Testis single, outstretched, extending to near base of esophagus. Spicula curved, with anterior third almost oblong in profile. Bursa rising about opposite proximal end of spicula and extending almost to the somewhat digitate terminus.

Biology: Cottony masses of nemas are formed as the plants mature and dry. These remain in the fields from about November until the young plants are growing in June. Then they become active, climb up on the stems during humid periods, and invade the growing point. Later they attack the stems and leaves in the last, or next to the last, leaf-bearing nodes. Plants are severely stunted, often with withered leaves which sometimes show brown areas near the nodes. When the inflorescence is invaded, the stem is black and withered and grain heads fail to form or are withered and contain only shriveled grain. At times the heads make a partial development but are twisted and deformed, although a small amount of grain may be produced. This condition is sometimes known as "pucca ufra."

Butler does not mention the life stage at which the nemas enter the plant, but he does state that the cottony masses are made up of individuals coiled in a tight spiral. From this we may infer that these are preadults similar to those of other species of the genus *Ditylenchus.* He states that they feed ectoparasitically on the epidermal cells of the young seed head, the peduncle, the part of the stems just above the upper nodes, and the young leaves rolled about the bud above the growing point. Under field conditions the first infested plants are noted when about half grown, or 2.5 to 3 feet tall. Developing heads are found to contain enormous numbers of nemas in all stages from eggs to adults. At no time are they found living endoparasitically in plant tissues.

Control: As previously mentioned, none of the many varieties of rice are known to be resistant to the nemas. Some of the early Aswina varieties partly avoid severe infestation, and the boro crops usually escape because they grow during the dry season, when the nemas are unable to travel up the stems. When artificially inoculated under humid conditions, these varieties proved to be equally susceptible.

Production of jute in certain areas provides a break between rice crops and gives control, but this is not practical on early-submerged land because an inferior fiber is produced.

Burning the stubble, plowing the field, and allowing it to lie fallow during the hot season gave satisfactory control in certain fields.

Ditylenchus askenasyi (Bütschli, 1873) Goodey, 1951

Synonyms: *Tylenchus askenasyi* Bütschli, 1873; *Anguillulina askenasyi* (Bütschli) Steiner, 1936

Bütschli described this species from moss collected near Feldburg, Germany, where specimens were found in discolored terminal swellings on the branches of moss, *Hypnum cupressiforme* Hooker. The accompanying description from Steiner (1936) is from specimens secured from galls on the common fern moss, *Thuidium delicatulum,* originating near Morgantown, West Virginia. Bütschli's specimens were about 40 per cent longer than Steiner's, but this difference in size may be due to host-induced variation. Galls measure about 0.7 by 0.85 mm and contain 7 to 12 adult nemas, together with 200 to 300 larvae and eggs. Both adults and larvae revived after being dried for 8 months.

Morphology: $\female$: 0.98–1.2 mm; a = 28–31; b = 8–11.5; c = 8.5–12.5; V = 73–78
$\male$: 0.92–1.2 mm; a = 24–31; b = 8.1–10.7; c = 8.5–14.5

Body usually assuming a somewhat spiral form. Vulva-anus distance about twice tail length. Lateral fields marked by about 10 very fine incisures. Spear only slightly longer than width of lip region, its knobs conspicuous; basal bulb of esophagus elongate-pyriform, set off from intestine, uterus outstretched, the oöcytes arranged in single file. Posterior uterine branch about twice as long as body width. Bursa extending only about half the tail length, narrower than those of other *Ditylenchus*.

Ditylenchus gallicus (Steiner, 1935) Filipjev, 1936

Synonym: *Anguillulina gallica* Steiner, 1935

This species was found in elm burls, *Ulmus* sp., from France and belongs in the group of *Ditylenchus* frequently found associated with bark beetles, although there was no evidence of beetles present in this instance. Numerous larvae emerged from the wood when it was immersed in water, while the adults remained buried in the wood, from which they were dissected.

Morphology: ♀: 1.0 mm; a = 38; b = 14; c = 43; V = 92
                      ♂: 0.6–1.0 mm; a = 40; b = 12; c = 38

Larval tails pointed, while those of females are blunt and rounded or, rarely, truncated. The posterior portion of the larval esophagus is unusually long compared with those of adults. Larval excretory pore anterior to median bulb, but in adults the pore is about opposite base of esophagus, a most unusual variation. Vulva broad with massive labia. Posterior uterine branch not present. Tail only about half as long as vulva-anal distance. Lateral field about one-third as wide as body. Phasmids and deirids not observed. Eggs almost spherical. Male tail arcuate-conoid, with bursa extending from the terminus to one body width anterior to anus. Spicula as long as tail. Gubernaculum thin, slightly arcuate. Spear about as long as head width, bearing only slightly developed knobs.

Identification may be made by the weak, faintly knobbed stylet, ventral narrowing of the female posterior to the vulva, absence of a posterior uterine branch, and the very short male tail enveloped by the bursa.

Ditylenchus brenani (Goodey, 1945a) Goodey, 1951

Synonym: *Anguillulina brenani* Goodey, 1945a

This interesting little species combines characters of both *Ditylenchus* and *Anguina*. The robust spiral females resemble the latter genus, while the esophagus, gonads, spicula, and bursa are more like those of the former. It is representative of several species which do not entirely fit into the diagnoses of either genus.

Morphology: ♀: 0.8 mm; a = 15–19; b = 5–7; c = 12–14; V = 78–83
                      ♂: 0.7 mm; a = 24–28; b = 4.3; c = 9–11; T = 60

Female body coiled in a complete circle. Lip region set off by constriction. Stylet about 10 μ long. Median esophageal bulb somewhat elongate, basal bulb with a short ventral lobe extending over the anterior end of the intestine. Junction of esophageal lumen and intestine an obscure muscular valvular apparatus. Ovary with double flexure, the cells of the flexed portion apparently arranged in two lines. Eggs 35 by 70 μ. Posterior uterine branch extending more than halfway to rectum. Terminus acute. Spiculum with unusually broad haft. Bursa rising near anterior end of spicula and extending only one-third length of tail. Testis outstretched, the spermatocytes lying in a single line.

This species is readily distinguished from *Ditylenchus askenasyi* by the shorter, more robust bodies, the ventral extension of the esophageal bulb, smaller eggs, and double flexure of the ovary. Goodey mentions that nemas have been reported from fifty other species of moss, but their specific identities are not known.

Biology: Young nemas either make their way into the growing point or climb to the terminus of the shoots, where one or two of each sex meet and feed on the terminal tissues. Infested leaves form an arched, gall-like cavity 0.5 to 0.75 mm long and 0.3 to 0.45 mm wide. The gall "floor" consists of granular cells which probably act as a nutritive zone. Young galls are green, while older ones become brown.

Host and distribution: *Pottia bryoides* collected near Headington Wick Copse, Oxford, England. This tiny moss grows on rough, calcareous soil; often the shoots are only 2 to 5 mm long.

Ditylenchus intermedius (deMan, 1884) Filipjev, 1936

Synonyms: *Tylenchus intermedius* deMan, 1884; *Anguillulina intermedia* (deMan) Goodey, 1932

Although this species has frequently been recorded by many workers, there is considerable doubt as to its identity. DeMan described and illustrated a rather slender nema, a = 50 to 60, while the measurements of other writers usually indicate wider specimens, a = 25–35. Actually, this name appears to have been used as a dumping ground to accommodate a number of closely related forms. Only an extensive study of the many forms involved will make it possible to identify the various species properly. Following is deMan's description:

Morphology: ♀: 0.9 mm; a = 50–60; b = 6; c = 8–10; V = 70
           ♂: 1.0 mm; a = 50–60; b = 6; c = 12

Body cylindroid from middle of neck to near anus. Vulva a depressed transverse slit. Tail uniformly conoid to the acute terminus. Vulva-anus distance about 1½ times tail length. Lip region half as high as wide. Spear about twice as long as lip width, bearing obscure knobs. Median bulb of esophagus narrow, elongated, basal bulb pyriform, well set off from intestine. Anterior cells of intestine hyaline (according to deMan's illustration). Ovary outstretched. Posterior uterine branch slightly longer than body width. Bursa extending about three-eighths of tail length.

Habitat: Damp soil, Sydenham, England.

Ditylenchus pinophilus (Thorne, 1935) Filipjev, 1936

Synonym: *Anguillulina pinophila* Thorne, 1935

This species is one of the most numerous associates of the mountain pine beetle, *Dendroctonus monticolae,* in lodgepole pine, *Pinus contorta,* in the Uintah and Wasatch Mountains of Utah. It is included herein as typical of the many *Ditylenchus* associated with bark beetles which carry the young nemas under the elyrta as they fly from tree to tree. Doubtless they feed on fungi growing in the frass of beetle tunnels (Wachek, 1955; Rühm, 1956).

Morphology: ♀: 1.5–2.5 mm; a = 25; b = 13; c = 33; V = $^{80}91^3$

♂: 1.0–1.5 mm; a = 33; b = 6; c = 36; T = 65

Lateral field smooth, refractive. Lip region set off by slight constriction, twice as wide as high. Spear with small but distinct knobs. Esophagus typical of the genus, the median bulb one-half to two-thirds as wide as neck. Vulva a depressed slit. Ovary outstretched, sometimes reaching base of esophagus, the oöcytes arranged in single file. Posterior uterine branch extending one-half to three-fourths distance to anus, often functioning as a spermatheca. Senile females occasionally viviparous. Male tail ventrally arcuate, enveloped by the bursa. Testis outstretched, the spermatocytes arranged in single file. Spicula three-fourths

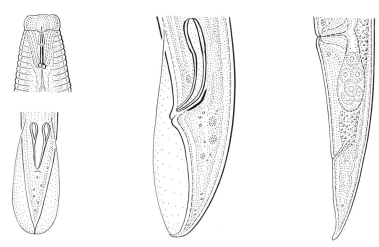

Fig. 6-13. *Ditylenchus pinophilus.* (*After Thorne. Courtesy of U.S. Department of Agriculture.*)

length of tail, arcuate in distal half. Gubernaculum thin, flat, slightly arcuate. Phasmids somewhat posterior to middle of tail in both sexes. Deirids not observed.

Like most nemas associated with bark beetles, there is considerable morphological variation in the populations found with different species of insects. One is confronted with the problem of deciding if they are to be identified as distinct species or as host variants of the same species. Regardless of the taxonomic method followed, the investigator will find difficulty in arriving at a satisfactory solution of the problem.

Genus *Pseudhalenchus* Tarjan, 1958

Diagnosis: Moderately slender nemas in which the sexes are similar in form. Body cylindroid from near the nerve ring to the anal region. Labial framework lightly sclerotized. Spear with distinct knobs. Median bulb of esophagus fusiform. Basal portion of esophagus a long lobe extending over anterior end of intestine. Junction of esophageal lumen and intestine an obscure muscular valve. Nerve ring at base of isthmus. Excretory pore adjacent to hemizonid. Vulva near 75 per cent. Ovary outstretched, with oöcytes usually in single file. Spermatheca present. Posterior uterine branch rudimentary. Bursa subcaudal. Spicula and gubernaculum tylenchoid.

Type species: *Pseudhalenchus minutus* Tarjan, 1958

Pseudhalenchus resembles *Tylenchus* and *Ditylenchus,* with the basal bulb extended in a long lobe as in *Halenchus* and *Deladenus.*

Pseudhalenchus minutus Tarjan, 1958

Morphology: ♀: 0.4 mm; a = 30; b = 3.3; c = 8.3; V = $^{30}73$

♂: 0.33 mm; a = 33; b = 3.3; c = 7.9; T = 32

Characters of the genus. Body slightly arcuate when relaxed. Lateral field marked by four incisures. Lip region bearing five annules. Female spear 7 to 10 μ long, male 8 μ. Spear knobs inclined posteriorly. Hemizonid adjacent to excretory pore. Anterior portion of esophagus half as wide as neck, terminating in a fusiform median bulb with a weak valvular apparatus. Posterior uterine branch shorter than body diameter. Spicules arcuate, cephalated. Gubernaculum thin, slightly bent.

Habitat and distribution: Soil about roots of citrus, strawberry, and other plants in various parts of Florida.

Chapter 7

Genus *Anguina* Scopoli, 1777 [1]

Diagnosis: Tylenchinae. Typical gall-forming endoparasites of seeds, stems, and leaves of cereals, grasses, and other plants. Lateral fields appearing as plain bands or as bands marked by four or more fine incisures, usually not visible on full-grown adults. Deirids and phasmids not observed. Amphid apertures at apices of lateral lips, visible only from a face view. Six minute papillae are grouped about the oral opening, while four submedian ones are located on the outer margins of the submedial lips. Ovary extending forward, usually with one or two flexures. Oöcytes usually in multiple series arranged about a rachis. Posterior uterine branch rudimentary. Males straight or slightly arcuate when relaxed by gradual heat. Testis outstretched or reflexed once or twice, often with spermatocytes developing in several rows arranged about a rachis. Bursa enveloping tail, or nearly so.

Type species: *Anguina tritici* (Steinbuch, 1799) Filipjev, 1936
Anguina is composed of a diverse group of species producing distinctive host symptoms which usually can be correlated with morphological characters for species determination. Members of the group are not uncommon in native grasses and other plants. They present difficult problems in identification because they are generally found in dry material and are unsatisfactory for detailed study. Extensive investigations with established colonies are desirable for most species, because the existing descriptions fail to include many pertinent points.

Body measurements and proportions frequently are of little value except in examples of extreme diversity of length, because mature adults usually are distorted by pressure of developing gonads. Numbers of lines in the lateral fields are sometimes distinctive, but these usually must be observed early in the development of both sexes since they rarely are visible on mature specimens. *Anguina tritici* and its close relatives have two flexures in the ovary, while in *A. graminophila* and related species there appears to be only one flexure. In *A. microlaenae* and *A. amsinckia* the ovary is outstretched. A small cardiac valve is present in certain species, but in *A. millefolii, A. balsamophila,* and perhaps other species there is only an obscure muscular valvular apparatus, and a basal lobe of the esophagus may extend back over the anterior end of the intestine.

---

[1] Chitwood (1935) reestablished *Anguina* as a valid genus and made *Anguillulina* Gervais and van Beneden a synonym, in accordance with the international rules of zoological nomenclature, which validated old generic names which were established without mention of a species.

159

Several species have a stricture separating the basal bulb from the isthmus, sometimes forming a conspicuous storage reservoir for salivary gland secretions.

Anguina tritici (Steinbuch, 1799) Filipjev, 1936

Synonyms: *Vibrio tritici* Steinbuch, 1799; *Vibrio tritici* Bauer, 1823; *Anguillula graminearum* Diesing, 1851 in part; *Anguillulina tritici* Gervais and v. Beneden, 1859; *Tylenchus tritici* (Steinbuch) Bastian, 1865; *Anguillula scandens* Schneider, 1866

Historical: As recounted in Chapter 1, the typical cockles apparently were known to Shakespeare, as well as the fact that these abnormal, seedlike galls did not produce plants. In England they are also known as *earcockles, purples,* and *peppercorns* and in Germany as *Radenkrankheit* (cockle disease). In France the disease was confused with bunt or stinking smut and is known as *blenielle*. In the United States the most common names are *eelworm disease, cockle wheat, hard smut,* and *nematode galls* according to Leukel (1924).

After Needham's discovery of the causal agent (1743) no additional information was recorded until Roffredi (1775, 1776) reported that he had observed different stages in the development of the worms while he was investigating their life cycle in growing wheat heads. It was not until 23 years later that Steinbuch (1799) finally designated the scientific name *Vibrio tritici,* which Bauer (1823) used again, not knowing of Steinbuch's previous work

Davaine (1857) determined the complete details of the life history, and during the following 50 years numerous references appeared in the literature from Germany, England, and France One of the most outstanding contributions was that of Marcinowski (1909). In the United States, Johnson (1909) reported the pest from California, New York, West Virginia, and Georgia. The range was further extended by the surveys of Byars (1920a) and Leukel (1924) to Virginia, Maryland, North Carolina, and South Carolina. However, the galls found in a mill in Maryland were later traced to Virginia, and the records from California and New York have not been verified by later discoveries.

The pest is doubtless one of the most ancient economically important nematode parasites and has been disseminated through infested seed to practically all the wheat-producing regions of the world. It is well known throughout most of the countries of Europe, with numerous records from such widely separated areas as Asiatic U.S.S.R., Israel, Syria, Pakistan, India, China, Australia, New Zealand, Egypt, and Brazil. Losses as high as 30 to 70 per cent are not unusual, and the annual toll from the world's wheat crop probably reaches many millions of bushels.

Morphology: ♀: 3.8 mm; a = 20; b = 13; c = 31; V = $^{83}91^3$

♂: 2.4 mm; a = 25; b = 9; c = 30; T = 80

Obligate plant parasite with obese body, that of the female being spiral in form and practically immobile, while the male is straighter and more active.

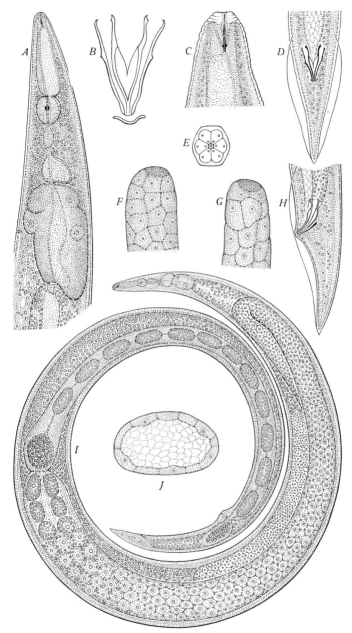

Fig. 7-1. *Anguina tritici.* *A*—Neck of female with greatly developed esophageal glands. *B*—Spicula. *C*—Female head. *D*—Male tail, ventral. *E*—Face view. *F, G*—Ends of ovary and testis, showing cap cells. *H*—Male tail, lateral. *I*—Female. *J*—Cross section of ovary. (*After Thorne. Courtesy of Helminthological Society of Washington.*)

Striae usually visible only on the neck region. Lateral fields indistinct, consisting of narrow bands marked by numerous minute incisures which often are invisible on well-developed specimens. Spear 8 to 10 μ long, with small basal knobs. Esophagus of gravid female frequently with abnormally developed glandular structures. Between the nerve ring and the basal bulb is a secondary "storage" gland, set off from the bulb by a definite constriction. In this the dorsal gland secretions apparently collect until it may become greatly distended; or the secretions may be used and the gland reduced to a small ovate swelling. Cardia small, often obscure. Ovary greatly developed, usually with two flexures, the oöcytes arranged about a rachis. In cross section the ovary appears as a pulpy cellular tissue surrounded by a relatively thin layer of developing oöcytes (Fig. 7-1*J*). A spherical spermatheca lies adjacent to the outlet of the ovary. The posterior uterine branch also serves as a spermatheca. Several eggs, each about as long as the vulva body width, may be present in the oviduct at one time.

Testis with one or two flexures, the spermatocytes arranged about a rachis. Spicula broad, short. Gubernaculum thin, troughlike. Bursa enveloping tail.

The above description is based on specimens from infested wheat collected in Georgia by A. L. Taylor. Goodey (1933) records females 5.0 mm long.

Biology: Cool, moist climates are especially favorable for the development of *Anguina tritici*. A film of moisture must be present when the young wheat plants are developing; otherwise the very active larval nematodes cannot travel from the soil to the growing point of the plant.

Second-stage larvae lie quiescent in the galled grains which remain in the field at harvest or are planted with the seed. They are liberated when relaxed by moisture during periods of favorable growing temperatures. As the young host plants develop, these larvae make their way to the growing points, where they await the lengthening of the culm which will carry them up to the seed head. It is possible that during this waiting period they feed ectoparasitically on the tissues of the growing point and leaf bases.

As the stems develop and the embryo seeds form, several nemas of both sexes enter each seed, begin feeding, soon become adult females and males, and mate. Each female produces hundreds, if not thousands, of eggs, from which first-stage larvae soon hatch and moult to reach the second stage. In this stage they remain until released from the gall which has been formed during the reaction of the seed tissues to the products of the salivary glands of the nemas. Limber (1938) found that the number of larvae in galls from China varied from 800 to 26,000, while in a similar study of galls from India they ranged from 3,600 to 32,400, the numbers usually varying according to the size of the galls, which weighed from 2.5 to 9.2 mg.

Frequently some larvae make their way into the leaves and produce galls, and occasionally a few individuals may mature there (Byars, 1920a). Wrinkling and twisting of the leaves is a characteristic symptom of their presence. This may be caused by feeding at the leaf base and not by direct invasion. Severe infestation may cause death of the plants during the very young stages. Leukel (1924) found that, of eighty seedlings exhibiting early symptoms of infestation, fifteen produced gall-free heads. However, many seedlings which showed no symptoms were found to harbor numerous larvae when examined microscopically. Working with

Fig. 7-2. Young wheat plant infested with *Anguina tritici*. (*After Leukel. U.S. Department of Agriculture photographs.*)

rye, Leukel found that the number of galls per infested head of grain varied from one to sixty-seven. These numbers probably were correlated with the population present when the seed stems began growing. In some instances of very severe infestation heads failed to develop. Infested heads usually are identified by their smaller size, irregular contour, and a tendency to ripen more slowly than uninfested ones. Examination reveals the small, dark-colored cockles so typical of the disease.

Marcinowski (1909) studied the details of gall formation and found that the galls were produced from undifferentiated flower buds. Staminate tissues were first involved, then carpellate tissues. Finally tissues lying between carpels and stamens were included. Leukel observed that as many as five galls may replace a single kernel. Therefore, the number of galls present in a sample of grain does not represent that many parasitized kernels.

Symptoms: Presence of *Anguina tritici* is usually indicated by dying small plants, wrinkled and twisted leaves of young plants, reduced and

Fig. 7-3. Normal head of wheat between two heads infested with *Anguina tritici*. (*After Leukel. U.S. Department of Agriculture photograph.*)

irregular heads, and presence of the characteristic cockles. All symptoms should be verified by microscopic examination.

Control: One or two years of nonhost crops are sufficient practically to eliminate nemas remaining in the field after harvest. Apparently they are not dependent on plant diffusates to stimulate their activity. When revived from their quiescence by favorable moisture and temperature, they leave the galls and search for a host plant. If they do not find a host, they continue searching until their stored food supplies are exhausted and death follows.

Clean seed is a most important item. In the United States it can usually be secured from areas where the pest is not known. But in many countries securing such seed presents a difficult problem which is sometimes solved by the use of modern mechanical cleaning apparatus which removes most of the cockles. If such machinery is not available, the galls can be floated off in a 20 per cent salt solution made by adding 40 pounds of common salt to 25 gallons of water. Floating galls and other debris should be skimmed off, the salt solution drawn off for further use, and the sound wheat rinsed thoroughly and dried by spreading in a thin layer on a floor or canvas, where it can be stirred to hasten the

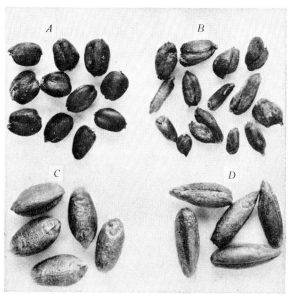

Fig. 7-4. *A, B*—"Cockles" of wheat and rye formed by *Anguina tritici. C, D*— Normal grains of same. (*After Leukel. U.S. Department of Agriculture photograph.*)

drying. Galls and brine should be disposed of where livestock and poultry will not find them (Byars 1920a).

Hot water. Experiments by Limber (1938) indicated that a two-hour presoak period followed by not less than two hours at 122°F was necessary to kill all the nemas. After treatment the grain must immediately be dried in the manner just mentioned.

Resistant varieties. Numerous varieties of wheat have been tested for possible resistance, but none has shown any promise except Kanred. This is a hard winter wheat which is not adapted to most of the areas in which the nematode occurs.

Host plants. Anguina tritici is generally regarded as a pest of wheat; yet it also readily attacks rye, emmer, and spelt. Henslow (1841) and certain other workers report slight infestations of oats and barley. No doubt variations in host preference occur in certain populations, and extensive investigations of colonies from different areas will probably expand the host range. That different populations do exist is evident from data on measurements of specimens from China. Byars and Limber both found these specimens to be somewhat smaller than those from other countries.

Dormancy studies. Galls stored under laboratory conditions of temperature and humidity at the Salt Lake City, Utah, Station of the Nematology Section, U.S. Department of Agriculture, showed that the nemas in one lot were 100 per cent alive after 28 years (Fielding, 1951). A recent (1958) examination of the same material indicated that 60 per cent are still alive.

Fungus enemies. Zopf (1888) observed *Arthrobotrys oligospora* trapping the nemas in loops, after which the hyphae penetrated the cuticle and fed on the body contents. Marcinowski found that the smut fungus, *Tilletia tritici,* prevented development of the parasite. Atanasoff (1925) observed that the second-stage larvae carry pycnospores of *Dilophosphora alopecuri* on their bodies. This is a serious parasite of wheat; its development not only destroys the grain but sometimes prevents the formation of galls, and it thus acts as a partial control of the pest.

Cheo (1946) in China experimented with a bacterial disease of wheat, *Bacterium tritici,* which previously had been reported from India, Egypt, and western Australia. Inoculations demonstrated that the bacterium must be associated with *Anguina tritici* before infection can be established. Cheo described the symptoms as follows:

> The diseased plant is characterized by a curling of the emerging leaves with gummy exudations. The culms may grow until heading, and the spike is usually narrower and shorter than the normal one. All of the spikelets, instead of producing normal grains, may be full of a bacterial mass. Glumes are externally covered with a bright yellowish, slimy bacterial growth. Not infrequently the diseased spikes become curled and distorted before heading.

Bentgrass nematode, *Anguina agrostis* (Steinbuch, 1799) Filipjev, 1936

Synonyms: *Vibrio agrostis* Steinbuch, 1799; *Vibrio phalaridis* Steinbuch, 1799; *Anguillulina graminearum* Diesing, 1851 (in part); *Tylenchus agrostidis* Bastian, 1865; *Tylenchus phlei* Horn, 1888; *Tylenchus agrostis* (Steinbuch) Goodey, 1930; *Anguillulina agrostis* (Steinbuch) Goodey, 1932b

Historical: Since Steinbuch first recorded *Vibrio agrostis* from galls in the seed heads of colonial bentgrass, *Agrostis capillaris,* = *A. tenuis,* there have been numerous reports of galls found in various species of grass. Unfortunately, satisfactory diagnostic descriptions of the nemas have not been given. It was not until Goodey (1930) made a study of specimens from redtop, *A. alba,* creeping bentgrass, *A. stolonifera,* = *A. palustris,* and *A. vulgaris,* = *A. tenuis,* that we finally had a fairly adequate description of the species involved.

Marcinowski (1909) had made extensive observations on the host range of nemas from the above-mentioned species and also from velvet bent-grass, *A. canina,* finding all susceptible. She also listed as susceptible sheep fescue, *Festuca ovina, Koeleria glauca, Phleum boehemeria,* annual bluegrass, *Poa annua,* and alpine bluegrass, *Poa alpina.* As hosts of *Anguina phalaridis* she found Kentucky bluegrass, *Poa pratensis,* prairie junegrass, *Koeleria cristata,* and *Phleum boehemeri.* These data indicated that the nemas had different host preferences, although Goodey (1933) considered *Anguina phalaridis* a synonym of *Anguina agrostis.* Additional investigations of this relationship are desirable.

In the Pacific Northwest states, Courtney and Howell (1952) studied the host range of *Anguina agrostis* and found that *A. palustris, A. canina, A. tenuis, A. alba,* and spike bentgrass, *A. exarata,* were all readily infested. However, eight grass species of the genera *Festuca, Phleum, Poa, Holcus,* and *Anthoxanthum* were not attacked. Apparently the population with which Marcinowski worked had a wider host range than those studied by Goodey and by Courtney and Howell.

However, there is a population in Oregon of *Anguina agrostis* which does infest Chewing's fescue, *Festuca rubra* var. *commutata,* but does not transfer to *Agrostis* species. Courtney (1958, personal communication) states that the infested seeds of fescue appear much the same as uninfested and that the galls can be found only by dissecting the palea from each seed. However, the galls are much lighter than the healthy seed and can be separated by mechanical means.

A most interesting and important point concerning the fescue galls is that they are toxic to livestock. After feeding on them, cattle, sheep, and horses suffer from nervous disorders characterized by falling, trembling of muscles, and lack of coordination (Shaw et al., 1949). In several instances this affliction has resulted in the death of animals.

Morphology: ♀: 1.5–2.7 mm; a = 19; b = 9; c = 36; V = 87
♂: 1.1–1.8 mm; a = 26; b = 6; c = 21

The above measurements by Goodey correspond fairly well with those from specimens collected by Courtney in Oregon. While similar in many respects to *Anguina tritici,* this species is much smaller, and esophageal development is less conspicuous. Lateral fields of males and young females about one-sixth to one-eighth as wide as body, bordered by two refractive lines with four much finer lines between them, all of which are invisible on adult females and most males after the bodies become distended by the gonads. Gonads with two flexures; spicula somewhat less robust than those of *A. tritici.* Eggs much larger in proportion to the body width than those of *A. tritici.*

Type host: *Agrostis capillaris,* = *A. tenuis*
Type distribution: Europe and the Pacific Northwest of the United States
Biology: Second-stage larvae are released from galls when they become moistened in plant residues or soil and make their way to the growing points of young plants. Here they probably feed ectoparasitically until the stems form and they are elevated to the inflorescence. There they enter the tissues of developing ovules and produce elongated,

spindle-shaped purple galls at the expense of the various flower parts. Goodey states that usually one of each sex is present in each gall but occasionally one male and two or three females are found and rarely one female with two or three males. However, Courtney and Howell observed that one to three females and an equal number of males usually were present in each gall. Each female produced approximately 1,000 eggs during the two-week deposition period, and these immediately hatched and moulted to become second-stage larvae. The life cycle was

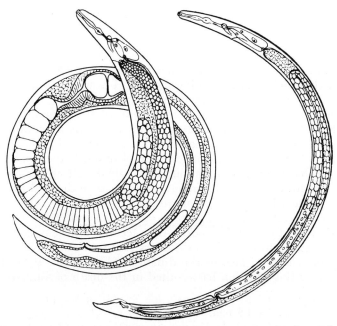

Fig. 7-5. *Anguina agrostis.* (*After T. Goodey. Courtesy of Journal of Helminthology.*)

accomplished in three or four weeks, depending on the rate of plant development. In some instances galls had been formed, and second-stage larvae were in dormancy. On the same plant, nemas in various stages of growth were still present in galls which were just developing. Only one generation occurs each year

Dispersal: Transportation of infested seed and straw containing galls by means of machinery, trucks, bags, water, and even clothing of workmen is the principal method of distribution. In one instance cited by Courtney and Howell, several dozen galls were found adhering to a pair of rubber boots after the wearer had walked a few hundred feet through an infested, wet, bentgrass field just prior to harvest. By collecting blowings from threshers on Tanglefoot flypaper, these investigators found that galls were carried at least 300 feet from blower-type machines without aid from air currents or winds, which would doubtless have greatly increased the range of the galls, even carrying them to adjacent fields.

Control: Plowing infested sod to a depth of 6 and 12 inches was demonstrated as a successful control method by Courtney and Howell. This necessitated turning the sod completely under to prevent any growth.

Fig. 7-6. Healthy and infested (right) panicles of Astoria bentgrass. Note transformation of seed to enlarged galls due to *Anguina agrostis.* (*Photograph by J. R. Hardistan, U.S. Department of Agiculture.*)

One year of nonhost crops in which no bentgrass is permitted to grow gives control. This condition is very difficult to achieve; fallow may be more satisfactory if it can be afforded. Under Oregon conditions heavy pasturing, close clipping, and flooding failed to give even partial control, and chemicals were too expensive to justify their use.

Sanitation practices should include cleaning of threshing machines, trucks, and other equipment, including seed bags and clothing of workmen, before moving from infested to clean fields. Such practices are exceedingly difficult to carry out under average commercial conditions.

If sources of clean seed are not available, hot-water treatment of seed for 15 minutes at 126°F is successful. This should be preceded by a two-hour soak in water to which a wetting agent like Vatsol O.S. has been added. However, this is not effective if galls are still covered by the inner palea of the inflorescence. A reduction in germination of about 5 per cent usually follows this treatment.

Fescue leaf gall nematode, *Anguina graminis* (Hardy, 1850) Filipjev, 1936

Synonyms: *Vibrio graminis* Hardy, 1850; *Tylenchus graminis* (Hardy) Marcinowski, 1909; *Anguillulina graminis* (Hardy) Goodey, 1932b

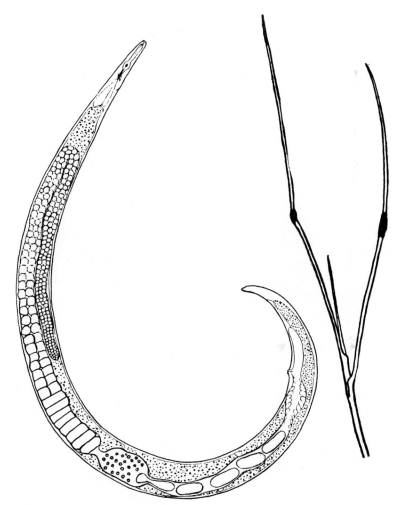

Fig. 7-7. *Anguina graminis,* female and galls on *Festuca ovina.* (*After T. Goodey. Courtesy of Journal of Helminthology and Methuen & Co., Ltd.*)

Galls on the leaves of fescues were first observed by Hardy, who described the nemas as "vibrios." It was not until Goodey (1932) collected specimens and gave an adequate description of their morphology and biology that they became recognized as a valid species. The following data are largely from his papers.

Morphology: ♀: 1.9–2.7 mm; a = 20; b = 10; c = 29; V = 85

        ♂: 1.1–1.6 mm; a = 22; b = 6; c = 17

Typical body pose slightly arcuate to open C form, not coiled as in *Anguina tritici* and *A. agrostis*. Gonads with only one flexure extending back near mid-body, and with six or eight cells in a circumference arranged about the rachis. Spear about 10 μ long. Second-stage larvae 0.7 to 0.8 mm long, resistant to desiccation.

Biology: Second-stage larvae enter the leaf tissues as the young blades rise from the crown and congregate in small groups in the fine, slender leaves, where they produce galls 1 to 4 mm long and 1 or 2 mm wide. These are formed by an infolding of the leaf and at first are yellowish green, later becoming deep purple. They resemble knots or swollen nodes. Sections show that all portions of the leaf tissues have become enlarged and hypertrophied, the cells being much larger than normal. Cavities are formed in the mesophyll in which the nemas are found.

Hosts and distribution: Sheep fescue, *Festuca ovina,* hard fescue, *F. ovina* var. *duriuscula,* and red fescue, *F. rubra,* are all known as hosts. So far as is known, *Anguina graminis* is confined to Europe.

Anguina graminophila (Goodey, 1933a) n. comb.

Synonyms: *Anguillulina graminophila* Goodey, 1933; *Ditylenchus graminophilus* (Goodey) Filipjev, 1936

According to Goodey, nemas producing galls on the leaves of fine bent-grass were recorded by Karsch as early as 1880, but 50 years elapsed before a complete study was made of the species and a specific name assigned. The multirowed cells of the gonads and posterior position of the vulva indicate that the species is an *Anguina,* not a *Ditylenchus.*

Morphology: ♀: 1.6–2.5 mm; a = 26–33; b = 10; c = 25; V = 86–90

        ♂: 1.4–2.0 mm; a = 30–43; b = 8; c = 20–26

Body with a marked constriction immediately behind vulva; lip region with six prominent rounded lips, set off by constriction, their sclerotized framework extending back into the head to an unusual degree. Base of esophagus overlapping intestine a short distance. Vulva located farther back than is usual in the genus. Ovary extending past base of esophagus, usually with two flexures. Oöcytes arranged in two lines except in region of multiplication, where there are four to six lines, probably arranged about a rachis. Posterior uterine branch very rudimentary, the most important diagnostic character of the species. As many as 14 eggs may occur in the uterus at one time.

Males more slender than females. Bursa unusually long, extending from near terminus to a point more than one tail length anterior to anus. Testis outstretched, with spermatocytes in several rows.

Biology: Preadult larvae enter the young leaves while they are still within the sheaths and congregate in groups of two or three to as high as twelve of each sex. These groups produce greenish-yellow galls 1 to 15 mm long, usually located near the bases of the leaves. Transverse sections reveal that cell hypertrophy and multiplication involve epidermal, mesophyll, and vascular tissues. Cells over the vascular bundles form ridges, while those between are depressed into furrows. The nemas live

Fig. 7-8. *Anguina graminophila,* female and galls on *Agrostis vulgaris.* (*After T. Goodey. Courtesy of Journal of Helminthology and Methuen & Co., Ltd.*)

in cavities within the galls, which have a red color due to a purplish-red sap in the cells immediately under the epidermis. Great numbers of eggs are produced, from which larvae about 0.4 mm long emerge. The first moult occurs when they are about 0.54 mm long, the second at 0.65 mm, the third at 0.9 to 1.1 mm, and the fourth at 1.2 to 1.43 mm, the last being the preadult stage. These larvae escape from the galls and enter the young, ensheathed leaves of the following crop.

Type host: Fine bentgrass, *Agrostis alba* L. (*A. vulgaris* With.)

Distribution: St. Albans, Hertfordshire, England, and probably Germany. In the United States it was collected on colonial bentgrass, *Agrostis tenuis,* near Corvallis, Oregon, by F. P. McWhorter and identified by Steiner and Buhrer (1933b). Goto and Gibler (1951) recorded a small infestation about 9 feet in diameter on bluejoint grass, *Calmagrostis canadensis,* growing on low land near St. Paul, Minnesota. Illustrations are from specimens collected by T. Goodey.

Anguina microlaenae (Fawcett, 1938) Steiner, 1940

Synonym: *Anguillula microlaenae* Fawcett, 1938

Morphology: ♀: 1.3–3.0 mm; a = 12–19; b = 9–19; c = 15–32; V = 88
♂: 1.1–2.0 mm; a = 17–23; b = 8–14; c = 16–26

The very robust, coiled body may be as wide as the length of the neck. Lip region low, flattened; stylet 8 to 9 μ long. Fawcett illustrates the median bulb of the esophagus as elongated and tapering both ways; basal bulb in three lobes, the dorsal extending back over the intestine. Ovary single, outstretched, six or eight oöcytes in circumference, the narrow anterior end extending to the esophagus. Posterior uterine branch shorter than vulva body diameter. The tail is illustrated as being slightly shorter than the vulva-anus distance, but the measurements indicate that it is extremely variable in length. Eggs 37 to 52 by 85 to 120 μ. First-stage larvae 0.5 to 1.0 mm long, able to withstand desiccation. Testis outstretched, apparently about six spermatocytes in circumference.

Described from galls on shoots, leaves, and inflorescence of *Microlaena stipoides* collected near Victoria, Australia.

Anguina tumefaciens (Cobb, 1932a) Filipjev and Schuurmans Stekhoven, 1941

Synonyms: *Tylenchus tumefaciens* Cobb; *Anguillulina tumefaciens* (Cobb) Goodey, 1933

Bradley grass, *Cynodon transvaalensis,* collected from lawns in the vicinities of Johannesburg and Pretoria, South Africa, bore ovoid galls 2 to 8 mm long in which as many as nine adult nemas and hundreds of eggs and larvae were found. Galls were present on stems, on leaves, and rarely in flower heads, some occurring singly, others in tandem or small groups. Injury was sufficient to cause dying out in small areas.

Morphology: ♀: 1.4 mm; a = 22; b = ?; c = 31; V = [80]88[44]
♂: 1.2 mm; a = 31; b = ?; c = 17; T = 80

Head set off by slight constriction. Body narrowing rapidly behind vulva. Ovary reflexed; one egg at a time in uterus. Posterior uterine branch present.

Tail sometimes bent dorsally (perhaps owing to cold fixative). Bursa narrowed near middle, enveloping all but a short portion of tail. Spicula and gubernaculum of the usual form.

Nothing is known of the life history, but it probably follows the general pattern of grass-infesting nemas. Cobb recommended burning infested areas after spraying with flammable liquid, use of clean seed, and recleaning of suspected seed.

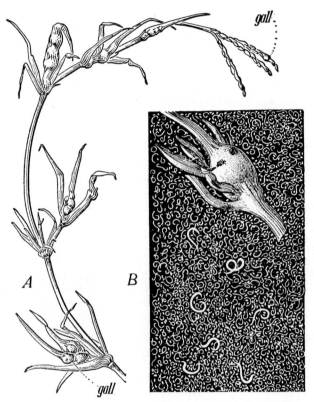

Fig. 7-9. *A*—Stem of *Cynadon transvaalensis,* showing galls formed by *Anguina tumefaciens.* *B*—Gall and part of the nemas found in it. *(After Cobb. Courtesy of Washington Academy of Sciences.)*

Anguina spermophaga Steiner, 1937

Morphology: ♀: 1.7 mm; a = 37; b = 10; c = 34; V = 87–91
                ♂: 1.4 mm; a = 33; b = 9; c = 23

Female body rather spindle-shaped, the terminus ending in an acute, digitate point. Ovary with double flexure, the terminus usually extending nearly to base of esophagus; ova 31 by 67 μ. Posterior uterine branch about as long as vulvar body width. Stylet weak, with only slight basal knobs.

Male body cylindroid, also ending in a mucronate terminus. Bursa rather large for an *Anguina,* rising in front of the spicula and extending to the base of the mucro, where it is expanded in two lobes, the most outstanding diagnostic character of the species.

Described from the inflorescence of *Saccharum spontaneum* grown at the former Experimental Station at Arlington, Virginia, from seeds collected in Turkestan (U.S.S.R.).

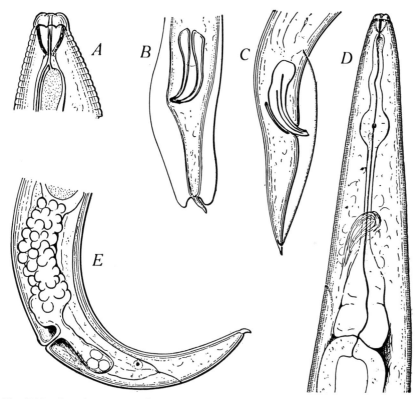

Fig. 7-10. *Anguina spermophaga.* A—Head. *B, C*—Male tail, ventral and lateral views. *D*—Female tail. *E*—Anterior end of female. (*After Steiner. Courtesy of Helminthological Society of Washington.*)

Anguina australis Steiner, 1940

Morphology: ♀: 2.4 mm; a = 20; b = 19; c = 14–20; V = 88–93
♂: 1.5 mm; a = 20; b = 12; c = 14–16

Females coiled in a circle, males straight or slightly bent ventrally. Lateral fields marked by four lines, the central band with minute diagonal and crisscross markings. Median esophageal bulb spheroid, posterior bulb obscured by pressure of ovary, which is reflexed near the nerve ring. Posterior uterine branch present. Bursa rising about opposite proximal ends of spicula and extending to near terminus. Spicula and gubernaculum of the usual form, testis reflexed.

This species produces pustulelike galls on the leaves of a grass, *Ehrharta longifolia,* collected in Australia. When the inflorescence is invaded, seed development is prevented and glumes may be swollen and deformed by several massed galls. Size of galls varies from 700 to 1,270 by 600 to 1,200 μ.

Anguina millefolii (Löw, 1874) Filipjev, 1936

Synonyms: *Tylenchus millefolii* Löw, 1874; *Anguillulina millefolii* (Löw) Goodey, 1932b

Fig. 7-11. *Anguina millefolii* injury on yarrow, *Achillea millefolium.* (*After Marcinowski.*)

Galls produced by this species on the leaves of yarrow, *Achillea millefolium,* were first observed by Löw. Müller (1880) found similar bodies on *A. tanacetifolia.* Marcinowski (1909) presented a rather complete account of the species, including fairly good illustrations showing the anatomy and symptoms on the host plants. T. Goodey collected specimens in England and kindly forwarded part of them to the writer. The following measurements are from Marcinowski:

Morphology: ♀: 2.3 mm; a = 21; b = 10; c = 18; V = 88
                ♂: 1.6 mm; a = 26; b = 8; c = 18; T = 78
    Female body forming a complete circle or a slightly open C. Lateral fields not visible on adult specimens. Spear about 9 μ long. Valve far forward in median esophageal bulb. Basal bulb of esophagus set off from isthmus by a narrow

constriction, then extending back and overlapping the intestine. Lumen of esophagus lying ventrally in the basal bulb, joining the intestine by an obscure connection operated by a sphincter muscle. Isthmus of esophagus sometimes expanded to form a small reservoir for the gland secretions. Ovary outstretched, with short double flexure near base of esophagus. Spermatheca about as long as body width, usually filled with granular spermatozoa. Posterior uterine branch about as long as vulva body diameter, with a few rudimentary cells attached. Tail one-half to three-fourths as long as vulva-anus distance.

Male somewhat cylindroid except at extremities. Testis outstretched, with spermatogonia arranged as elongate, diagonal cells which present a "herringbone" appearance. Spicula and gubernaculum of the usual type. Bursa narrow, rising well in front of the spicula and extending almost to terminus, which is somewhat spicate and slightly bent dorsally in dead specimens.

Biology: Marcinowski illustrates the larvae as resembling those of *Heterodera schachtii* in size and body proportions, with an average length of 0.36 mm and a = 21. Larvae and adults were found in the galls, but nothing is known of the various stages of growth and the life history.

According to Marcinowski's illustrations galls may occur at any point on the slender leaves and range from 3 to 6 mm long. When attack is concentrated on the terminal portion of the stem, twisting and deformity are common.

Distribution appears to be limited to Europe.

Anguina balsamophila (Thorne, 1926) Filipjev, 1936

Synonyms: *Tylenchus balsamophilus* Thorne, 1926; *Anguillulina balsamophila* (Thorne) Goodey, 1932b; *Ditylenchus balsamophilus* (Thorne) Filipjev & Stekhoven, 1941

This species was described from specimens collected in Utah, where it is frequently observed as the causal agent of galls on the leaves of arrowleaf balsamroot, *Balsamorrhiza sagittata*. In the original description the basal portion of the esophagus was described and figured as a small pyriform bulb. Actually this bulb was the storage reservoir for esophageal gland secretions. The main bulb was greatly enlarged and extended back over the anterior end of the intestine.

Morphology: ♀: 2.6–3.4 mm; a = 17; b = 7; c = 30; V = $^{76}88^{3}$
        ♂: 1.5–2.0 mm; a = 30; b = 7; c = 20; T = 81

Cuticle marked by four incisures occupying about one-eighth the body width. These are not visible on fully developed specimens. Body widest near middle. From a face view the amphid apertures and four very small papillae are seen grouped closely about the oral opening. Ovary outstretched except for a short double flexure which usually is present near the anterior end. Granular, ovoid spermatozoa are present throughout the uterine tract, although most of them are congregated about the entrance to the ovary. Eggs 37 by 60 μ, as many as six or eight present in the uterus at one time. Posterior uterine branch about as long as vulvar body width. Vulva-anus distance about 1½ times tail length.

Male body more cylindroid except near extremities. Bursa gradually rising from the body contour well anterior to the spicula and extending slightly past middle of tail (not rising abruptly as shown in the original illustration). Testis outstretched, sometimes with double flexure near anterior end.

Larvae are about 0.4 mm long when they hatch and soon develop into slender nemas about 1.0 mm long. In this stage the developing gonads can be seen, a fact indicating that the larvae are preadults, rather than second-stage larvae as in other *Anguina*.

Fig. 7-12. Galls on leaf of *Balsamorrhiza sagittata,* produced by *Anguina bal-samophila. (After Thorne. Courtesy of Journal of Parasitology.)*

Biology: The overwintering preadults make their way to the growing point early in the spring, where they enter the tender tissues of the young leaves before the petioles are formed. As the leaves develop, they congregate in small groups of three to eight of each sex and produce large, hollow galls varying from 1 to 4 mm in length and 1 or 2 mm in height on the undersurface of the leaves. Externally the galls are a faint lavender, while internally they become purple or deep maroon. Each is filled with a vascid fluid in which the nemas lie. It is not known whether they feed on this fluid or on the contents of the enlarged cells surrounding the cavity. Small bubbles of air are always present. Egg deposition begins about three weeks after entering the leaves. Galls may be distributed over the entire leaf, but usually groups are found in the lower lobes of the leaves, where considerable distortion and frilling may occur. In rare instances the leaf may be killed by excessive infestation. Severely infested plants are sometimes reduced to one-fourth their normal size.

During July and August the leaves die, and the preadult nemas become quiescent. By spring the leaves are partly decayed and the nemas escape.

Hosts: Hosts include cutleaf balsamroot, *Balsamorrhiza macrophylla,* and mule-ears, *Wyethia amplexicaulis.* Where *B. sagittata* is predominant, *W. amplexicaulis* rarely is attacked. The reverse is true in heavy stands of *Wyethia.* Where two, or all three, hosts are prevalent, little or no host preference is displayed. Courtney found the common sunflower, *Helianthus annus,* infested in Washington state.

Galls on *Balsamorrhiza macrophylla* protrude both above and below the leaf. Those on *Wyethia amplexicaulis* are much less developed, and often the centers become dry and shrunken, giving the leaf a pock-marked appearance.

Distribution: Utah, western Colorado, Idaho, and Washington.

J. B. Goodey (1948) studied sections of *Balsamorrhiza sagittata* and found the gall cavity irregular and surrounded by an inner zone of three or four cells in depth. Some cells in this zone were collapsed, and often their contents stained deeply. Outside this zone was a layer of vascular tissue containing tracheids and phloem elements which constitute an assimilatory tissue. Then followed a layer of spongy mesophyll and palisade cells lying beneath the epidermis. Epidermal cells were more thickened than those of a normal leaf.

Anguina klebahni Goffart, 1942

This unusually small species infests the flowers of a primrose, *Primula florindae,* and was collected in Hamburg, Germany. Goffart gives the following measurements:

Morphology: ♀: 0.8–1.1 mm; a = 38–47; b = 11–14; c = 12–16; V = 69–80
♂: 1.1–1.2 mm; a = 39–47; b = 11–13; c = 13–16

Female body coiled until the ends overlap. Median esophageal bulb more than half the distance back to the intestine. Apparently no storage reservoir between basal bulb and nerve ring. Ovary with 10 or 12 cells in a circumference, extending forward to near base of esophagus.

Anguina amsinckia (Steiner and Scott, 1935) n. comb.

Synonym: *Ditylenchus dipsaci* var. *amsinckiae* Steiner and Scott, 1935
Conspicuous galls were observed on *Amsinckia intermedia* near Winters, California, by Grace M. Cole in the spring of 1930. Cole gave the specimens to C. E. Scott, who forwarded them to G. Steiner for identification. The host is one of the common plants in the interior valleys of California and subsequently infested material was collected near Napa,

Planada, and Woodland. The species is of biological interest only since the host is not economically important. The following description is from specimens collected by Scott with measurements from the original description.

Morphology: ♀ : 1.0–1.4 mm; a = 31; b = 8; c = 22; V = [7083]–91[4]

♂ : 1.0–1.3 mm; a = 30; b = 7; c = 15; T = 68

Lateral field a narrow band marked by eight minute incisures near middle of body. Lip region low and rounded. Striae near head easily visible but obscure over most of body. Spear about 10 μ long, with strong, sloping knobs. Median bulb about two-thirds as wide as neck, with prominent refractive valve. Nerve

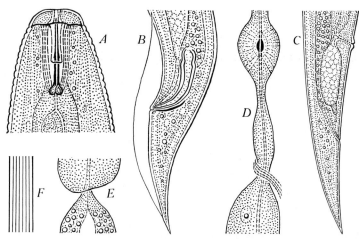

Fig. 7-13. *Anguina amsinckia.* *A*—Female head. *B, C*—Posterior portions of male and female. *D*—Esophageal region. *E*—Junction of esophagus and intestine. *F*—Lateral field. (*Specimens courtesy of C. E. Scott.*)

ring at base of elongated isthmus, which sometimes is expanded into a reservoir for accumulated salivary secretions. Esophagus connected to intestine by an obscure muscular valvular apparatus. Excretory pore about one body width posterior to nerve ring. Hemizonid not observed on the many specimens examined. Ovary usually with two flexures, the terminus frequently extending forward to the esophagus. Oöcytes in four to six lines, probably arranged about a slender rachis. Often both the elongated spermatheca and uterus are filled with spermatozoa. Eggs average about 30 by 90 μ and sometimes contain well-developed larvae before deposition. Posterior uterine branch extending two-thirds the distance to anus, a few rudimentary cells attached to its posterior end. Occasionally a few spermatozoa are present in it. Testis reflexed two to four times body width. Spicula massive, arcuate, resting on a simple, trough-like gubernaculum. Bursa usually without visible striae, extending from near terminus to a point well anterior to the spicula.

Biology: The life history of *Anguina amsinckia* has not been determined, but no doubt the immature nemas make their way to the growing point of the plant during the late winter and spring rains and enter the tissues of the stems and seed heads. Here they congregate in small groups and produce galls 5 to 10 mm long. After maturity the plants fall to the ground, where the nemas lie quiescent until revived by rains.

Anguina picridis Kir'anova, 1944

This species produces clublike galls on the stems of an orchid, *Acroptilon picris.* Morphological information not available.

Anguina poophila Kir'anova, 1952

Information on host and morphology not available.

Paranguina agropyri Kir'anova, 1955

Cuticle bearing peculiar sculptured patterns. Basal bulb of esophagus lobed.

Host: Kir'anova illustrates this species as producing gall-like swellings on quack grass, *Agropyron repens,* causing a breakdown of tissues and general destruction of the stem base.

Chapter 8

Subfamily HOPLOLAIMINAE Filipjev, 1934

Diagnosis: Tylenchidae. Sexual dimorphism of head region frequently present. Cuticle strongly striated. Lateral fields usually marked by four incisures. Labial annules often divided into numerous tilelike elements. Cephalic framework heavily sclerotized, sometimes yellowish in color. Spear massive, with strongly developed knobs. Basal portion of esophagus lobelike, extending back over intestine. Junction of esophagus and intestine an obscure valvular apparatus. Intestinal granules coarse, refractive. Ovaries two, outstretched. Spermagonium present in monosexual species. Vulva near middle of body. Female terminus hemispheroid to convex-conoid, sometimes bluntly digitate ventrally. Bursa enveloping tail. Testis outstretched. Gubernaculum bearing titillae. Ectoparasites or vagrant endoparasites of numerous plant species.

Type genus: *Hoplolaimus* Daday, 1905

Development of a posterior lobe on the base of the esophagus and the loss of a true basal bulb and cardiac valve are characteristics of the Subfamily Hoplolaiminae. Discussing this development, Steiner (1945) made the following comment:

> The loss of a distinct terminal bulb together with an increase in size of the esophageal glands appears to represent an evolutionary process related to the mode of feeding and kind of food ingested by these forms, wherein digestion is becoming partly or wholly extra-oral and is creating a correlated transformation of the intestine into a storage organ with reduced lumen and vestigial rectum.

Members of this subfamily are among the most numerous of nemic groups found about plant roots. Rarely is a sample collected which does not contain specimens of one or more species. In turf samples these nemas frequently outnumber all other species combined. They are characterized by strongly developed spears which immediately mark them as suspected plant parasites, and investigations have demonstrated that these suspicions are well founded. Usually they feed as ectoparasites, with not only the spear inserted into the root but also the anterior portion of the body. Here they remain in a sedentary position for considerable lengths of time, feeding on the contents of cells into which salivary secretions have been injected. Stained roots frequently show extensive areas into which secretions have penetrated without evident necrosis. Other species live as migratory endoparasites which destroy

182

root-cells as they feed through the tissues. Injury is characterized by stunting and gradual decline, which eventually may result in death of the host. Various species of grass in pastures, lawns, and golf courses are especially subject to attack. "Overgrazing" of pasture and range lands by livestock is often associated with nemas feeding on roots of forage plants. Losses usually are not obvious or spectacular; yet in the aggregate they reach many millions of dollars each year.

Species of Hoplolaiminae compose two natural groups which usually may be readily recognized by their typical body postures when relaxed by gentle heat. Those belonging to the genera *Hoplolaimus* and *Scutellonema* usually are straight or only slightly arcuate when relaxed. The other group assumes spiral or open C forms, which prompted Steiner to refer to them as "spiral nematodes."

The amphid apertures and four labial papillae of *Hoplolaimus* and *Scutellonema* are located just under the margin of the labial disc. In spiral forms the amphid apertures are at the apices of the lateral lips. Six papillae are grouped close about the oral opening, and an outer circlet of eight is arranged with two on each submedian lip.

Spiral species are divided into two genera. Forms in which one or more of the cephalic annules are subdivided into tiny blocks belong in *Rotylenchus*. Those in which the cephalic annules are not subdivided are grouped in *Helicotylenchus*.

Key to genera of Hoplolaiminae

1. Body usually straight when relaxed, phasmids very large.................. 2
   Body spiral in form, phasmids porelike............................... 3
2. Spear knobs compressed, forward-pointing....................*Hoplolaimus*
   Spear knobs broad, cupped or rounded.....................*Scutellonema*
3. One or more annules of lip region tiled.....................*Rotylenchus*
   Annules of lip region not tiled..........................*Helicotylenchus*

Taxonomy of Hoplolaiminae is in a most unsatisfactory state, and many adjustments must eventually be made in both genera and species. Golden (1956) presented an excellent review of spiral forms and should be consulted for information on species up to that time. Andrassy (1958) attempted to revise the taxonomy of the subfamily but failed to recognize certain important morphological characters in separating the various genera. Perry (1959) contributed important information on morphology of spiral forms and described four new species.

Only a few representative types are included herein to give the reader a survey of the various forms included in the subfamily. S. A. Sher is assembling a monograph of the entire group, which will include over sixty species.

Lance nematodes, genus *Hoplolaimus* Daday, 1905

Diagnosis: Body assuming an almost straight position when relaxed. Lip region set off by constriction, one or more of the annules subdivided into minute, tilelike elements. Cephalic framework massive, often yellowish in color. Spear with forward-pointing knobs which may be furcate. Distal position of gubernaculum protrusile, bearing titillae. Telemon present but often obscure. Phasmids unusually large, scutellumlike, sometimes located erratically along the lateral fields. Deirids not observed.

Type species: *Hoplolaimus tylenchiformis* Daday, 1905

Andrassy (1954) examined Daday's original specimen and noted that the lip region is characterized by a wide basal annule which is divided into 24 tilelike elements. Anterior to this annule are two narrower annules surmounted by the labial disc, none of which is sculptured. Measurements of Daday's specimens from an island in the Paraguay River are: ♀: 1.1 mm; a = 14; (doubtless flattened); b = 6.7; c = ?. Additional studies of the species are desirable.

Crown-headed lance nematode, *Hoplolaimus coronatus* Cobb, 1923

This species was first collected by J. R. Christie from soil about a mermis "nest" near Falls Church, Virginia. Later collections were made by the writer from the type locality and from the Arlington Experimental Farm, now buried under the Pentagon Building across the Potomac River from Washington, D.C. The following description and accompanying illustrations were made from these specimens.

Numerous collections from the Eastern and Central states indicate that considerable variation occurs, especially in head characters. The basal cephalic annule is divided into tilelike elements which range from twenty-four to forty according to specimens examined and reports of other workers. In some collections only the basal annule is tiled, while in others the entire lip region is subdivided, but not so elaborately as Cobb illustrated. Detailed studies probably will reveal that three or four species are involved in the complex.

Morphology: ♀: 1.2–1.6 mm; a = 33; b = 6.1; c = 65; V = $^{30}55^{26}$
         ♂: 1.2 mm; a = 34; b = 6.3; c = 32; T = 52

Lateral fields marked by four incisures forming three bands which are aerolated by transverse striae. Deirids and hemizonids not observed. Phasmids appearing as large depressions, with glandlike organs extending into the lateral cords. On one female the left phasmid was located at a latitude of 16 per cent, while the right was near 84 per cent. On most males the left phasmids were back near the tail, while the right were far forward, near 30 to 50 per cent. But on each sex phasmid arrangement is variable, and many other combinations of location may occur.

The sexual dimorphism mentioned by Cobb is readily recognized in the forms of the lip regions, those of the females being rather bluntly conoid, the males more spheroid. The tiling of the labial annules often involves the entire lip region of the female, while in the male only the basal annule may be divided into small hemispheroid elements. Naturally the cephalic framework is altered to accommodate the differently formed lip regions.

The amphids and apparently only four of the cephalic papillae are located beneath the edge of the labial disc, not on the outer contour of the lips as in the spiral members of the subfamily. Labial framework yellow, massive, dividing

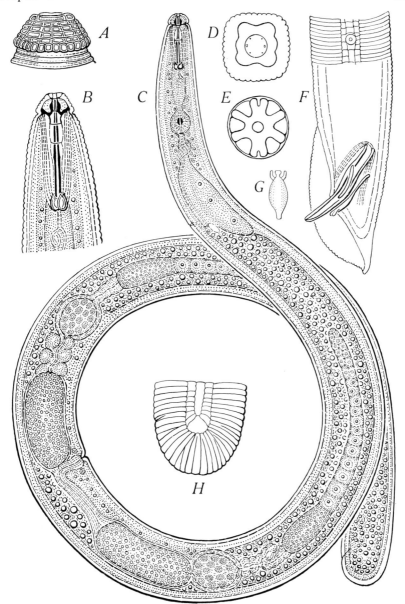

Fig. 8-1. *Hoplolaimus coronatus.* *A*—Lip region. *B*—Head. *C*—Female. *D, E* —Face view and basal plate of cephalic framework. *F*—Male tail; note anterior location of large phasmid. *G*—Gubernaculum; note titillae. *H*—Female tail.

the head into the usual six sectors, of which the lateral are smaller than the submedian. Dorsal and ventral segments of the framework somewhat duplex where they join the basal cephalic ring. In some males they may even be trifurcate, as described by Krueger and Linford (1957). Spear strongly developed, with elongate, furcate, forward-pointing knobs lying close to its base. Median esophageal bulb spheroid, basal bulb an elongated gland extending back over anterior end of intestine, usually in a dorsal position. Junction of esophageal lumen and intestine an obscure muscular valve. Intestine of female extending back into tail, completely filling the cavity. Rectum short, extending in and forward to join the ventral side of the intestine.

Ovaries outstretched, with developing oöcytes arranged as illustrated. Spermatheca spheroid, usually filled with granular spermatozoa. Testis outstretched, the spermatocytes arranged in two lines. Bursa enveloping tail. Spicula almost straight, resting on a troughlike gubernaculum which bears a typical pair of distal titillae. Telemon slightly curved, lying between the spicula and difficult to observe in many instances.

Biology: Numerous specimens of lance nematodes generally are found within the host roots and in the soil surrounding them. Soil screenings usually contain the various stages of immature forms together with adults of both sexes, the females frequently containing eggs. Steiner (1927) presented the first photographs of the species inhabiting corn roots and reported finding specimens in the roots of clover, alfalfa, sugar cane, and numerous other plants. Later (1949) he found sixty-five specimens in a 1-inch piece of root from a seedling longleaf pine and observed that during drought periods young plants were killed by nematodes combined with associated fungi and bacteria.

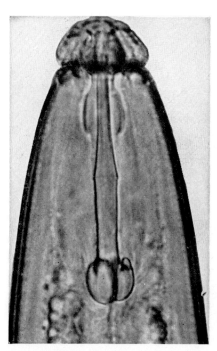

Fig. 8-2. Spear of *Hoplolaimus coronatus.* *(Photograph by H. W. Lyon. Courtesy of the Department of Plant Pathology, Cornell University.)*

Krusberg and Sasser (1956) sampled the rhizosphere of cotton plants severely infested with lance nematodes and found that 1,495 were present in each pint of soil, compared with 125 in soil from lightly infested portions of the same field. Studies on population increase in 8-inch pots under greenhouse conditions revealed that colonies of 500 specimens built up to 12,883 in 344 days (average of seven pots). However, only slight stunting was observed in young cotton plants grown in the pots. By growing seedlings in test tubes these workers were able to observe that the nemas freely moved from root to root and that both ecto- and endoparasitic feeding occurred. Brownish-yellow discoloration of the epidermal cells marked the point of penetration and attacked areas exhibiting definite lesions. Discolored cells were present along the route followed by the nemas as they traveled through the tissues.

The nemas usually were found two or three cell layers inside the epidermis, lying parallel with the longitudinal root-axis, and with the anterior end curved down into the conducting tissue. Occasionally a nema penetrated directly into the stele, leaving part of the body outside the root. Cortical damage extended one to four cells beyond the nemas, and cavities were formed where they stopped to feed. Walls of damaged cortical cells appeared to be thicker, and certain cells apparently built up a membrane across the broken area. Endodermal injury was similar to that of the cortex but less extensive. Damage was noted two to four cells from the route of the nemas, and many of these cells were killed. Stained walls of empty cells appeared to be thicker than normal. Penetration of phloem cells always occurred, and feeding took place in the parenchyma and other elements of the phloem tissues. In some cells of the phloem parenchyma, abnormal division occurred and formed cork tissue. Xylem elements were sometimes punctured, and injury also occurred in xylem elements adjacent to damaged parenchyma. The amount of affected xylem corresponded to the extent and age of nematode damage. Nematodes were not observed to penetrate entirely through the vascular tissue. Tylose production was noted in damaged cells in amounts corresponding to the age of the injury. Under severe infestation tyloses caused plugging of injured xylem elements and probably were partly responsible for stunting of the plants.

Kruger and Linford worked with a population in which females ranged from 1.6 to 2.0 mm and males from 1.4 to 1.9 mm in length. These reproduced rapidly in pots of red clover, beginning with colonies of only forty to fifty nemas. These workers observed that females and young were found more frequently within roots than were mlaes. Moulting males were dissected from roots, but most of those found feeding had only the anterior end inserted in the tissues.

Hosts and distribution: Numerous records have revealed that *Hoplolaimus coronatus* is distributed in the Atlantic coast states from New England through Florida. In the Mississippi River basin it occurs from the Gulf of Mexico north through Wisconsin and Minnesota. Distribution to the west is marked by a single collection from soil about native shrubs in the foothills west of Longmont, Colorado. S. A. Sher (1958, personal communication) reported a collection from southern California, and Goodey (1951) records young specimens from Benkvalen, Sumatra. Wherever host plants have beeen studied, the species appears to attack a wide variety of plants, ranging from grasses, grains, corn, cotton, and sugar cane to apple and pine trees.

Competitive species: Krusberg and Sasser made the interesting observation that *Meloidogyne* sp. and *Pratylenchus* sp. were present in only small numbers where *Hoplolaimus coronatus* was abundant. This fact indicates that *H. coronatus* was the dominant species and that other plant parasitic forms were unable to compete against them.

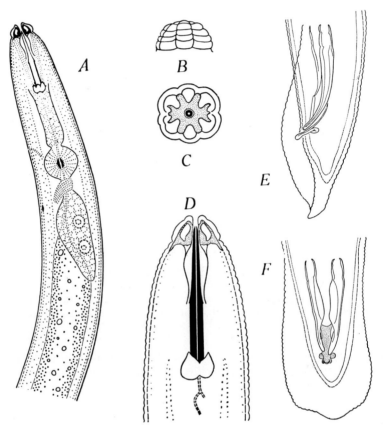

Fig. 8-3. *Hoplolaimus proporicus.* *A*—Anterior portion of body. *B*—Cuticle pattern of lip region. *C*—Basal cephalic framework. *D*—Head in saggital section. *E, F*—Male tail in lateral and ventral views. (*After J. B. Goodey, Nematologica. Courtesy of E. J. Brill.*)

Hoplolaimus proporicus J. B. Goodey, 1957a

Morphology: ♀: 1.0–1.6 mm; a = 25–35; b = 5.7–9.7; c = 49–164; V = 55–59
♂: 1.0 mm; a = 31; b = 6.5; c = 34

Lateral fields absent, annules extending completely around body. Phasmids similar to those of *Hoplolaimus coronatus,* erratically located. Lip region divided into six sections by longitudinal striae, but the elements are not subdivided into tilelike blocks. Amphid apertures minute, slitlike, located at outer edge of lateral lips. Lateral sectors of cephalic framework much narrower than submedian. Dorsal and ventral elements of cephalic framework trifurcate. Spear 41 μ long, with typical, forward-pointing knobs. Excretory pore located nearly opposite anterior end of median esophageal bulb; hence the specific name *proporicus*. Hemizonids about one neck width posterior to latitude of excretory pore. Intestine and reproductive system similar to those illustrated for *H. coronatus*. Female tails varying from bluntly spheroid to bluntly conoid. Bursa and spicula typical. Gubernaculum with titillae and a thickened transverse element, the entire organ being of an unusual and rather complicated form.

Hosts and distribution: This species was found in decaying roots of oil palm seedlings, *Elaeus guineensis* Jacq., from the Cameroons, West Africa. Later it was found infesting the same species and also *E. melanococca* Gaertn. in Nigeria. Nemas were present in lateral roots, not in advancing borders of the lesions. Apparently the species was not involved with the disease known as "blast" from which the trees were suffering.

Genus *Scutellonema* Andrassy, 1958

Diagnosis: Sexual dimorphism present, the female head being bluntly conoid, while that of the male is more spheroid. Lateral fields aerolated, especially near the extremities. Phasmids scutellumlike, located near latitude of anus. Deirids not observed. Lip region quadrangular, the annules plain. Amphid apertures and four papillae located just under margin of labial disc. Dorsal and ventral sectors of cephalic ring bifurcate. Esophageal glands only slightly overlapping anterior end of intestine. Ovaries outstretched, with spermatheca in the uterine branches. Spicula slightly arcuate, resting on a troughlike gubernaculum bearing titillae similar to those of *Hoplolaimus* and *Rotylenchus*. Bursa enveloping tail.

Type species: *Scutellonema blaberum* (Steiner, 1937) Andrassy, 1958
Location of the amphid apertures and labial papillae and highly developed phasmids indicate a close relationship of *Scutellonema* to *Hoplolaimus*.

Scutellonema blaberum (Steiner, 1937) Andrassy, 1958

Synonym: *Rotylenchus blaberus* Steiner

Morphology: ♀: 0.95 mm; a = 28; b = 7.4; c = 26–33; V = 57
♂: 0.85 mm; a = 29; b = 4.8; c = 29
Body cylindroid except at extremities. Lateral fields aerolated near latitude of neck base and on tail. Female phasmid smaller than that of male, located anterior to latitude of anus. Male phasmid much larger than that of female, located on anterior portion of tail. Lip region distinctly set off, marked by seven or eight annules which are not divided into sections. Cephalic framework sclerotized, refractive. Stylet strongly developed, 28 μ long, with large, forward-pointing knobs. Basal portion of esophagus not extending back over intestine. Gubernaculum distally folded, doubtless with titillae as in *Scutellonema bradys*. Bursa enveloping the irregularly conoid, slightly arcuate tail.

Host and distribution: Yams, *Dioscorea* sp., intercepted at Boston, Massachusetts, were 50 per cent infested with *Scutellonema blaberum*.

Symptoms: Bright yellow spots about ¼ inch deep contained numerous females, males, and larvae.

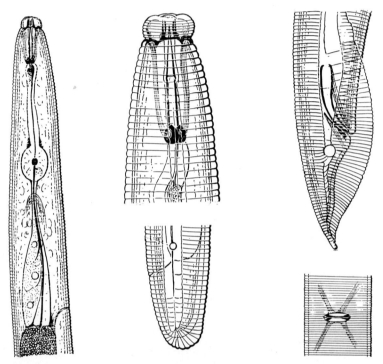

Fig. 8-4. *Scutellonema blaberum.* *A*—Anterior portion. *B*—Head. *C*—Detail of lateral field on neck. *D, E*—Female tails showing variations in position of phasmids. *F*—Female tail in sinistroventrosubmedial view. *G*—Vulva. *H*—Posterior portion of male. (*After Steiner. Courtesy of Helminthological Society of Washington.*)

Scutellonema bradys (Steiner & LeHew, 1933) Andrassy, 1958

Synonyms: *Hoplolaimus bradys* Steiner & LeHew; *Anguillulina bradys* (Steiner & LeHew) Goodey, 1935a; *Rotylenchus bradys* (Steiner & LeHew) Filipjev, 1936

Morphology: ♀: 1.2 mm; a = 27; b = 10; c = 39; V = 58
　　　　　　 ♂: 1.0 mm; a = 30; b = 9; c = 40

Body cylindroid except near extremities. Lateral fields aerolated. Female phasmids slightly anterior to latitude of anus, those of male somewhat posteriad. Female lip region bluntly conoid, that of male more spheroid and distinctly set off. Female lip region marked by seven or eight annules which are not divided into elements. Male lips with six annules. Cephalic framework strongly sclerotized, lateral sectors considerably smaller than the submedian. The minute amphid apertures and four labial papillae apparently lie just beneath the margin of the labial disc. Stylet very strong, averaging 27 μ long, with broad, cupped basal knobs. Dorsal esophageal gland outlet close to base of spear. Hemizonid obscure, five or six annules anterior to excretory pore. Lobes of esophagus extending but little over anterior end of intestine. Ovaries outstretched, with spheroid spermatheca. Female intestine extending into tail cavity. Rectum attached ventrally to intestine as in *Hoplolaimus coronatus*. Bursa enveloping tail. Spicula slightly arcuate, resting on a cephalated and reflexed gubernaculum bearing titillae similar to those of *H. coronatus*.

Host and distribution: Yams, *Dioscorea* sp., Jamaica, West Indies. Goodey (1935a) recorded infested yams introduced into England.

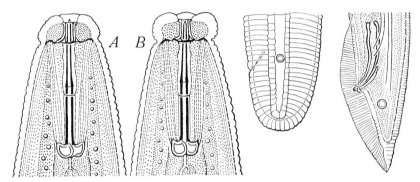

Fig. 8-5. *Scutellonema bradys. A*—Female head. *B*—Male head.

Symptoms: Brownish discolored areas extended throughout the tuber in which the nemas were present in great numbers.

Genus *Rotylenchus* Filipjev, 1936

Diagnosis: Hoplolaiminae. Usually assuming a somewhat spiral form when relaxed by gradual heat. Lateral fields with little or no aerolation. Phasmids small, located near latitude of anus. One or more labial annules tiled or divided into sectors. Spear with broad, spreading knobs. Basal esophageal lobes variable in form and size. Female gonads outstretched, with spermatheca. Bursa enveloping tail. Gubernaculum cephalated and bearing titillae.

Type species: *Rotylenchus robustus* (deMan, 1876) Filipjev, 1936
Rotylenchus represents a group of species with morphological characters of both *Hoplolaimus* and *Helicotylenchus*. The small, regularly placed phasmids of *Helicotylenchus* combined with the tiled labial annules of *Hoplolaimus* constitute the chief diagnostic features.

Rotylenchus robustus (deMan, 1876) Filipjev, 1936

Synonyms: *Tylenchus robustus* deMan, 1876; *Hoplolaimus uniformis* Thorne, 1949. Not *Anguillulina robusta* (deMan) Goodey, 1932b
The involved nomenclature of this species was clarified by Loof and

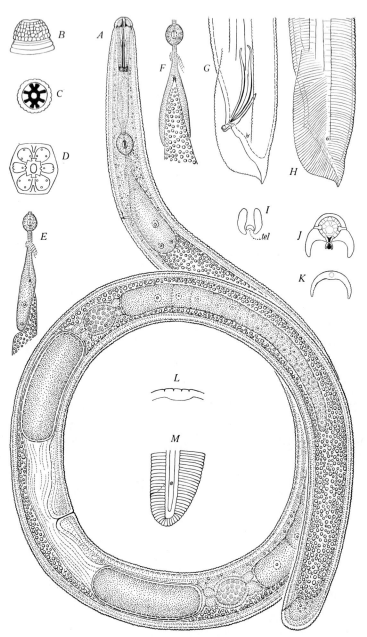

Fig. 8-6. *Rotylenchus robustus.* *A*—Female. *B*—Lip region. *C*—Basal plate of cephalic framework. *D*—Face view. *E*—Esophageal glands of young female. *F*—Right side of gland region shown in (*A*). *G, H*—Structures of male tail. *I*—Section through spicula and telemon. *J*—Section through anal region of male, showing gubernaculum and phasmids. *K*—Section through bursa near terminus. *L*—Section through lateral field. *M*—More conoid type of female tail. (*After Thorne. Courtesy of Helminthological Society of Washington.*)

Oostenbrink (1957). Thorne (1949) erroneously described it as *Hiplolaimus uniformis.* His description was based on specimens collected by J. W. Seinhorst near Goree, Netherlands. Oostenbrink (1954) added considerable information on the species from specimens assembled from other parts of that country.

Morphology: ♀: 1.4 mm; a = 31; b = 7.1; c = 80–120; V = $^{32}54^{30}$

♂: 1.4 mm; a = 38; b = 7.5; c = 49; T = 53

Body assuming a somewhat coiled position when relaxed by gradual heat. Lateral fields marked by four incisures. The bands between them sometimes marked by the transverse striae. Sexual dimorphism of head similar to that found in *Hoplolaimus.* Deirids not observed; hemizonid slightly anterior to excretory pore. Phasmids porelike. Lip region set off by constriction, the labial annules usually divided into tiny blocks. A face view reveals the full complement of 6 and 10 cephalic papillae. Amphids located at outer contour of lateral lips. Cephalic framework massive, yellowish. Stylet 40 to 50 µ long, the knobs slightly cupped. Esophagus base an enlarged, variable-sized lobe extending back over the anterior end of the intestine, its lumen ending in an obscure muscular valvular apparatus. Female gonads outstretched, each with a spermatheca. Bursa enveloping tail. Spicula slightly arcuate, resting on a cephalated gubernaculum bearing titillae. An obscure telemon lies between the spicula.

Hosts and distribution: *Rotylenchus robustus* is an ectoparasitic species feeding on the roots of various plants, although little is known of its actual host range. The economic importance of this species was first recognized by Seinhorst (1954), who demonstrated that it produced severe injury to peas. This was characterized by reduced and decayed roots, a condition accompanied by extreme stunting of top growth. Slootweg (1956) found *R. robustus* associated with lesions on the roots of *Lilium speciosum* var. *rubrum.* As the old roots died, the young ones developed lesions which coalesced to form necrotic areas, and many adventitious roots were produced. A fungus, *Cylindrocarpon radicicola,* apparently was a secondary organism following the nemas. Kuiper and Drijfhout (1957) reported a destructive disease of carrots characterized by a severe reduction in roots and stunting of top growth which definitely was associated with *R. robustus.*

In the United States *Rotylenchus robustus* has been found in Rhode Island, in New Jersey, on Long Island, New York, and near San Francisco, California. Slight morphological differences are found in the various populations, but these are not of sufficient importance to justify establishing new species. Stylet lengths vary from an average of 40 to 50 µ in populations from the Netherlands to 45 µ on Long Island and 50 µ in New Jersey. Body lengths and proportions vary in a somewhat similar manner.

Rotylenchus goodeyi (Goodey, 1932b) Loof and Oostenbrink, 1958

Synonyms: *Anguillulina robusta* Goodey, 1932b; *Rotylenchus robustus* Filipjev and Stekhoven, 1941, and Thorne, 1949, Goodey, 1951, and Golden, 1956; *Gottholdsteineri goodeyi* (Goodey) Andrassy, 1958

Little is known of the biology of this species, but like other *Rotylenchus* it doubtless is ectoparasitic on the roots of various plants with which it is associated. Pathogenicity has not been demonstrated.

Morphology: ♀: 1.0–1.2 mm; a = 34; b = 7; c = 50–60; V = $^{3254-63}28$
   ♂: 0.8–1.0 mm; a = 25; b = 6.1; c = 40–50; T = 40

Lateral field marked by four incisures. Female tail hemispheroid to slightly convex-conoid. Deirids not observed. Hemizonid located just anterior to

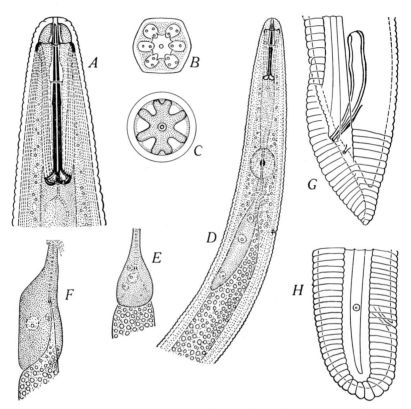

Fig. 8-7. *Rotylenchus goodeyi.* *A–C*—Head, face view, and basal cephalic framework. *D*—Anterior end. *E, F*—Variations in basal esophageal lobes. *G*— Male tail. *H*—Female tail somewhat longer than usual. (*After Thorne. Courtesy of Helminthological Society of Washington.*)

excretory pore. Phasmids of both sexes usually slightly anterior to latitude of anus. Lip region marked by four striae. From a face view the amphid apertures are visible as minute pores on the outer margin of the lateral lips, while the papillae consist of an inner circlet of six and an outer circlet of eight. Cephalic framework strongly sclerotized, the dorsal and ventral sectors of the basal plate being slightly furcate. Stylet averaging about 30 μ long, with knobs sloping backward. Dorsal esophageal gland outlet near the base of stylet. Basal lobe or esophagus variable in size, usually in a dorsal or subdorsal position. Oöcytes in tandem except for a short region of multiplication. Testis outstretched. Spicula slightly arcuate, resting on a trough-shaped gubernaculum which is reflexed ventrally at its terminus. Bursa enveloping tail, the cuticular striae forming a crenate margin.

Distribution: Several species are probably represented in reports from many countries, and only extensive collecting and detailed studies will clarify the taxonomy.

Spiral nematodes, genus *Helicotylenchus* Steiner, 1945

Synonym: *Gottholdsteineria* Andrassy, 1958

Diagnosis: Tylenchinae. Body usually in an arcuate or spiral form. Lip region annulated. Body annules coarse, continued around the contour of the tail. Lateral fields marked by prominent incisures, the bands between them sometimes aerolated. Deirids not observed. Phasmids usually anterior to latitude of anus, although occasionally near middle of tail. Labial framework strongly sclerotized. Amphids and labial papillae visible only from a face view. Stylet 20 μ or longer, with strongly developed knobs. Outlet of dorsal esophageal gland located from near stylet base to one-half the stylet length behind the spear in *Helicotylenchus nannus*. Median esophageal bulb spheroid. Basal bulb an elongated gland extending dorsally over anterior end of intestine, frequently variable in size. Junction of esophagus and intestine an obscure muscular valve. Females amphidelphic, the oöcytes usually arranged in tandem except for a short region of multiplication. Monosexual species with spermagonium and small spermatheca adjacent to uterine valve. Bursa enveloping tail. Spicula arcuate, resting on a slightly curved gubernaculum which distally may be thickened or recurved.

Type species: *Helicotylenchus nannus* Steiner, 1945
Helicotylenchus includes about fifteen known species which are ecto-parasitic on the roots and underground parts of plants. So numerous are they that a pound of soil from about the roots of almost any plant will usually contain specimens of one or more species. These nemas are especially prevalent in lawns, golf greens, pastures, meadows, and range grazing lands. The common field and vegetable crops, as well as ornamental shrubs, fruit and forest trees, and even weeds, serve as hosts.

Golden (1956) and Perry (1958) have made the principal contribution to our knowledge of the life history, distribution, host relationship, and morphology of the spiral nemas. By following their methods, demonstration of pathogenicity for other species should be merely a matter of routine. An extensive synonomy of species names in the genus is recorded by Golden (1956) and Andrassy (1958).

Helicotylenchus nannus Steiner, 1945

Morphology: ♀: 0.6 mm; a = 24; b = 6; c = 39; V = 64
Body usually forming an open spiral. Lateral fields marked by four incisures, the bands between them not aerolated. Phasmids very small, well forward of anal latitude. Tail with 9 or 10 annules ventrally. Lip region marked by three striae. Cephalic framework well sclerotized. Stylet 26 to 28 μ long. Position

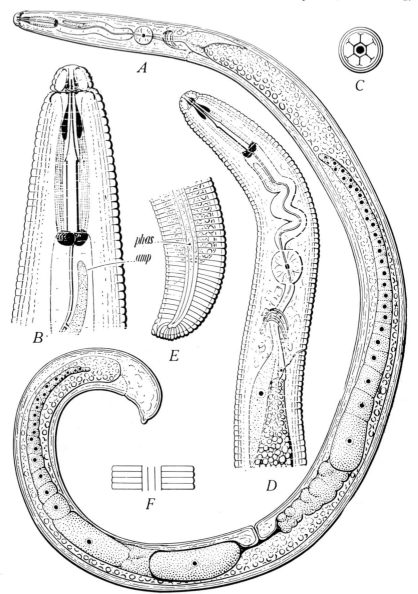

Fig. 8-8. *Helicotylenchus nannus.* *A*—Female. *B*—Head. *C*—Face view. *D*—Anterior end. *E*—Female tail. *F*—Lateral field. (*After Steiner. Courtesy of Helminthological Society of Washington.*)

of dorsal esophageal gland outlet a conspicuous feature, being 8 to 14 μ behind stylet. Basal portion of esophagus overlapping intestine. Junction of esophageal lumen and intestine an obscure muscular valve. Females amphidelphic, both ovaries outstretched, usually on same side of intestine. Uteri with spermagonia.

Hosts and distribution: *Helicotylenchus nannus* was first collected from the roots of lima beans in a greenhouse at Beltsville, Maryland. Later it was found associated with the roots of a number of different species of plants throughout the Southern states and as far north as Wisconsin. Pathogenicity has not been demonstrated.

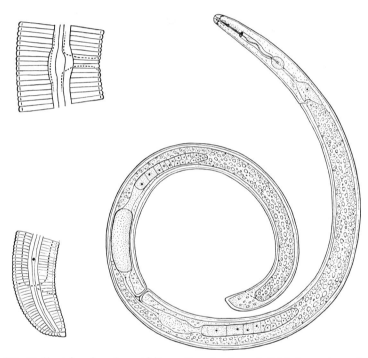

Fig. 8-9. *Helicotylenchus buxophilus.* Female, lateral field in region of vulva, female tail. (*After Golden. Courtesy of University of Maryland Experiment Station.*)

Helicotylenchus buxophilus (Golden, 1956) Perry, 1959a

Synonyms: *Rotylenchus buxophilus* Golden, 1956; *Gottholdsteineri buxophilus* (Golden) Andrassy, 1958

Morphology: ♀: 1.1 mm; a = 31; b = 7.0; c = 43; V = $^{26}65^{25}$

Lateral fields marked by the usual four incisures, which are much wider for a short distance opposite the vulva. Phasmid about one body width anterior to latitude of anus. Tail dorsally convex-conoid, with 13 annules on ventral side according to Golden's figure. Annules of subcuticle only half as wide as those on cuticle. Lip region bearing 5 annules. Stylet 33.5 μ long, with strong, rounded basal knobs. Hemizonid just anterior to excretory pore. Esophagus, gonads, and other organs typical of the genus. Perry (1959) found spermagonia present in the gonads.

Golden was the first to establish definitely the economic importance of spiral nematodes by demonstrating pathogenicity of this species on boxwood. Previously, only random observations had been made of occasional specimens found attached to roots.

Biology: Golden found five stages in the life history of *Helicotylenchus buxophilus:* The eggs, in which the larvae developed to a length of 264 μ and grew to 414 μ before the first moult; two more moults, when the larvae were 620 and 936 μ long; the adult stage, in which an average length of 1.088 mm was attained. Except when moulting, the nemas at all stages were capable of attacking the host.

Experiments in 6-inch pots demonstrated that in one year 250 specimens introduced about the roots of young boxwood built up to a population of 9,300. Numerous individuals were found attached to the smaller roots, and points of entrance were marked by tiny brown necrotic pits and lesions. Feeding usually was accomplished by inserting only the stylet, but in some instances the anterior end of the nema was forced into the root to a depth of five or six cells. Actual feeding damaged the roots by destroying the cells, injection of digestive secretions, and removal of cells' contents. Invading secondary fungi and bacteria probably were responsible for further injury after the nemas moved to new locations on the roots.

Hosts and distribution: English boxwood, strawberry, privet, tomato, lima bean, and rye were favorable hosts for the boxwood populations of *Helicotylenchus buxophilus.* Azalea and rose failed to maintain large numbers of the nemas. Golden's survey of Maryland revealed infestations of *H. buxophilus* in fourteen counties. During this survey barberry and peony were also found infested. Boxwood from Pennsylvania, South Carolina, West Virginia, and Virginia was found infested. One sample of barberry from Kentucky was infested.

Control: Soil fumigants are effective under ordinary conditions and may be used for protection of annual crops. However, boxwood, privet, and other perennials present more difficult problems, which may be alleviated to a certain extent by dichlorobromopropene fumigants when properly applied.

Helicotylenchus digonicus Perry, 1959

Morphology: ♀: 0.6–0.7 mm; a = 23–25; b = 4.7–5.9; c = 53–70; V = $^{31}62^{25}$
Body widest in vulvar region, tapering toward the extremities. Lateral field marked by four incisures. Phasmids porelike, two to four annules anterior to latitude of anus. Tail dorsally convex-conoid to a pointed terminus, but occasionally bluntly rounded. Lip region continuous with body contour, marked by three or four annules. Amphid apertures at outer margins of lateral lips. Cephalic papillae consisting of six grouped about the oral opening and an outer circlet of eight, two on each submedian lip. Stylet 25 to 29 μ long, with

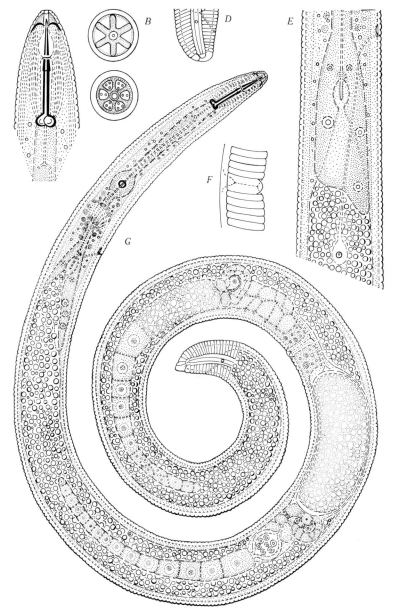

Fig. 8-10. *Helicotylenchus digonicus. (After Perry. Courtesy of University of Wisconsin Experiment Station.)*

200   *Principles of Nematology*

rounded basal knobs. Outlet of dorsal esophageal gland well behind spear
knobs, o = 32–36. Hemizonid adjacent to excretory pore. Base of esophagus
a flattened lobe extending back past anterior end of intestine, in either a right
or a left subventral position. Junction of esophageal lumen and intestine
an obscure chamber operated by a minute sphincter muscle. Small lateral vulvar
flaps present. Ovaries outstretched, the oöcytes usually in single file. Anterior
ovary rarely reflexed one or two times. Spermagonium present in each uterus.

Perry's identification of the spermagonium was an interesting contribution to our knowledge of egg fertilization in monosexual *Helicotylenchus*. Production of comparatively large, normal-appearing spermatozoa
in this organ constitutes a very definite instance of digonic hermaphroditism. Apparently this organ is unique for *Helicotylenchus* or has
been overlooked in other genera.

Biology: Pastures, lawns, and golf courses in southern Wisconsin frequently exhibit symptoms of decline and dying during the period between late June and early September. Symptoms are especially evident
in plantings of Kentucky bluegrass, *Poa pratense* L., and occur so frequently that the condition is commonly known as "summer dormancy."
Characteristic symptoms are thin stands with pale, slender or dying
leaves and with short, discolored dead roots. While investigating nematode populations from these fields, Perry (1959) found that *Helicotylenchus digonicus* frequently was the dominant plant parasitic species
present.

Nemas were found overwintering in the top 2 to 4 inches of soil, which
usually freezes to a depth of 2 feet or more during the winter. All stages
of the life cycle were present except gravid females. With the advent of
spring, plants began producing new roots, and on these the nemas rapidly increased to enormous numbers. While temperatures were cool and
moisture was abundant, no injury was apparent. However, examination
frequently revealed specimens of *Helicotylenchus digonicus,* their heads
penetrating into roots. Occasionally, the entire body was observed
within the cortical cells and phloem elements. Resultant damage was
evident in discolored spots which frequently involved entire roots, a
condition causing severe stunting or death. Often the cortex hung loosely
about the shrunken root.

With high temperatures and reduced moisture the plants rapidly declined and crab grass, white clover, and other plants often obscured the
bluegrass. Destruction of roots brought starvation to the nematodes,
and by the end of the summer populations were drastically reduced. Fall
rains and lower temperatures were again favorable for growth, and
plants were in good condition when freezing temperatures returned. By
this time nemic populations were well established and went into dormancy to await return of spring.

Histological sections revealed that after penetrating the epidermis the
nemas first fed on cortical cells. As these tissues were destroyed, they
penetrated deeper and finally reached the central cylinder, where they

fed on phloem and perhaps xylem elements. Nemas were especially numerous in areas where the cortex had sloughed off, a fact indicating that they preferred cells of the central cylinder. Invasion of sacrophagus nemas, fungi, and bacteria into the lesions doubtless accelerated final root destruction.

Helicotylenchus digonicus frequently was found floating on screen residues after soil samples had been processed. In some instances it was possible to secure almost pure populations by merely pouring off the top portion of the beaker. Other species of *Helicotylenchus* and *Tylenchorhynchus* often may be collected in a similar manner.

Hosts and distribution: In addition to Kentucky bluegrass, corn and beans maintained colonies of *Helicotylenchus digonicus*. However, neither of these crops was visibly injured.

Control: Applications of emulsified VC-13 and Nemagon applied as drenches gave marked improvement in growth. In mixed lawns Kentucky bluegrass remained dominant throughout the summer, while in adjacent control areas white clover almost submerged the weakened infested grass plants. Applications of PRD severely injured grass for two or three weeks, but after this period recovery was rapid and growth comparable with that on other fumigated plots. In one instance, evidence of partial control existed in the third summer, especially on the Nemagon plot. Under field conditions, applications of EDB may almost eradicate spiral nemas, according to Nusbaum (1955).

Helicotylenchus erythrinae (Zimmermann, 1904) Golden, 1956

Synonyms: *Tylenchus erythrinae,* Zimmermann, 1904; *Tylenchus pseudorobustus* Steiner, 1914; *Aphelenchus dubius* var. *peruensis* Steiner, 1920; *Tylenchus spiralis* Cassiday, 1930; *Tylenchorhynchus robustus* var. *erythrinae* (Zimmermann) Bally and Reydon, 1931; *Anguillulina multicincta* (Cobb) Schuurmans-Stekhoven and Tenuissen, 1938; *Anguillulina erythrinae* (Zimmermann) Goodey, 1951 (in part)

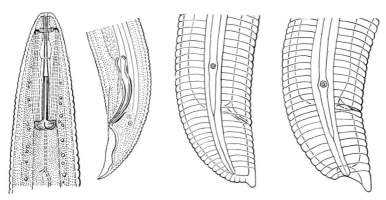

Fig. 8-11. *Helicotylenchus erythrinae.* *(From Java specimens.)*

Morphology: ♀ : 0.7 mm; a = 30; b = 5.6–7.0; c = 35–50; V = ^{26}66$3^{18}$
                      ♂ : 0.5 mm; a = 28; b = 4.2; c = 25; T = 37

Body usually forming at least one complete spiral. Lateral field marked by the usual four incisures. Phasmid 8 to 12 annules anterior to latitude of anus. Tail variably digitate. Lip region continuous with body contour, marked by 4 or 5 annules. Cephalic framework strongly sclerotized. Spear 22 to 24 μ long, with slightly cupped knobs one-third as wide as base of head, o = 35–37. Median bulb ovoid, about one-third neck width. Hemizonid adjacent to excretory pore. Basal portion of esophagus extended in flattened lobes. A conspicuous spherical spermatheca present in each uterus. Bursa crenate, rising about opposite middle of spicula and enveloping the conoid, arcuate tail. Male head less conspicuously striated, and spear knobs not so strongly developed as those of female.

The above description is based on specimens collected at various points on Java. Other species of *Helicotylenchus* are present on that island, but the above forms appear to correspond most closely to Zimmermann's description.

Helicotylenchus erythrinae represents a large group of closely related species which are found in large numbers throughout the world. Intensive collecting and careful analysis of specimens will probably reveal that some of forms placed in synonymy are valid species.

Hosts and distribution: Zimmermann described this species from specimens associated with roots of dadap, *Erythrina lithosperma* Blume, in Java. It also commonly occurs about the roots of coffee, cloves, corn, tobacco, rice, and numerous other plants in that country. Doubtless it is cosmopolitan in distribution.

Chapter 9

Subfamily PRATYLENCHINAE Thorne, 1949

Diagnosis: Tylenchidae. Lip region one-half to three-fifths as wide as spear length, frequently low, flattened. Tails at least twice as long as anal body diameter, except in *Nacobbus* and *Rotylenchulus*, and in these two genera the females are saccate and reniform, respectively. Bursa enveloping tail. Phasmids located well behind latitude of anus. Deirids rarely observed. Spear strong with well-developed knobs. Median esophageal bulb spheroid. Basal portion of esophagus consisting of an elongated lobe extending back over anterior end of intestine. These glandular lobes vary in form and position and contain three large esophageal gland nuclei. Ovaries one or two.

Type genus: *Pratylenchus* Filipjev, 1934

Pratylenchinae includes those rather broad-headed plant parasitic nemas which form a very natural group because of the close similarities of the larval stages and of the structures of the heads, spears, esophagi, and male tails. However, there are divergent characteristics which eventually may necessitate raising the group to family rank and separating such aberrant genera as *Nacobbus* and *Rotylenchulus* from the more simple forms like *Pratylenchus* and *Radopholus*. Extensive collecting, especially in the tropics, should reveal more genera and numerous species of this subfamily.

Key to genera of Pratylenchinae

1. Female a typical active nema.. 2
   Female greatly enlarged, saccate.................................. 4
2. Two ovaries present.......................................*Radopholus*
   One ovary present... 3
3. Female tail bluntly rounded...........................*Pratylenchus*
   Female tail ending in a point.....................*Chitinotylenchus*
4. Female with one ovary and elongated posterior.................*Nacobbus*
   Female reniform, with two ovaries......................*Rotylenchulus*

Root-lesion nematodes, genus *Pratylenchus* Filipjev, 1934 [1]

Historical: *Pratylenchus* species were first described by various workers as members of the genus *Tylenchus,* and in this classification they remained until Goffart (1929) and Goodey (1932b) assigned them to *Anguillulina* in accordance with the taxonomic revision of Baylis and

---

[1] Members of this genus are also sometimes known as "meadow nematodes."

Daubney (1926). When Filipjev (1934) established the genus *Pratylenchus* for their reception, some investigators immediately accepted the validity and convenience of this action, while others continued to recognize *Anguillulina*. The many synonyms resulting from these transfers are recorded in detail by Sher and Allen (1953).

Bastian (1865) was the first to observe a member of this group and described it as *Tylenchus obtusus*. His description and figures indicate a typical *Pratylenchus*, with plump body about 0.87 mm long and with a broad head, short strong stylet with large basal knobs, single anterior ovary, and short, bluntly rounded tail. Unfortunately, the identity of this species remains unknown because Bastian's description is inadequate for purposes of specific identification, and additional collections have not been made from the type locality near Broadmoor, Berkshire, England.

DeMan (1880) described *Tylenchus pratensis*, = *Pratylenchus pratensis*, from specimens collected near Leiden, Netherlands, and later (1884) recorded its presence in a meadow near Sydenham, England. In his 1884 paper he included a full-length drawing of a female and illustrated certain diagnostic characters which made it possible to identify the group to which the species belonged. However, deMan failed to record the number of annules on the lip region, the lobelike base of the esophagus, and details of the spear, male tail, and lateral fields by which the species could definitely be determined. T. Goodey collected specimens near Sydenham from which the writer (1949) emended the generic and specific diagnoses.

Zimmermann (1898) first recognized that nemas of this group were of economic importance when he discovered *Tylenchus coffeae*, = *Pratylenchus coffeae*, severely infesting coffee roots in Java. Description of the species was supplemented by an account of the symptoms produced and illustrations of stages in the life cycle. Zimmermann also made the first demonstration of *Pratylenchus* pathogenicity by growing young coffee plants in both infested and clean soil.

Cobb (1917) described *Tylenchus penetrans*, = *Pratylenchus penetrans*, and reported that this species attacked potato tubers and the roots of cotton, camphor, and violets. However, Cobb had a mixed collection, and while his description refers to *T penetrans*, his illustration shows a species which Steiner (1943a) named *P. scribneri*. This illustration by Chambers gave us our first detailed study of the morphology of the genus. Cobb next (1919) reported *T. musicola*, = *P. coffeae*, as a parasite of banana roots sent to him from Barbados, West Indies.

Rensch (1924a) failed to recognize the proper genus for specimens which he found in the roots of cereals and numerous other plants in Germany and described them as *Aphelenchus neglectus*. Loof (1957) again collected specimens, reestablished the species name as *Pratylenchus neglectus*, and stated that it closely resembles *P. minyus*.

Steiner (1927) reviewed the works of Cobb and Rensch and decided that *Aphelenchus neglectus* and *Tylenchus penetrans* were synonyms of

Pratylenchus pratensis. Steiner emphasized that this species was a widespread and economically important plant parasite. In his paper he presented photographs showing nemas within the roots of lily of the valley, wheat, rye, and cotton. These constitute our first photographic records of *Pratylenchus* inhabiting and depositing eggs in root tissues.

Godfrey (1929) described *Tylenchus brachyurus*, = *Pratylenchus brachyurus*, as the causal agent of a destructive disease of pineapples and other plants in Hawaii. His detailed account of the etiology of this disease was a good contribution to our knowledge of the nature of the damage done to root-tissues by nemas of this genus.

Thorne (1934) wrote of a severe root-rot of figs near Merced, California, produced by *Anguillulina pratensis*, = *Pratylenchus vulnus*. Ark and Thomas (1936) recorded *A. pratensis*, probably *P. penetrans*, attacking roots of apple trees near Sebastopol, California.

Between 1936 and 1953 numerous papers appeared on *Anguillulina pratensis* and *Pratylenchus pratensis*, but in most instances the actual identity of the nemas remains unknown. Among the most valuable contributions are those of Hastings (1939) on life history and Gadd and Loos (1941a, 1941b, 1941c) on life cycle and biology.

Jensen (1950) wrote a dissertation (unpublished) on the biology and morphology of a root-lesion nematode attacking walnut roots in California. Allen and Jensen (1951) compared Jensen's species with specimens from sites where other species had been reported in the state, concluded that only one form was involved in most instances, and named it *Pratylenchus vulnus*. Their measurements of numerous specimens indicated that far more variations in size and body proportion occur than had previously been recorded for a single species.

Confusion in the nomenclature of *Pratylenchus* was largely eliminated by Sher and Allen (1953). In this outstanding work they compiled all pertinent data on the genus and revised the taxonomy. Diagnoses of seven species previously described were emended and three new species added to the genus. This contribution made it possible to determine these ten species with a good degree of accuracy. However, the group is difficult taxonomically and requires intensive study before proficiency in identification can be achieved.

Since 1953 *Pratylenchus* has attracted the attention of numerous workers, and many observations have been published on distribution, hosts, biology, and control. Outstanding among these papers have been the works of Mountain in Canada and Oostenbrink and his associates in the Netherlands. Extensive collecting has revealed that geographical variants occur among certain species which fail to conform to each detail of the original diagnosis, a fact complicating the problem of identification in many instances.

Association with fungi and bacteria: *Pratylenchus* frequently make the initial openings in roots through which plant pathogenic fungi and bacteria enter. The combined action of these associated organisms produces conspicuous lesions, and this effect prompted Godfrey (1929) to propose the descriptive name "root-lesion nematodes." However, it is not unusual to find considerable numbers of *Pratylenchus* in root-tissues without evidence of necrosis. Delicate, succulent roots are very susceptible to mass invasion and often die before definite lesions are produced. Injury to apples, prunes, cherries, walnuts, and other woody perennials may be largely confined to the smaller roots and frequently is accompanied by the production of masses of fibrous dead and dying roots. Perhaps the most extreme examples of lesion formation are those produced on fig roots by *P. vulnus*. In one instance, roots up to 3 inches in diameter were completely severed, and so extensive was the damage that trees several inches in diameter could be pushed over.

Although this obvious association of *Pratylenchus* and other organisms must have been noted by Zimmermann, Cobb, Steiner, and others, the first reference is that of Godfrey (1929), who observed unidentified fungi and bacteria in lesions produced by *P. brachyurus*.

Ark and Thomas (1936) found *Pseudomonas fluorescens* and another unidentified bacterium associated with *Anguillulina pratensis,* probably *Pratylenchus penetrans,* in apple roots near Sebastopol, California. They demonstrated that, unless *Pratylenchus* was present, young apple seedlings when experimentally inoculated did not become infected by the bacterium. Hildebrand and Koch (1936) emphasized the importance of this genus of nemas in the root-rot complex of strawberry and tobacco in Canada.

Hastings and Bosher (1938) found *Anguillulina pratensis,* = *Pratylenchus penetrans* (Bosher, personal communication, 1958), and a fungus, *Cylindrocarpon radicicola,* in lesions on the roots of narcissus, strawberry, apple, cherry, and raspberry in British Columbia. When freed from the fungus, the nemas reduced the growth of potato, carrot, red clover, tomato, spinach, and violet seedlings by 50 to 75 per cent, and oat seedlings by less than 4 per cent. In similar experiments with the fungus only, growth was reduced by 6 to 11 per cent. Reduction of growth by nematodes and fungus combined was usually greater than the sum of the losses caused by pure colonies of both organisms.

Association of *Pratylenchus* spp. with brown root-rot of tobacco has been noted by several investigators; yet no plant pathogenic fungus or bacterium has been consistently found accompanying the nemas. Graham (1951) in South Carolina found *P. zeae* and *P. brachyurus* in brown rot lesions and decided that they were the causal agents. He also noted that incidence of rot was influenced by temperature; slight to moderate injury from 60 to 70°F, moderate to severe from 70 to 80°F, and severe at 90°F. Mountain (1954) found *P. minyus* abundant in the tobacco fields of southern Ontario, where brown root-rot was prevalent. By studying colonies of *P. minyus* under aseptic conditions he found that they produced brown lesions in the absence of other organisms. Experimental-plot data and field observations added further evidence of the importance of nemas in brown rot. Soil-fumigation experiments demonstrated that removal of the nemas also eliminated the disease.

Mountain observed that under Ontario conditions there was only slight root injury when temperatures were below 70°F, while at 100°F severe damage occurred.

Benedict and Mountain (1956) reported *Pratylenchus minyus* and *Rhizoctonia solani* as consistently associated with root-rot of winter wheat in southern Ontario. Field symptoms consisted of large patches of yellowed and stunted plants which seriously reduced yields in over 32 per cent of the wheat acreage in Essex, Kent, and Lambton counties. *Pratylenchus minyus* was present at all stages of its life cycle, while *R. solani* had ramified through leaf sheaths and the subcortical stem, as well as through the root-tissues. The fungus was also found on diseased roots and stems at, or near, the soil surface. *Pratylenchus minyus* was especially prevalent from October through April when root-degeneration was taking place. Infested plants produced few new roots in the spring to take the places of those which were damaged or destroyed. Reduction of either the nematode or the fungus population increased plant growth to a marked degree. Control of both organisms by methyl bromide produced twice the growth secured from infested soil.

Mountain gives an interesting account of his observations after the nemas entered tobacco roots:

> After four to six days the nematodes within the root began to move about quite readily, and about this time the cortical tissue began to break down. The tissues in the invaded area turned brown and appeared to be killed. In one culture, which was kept free of contaminants for over a month, all of the nematodes of the lesion had died within that time. The cortical cells surrounding the nematodes were killed and disrupted and it was assumed that the nematodes died of starvation. The epidermal cells also appeared to be necrotic, but retained their original shape and did not disintegrate. The cells of the rest of the root appeared to be alive. It thus appears that under aseptic conditions the lesion did not approach the stage of advancement observed in the soil. This suggests that subsequent breakdown may be correlated with the activity of various secondary organisms.

The above examples of demonstrated pathogenicity indicate that *Pratylenchus* and associate fungi and bacteria unite to produce the destructive lesions found on the roots of host plants. Techniques developed by various workers now make it possible to repeat such demonstrations provided that natural ecological conditions are simulated to a degree that the nemas will thrive on a suitable host. But as Oostenbrink (1957) observed, *Pratylenchus* do not respond favorably to the ordeal of soil washing, separation, and inoculation and a large portion of the specimens fail to survive. When greenhouse facilities are not available, soil fumigants properly applied to plots and fields will usually prove that removal of the nemas will reduce or eliminate certain fungus and bacterial infections.

Host plants: Reports on host plants of *Pratylenchus* were fairly accurate until 1929. However, from that year until 1953 the records are practically worthless because they were thoroughly confused under the two names, *Anguillulina pratensis* and *Pratylenchus pratensis*. During this period each of these names was assumed to include *P. coffeae, P. penetrans, P. brachyurus,* and *P. neglectus,* which unfortunately had been made synonyms of the two above-mentioned names. Species identification has been more accurate since Sher and Allen (1953) monographed the genus, and host studies indicate that each species has a wide range within certain groups of plants.

Host preferences: During recent years some species of *Pratylenchus* have been observed to exhibit preferences for certain plants, and detailed studies of each species in relation to the plants with which it is associated are thus required. Several of the known species either are indigenous to the different continents or have been distributed through infested plant material. Host preferences of populations long separated from one another may differ greatly, and the possibilities of varying biotypes is ever present. Identification of each species and host studies in each locality in which it occurs will be imperative before crop rotations can be recommended for control. Mixed populations of two or more species are not unusual and present special problems, since a rotation suitable for the control of one species may be favorable to the propagation of another.

Host response: Evaluation of crops showing little or no damage from *Pratylenchus* must be based not only on their growth and vigor but also on the numbers of nemas actually living within their roots. Corn and rye may produce "normal" yields, yet may harbor populations large enough to damage severely susceptible crops like tobacco (Graham, 1951). Hastings and Bosher (1938) reported that oats were reduced only 4 per cent in growth, whereas potatoes, red clover, and other crops were damaged 50 to 75 per cent. Corn, wheat, and oats observed in Utah were severely infested with *P. thorni* while their roots were young and succulent. Later in the season as the roots became woody and inhospitable, it frequently was impossible to find specimens within the tissues although they were numerous in the surrounding soil. Similar infestations of young wheat have been observed in eastern Nebraska and northern Idaho. Root examinations should always be supplemented with adequate soil sampling. It is not unusual to find periods during the year when populations fluctuate to a marked degree and combined root and soil examinations may fail to produce reliable data on the numbers present.

Vigorous-growing young orchard trees frequently make an apparently normal growth for several years in the presence of large populations of *Pratylenchus*. But when competition for moisture and soil nutrients develops, growth is checked and decline begins. Old orchard trees may exhibit extensive decline and dieback symptoms; yet soil and root samples may fail to reveal populations deemed sufficient to produce such extensive injury. In such instances, reduction of growth has reduced food sources until nematode reproduction has been limited to a corresponding degree. Under these conditions it may be necessary to dig 10 or 15 feet of trenches before a sufficient number of small roots can be found for examination. Populations in orchards frequently appear to pass through cycles which probably are associated with periods of root growth and of favorable moisture and fertility.

Control: Host ranges of *Pratylenchus* spp. indicate that in occasional instances there will be opportunities to use crop rotations in their control. Of special interest is the work of Oostenbrink, Kuiper, and s'Jacob (1957), which demonstrated that marigolds, *Tagetes* hybrids, are very effective in reducing populations of *P. pratensis* and *P. penetrans* to negligible numbers. The possible value of crop rotations will be discussed later for each of the several species for which data are available.

Summer fallow in dry climates appears to reduce populations through exposure to heat and drying and by eliminating host plants. Mountain (personal communication) found that fallow from June 1 to October 1 drastically reduced the population. During winter months when metabolism was low, there was little food consumption and the nemas lived through the winter with no appreciable loss in numbers.

Soil fumigants give effective control provided that host-plant roots are either removed from the field or allowed to decay before fumigation; otherwise nemas within the roots escape. Allen and Raski (1952) attempted to clear nursery soil on which tuberous begonias were grown but found that even 600-pound applications of D-D and CBP failed to accomplish complete eradication. A combination of shallow-rooted crops, summer fallow, and fumigation doubtless would be preferable in fields where nursery stock will be grown.

Biology: Members of the genus *Pratylenchus* are typically vagrant parasites of plant roots, although in rare instances they may inhabit aboveground portions. In one instance the writer observed specimens as much as 2 inches aboveground in lesions beneath the cortex of a coleus. This plant had been grown from a cutting planted in heavily infested soil, and as the roots died, the nemas made their way up into the stem. Cobb (1922) reported *Tylenchus mahogani,* = *P. coffeae,* including the bark of mahogany, a most unusual habitat. Merzheevska (1951) occasionally found *P. tumidiceps* in stalks and leaves of barley and oats.

Manner of attack: Both young and adult nemas enter roots by forcing their way through or between the cortical cells and then feed on the cell contents as they migrate through the tissues. Mountain (1955) established colonies of *Pratylenchus minyus* on aseptic corn and tobacco roots, where he observed details of their feeding and development. Permanent openings were made at points of entrance which, under field conditions, would provide access for fungi and bacteria. Breaking down of root-tissues progressed with invasion, but without evidence of hypertrophy. Attack was made most frequently on the older, mature region, where the nemas first fed on epidermal cells. In 4 to 6 hours they had invaded the cortical cells, and frequently in 8 to 10 hours they were completely within the tissues. Those attacking the growing point appeared to feed on the meristematic cells in the growing region and caused growth to cease within a day or two; they then moved on to more mature portions of the roots. In no instance were they observed to penetrate roots at the growing point.

Life cycle: *Pratylenchus pratensis* was reported by Hastings (1939) as completing its life cycle in oat roots in 54 to 65 days, of which 25 to 31 were spent in larval stages and 29 to 34 days from the adult to the young of the next generation. An average of one egg was deposited each day by each female, and as many as sixteen were deposited in one place by a single female. Because of the migratory habit of the nemas the total number of eggs per female was not determined. Nemas at all stages were able to enter roots.

Gadd and Loos (1941a, 1941b, 1941c) reported the life cycle of a *Pratylenchus* (probably *P. coffeae*) as requiring 45 to 48 days in tea roots. Of this time, 15 to 17 days were necessary for eggs to hatch, 15 to 16 days were spent as larvae, and it took 15 days from maturity to egg production. Of 318 larvae observed to reach the adult stage only 32 became males. When males were absent, egg laying was usually delayed. Nemas in *Tephrosia vogelii* roots developed normally, while in *Deamodium gyroides* egg production was normal during the first week but later diminished. In *Crotaloides anagyroides* and turnips only a few eggs were laid, and many nemas left without depositing eggs.

Jensen (1950) described and illustrated four stages in the life cycle of *Pratylenchus vulnus,* a species containing numerous males. Host range varied among various plant families from susceptible to slightly susceptible and immune.

Pratylenchus zeae in corn required 35 to 40 days to complete the life cycle according to Graham (1951). Mountain (1955) assumed that under aseptic conditions the life cycle of *P. minyus* was completed in about 28 days.

In temperate climates overwintering takes place either in roots or in soil, and all stages in the life cycle except that of the egg-producing female may occur. In Java, under tropical conditions, there appeared to be a break in the reproductive cycle from November through February: gravid females were not observed during these months. However, large populations were present both in roots and in soil during this period.

During periods of drought, the nemas lie quiescent, awaiting the coming of moisture and the resumption of plant growth. Under these conditions they are susceptible to drying if the soil is plowed and fallowed through the hot summer months, especially when they have become concentrated near the surface through the growing of shallow-rooted crops.

Nothing is known of the feeding habits of *Pratylenchus* while living free in soil. Under field conditions the nemas remain normal in appearance, with intestinal cells apparently well filled with stored food granules. During drought and winter hibernation their metabolism probably is reduced to a minimum, and stored supplies carry them through such periods. Mountain (1958, personal communication) reported that he had observed them feeding on root-hairs of tissue cultures but that they failed to survive unless they entered the roots and fed endoparasitically. He did not see them feeding on fungus mycelia or even appearing to be attracted to them.

Competitive nemas: Where *Pratylenchus penetrans* or *P. minyus* is found associated with the American dagger nematode, *Xiphinema americanum*, it has frequently been noted that the latter is the dominant species. Often only an occasional specimen of *Pratylenchus* is found, even about cherry trees, which are among their favorite hosts. Apparently the relatively large, active xiphinemas destroy the roots before the small, sluggish pratylenchs can reach them.

Morphology: All species of *Pratylenchus* are so characteristic in their general appearance that little difficulty will be experienced in identifying them with the genus, although immature stages may sometimes resemble the young of *Nacobbus, Radopholus,* or *Rotylenchulus.* But the species are often exceedingly difficult to recognize because their differentiating characters are minute and frequently obscure, even on well-prepared specimens. Adult nemas taken from soil are usually somewhat shorter and more slender than those from roots in which they have been feeding and reproducing.

Diagnostic characters usually include the number of annules on the lip region, form of spear knobs, position of vulva, tail length compared with vulva-anus distance, and tail form. The following generic diagnosis is from Thorne (1949), while the species measurements and descriptions are largely from Sher and Allen (1953):

Diagnosis: Pratylenchinae. Stout, cylindroid nemas less than 1.0 mm in length, with relatively broad heads and bluntly rounded tails. Lateral field marked by four incisures, except six in *Pratylenchus hexincisus* and variable in rare specimens of certain other species. Incisures of adult females frequently absent owing to stretching of the cuticle. Deirids rarely visible, located near latitude of excretory pore. Phasmids located one-third of tail length or more behind latitude of anus. Lip region bearing two to four annules (one to three striae) set off by a narrowing of the head. Cephalic framework sclerotized, refractive. Spear strong, 14 to 19 μ long, with massive basal knobs. Median esophageal bulb spheroid, more than half as wide as neck. Basal bulb extending back over intestine, usually in a lateroventrad position. Three prominent esophageal gland nuclei. Esophageal lumen and intestine joined by an obscure muscular valve. Excretory pore prominent, about opposite nerve ring. Hemizonid slightly anterior to excretory pore. Intestine packed with numerous dark granules. Slender, muscular rectum ending in a transverse, slitlike anus. Vulva a depressed transverse slit, vagina extending in and slightly forward. Anterior ovary outstretched, with oöcytes arranged in a single file except for a short region of multiplication. Posterior uterine branch rudimentary.

Males known in about half the species. Bursa enveloping tail, with phasmids located near its base. Spicula slightly arcuate, resting on a thin, troughlike gubernaculum. Testis outstretched, with spermatocytes irregularly arranged, especially in the region of multiplication.

Type species: *Pratylenchus pratensis* (deMan, 1880) Filipjev, 1936

Because of the similarity of the various species the following descriptions include only measurements and certain characters of diagnostic value. The accompanying illustrations of the ten best-known species show their most important diagnostic characters.

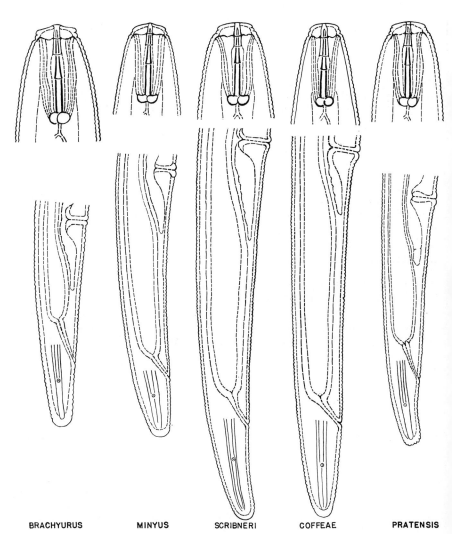

BRACHYURUS   MINYUS   SCRIBNERI   COFFEAE   PRATENSIS

Fig. 9-1. *Pratylenchus* spp. Note two annules in lip regions of *brachyurus, minyus, scribneri,* and *coffeae;* three annules on *pratensis, penetrans, thornei, zeae,* and rarely on *vulnus;* and four annules on *vulnus* and *goodeyi.*

Pratylenchus brachyurus (Godfrey, 1929) Filipjev & Stekhoven, 1941

Synonyms: *Tylenchus brachyurus* Godfrey; *Pratylenchus leiocephalus* Steiner, 1949

Morphology: ♀: 0.45–0.75 mm; a = 20–29; b = 5.6–6.1; c = 17–21; V = 83–89
♂: 0.46–0.56 mm; a = 27–29; b = 6; c = 21; T = 51–53

Lip region bearing two annules. Spear 19 to 22 μ long, with strongly developed, rounded knobs. Spermatheca and spermatozoa not observed in uterine tract; vulva located farther back than usual in the genus. Vulva-anus distance less than twice length of tail. Terminus bluntly rounded. Males rare; absence

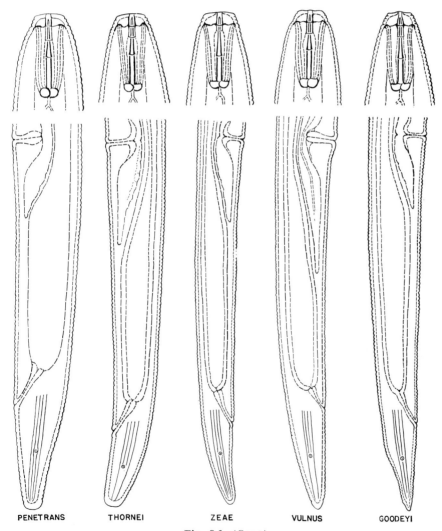

PENETRANS   THORNEI   ZEAE   VULNUS   GOODEYI

Fig. 9-1. (*Cont.*)

of spermatozoa in the females indicates that the few observed may not be functional.

Pratylenchus brachyurus very closely resembles *P. minyus,* from which it is distinguished by the rounded spear knobs and more prominent annulations of the tail.

Symptoms: Godfrey observed that lesions on pineapple roots began as elongate brown spots which became darker with age. Borders of the lesions were sharply delineated by dead, discolored epidermal cells from which the affected tissues extended inward to the stele. Coalescing lesions eventually involved the entire cortical region; then the vascular tissues died, and the root was destroyed. Variations in susceptibility were evident in the several hosts. Roots of cowpeas suffered pronounced damage, while those of tomato and sugar cane were affected but little.

Host plants and distribution: Pineapples and numerous other plants, Hawaii; depressed lesions on potato tubers, Pretoria, South Africa; peanut shells and roots, Georgia; strawberry, Florida and Wisconsin; lespedeza, cotton, okra, Louisiana; cotton, corn, tobacco, South Carolina; and from both cultivated and virgin soil at various other points in the United States where it probably is indigenous.

Pratylenchus minyus Sher and Allen, 1953

Morphology: ♀: 0.31–0.55 mm; a = 18–26; b = 4–6.3; c = 16–22; V = 80–88
            ♂: 0.34 mm; a = 22; b = 4.8; c = 20

Lip region bearing two annules. Spear 16 to 18 μ long, with anteriorly cupped knobs. Vulva located far back, the vulva-anus distance equal to not more than twice the tail length. Posterior uterine branch about as long as body width. Spermatheca and spermatozoa not seen in uterine tract. Tail bluntly rounded. Males rare and probably not functional.

Pratylenchus minyus closely resembles *P. brachyurus,* from which it is distinguished by the anteriorly cupped spear knobs and finer annulations of the tail. Occasional specimens from Wisconsin possess spear knobs which are intermediate in form between the two species, a variation which makes their identification very difficult or impossible.

Hosts and distribution: Sher and Allen report *Pratylenchus minyus* from soil about the roots of pear, grape, dandelion, and date palm in California and thus indicate its wide host range. The species is also present in both cultivated and virgin soil throughout the United States, where it is doubtless indigenous. Mountain (1954) found it abundant in tobacco fields of Ontario and noted that the build-up of populations was most rapid on corn, rye, and red clover.

Control: Recommended applications of recognized soil fumigants. Mountain observed that the Green Briar variety of tobacco produced 18 pounds per plot compared with 2 pounds for Harrow Velvet. Yet the nematode populations associated with both varieties showed no significant differences in numbers, a strong degree of tolerance in Green Briar thus being indicated. Mountain also found that strawberry and timothy reduced populations to negligible numbers.

Pratylenchus scribneri Steiner, 1943a

Synonym: *Tylenchus penetrans* Cobb (1917) in part

Morphology: ♀: 0.49–0.67 mm; a = 20–26; b = 5.2–6.7; c = 15–19; V = 74–78
♂: 0.40 mm; a = 27; b = 5.5; c = 17; T = 42

Lip region bearing two annules. Spear 15 to 17 μ long, with broad, rounded, slightly cupped knobs. Vulva-anus distance averaging about three times tail length. Posterior uterine branch usually slightly longer than vulva body width. Spermatozoa and spermatheca not observed, and the rare males probably are not functional. Tail slightly cylindroid in posterior half, ending in a broad, rounded terminus.

In many respects *Pratylenchus scribneri* resembles *P. brachyurus,* but it usually is larger, the vulva is more anterior in position, and the spear

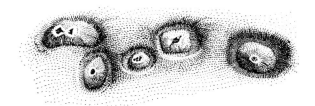

Fig. 9-2. Pustules on potatoes caused by *Pratylenchus scribneri. (After Cobb. Courtesy of U.S. Department of Agriculture.)*

knobs are slightly cupped. The partly cylindroid tail is distinctly different from the tails of other species possessing two labial annules.

Steiner wrote the description of this species, which was published by Sherbakoff and Stanley (1943). However, Scribner (1889) had mentioned its presence in potato tubers and had described the typical symptoms; hence Steiner was prompted to assign the name *scribneri.* Cobb (1917) found specimens in potato tubers and assigned them to a complex of species which he named *Tylenchus penetrans.* Chambers illustrated Cobb's paper with an excellent full-length drawing of a female and a sketch of the typical injury to potato tubers. Severe injury to a potato crop was observed by M. L. Schuster (1941, unpublished notes) on Prairie Island, Platte River, Nebraska. Christie and Birchfield (1958) reported the species as a destructive parasite of amaryllis in Florida.

Host plants and distribution: Causal agent of depressed lesions in potato tubers, Tennessee and Nebraska; amaryllis roots, Florida.

Control: Recommended applications of recognized soil fumigants.

Pratylenchus coffeae (Zimmermann, 1898) Filipjev & Stekhoven, 1941

Synonyms: *Tylenchus musicola* Cobb, 1919; *Tylenchus mahogani* Cobb, 1922

Morphology: ♀: 0.45–0.70 mm; a = 25–35; b = 5–7; c = 17–22; V = 76–83
♂: 0.45–0.70 mm; a = 26–40; b = 6–7; c = 17–24; T = 45–52

Lip region with two annules. Spear 15 to 18 μ long, with rounded knobs. Vulva-anus distance about twice tail length in Zimmermann's specimens but

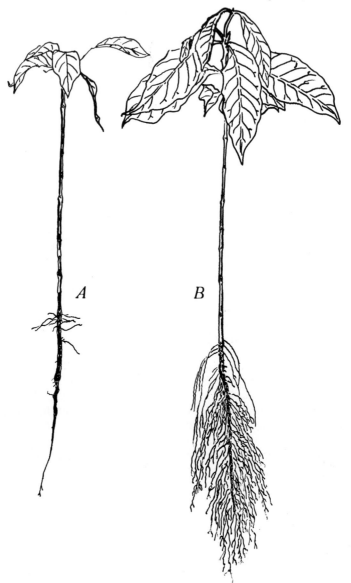

Fig. 9-3. *A*—Coffee seedling infested by *Pratylenchus coffeae.* *B*—Control. First recorded demonstration of *Pratylenchus pathogenicity.* *(Sketched from Zimmermann, by Mario San Juan.)*

nearly three times that distance in those collected by Colbran in Australia. Posterior uterine branch usually shorter than vulva body diameter. Tail symmetrically convex-conoid to the rounded terminus. Vulva from Java specimens near 83 per cent but only 75 per cent in the Australian population.

Pratylenchus coffeae appears to be most closely related to *P. scribneri*, from which it is distinguished by the rounded spear knobs, shorter posterior uterine branch, and symmetrically convex-conoid tail.

Hosts and distribution: *Pratylenchus coffeae* attacks a wide range of plants varying from coffee, bananas, abaca, and apples to peas, beans, cabbage, cauliflower, and tomatoes. Of special interest was the colony described by Cobb from mahogany bark collected in Barbados, British West Indies. In the United States it has been found in camellia, California; vetch, Kentucky; and strawberry, Wisconsin.

Control: Colbran (1953, 1954) found that certain apple root-stocks were less susceptible to *Pratylenchus coffeae* than were others, although all were infested to some degree. He also reported that replacement of soil in planting sites aided in establishing trees. Growth of apple seedlings in pots was increased more than eight times by fumigating the soil with D-D and formalin. Three inches of sawdust as a mulch for nine months reduced populations to small numbers. Moist soil kept free of host plants for nine months showed steadily decreasing populations, ranging from 210 per 40-g sample in April to none in December.

Pratylenchus pratensis (deMan, 1880) Filipjev, 1936

Synonyms: *Tylenchus pratensis* deMan; *Anguillulina pratensis* (de-Man) Goffart, 1929

Morphology: ♀: 0.37–0.70 mm; a = 22–32; b = 4–6; c = 19–24; V = 80–85
♂: 0.32–0.54 mm; a = 22–31; b = 6; c = 16–20; T = 45–57

Lip region bearing three annules. Spear 17 to 19 μ long, with strong, slightly cupped knobs. Vulva-anus distance about three times tail length. Tail somewhat cylindroid in posterior half, ending in a blunt, rounded terminus completely surrounded by annules. Spermatheca filled with spermatozoa, which proves that males of this species are functional.

DeMan's description of *Pratylenchus pratensis* was very meager, and accurate identification is difficult. It is even possible that more than one species were in his collections from near Leiden, Netherlands, and Sydenham, England. However, the form collected by Goodey near Sydenham is also known to occur in the Netherlands, and the emended diagnosis has been generally accepted.

Most of the literature on *Pratylenchus pratensis* is of questionable value because of the extensive synonymy involved, as previously recounted. Records made since the species diagnosis was emended by Thorne (1949) appear to represent correct identifications, and only these are covered in the following discussion.

Host plants and distribution: Sher and Allen report *Pratylenchus pratensis* from narcissus, Netherlands; lily-of-the-valley pips, Germany; soil

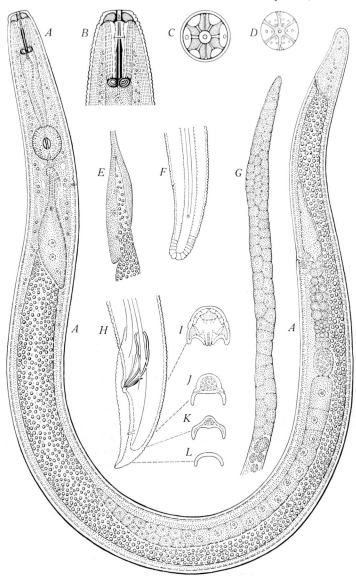

Fig. 9-4. *Pratylenchus pratensis.*   *A*—Female.   *B*—Head.   *C*—Basal plate of cephalic framework.   *D*—Face view.   *E*—Basal portion of esophagus, showing connection with intestine.   *F*—Female tail.   *G*—Testis.   *H*—Male tail showing lateral field and phasmid.   *I–L*—Cross sections through anal region, phasmids, and posterior parts of tail.   (*After Thorne.   Courtesy of Helminthological Society of Washington.*)

about grass, cherry, and other plants, New York; strawberry, Kentucky; cabbage field, Washington; Croft lily and Ladino clover, Oregon. Infested plant material has doubtless carried the pest to many parts of the world, or it may have been indigenous to more than one continent. Oostenbrink (1954) found 3,620 specimens in 200 g of soil from a cornfield, and 10 g of rye roots contained 32,800. The species is widespread in the lighter soils of the Netherlands.

Control: Oostenbrink (1954a, 1956) reported extensive observations which proved that cereals are very favorable hosts for *Pratylenchus pratensis*, while numbers declined during the culture of beets and woody perennials. Oostenbrink, Kuiper, and s'Jacob (1957a) found that marigolds, *Tagetes* hybrids, were very efficient in reducing populations of this species.

Pratylenchus penetrans (Cobb, 1917) Filipjev & Stekhoven, 1941

Synonym: *Tylenchus penetrans* Cobb

Morphology: ♀: 0.43–0.65 mm; a = 17–30; b = 5.7–6.5; c = 15–21; V = 78–83
♂: 0.44–0.56 mm; a = 23–30; b = 5.2–6.0; c = 15–20; T = 43–52
Lip region bearing three annules. Spear 16 to 18 μ long, with broadly rounded knobs. Spermatheca present, usually filled with spermatozoa. Posterior uterine branch about as long as vulva body width. Tail dorsally convex-conoid, the posterior portion being somewhat subcylindroid and ending in a broadly rounded terminus.

Pratylenchus penetrans is distinctive because of the rounded spear knobs and subcylindroid posterior portion of the tail. It is one of the few species in which males are numerous.

Host plants and distribution: *Pratylenchus penetrans* is known throughout the United States, southern Canada, and Europe. Records indicate that it is has one of the widest host ranges of any species in the genus. Many hosts are of economic importance, and severe losses have occurred in numerous instances. Decline and dieback of cherry trees in Michigan were a threat to the industry until the advent of soil fumigants and rigid nursery inspection. Mountain and Boyce (1958) reported that *P. penetrans* presented a serious problem in peach replant. Probably no other nematode species has been more widely distributed through infested nursery stock. Reduction of potato yields through infestation of the roots was demonstrated by Oostenbrink (1957), and similar damage has been seen in small areas in Wisconsin fields.

Jensen (1953) found that all of 33 species and varieties of plants tested were susceptible to *Pratylenchus penetrans*. Oostenbrink, s'Jacob, and Kuiper (1957) found the same to be true in the Netherlands, where they tested 164 plants, but they observed marked differences in the relative susceptibility of certain species. Populations from 10-g root samples varied from 23 in marigolds to 106,000 in vetch. Beets were least infested of the common field crops. Oats, rye, and barley showed little actual damage, but all three ranked high as favorable hosts. Outstanding reduction of populations was noted during the culture of marigolds, and

Oostenbrink (1958, personal communication) stated that the few nemas which invaded the roots failed to reproduce.

Control: Soil fumigants properly applied give good control. Present information indicates that crop rotations will be of no value because of the wide host range, with the possible exception of sugar beets. While marigolds are very effective in control, they are neverthelesss impractical because of their limited value except when produced for seed.

Fig. 9-5. Left, five potato tubers from an area severely infested with *Pratylenchus penetrans*. Right, tubers from an adjacent uninfested area. (*Courtesy of Department of Plant Pathology, University of Wisconsin.*)

Pratylenchus thornei Sher and Allen, 1953

Morphology: ♀: 0.45–0.77 mm; a = 26–36; b = 5.5–8; c = 18–22; V = 73–80
♂: 0.57 mm; a = 31; b = 5.8; c = 20; T = 30

Lip region bearing three annules. Basal plate of cephalic framework a conspicuous feature, the outer margin strongly developed and extending back a distance equal to the width of two adjacent annules. Spear 17 to 19 μ long, with strong knobs which are almost truncate anteriorly. Neither spermatheca or spermatozoa observed in the uterine tract. Posterior uterine branch about 1½ times the vulva body diameter. Tail dorsally convex-conoid to the blunt, rounded terminus. A single male was reported by Sher and Allen.

Host plants and distribution: *Pratylenchus thornei* is a serious parasite of cereals and corn in limited areas in Salt Lake County, Utah. Young, succulent roots of wheat and oats are especially susceptible to attack, and severe stunting often follows. Wheat heads from the dwarfed infested plants frequently bore less than a dozen shrunken grains. Oats and corn were also reduced in growth and subject to severe attack by smut. After the roots became hard and inhospitable, the nemas migrated into the soil, where they remained until the next crop was planted.

Fig. 9-6. Wheat infested with *Pratylenchus thornei;* ×⅓.

They were not observed to enter the roots of sugar beets, alfalfa, or potatoes. Oostenbrink (1954a) found this species associated with decline of peas in the Netherlands. Sher and Allen reported specimens from soil about the roots of numerous plants in several localities in California but failed to find them within tissues.

Control: Rotations of alfalfa and sugar beets for several years reduced populations to negligible numbers in Utah. Since infestations in that state were found only on rather heavy clay loams, soil fumigation was impractical.

Pratylenchus subpenetrans Taylor and Jenkins, 1957

Morphology: ♀: 0.33–0.48 mm; a = 18–28; b = 5.0–7.2; c = 16–21; V = 77–83
               ♂: 0.33–0.47 mm; a = 24–32; b = 5.0–7.4; c = 15–21; T = 40–50
Lip region with three annules. Female spear 15 to 16.5 μ long, with spherical knobs; male spear slightly shorter. Borders of labial framework heavily sclerotized and projecting back about 2 μ. Vulva-anus distance about twice tail length. Posterior uterine branch about 1½ times as long as vulva body diameter. Tail uniformly convex-conoid to small, rounded terminus. Males about as numerous as females.

As the name signifies, *Pratylenchus subpenetrans* resembles a small form of *P. penetrans,* from which it is distinguished by the heavily sclerotized margin of the cephalic framework and the longer postuterine branch bearing rudimentary uterine tissues.

Host plants and distribution: Soil about roots of tall fescue, *Festuca elatior,* Prince Georges County, Maryland.

Pratylenchus hexincisus Taylor and Jenkins, 1957

Morphology: ♀: 0.34–0.54 mm; a = 18–29; b = 5.9–8.4; c = 16–23; V = 75–82
Lateral fields marked by six incisures except toward the extremities. Frequently some of the incisures near mid-body are broken into short sections. Lip region with two annules, spear 14.5 to 15.4 μ long, bearing rounded knobs. Posterior uterine branch about as long as vulva body width. Tail conoid to small, rounded terminus.

Pratylenchus hexincisus is distinctive because of the six incisures of the lateral field. However, occasional specimens of other species bear five or six and sometimes as many as ten incisures, and therefore this character is not always diagnostic. The general body form is somewhat like that of *P. minyus,* but the rounded spear knobs are more like those of *P. brachyurus.* The conoid tail is distinctly different from the broad, subcylindroid tail of *P. scribneri.*

Host plants and distribution: Type specimens collected in Kent County, Maryland, about roots of corn. Also reported from Indiana by Virginia Ferris and from South Dakota by Fields Caveness (personal communications).

Pratylenchus zeae Graham, 1951

Morphology: ♀: 0.36–0.58 mm; a = 25–30; b = 5.4–8; c = 17–21; V = 68–76
Lip region bearing three annules. Spear 15 to 17 μ long, with broad, flattened knobs. Spermatheca and spermatozoa not seen. Posterior uterine branch 1 to 1½ times as long as vulva body diameter. Vulva-anus distance 3 to 4 times length of tail; tail somewhat subcylindroid in posterior half, ending in a small but rounded terminus. All four lateral incisures extending past phasmid to near terminus. Male unknown.

Pratylenchus zeae is distinguished from *P. vulnus,* its closest relative, by the more anterior position of the vulva and the usually shorter posterior uterine branch. It is also distinguished by the absence of males, which are numerous in *P. vulnus.*

Host plants and distribution: As the name indicates, this species is typically a parasite of corn, in which it has been reported in South Carolina and Georgia. Graham also reports that it is frequently found in crab grass, *Digitaria* sp., and occasionally in tobacco. Both corn and crab grass contained large populations without marked injury to the plants.

Control: Cotton and peanuts appeared to be uninfested by *Pratylenchus zeae,* and rotations with these crops should reduce populations provided that crab grass and similar weed hosts are also controlled.

Pratylenchus vulnus Allen and Jensen, 1951

Morphology: ♀: 0.46–0.91 mm; a = 25–39; b = 5.3–7.3; c = 15–25; V = 78–82
♂: 0.46–0.74 mm; a = 28–39; b = 5.3–7.4; c = 18–26; T = 36–66
Lip region almost continuous with neck contour, marked by three or four annules. Spear 16 μ long, with broad knobs which are anteriorly truncate. Ovary often extending forward to esophageal gland. Spermatheca elongated.

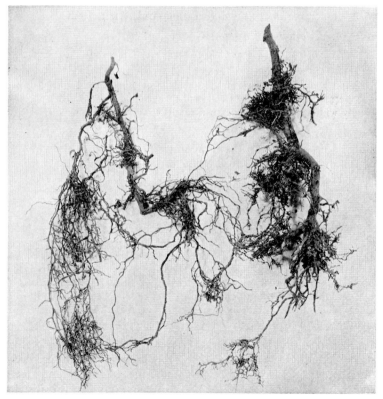

Fig. 9-7. Cherry roots infested with *Pratylenchus vulnus.* (*Specimens courtesy of W. W. Winslow.*)

Posterior uterine branch twice as long as vulva body diameter, bearing a few cells representing a rudimentary ovary. All four lateral incisures extend to near terminus. Tail conoid to narrow, blunt terminus. Males numerous.

Pratylenchus vulnus is typically a parasite of fruit trees, vines, and berry plants. It is usually recognized by the numerous, slender young females and the abundance of males. Length of posterior uterine branch of Utah specimens only about equal to vulva body diameter.

Host plants and distribution: Allen and Jensen found *Pratylenchus vulnus* a widespread pest of fruit trees and vines in California. Later (1953) Jensen reported that, of sixty plants tested, twenty-nine were susceptible to infestation. Of these, alfalfa, cabbage, and the Graminaceae were only occasionally entered, and reproduction did not occur. They also recorded specimens from Arkansas, Maryland and Oregon, and the writer found infestations in raspberries in Utah and chrysanthemums in Wisconsin.

Control: If grown for two or more years, grains and alfalfa should reduce populations. Annual crops will concentrate populations near the surface, where they will be more vulnerable to soil fumigants.

Pratylenchus goodeyi Sher and Allen, 1953

Synonym: *Tylenchus musicola* Goodey, 1928

Morphology: ♀: 0.66 mm; a = 27–37; b = 5.8; c = 17; V = 74
♂: 0.56 mm; a = 26; b = 5.6; c = 18

Lip region bearing four annules. Spear 17 μ long, with slightly cupped annules. Spermatheca oval, uterus short, posterior uterine branch as long as vulva body width. Tail tapering to a small, conical terminus.

Pratylenchus goodeyi is distinguished from *P. vulnus* by the four annules of the lip region and the more anterior position of the vulva.

Host plants and distribution: Roots of banana, *Musa sapientum*, Kew Gardens, England.

Pratylenchus tumidiceps Merzheevska, 1951

Morphology: ♀: 0.3–0.5 mm; a = 28; b = 3.8–5.1; c = 20–30; V = 76
♂: 0.3–0.4 mm; a = 28; b = 4.0–5.1; c = 15

Width of body from head to anal opening almost uniform except for a slight expansion in vulvar region. Head truncate with six small lips occupying about one-third of its width, at the base of which are 12 easily seen elevations. Spear 13 to 15 μ long, with prominent knobs. Female tail conical, with rounded terminus. Male tail length about equal to twice the anal body diameter. Bursa prominent. One male to eight or nine females found.

The description indicates a rather small, aberrant form, distinctive because of the almost cylindroid body from lip region to anus.

Host plants and distribution: Soil and roots of barley and oats, less frequently in stalks and leaves. Small numbers found in five districts of U.S.S.R.

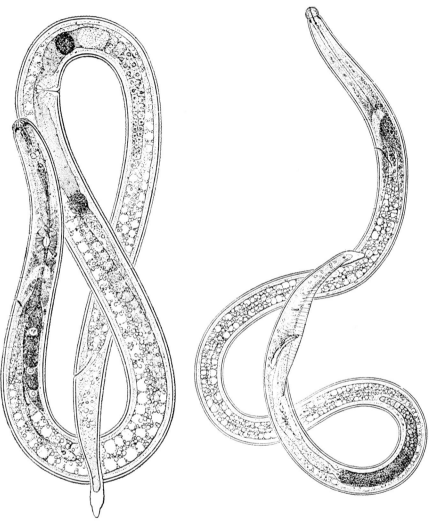

Fig. 9-8. *Radopholus similis,* female and male. (*After Cobb. Courtesy of U.S. Department of Agriculture.*)

Genus *Radopholus* Thorne, 1949

Radopholus constitutes an important group of endoparasitic nemas inhabiting plant roots. Generally the nemas occur in tropical or subtropical regions, although certain species are found in temperate zones.

Diagnosis: Pratylenchinae with two ovaries. Heads resembling those of *Pratylenchus*, with the lip region set off by a slight narrowing of the head contour. Spears are also similar to those of *Pratylenchus*, except in the males of *Radopholus similis*, in which the spear is rudimentary. Esophageal lobe elongated, extending back over the intestine. Ovaries two, outstretched, each uterine branch with a spheroid spermatheca. Deirids not observed. Hemizonid just anterior to excretory pore. Phasmids usually conspicuous. Spicula slightly arcuate, cephalated. Bursa enveloping about two-thirds of tail.

Type species: *Radopholus similis* (Cobb, 1893) Thorne, 1949

Radopholus includes two rather divergent groups of plant parasitic nemas: *R. similis* and the closely related species, *R. inaequalis* and *R. neosimilis,* are all well under 1.0 mm in length, sexual dimorphism is present, the tail termini are not mucronate, and the esophageal gland lobe lies in a dorsal position. In contrast to this group, *R. gracilis, R. oryzae,* and *R. lavabri* are 1.0 to over 3.0 mm long, sexual dimorphism does not occur, the tails are frequently mucronate, and the esophageal gland lobe extends in a ventral position.

Burrowing nematode, *Radopholus similis* (Cobb, 1893) Thorne, 1949

Synonyms: *Tylenchus similis* Cobb; *Tylenchus biformis* Cobb, 1907; *Tylenchus acutocaudatus* Zimmermann, 1898?; *Anguillulina similis* (Cobb) Goodey, 1932b; *Rotylenchus similis* (Cobb) Filipjev, 1936

Historical: While investigating a serious disease of bananas, *Musa sapientum,* in Fiji in 1890–1891, Cobb observed males of a new species of plant parasitic nematode which he later (1893) described as *Tylenchus similis.* Zimmermann (1898) found females of a species which he named *T. acutocaudatus* associated with diseased coffee roots in Java. This probably was *R. similis.* While studying roots of diseased sugar cane, *Saccharum officinarum,* on Kauai, one of the Hawaiian Islands, Cobb next (1907) found both males and females of a species which he named *T. biformis.* Extensive observations left no doubt as to the plant parasitic nature of this species.

Several years later Cobb received diseased rhizomes of the Gros Michel variety of banana from Jamaica and from this material secured specimens which convinced him that *Tylenchus biformis* actually was *T. similis,* and a more complete description of the species was published (1915). During the following 40 years there were several reports of the species which established its distribution throughout the tropical and subtropical regions of the world. Today it ranks high among the most important plant parasitic nemas in the tropics. Perhaps it is the major economically important species in those regions.

Morphology: ♀: 0.5–0.7 mm; a = 22; b = 5.9; c = 10; V = [435]4[38]

♂: 0.5–0.7 mm; a = 29; b = 5.2; c = 8.7; T = 32

Female. Lip region rounded, marked by three striae, set off by a slight narrowing of the head contour. Cuticle distinctly striated. Lateral fields marked by four incisures, the lateral ones minutely crenate. Deirids not observed. Phasmids a little less than one body width behind the latitude of the anus. Tail conoid to the blunt, rounded terminus. Spear strong, with well-developed knobs. Median bulb of esophagus subspherical. Isthmus about as long as body width. Junction of esophageal lumen and intestine very obscure. Basal lobe of esophagus two to four times as long as body width, extending back over anterior end of intestine. This lobe usually is in a dorsal position and contains the three gland nuclei. Anterior ovary frequently extending forward to median bulb of esophagus. Posterior ovary sometimes reaching into tail and occasionally reflexed forward one to three body widths. Oöcytes in single file except for a short region of reproduction. Eggs about twice as long as body diameter.

Male. Lip region subspheroid, with or without fine striae, set off by constriction. Cuticle distinctly annulated. Lateral fields marked by four incisures, ending on the tail, as illustrated. Phasmids near base of bursa, about one body width posterior to the latitude of the anus. Bursa crenate, rising at a point well in front of the spicula and extending two-thirds the length of the tail. Spear very slender, with tiny basal knobs. Esophagus reduced, the median bulb apparently being valveless. Testis outstretched, one-fourth to one-third the body length. Spicula slightly arcuate, cephalated. Gubernaculum thin, troughlike, slightly less than half as long as spicula.

The above measurements are representative of the species, but variations of 10 per cent and even more can be expected in any population. Specimens from favorable or unfavorable hosts may exhibit marked differences in size, body proportions, and development of gonads. Considerable variation will also be found after the final moult, depending on the time the individuals have been feeding, sexual maturity, and egg production. Variations in form of lip region and tails were well illustrated by van Weerdt (1958).

Cobb (1915) stated that the lip region was marked by about eight or ten minute annules, and van Weerdt (1958) records six or seven, some specimens having only three or four. The writer has observed four in most instances, a few individuals having five or six. Cobb's figure (1915) indicates that the three esophageal gland nuclei may lie in separate lobes, and van Weerdt agrees with this arrangement. However, the writer has not observed this to be true.

Steiner and Buhrer (1933a) discussed *Radopholus similis* as a parasite of tea roots collected in Java by R. Menzel in 1928. Their morphological studies revealed that the cephalic framework of the female is strongly sclerotized and hexaradiate. Six perioral papillae are present, closely grouped about the oral opening, and the four submedian lips each bear a single papilla. Amphid apertures are located at the apices of the lateral lips. The sexual dimorphic male has little, if any, sclerotization of the labial framework. Only the four submedian papillae are present, and the amphid apertures were not observed.

Biology: Burrowing nematodes at all life-cycle stages are usually found in and around the roots of infested plants. They enter the roots at any desired point, and then they break down the walls of the cells and feed on the contents. As they migrate through the tissues, numerous eggs are produced and colonies develop along the paths made by the females. As the nemas congregate in certain areas, cell destruction increases to a point at which discolored lesions are formed. As these lesions develop, they frequently extend into the central cylinder, coalesce, and sever the root. During lesion formation the nemas are followed by soil fungi and bacteria, which aid in completely destroying the infested tissues. Root destruction retards plant growth, and in advanced stages the plant becomes stunted and unthrifty and frequently dies. As plant growth declines, the nemas migrate into the soil in search of new roots, and if these are not found, the population may become drastically reduced through starvation.

Hosts and distribution: A few new hosts usually were added in each publication on this nematode until about twenty had been recorded in 1953, when it was discovered in Florida. Intensive investigations of possible host plants in that state revealed that the host range is unusually wide, and by 1959 the nematode had been found infesting upward of 150 species. Among citrus plants alone Feder et al. (1958) report nearly 400 species, varieties, and relatives as all being susceptible to attack. Not only are important crops involved, but also ornamentals, weeds, grasses, and other plants ranging from tea, coffee, sugar cane, bananas, and citrus to sweet potato, beans, squash, tomato, and corn. In fact, nonsusceptible plants are relatively scarce, among them being lychee, *Crotalaria,* turnips, kale, and lettuce. Investigations in other areas will doubtless increase the list to many hundreds of plant species.

Host investigations have revealed that degree of susceptibility is exceedingly variable and that one host may be severely injured, while another will exhibit little or no injury. Godfrey (1931) observed that although pineapples were susceptible to attack they were not seriously injured, and numerous similar instances were observed by Feder et al.

The presence of physiologic races which may attack one plant but not another was reported by DuCharme and Birchfield (1956). They found that one population originating from bananas did not infest citrus, while another population readily infested both bananas and citrus. Van Weerdt (1957) found marked differences in the abilities of various populations to transfer from one host to another.

ROOT AND RHIZOME NECROSIS OF BANANA

The burrowing nematode has been transported, or may have been indigenous, to most of the banana-producing regions of the world, and the typical injury caused by them is known as root and rhizome necrosis. According to publications of the United Fruit Company and of C. A. Loos (1957) and an anonymous publication (1958), these nemas frequently are associated with *Fusarium oxysporum* f. *cubense* E. F. S.

Sny. & Hans. This fungus is recognized as the causal agent of "Panama disease," which destroyed over 100,000 acres of bananas in Central and South America during the first 25 years of the present century. This disease is still the limiting factor in the production of the Gros Michel banana, which is the most popular variety for the American market. Just what part the nematodes play in the disease complex remains to be determined.

Symptoms: Root and rhizome necrosis is manifested by varying degrees of retarded growth, leaf yellowing, and falling of mature plants. Advanced stages of infestation show extensive lesions of the roots, especially near the rhizome. Often the rhizome is attacked, the result being blackened, rotting pockets in the outer cortical region. The nemas are found congregated in the adjacent healthy tissues.

Control: In certain level plantations flood fallowing for about six months destroys not only the *Fusarium* organisms but also the burrowing nematodes. After flooding, uninfested banana rhizomes are planted, and these produce satisfactory crops for several years. When clean rhizomes are not available, cutting out and trimming off visible lesions, and treatment with hot water as an accompaniment, constitute a fairly satisfactory method of reducing injury. However, the most careful trimming and hot-water treatment often fail to remove all the nemas, and lethal populations may build up within two or three years after planting.

YELLOWS DISEASE OF PEPPER

Historical: The Indonesian island of Bangka once was one of the world's principal sources of pepper, *Piper nigrum* L. Although the island area is only 4,600 square miles, over 22 million pepper trees were growing there at one time. (A pepper "tree" is a teakwood or concrete post set in the field with two pepper vines entwined about it.) Many of the "gardens," as they are known, were in production for as long as 40 to 60 years without appreciable loss in yield. But in the early 1930s occasional trees began to develop what became commonly known as "yellows" disease, and by 1950 the scourge had spread over the island until fewer than 2 million trees remained. Where formerly a garden produced for several decades, a planting now survives for only 3 to 5 years. Loss of the industry has become a major disaster to the inhabitants of the island since it was their principal source of income.

An interesting point in pepper culture on Bangka is the method of planting. As the jungle growth is cleared from the prospective garden, the wood is piled for burning and on each pile a quantity of soil is placed, which becomes at least partly sterilized by the heat. At planting time the supporting posts are first set, and slanting trenches are dug on opposite sides of each post. Burned soil is then placed on the slope of each hole to a depth of 5 or 6 inches. A 3- or 4-foot-long pepper vine cutting is laid on it and covered with more burned soil. The rapidly growing vines establish good root systems before nematodes or other pests can reach them. Johar Munzir, chief of the Bangka Agricultural Agency, informed the writer that his people had "always" used this method of planting. Apparently some Indonesian farmer long ago observed that plants growing on burning sites made a superior growth and introduced this method of establishing the pepper gardens.

Fig. 9-9. *A*—Pepper seedling infested with three females of *Radopholus similis*. *B*—Uninfested seedling. (*Photograph by H. J. van der Vecht, 1933, in De Plagen van de Cultuurgewassen in Indonesie, by L. G. E. Kalshoven, 1950, ed. W. van Hoeve, The Hague.*)

Association of *Radopholus similis* with yellows disease of pepper was first recorded by van der Vecht (1950), who made extensive field studies and demonstrated pathogenicity in the laboratory. The pest had doubtless been present in Bangka for many years. Perhaps it was present when the industry was established, because it appears to be generally distributed in the Orient and may have been indigenous to various areas. Pepper on Bangka was not appreciably injured until some other plant pathogen was introduced, and this combined with the nemas to incite the destructive yellows disease. A similar association apparently is present in Florida, where spreading decline of citrus has become so destructive during recent years, as noted by Christie (1957).

Symptoms: The first indication of yellows disease is the appearance of occasional yellowed leaves, which increase in numbers until within a year a large portion, or even all, of the foliage may become involved. Growth ceases soon after the yellowing becomes apparent, and production of pepper rapidly declines. Severe dieback and death of the plants eventually follow. The main roots are devoid of small feeder roots, and extensive necrosis of the larger laterals gradually develops.

Soil sampling in late December produced only small numbers of larval *Radopholus similis,* even from the roots of trees which were just beginning to exhibit symptoms of yellows. This paucity of nemas has also been a common characteristic of infestations in spreading decline of citrus. Similar conditions were observed about dying pepper trees at the Bogor Experiment Station.

Control: Christie reported that plantings in isolated areas escaped infestation for at least five years, but opportunities for isolation are limited. Applications of different organic and commercial fertilizers failed even to retard development of the disease. Resistant plants or varieties have not appeared in the infested areas.

SPREADING DECLINE OF CITRUS

Perhaps the most spectacular disease with which the burrowing nematode has been associated is that of "spreading decline" of citrus in Florida. Because of the great economic importance of the citrus crop to that state, several millions of dollars have been spent in survey, control, and research. According to Camp (1954) spreading decline was first observed sometime between 1926 and 1928 in a grove near Winterhaven. In 1935 and 1936 more infested groves were found in the same general vicinity. As the disease continued to spread, a campaign was begun in 1939 to discover the causal organism. In the late 1940s many new cases appeared over larger areas, and research was intensified, with state and Federal agencies cooperating.

Suit and DuCharme (1953) demonstrated that sour orange seedlings grown in pots of clay subsoil from diseased orchards showed the typical symptoms of spreading decline. Top and root growth were reduced, and burrowing nematodes were present in brown lesions on the roots. Therefore, the nemas were assumed to be the causal agents, an assumption which has been generally accepted. However, Feldmesser, Rebois, and Taylor (1959) found that, when the nemas were eliminated from soil, spreading decline continued to appear. In other experiments they applied wettable Captan, a fungicide, at rates of 25, 50, and 100 pounds per acre to pots of sterilized soil in which nematode infested young Duncan grapefruit were planted. Five months later the young trees in the 50 pound per acre pots had twice the root and three times the top growth of the control trees. However, the fungicide did not affect the

nematode population, and this circumstance indicated that some organism other than nematodes was present and had been controlled, at least
to a marked degree. All plants in the Captan-treated pots were darker
green in color than the chlorotic individuals in the controls. There appears to be little doubt that spreading decline is due not only to the
presence of burrowing nematodes but also to some associated organism
or organisms.

Symptoms: Spreading decline appears in citrus orchards as groups of
stunted or unthrifty trees with sparse leaves, small fruit, and retarded
terminal growth. Leaves on these trees have a tendency to wilt during
hot or dry periods but may respond to moisture and appear to make
some recovery. Examination of the root systems reveals that below 20
inches young feeder roots are reduced in number or may be absent, a fact
which accounts for the starvation effects on the top growth. Typical
lesions are present, and under extreme conditions so few roots remain
alive that it is difficult to find nemas in either the roots or the surrounding soil.

Migration: Under usual conditions in Florida citrus orchards spreading decline advances by an average of 1.6 trees per year according to
Suit and Ford (1950). Apparently the nemas move from the roots of
one tree to another, but in certain instances they appear to have made
their way under roadways 100 feet wide and even to have passed under
railroad rights of way.

Control: Eradication of *Radopholus similis* has been attempted on a
large scale in Florida. Decline areas are delineated by soil sampling,
and as a safety margin four rows of trees beyond those found infested
are added to the area. All trees in an area are then pulled and burned,
beginning near the center and working out toward uninfested parts of
the orchard. Roots are dug out by tractors and plows and burned with
the trees, and after this operation the land is worked down and prepared
for fumigation. An application of 60 gallons of D-D soil fumigant per
acre is then made at a depth of 12 inches and the surface thoroughly
sealed.

Soils of the infested area are very sandy and porous, and penetration by
D-D is much deeper than in heavier types. Diffusion to a depth of 6 or 8
feet should give effective control, because most of the nemas are in the top
5 feet of soil. However, in a few instances the nemas have been found
to a depth of 12 feet, beyond the range of economical fumigation. The
practice of fumigating immediately after the trees have been removed is
questionable. Citrus roots decay slowly, and nemas may remain within
them for several days, or even weeks, before they migrate out into the
soil, where they are vulnerable to fumigants.

There is a marked similarity between the yellows disease of pepper
on Bangka and spreading decline of citrus in Florida. This has been
noted by Christie (1957), who has had opportunities to make observations and studies on both problems.

Rice-root nematode, *Radopholus oryzae* (v. Breda de Haan, 1902) Thorne, 1949

Synonyms: *Tylenchus oryzae* v. B. de Haan, 1902; *Tylenchus apapillatus* Imamura, 1931; *Anguillulina oryzae* (v. B. de Haan) Goodey, 1936; *Rotylenchus oryzae* (v. B. de Haan) Filipjev & Schuurmans Stekhoven, 1941; *Rotylenchus apapillatus* (Imamura) Filipjev & Schuurmans Stekhoven, 1941

Historical: Von Breda de Haan discovered numerous nematodes inhabiting rice roots in Java and named the species *Tylenchus oryzae,* but his description was meager, and he gave no illustrations. The species remained in an *inquirendum* status until Goodey (1936) emended the description and made illustrations from specimens collected in Java by J. van der Vecht. The importance of the species in rice culture was somewhat controversial in that von Breda de Haan (1902) stated that it was the causal agent of "mentek," one of the most destructive rice diseases of Java, but failed to demonstrate pathogenicity by experimental work. It was not until 50 years later that van der Vecht and Bergman (1952) determined that under controlled experimental conditions the nemas did cause appreciable injury to rice plants, but they failed to produce symptoms of mentek. The complicated relationship between rice-root nematodes and the physiological and cultural aspects of mentek was ably discussed by van der Vecht (1953), and his conclusions were as follows:

> Although not many exact data on the degree of nematode infestation in mentek-diseased plants in the field have been collected, it appears that we may safely assume that the most destructive form of the disease is the result of severe root infestation together with extremely unfavorable growth conditions reducing the capacity to recover.
>
> Variations in the degree of severity of the disease from place to place are closely associated with, and probably mainly determined by, differences in soil properties. Particularly the heavy marl soils appear to lose their fertility upon submergence much sooner than others, and show much more pronounced seasonal variations. Extreme deviations from the usual growth conditions are more likely to occur on these soils than elsewhere.

Between September, 1951, and March, 1952, the writer collected extensively in Java, Bali, Sumatra, Thailand, and the Philippines. Specimens from Java were usually under 1.5 mm in length, similar to those described by Goodey. On Bali several individuals were found which were over 2.0 mm long, none of which contained eggs. Near Bangken, Thailand, many specimens about 2.0 mm long were found quiescent in dry clay loam of rice fields, awaiting the rainy season. Similar conditions prevailed near Manila, the Philippines. A collection made in August, 1959, by M. S. Siswopranoto of the Institute of Plant Diseases and Pests, Bogor, Java, contained complete series of males and females from recently moulted specimens to adults.

This wealth of material revealed a most unusual type of development.

After the final moult both males and females are about 1.0 mm long and have very immature gonads. During development they more than double their length and diameter before becoming sexually mature. In this process the cuticle expands to accommodate a body volume of six or eight times its original capacity. Thus the conflicting records of measurements by von Breda de Haan, Imamura, and Goodey were finally resolved. So great were the differences between young and adults that Imamura thought them to be two species, *Radopholus oryzae* and *R. gracilis.*

Morphology: Young ♀: 1.0–1.3 mm; a = 61; b = 12; c = 15; V = 22.51[20]
Young ♂: 1.0–1.2 mm; a = 56; b = 13; c = 14; T = 32
Adult ♀: 2.2–2.8 mm; a = 56; b = 13; c = 18–22; V = 35.50–60[32]
Adult ♂: 2.1–2.6 mm; a = 56; b = 11; c = 22–27; T = 45

The above measurements from Java specimens. The b proportions are measured from the junction of the esophagus and intestine. Body cylindroid except at extremities. Cuticle marked by striae 2.0 to 2.5 μ apart at mid-body. Lateral fields about one-third body width, marked by four incisures, the lateral ones crenate. Incisures rarely extend past middle of tail. Tails of both sexes ending in abruptly conoid, acute termini, which may be somewhat variable in form and position, occasionally being double. Deirids not observed. Phasmids near beginning of posterior third or fourth of tail, well beyond the ends of the lateral fields. Spear 17 to 20 μ long with strong, rounded knobs which are almost one-third as wide as head. Lip region with four or five annules. Amphids slitlike, located at margin of labial disc. Only four submedian cephalic papillae observed. Median bulb ovate, the valve often slightly anterior to

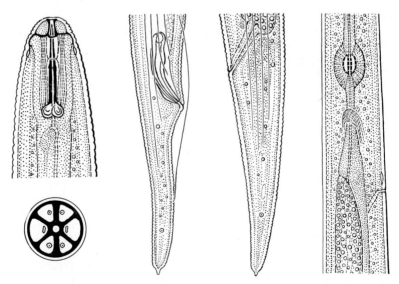

Fig. 9-10. *Radopholus oryzae.* Head and face views, male and female tails, and posterior esophageal region. (*Specimens courtesy of M. S. Siswopranoto, Institute of Plant Diseases and Pests, Bogor, Java.*)

center. Isthmus shorter than neck diameter. Excretory pore slightly posterior to junction of esophageal lumen and intestine. Hemizonid slightly anterior to pore, two or three annules wide. Esophageal glands extending ventrally in a lobe 7 to 12 times as long as body width. Ovaries outstretched, the oöcytes in single file except for a short region of reproduction. Spermatheca a prominent feature, about 1½ times as long as body width, conspicuous even in the youngest females. Testis outstretched. Spicula slightly arcuate, cephalated, resting on a thin, troughlike gubernaculum. Bursa rising anterior to proximal ends of spicula and extending one-half to three-fourths the tail length.

Radopholus oryzae is distinguished from *R. gracilis* by the higher, rounded lip region, more massive spear, less angular spear knobs, and shorter isthmus. Lateral incisures disappear near middle of tail and phasmids are more posteriorly located than those of *R. gracilis*. Tails are shorter and less subcylindroid.

Biology: From observations made in Java, Thailand, and the Philippines it appeared evident that various stages of immature and adult *Radopholus oryzae* live over in the soil between rice crops and during periods of drought. Specimens readily revived when washed from soil which had been stored dry in a room for eight months at the Bogor, Java, Experiment Station. Egg-producing females were not found quiescent in dry soil.

Roots are penetrated at almost any point except near the growing terminus, and after an opening is made by one nema others frequently use it. The long chambers between the parenchyma lamellae allow free movement throughout the root as the nemas search for suitable cells on which to feed. To determine the points at which feeding takes place, roots were lifted and immediately fixed in hot 5 per cent formaldehyde solution; they were then stained with acid fuchsin in lactophenol. Examination revealed that many nemas were killed just as they were coiled between the lamellae, with heads pressed against the cells surrounding the bases of root-hairs and spears inserted into the cells. Destruction of these cells results in death of the root-hairs. Occasionally a specimen was seen with the spear inserted in cells along the vascular bundle. Frequently specimens were killed in the act of entering or leaving the roots, as illustrated by van der Vecht and Bergman.

Reproduction: Although several investigators have studied the rice-root nematode, none has recorded the time of season during which eggs are produced. While the writer was in Java from mid-September to near the end of February, not one egg-producing female was observed among the hundreds of thousands of specimens seen. There are reports of unexplained cessation of growth of rice plants during April and May, and it appears that this may be due to rapid build-up of populations during those months.

Hosts and distribution: Van der Vecht and Bergman found rice-root nematodes inhabiting the roots of more than twenty species of plants in Java. Monocotyledonous plants, especially Cyperaceae and Gramineae, were readily attacked, and a few specimens were collected from the dicotyledons, *Marselia crenata* Presl, and *Rotala leptopetala* (Bl.). Nemas in various stages of development were found, a fact indicating that reproduction was taking place and that these plants were capable of carrying the pest over between rice crops.

Radopholus oryzae is known to occur in Indonesia on the islands of Java, Sumatra, and Bali and in India, Thailand, Japan, and the Philippines. Doubtless it is distributed throughout the rice-growing regions of Asia and the Pacific islands.

Under favorable agronomic conditions of moisture and fertility there is little evidence of injury to rice by *Radopholus oryzae,* and "normal" crops are produced on land where high populations of nemas are present in every acre. Growth habits of the rice plant are doubtless largely responsible for its ability to withstand infestation. According to van der Vecht and Bergman there are three periods of root production:

1. Seedling stage, in which the primary root is produced together with many slender, adventitious roots bearing numerous root-hairs.

2. Tillering period, when thicker and longer roots are produced in great numbers, beginning on the lower primary root-nodes and progressing upward. These roots have fewer root-hairs.

3. Toward the end of the tillering period a strong, ramified root system develops a heavy sod in the upper 3 to 5 inches of soil.

Most of the nemas developed in the roots of one period remain there until the roots of the following period are well established. Thus the plant is able to secure moisture and nourishment during critical periods of growth with little interference by the nemas.

Control: Maintenance of fertility is probably the primary factor in producing good crops on heavily infested land. This task is difficult in many rice-producing regions because there are no nearby sources of commercial fertilizers and transportation costs make such fertilizers very expensive. However, in most areas local agronomic practices have maintained high yields during hundreds of years of rice culture.

Van der Vecht and Bergman observed marked differences in susceptibility of certain rice varieties, and breeding and selection of resistant types offer a promising approach to increased yields. One of the most striking instances was that in which roots of the variety Gendjah Ratji contained only 3,740 nemas per plant, while those of the Tjina variety contained 15,300, although both had received the same amount of inoculum.

Radopholus gracilis (deMan, 1880) Hirschmann, 1955

Synonyms: *Tylenchus gracilis* deMan; *Chitinotylenchus gracilis* (deMan) Micoletzky, 1922; *Tylenchorhynchus gracilis* (deMan) Micoletzky, 1925; *Anguillulina gracilis* (deMan) Goodey, 1932b

Radopholus gracilis is typically an inhabitant of wet soil, where it has been found associated with the roots of various plants. After deMan found specimens in the Netherlands, various workers reported the pest from Denmark, Germany, Hungary, and Russia, as recounted by Hirschmann (1955). Imamura erroneously reported the adult of *R. oryzae* from Japan. Sher (1954) and Golden (1957) recorded the species from Hawaii and California, respectively.

Sanwal (1957) made a good detailed morphological study of a species which he identified as *Radopholus gracilis.* This form had a triangular gubernaculum, an indication that it belonged to a different species. The writer collected preadult specimens from Fish Lake, Utah, which have a very long esophageal isthmus and which doubtless are an undescribed species. Hirschmann made *Tylenchorhynchus behningi* Micoletzky, 1923, and *Radopholus gigas* Andrassy, 1954, synonyms of *R. gracilis.* Since several species doubtless are represented in the group, it appears advisable to retain them as valid species.

Hirschmann suggested that *Radopholus gracilis* and *R. oryzae* were synonymous. She kindly loaned the writer a few specimens from Germany which were compared with collections from Java and found to be distinctly different. The following measurements are from Hirschmann (1955):

Morphology: ♀: 1.4–2.7 mm; a = 50–69; b = 4.7–7.6; c = 13–20; V = 47–59
♂: 1.6–2.4 mm; a = 45–69; b = 5.0–5.8; c = 14–20

Lateral fields about one-third body width, marked by four incisures. Lip region truncate, only about one-fourth as high as wide, marked by four or five minute striae. Spear averaging 20 μ long, bearing strong basal knobs. Cephalids visible just posterior to cephalic framework. Details of esophagus as illustrated. On a favorable specimen the esophageal intestinal junction was clearly seen to consist of a spheroid valvular apparatus located within the anterior end of the intestine. Basal lobe of esophagus extending ventrally under the intestine a distance equal to five to seven body widths. Hemizonid not observed. Ovaries outstretched, the oöcytes arranged in single file except for a short region of reproduction. A prominent spermatheca present in each uterus. Female rectum extending into base of intestine, as illustrated on the one specimen examined. In specimens with shrunken body contents the two series of subdorsal and subventral suspension muscles were a prominent feature, as illustrated. Spicula arcuate, slightly cephalated, resting on a lineate, troughlike gubernaculum. Lateral incisures of male arranged somewhat like those of *Radopholus oryzae* except for the dorsal one, which extends almost to the terminus. Bursa rising well anterior to spicula and extending almost three-fourths the tail length. Tail of both sexes subcylindroid in terminal third, ending in an abruptly conoid, acute terminus. As Hirschmann illustrated, the terminus may be very variable in form. Phasmids near middle of tail, an important feature in differentiating this species from *R. oryzae.* Specimens received from Hirschmann were heavily infected with a sporozoan, apparently *Duboscquia penetrans.*

Radopholus gracilis is distinguished from *R. oryzae* by the low, truncate lip region, less massive spear, more angular spear knobs, and longer isthmus. Lateral incisures extend farther back on tail. Phasmids are near the mid-tail region. The longer tails with subcylindroid ends are especially distinctive.

Distribution: Various points in Europe and perhaps in America. The uncertain status of the species reported makes some records questionable. No evidence indicates that *Radopholus gracilis* is of economic importance.

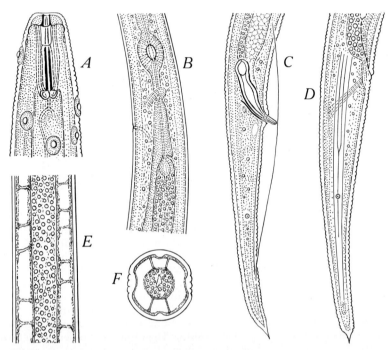

Fig. 9-11. *Radopholus gracilis. A*—Head of specimens infested with *Duboscquia penetrans. B*—Posterior portion of esophagus. *C, D*—Male and female tails. *E*—Mid-body region showing muscle bands supporting intestine. *F*—Cross section showing position of supporting muscle bands. (*Specimens collected by A. Meyl. Courtesy of Hedwig Hirschmann.*)

Radopholus lavabri Luc, 1957

This species closely resembles *Radopholus oryzae* in length and body proportions. Lip region rounded, marked by five fine striae. Female spear 42 to 45 μ long, or about three times the lip-region width. Spear knobs similar to those of *R. oryzae*. Lateral fields and tails also similar. Annules of cuticle often extending into lateral fields.

Type host: Roots of rice plants
Type locality: French Cameroons, West Africa

Radopholus inaequalis Sauer, 1958

Similar in size to *Radopholus similis*. Sexual dimorphism present. Lateral fields marked by as many as seven incisures. Female tails bluntly rounded with striae arranged around the terminus. Spear knobs pointing anteriorly.

Type host: Soil about the roots of *Condonocarpus cotinifolius* F. v. M. in virgin mallee scrub

Type locality: Near Lake Mournpoul, Victoria, Australia

Radopholus neosimilis Sauer, 1958

Slightly smaller than *Radopholus similis.* Sexual dimorphism present. Female tail length about three times anal body diameter, terminus broadly rounded, not striated. Lateral fields marked by four incisures.

Type host: Same as for *Radopholus inaequalis* above
Type locality: Same as for *Radopholus inaequalis* above

Genus *Chitinotylenchus* Micoletzky, 1922

Type species: *Chitinotylenchus paragracilis* Micoletzky, 1922

Morphology: $\female$: 0.7 mm; a = 32; b = 6.4; c = 11.4; V = ⁵⁶81
Lateral fields not observed. Lip region low, rounded, heavily sclerotized, apparently resembling that of *Radopholus gracilis.* Width of lip region about one-third that of neck base. Spear 13 μ long, the knobs extending backward, giving the appearance of a trifurcate base. Ovary outstretched. Tail rather short, plump, ending in a moderately sharp point.

Micoletzky's description and sketch of the head indicate that this genus resembles *Radopholus.* He noted this fact and gave the specific name *paragracilis* because he was reminded of *R. gracilis.* Only one female was collected.

Habitat: An alpine meadow, Steirmark, Austria.

Genus *Nacobbus* Thorne and Allen, 1944

Diagnosis: Pratylenchinae. Sexual dimorphism present, with the adult female transformed into a swollen, more or less irregularly shaped body, while the male remains a typical filiform tylenchoid nema with a short tail enveloped by a narrow bursa. Esophageal glands lying dorsal along anterior end of intestine. Plant parasites forming galls or swellings on host roots.

Type species: *Nacobbus dorsalis* Thorne and Allen, 1944
The males, young females, and larvae of this genus exhibit marked resemblance to nemas of the genus *Pratylenchus,* although the distended adult females filled with eggs are reminiscent of *Heterodera* and *Meloidogyne.* Of the three known species only one, *Nacobbus batatiformis,* is an economically important plant parasite. It will be discussed in detail, instead of the type species.

Cobb's root-gall nematode, *Nacobbus batatiformis* Thorne and Schuster, 1956

Synonym: *Heterodera schachtii* male tail and larvae of Cobb (1918)
Historical: In his description of the sugar beet nematode, *Heterodera schachtii,* Cobb illustrated a male, with short, tapering tail enveloped by a narrow bursa, and a small blunt-tailed larva which originated "from Colorado." Obviously these were not specimens of the sugar beet nema-

tode.   It was not until Allen collected *Nacobbus dorsalis* in California
that Steiner recognized some of the specimens as being closely related
to those described by Cobb.   Surveys reported by Caveness (1958) revealed the presence of *N. batatiformis* in several sugar beet growing
areas of eastern Colorado, and there is no doubt that this is the same
species illustrated by Cobb 40 years earlier.

Sugar beets bearing conspicuous galls were observed near Mitchell,
Nebraska, for many years, and these were assumed to have been produced by *Meloidogyne* spp.   In 1949, Schuster dissected some of the galls
and discovered that they were caused by a nematode very different from
Meloidogyne.   Specimens forwarded to A. L. Taylor were identified as a
Nacobbus which Thorne and Schuster (1956) named *N. batatiformis*.   A
survey by Schuster in western Nebraska during 1953 and 1954 revealed
that 32 per cent of 125 sugar beet fields were infested, many of them
suffering severe losses.   These data proved the economic importance of
the species.

Morphology: ♀: 0.7–1.4 mm
Body varying in form and size but usually somewhat spindle-shaped, with
irregular expansions and contractions produced by pressure of the root-tissues
during development.   Head and neck sometimes pressed into anterior end of
body until almost indistinguishable.   Posterior portion of body somewhat
conoid to truncated terminus, on which the vulva and anus are located.   Lip
region usually slightly elevated above head contour.   Spear length 15 to 18 μ,
bearing small basal knobs.   Corpus of esophagus strongly developed, frequently
irregular in form, and set off from median bulb by a narrow constriction.
Median esophageal bulb spheroid, with conspicuous radial musculature.   Esophageal glands forming a broad, thick lobe pressed against anterior end of intestine.   Intestinal cells packed with coarse, refractive granules.   Cell nuclei
frequently prominent.   Vulva a deep, transverse slit.   Uterus ending in an
ovate or pyriform spermatheca, which usually contains hundreds of spermatozoa.
Oöcytes arranged about a slender rachis.   Immediately behind the cap cell of
the ovary about 12 small oöcytes constitute a circumference, and as they increase
in size, the number is reduced to 8, then 6, and finally 4 when they are fully
developed.   Eggs thin-shelled, 49 by 83 μ, deposited before segmentation.
Usually the ovary has more convolutions than illustrated.

♂: 0.8–1.2 mm; a = 32; b = ?; c = 35–45; T = 62–78
Lip region continuous with body contour, bearing four annules and the
labial disc.   Lateral fields marked by four incisures.   Labial framework hexaradiate, heavily sclerotized.   Spear 20 to 25 μ long, with strong knobs which are
slightly cupped anteriorly.   Median esophageal bulb about half as wide as
neck.   Esophageal glands forming an elongate lobe extending dorsally over
intestine.   Hemizonid adjacent to excretory pore.   Deirids not observed.   Testis
occasionally extends as far forward as middle of esophageal lobe.   Spicula
26 μ long; gubernaculum a simple trough, about one-fourth as long as spicula.
Bursa enveloping the short arcuate tail.   Phasmid opening at base of bursa,
slightly posterior to middle of tail.

Larva: 0.32–0.38 mm; a = 18; b = 4.5; c = 15
Cuticle marked by very fine transverse striae.   Lateral field outlined by two
fine, bright lines.   Lip region, spear, and general body form resembling those
of a young *Pratylenchus*.   Tail bluntly rounded, even on larvae removed from

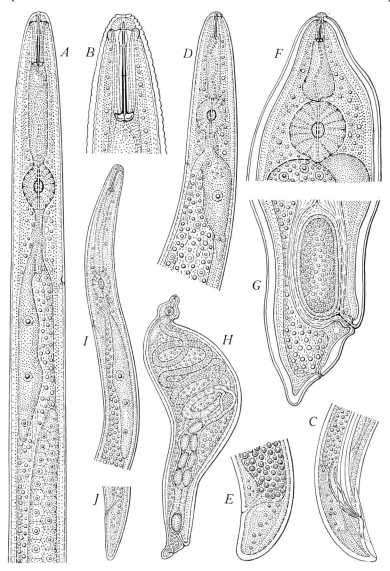

Fig. 9-12. *Nacobbus batatiformis.* *A–C*—Anterior portion, head and tail of male. *D, E*—Anterior and posterior portions of preadult female. *F, G*—Anterior and posterior portions of adult female. *H*—Female. *I, J*—Anterior and posterior portions of larva. (*After Thorne and Schuster. Courtesy of Helminthological Society of Washington.*)

eggs before hatching. First-stage larvae with pointed tails were not observed as in *Nacobbus dorsalis.* Esophageal gland lobes about as long as body width at time of hatching, but they develop rapidly and soon are three to four times as long as body width. Genital primordium a single cell with well-developed nucleus when larva emerges from egg.

Biology: Since the sugar beet is the most economically important known host of *Nacobbus batatiformis,* studies on the life cycle have largely been made with this crop. But the wide host range of taxonomically diverse plant species indicates that considerable variation in the life cycle may be expected when it is studied in detail on the various hosts. Doubtless, there will be only one generation on short-lived annuals, while on perennials there may be two or more. Under semidesert conditions existing throughout much of the range of this nematode, activity on the native hosts must necessarily be restricted to relatively short periods when moisture is present. On irrigated hosts the life cycle may be completed three or four times since favorable moisture conditions prevail throughout the season.

A few preadults overwinter, but apparently most of the population live through as eggs which hatch when the growing season begins. Larvae penetrate the roots and become established in favorable positions. Often a dozen or more will be grouped in one small area. Frequently three or four will be found immediately behind the root-tip. After the first

Fig. 9-13. Sugar beet infested with *Nacobbus batatiformis.* (*After Thorne and Schuster.*)

moult the immature nemas have an average length of about 0.5 mm and assume an open C form. Growth continues until they are 0.6 to 0.8 mm long, and at this stage they lie coiled within the galls. After a second moult they become juvenile females and males, and many of them migrate into the soil as the severely injured small roots die. Copulation might be expected to occur at this time, but among the many young females examined not one was spermatized.

The immature females then move to other roots, usually larger ones, and again enter and force their heads among the cells surrounding the central cylinder. Hundreds of these cells become hypertrophied, and frequently three to six females will be found in a single gall. As the gall develops, the posterior portion of the female extends toward the periphery and an opening is formed through which the eggs are discharged into a gelatinous matrix extruded by the female. Occasionally males are found entangled in this mass; this fact indicates that fertilization occurs after gall formation has begun.

Large galls frequently contain no living females, and only masses of darkened tissue mark the spots in which they developed. Galls usually bear numerous small rootlets; sometimes upward of fifty occur on one gall alone. In advanced stages portions of roots between galls and even portions of the beet will bear many of these rootlets.

Schuster's studies of the pathological histology showed a necrosis of the cell walls and increased cell division in the vicinity of the young nematode. Gall formation is the result of increase in cell size and numbers, and this increase results in a spindle or egg-shaped area near the head of the young female. The long axis of this spindle usually is parallel to the root axis.

The spindle appears to function as a unit. The individual cells may lose their identity in advanced stages, and the entire area may be of an amorphous tissue type with cell walls which do not take on the characteristic stain of normal cells. Cell walls commonly collapse, and enlarged cells result from "coalescence" of adjacent cells; cell enlargement also results from accentuated cell growth. Nuclei occasionally divide without concomitant cell division, and multinucleate cells result. As galls develop, the affected portions become granular in appearance and later yellow in color. Invasion outside the vascular cylinder results in galls, or "warts," on the surface of older tap-roots, arising almost entirely from cortical tissue.

Hosts and distribution: Extensive investigations of native and introduced hosts in western Nebraska were made by Schuster. The most common native hosts appeared to be three species of cactus: *Opuntia tortispina* Nutt., *O. fragilis* (Nutt.) Haw., and *Corypantha vivipara* Nutt. Isolated colonies from cacti and sugar beets gave reciprocal infestations, and the morphology and mode of reproduction of these colonies were similar. From these data it may be assumed that *Nacobbus batatiformis* is indigenous to the area and that it has adopted the sugar beet as one of its preferred hosts.

Knowledge of the distribution of *Nacobbus batatiformis* was greatly expanded by the work of Caveness and his associates (1958) during their survey of nematodes parasitic on sugar beets in the Great Plains area and neighboring states. Infestations were observed in thirteen counties in Kansas, Nebraska, Colorado, Wyoming, and Montana; this fact indicates that the species is indigenous to the entire region.

Schuster made extensive observations of host plants under field and experimental-plot conditions, supplemented by greenhouse tests. The presence of females producing viable eggs was the criterion by which plant species were determined to be susceptible. Degree of distortion and galling varied greatly, indicating that certain plants were more favorable hosts than others. Morphology of females also varied, those from sugar beets being plump and well developed, while others from *Salsa* and *Chenopodium* were misshaped by pressure of the hard, woody tissues.

A total of seventy-four plant species, including ninety-two varieties, representing fifteen families of the angiosperms, were tested for their reaction to *Nacobbus batatiformis*. All species tested of the Chenopodiaceae, Cruciferae, Cactaceae, and Zygophyllaceae gave susceptible reactions, whereas those of the Gramineae, Liliaceae, Malvaceae, Iridaceae, Amaranthaceae, and Convolvulaceae appeared to be nonsusceptible. Species of the Leguminosae proved to be nonsusceptible with the exception of *Pisum sativum,* on which rather small galls were produced. Some species of the Cucurbitaceae, Umbelliferae, Compositae, and Solanaceae were resistant, while others were susceptible. A complete list of the species tested was recorded by Thorne and Schuster (1956).

Nacobbus batatiformis will doubtless be found inhabiting a much wider range than that in which it is now known. Its importance as a potential plant parasite is attested by the fact that it attacks beet, rutabaga, broccoli, cabbage, turnip, radish, lettuce, pumpkin, cucumber, tomato, carrot, and pea, all of which are crops grown within its range. Distribution to new localities can be anticipated, since it can readily be carried in seedling plants, nursery stock, and soil.

Control: *Crop rotation.* Fortunately, alfalfa, clover, wheat, oats, rye, barley, corn, onion, and potato are not hosts of this nema. All can be used in rotations to reduce populations to a point where susceptible crops can again be produced.

Clean culture. Since mustards, lamb's-quarters, Russian thistle, and other weeds will harbor the nemas, they must be kept under control if crop rotations are to be successful.

Soil fumigation. Applications of recognized soil fumigants give satisfactory control. *Nacobbus batatiformis* is typically an inhabitant of light, sandy soils, and therefore no difficulties should be experienced in the application of chemicals.

Genus *Rotylenchulus* Linford and Oliveira, 1940

Diagnosis: Pratylenchinae? Marked sexual dimorphism. Adult female an irregular-shaped, reniform, saccate body. Male about same length as larva, slender, with moderately developed spear and narrow bursa extending almost to terminus. Young female resembling an immature *Pratylenchus* in general body form. Dorsal gland outlet about one spear length behind spear. Obligate plant parasites.

Type species: *Rotylenchulus reniformis* Linford and Oliveira, 1940

The taxonomic position of *Rotylenchulus* is doubtful. Linford and Oliveira gave the generic name because of certain similarities to the genus *Rotylenchus*, while the writer (1949) assigned it to Pratylenchinae. The Chitwoods (1950) placed it with *Nacobbus* in a new subfamily, Nacobbinae. Careful studies of specimens from many parts of the world will probably reveal that several species are involved and that they constitute a distinct subfamily or family.

Reniform nematode, *Rotylenchulus reniformis* Linford and Oliveira, 1940

Morphology: Larva: 0.3–0.44 mm; a = 21; b = 4; c = 13

♂: 0.33–0.5 mm; a = 24; b = 4.2; c = 11.8

Young ♀: 0.32–0.43 mm; a = 19; b = 31; c = 15

Mature ♀: Reniform portion of body 0.32–0.48 mm; width 0.12–0.17 mm

Cuticle finely annulated. Lateral fields of young and males marked by four fine lines. Lip region sclerotized, with six sectors. Labial annules not observed. Median esophageal bulb strongly developed, basal bulb extending over intestine, forming a large, irregular-shaped, flattened lobe in female. Excretory pore just posterior to median bulb. Outlet of dorsal esophageal gland a conspicuous feature because of its distance behind the spear. Posterior portion of female variably reniform, terminating in a spicate process. Vulva a transverse slit. Ovaries with several convolutions due to crowding. Male tail 1 to 1½ times as long as spicula; bursa narrow, not enveloping terminus. Phasmids slightly anterior to middle of tail.

Life cycle: The unusual life cycle of *Rotylenchulus reniformis* was covered in detail by Linford and Oliveira, and the following résumé is from their account. Although the newly hatched larvae have a well-developed spear 14 to 18 μ long, they have not been observed feeding. When held in water without plant roots, they soon pass through three superimposed moults to become young infective females and adult males. However, while in water they were unable to release the moulted cuticles.

By using the Linford (1940) root-observation boxes, it was possible to watch the young females force their way into the root-cortex until they were partly or completely embedded. Three days after feeding began, a slight swelling was observed on the posterior portion of the female, and 8 days later well-developed embryos were present in eggs deposited against the glass side of the box. When these eggs were transferred to water, they promptly began to hatch. Rate and duration of oviposition appeared to vary with individual females and with favorable or unfavorable hosts. Whippoorwill cowpeas gave counts as high as 78 per egg mass, with a mean of 54. Both eggs and empty shells reached a high of 196, with a mean of 121. The complete life cycle was accomplished in about 25 days, provided that the young females immediately located host roots.

Sex ratio of larvae hatched in water was approximately 1 to 1, but in soil washings males usually outnumbered young females. Developing females attracted numerous males, which coiled sluggishly about the body, although copulation was not observed. An average of 5.9 males were found in the gelatinous matrix secreted about the vulva into which eggs were deposited. Occasional males were found with females which were completely embedded within roots.

Hosts and distribution: Linford and Yap (1940) in Hawaii reported sixty-five host plants belonging to thirty families; thus the host range

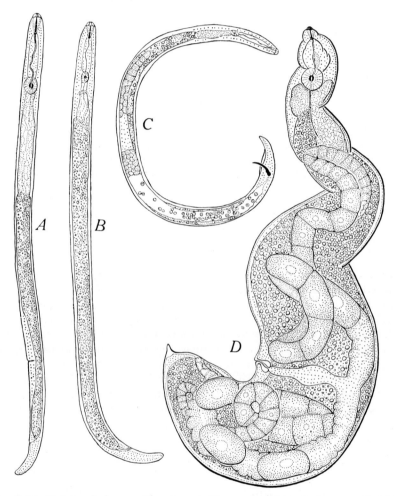

Fig. 9-14. *Rotylenchulus reniformis.* *A*—Young female. *B*—Larva. *C*—Male. *D*—Female. *(After Linford. Courtesy of Helminthological Society of Washington.)*

will cover hundreds of species. Among the most favorable hosts were Whippoorwill cowpea, bean, cucumber, eggplant, okra, pineapple, and many others. More limited reproduction was noted on radishes, indigo, and bush lima bean. Three species, bermuda grass, *Cynodon dactylon* (L.) Pers, *Leucaenea glauca* Benth., and *Stenotaphrum secundatum* Kuntze, were apparently very resistant to the entry of the nemas.

Smith and Taylor (1941) first reported the species in the United States, where it was found infesting cotton and soybeans near Baton Rouge, Louisiana. Steiner (1949) found it severely infesting tomato and coffee weed, *Cassia torro* L., in Florida. Martin (1955) found it in South Africa, and Peacock (1956) recorded numerous hosts in the vicinity of Accra, Gold Coast, Africa.

The writer observed the pest infesting tobacco, tea, clove, and other plants in Java, and clove in Sumatra, in 1951 and 1952. One collection was made in the Philippines. In tea nurseries severe losses were inflicted on young plants when the tap-root was attacked and killed early in their growth. If a strong tap-root became established, there was no apparent injury. In commercial tea plantings no damage was visible, while, in cloves, infestations were accompanied by decline and dieback. The pest is doubtless widely distributed throughout the tropics and frequently is of considerable economic importance. Infestations have probably been overlooked in many instances because of sand grains adhering to the gelatinous secretion surrounding the females.

GENERA OF UNCERTAIN POSITION

Genus *Atylenchus* Cobb, 1913a

Type species: *Atylenchus decalineatus* Cobb, 1914

Morphology: ♀: 0.6 mm; a = 34.5; b = 5.5; c = 7.1; V = $^{21}66$

♂: 0.6 mm; a = 35.5; b = 5.9; c = 10; T = 45

Body rather cylindroid from region of vulva to the blunt, rounded lip region. Posteriorly it ends in an attenuated tail. Cuticle marked by very coarse annules, which are subdivided by 10 deep furrows near middle of body. These decrease in numbers toward the head and on the tail. Lateral field marked by two crenate lines lying between cuticular ridges. Lip region bearing four outward-spreading setae sublateral, 7 to 9 μ long. Lip region with four to six annules. Amphid apertures near oral opening. Two minute papillae on each submedian lip. Stylet 14 to 16 μ long, with strong, rounded knobs. Esophagus tylenchoid, with ovate median bulb and elongate-pyriform basal bulb. Cardia oval. Deirid prominent, near latitude of nerve ring. Hemizonid not observed. Ovary outstretched, posterior uterine branch slightly shorter than body width.

This unusual tylench, together with *Eutylenchus setiferus*, probably represents a family group. The above measurements are from Cobb and much of the description from Chitwood and Tarjan (1957), whose specimens were rather similar in size and proportions to those reported by Cobb.

Habitat: Found by Cobb in soil from a cranberry bog, New Lisbon, New Jersey. Collected by Chitwood and Tarjan about roots of sugar cane and other plants, Lake Alfred and Gainesville, Florida. Also reported by Hirschmann (1954) from Germany.

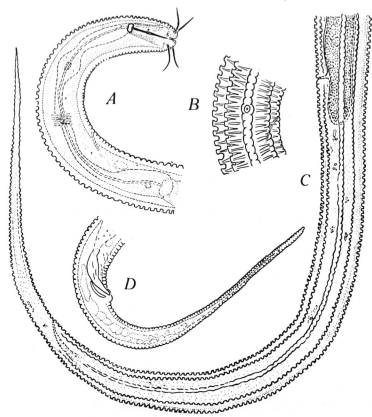

Fig. 9-15. *Atylenchus decalineatus.* *A*—Anterior portion of body. *B*—Deirid region. *C*—Posterior portion of female. *D*—Male tail. (*After Chitwood and Tarjan.*)

Genus *Eutylenchus* Cobb, 1913a

Type species: *Eutylenchus setiferus* Cobb, 1913a
Synonym: *Tylenchus setiferus* Cobb, 1893

Morphology: Body marked by coarse annules. Head armed with four strong, outspreading setae. Spear plain, with small knobs. Tail elongate to acute terminus bearing a broad, flaplike adanal bursa. Spicula slightly arcuate, pointed. Gubernaculum not observed.

Probably this species and *Atylenchus decalineatus* are related, but definite information must await collection of additional specimens.

Habitat: Soil about native plants, Harwood, New South Wales, Australia.

Chapter 10

Family NEOTYLENCHIDAE Thorne, 1949

Diagnosis: Median valvular esophageal bulb absent. Cephalic framework in either six or eight sector. Basal portion of esophagus variable, joined directly to intestine; definite basal bulb with cardia; basal bulb with short glandular extensions; elongated glandular extensions containing the gland nuclei or bearing a stemlike basal process extending into the intestine. Prodelphic, with ovary outstretched, rarely reflexed. Posterior uterine branch present or absent.

Type subfamily: NEOTYLENCHINAE Thorne, 1941

Neotylenchidae is composed of a diverse group of genera in which the absence of a valvular median esophageal bulb is the one common characteristic. Body tissues of most genera are more dense than those of other tylenchs, and hence detailed morphological examinations are frequently rendered very difficult. This is especially true of *Hexatylus, Deladenus,* and *Paurodontus.*

Certain Neotylenchidae appear to be closely related to members of the Family Tylenchidae: *Nothotylenchus* resembles *Ditylenchus, Nothanguina* is similar to *Anguina,* and *Thada* is reminiscent of *Tylenchus cancellatus.* Either there has been a parallel development of the two families, or these similar genera are descendants of common ancestors. However, in *Hexatylus, Paurodontus, Ecphyadophora,* and similar genera there are outstanding characteristics which merit generic and supergeneric standing.

Chitwood (1958) reduced the group to subfamily rank under the Family Tylenchidae, but the writer regards this action as unjustified. The classification admittedly is unsatisfactory in certain respects and must remain so until missing elements are collected. However, it is deemed more fitting to bring together the various groups where they may be more critically evaluated. Thus the taxonomy presented is of necessity based on convenience as well as on morphological characters.

Key to genera of Neotylenchidae

1. Esophagus base fused with intestine, not set off................*Hexatylus*
   Esophagus with a basal bulb or elongated glandular lobes............... 2
2. Basal esophageal bulb bearing a stemlike extension.................... 3
   Basal bulb not bearing a stemlike extension........................ 4
3. Spear knobs approximately symmetrical....................*Paurodontus*
   Submedian spear knobs much larger than the dorsal one.........*Stictylus*

Subfamily NEOTYLENCHINAE Thorne, 1941

Diagnosis: Neotylenchidae. Labial framework divided into eight sectors, two of which may be greatly modified. Base of esophagus frequently extended in an elongate lobe. Cardia not present. Ovary prevulvar. Posterior uterine branch rarely present. Males ditylenchoid.

Type genus: *Neotylenchus* Steiner, 1931a

Diagnosis: Neotylenchinae. Cephalic framework in eight sectors, of which certain ones may be greatly reduced. Basal bulb of esophagus joined to intestine by an obscure muscular valve. Spear usually with three definite basal knobs. Ovary outstretched or reflexed. Spicula, gubernaculum, and bursa ditylenchoid. A small genus of about ten species.

Type species: *Neotylenchus abulbosus* Steiner, 1931a
Synonym: *Hexatylus abulbosus* (Steiner) Goodey, 1933

Morphology: ♀: 0.76; a = 27; b = 5.5; c = 10.5; V = [67]86
             ♂: 0.74; a = 39; b = 11.2; c = 20
Form of neck and esophagus as illustrated. Distance from vulva to anus somewhat shorter than tail length. Cuticle marked by four incisures. Cephalic sectors of almost equal size. Female spear bearing forward-curved processes on the knobs; male spear absent. Ovary outstretched, sometimes reaching to excretory pore. Spicula and gubernaculum poorly developed. Bursa crenate, rising in front of spicula and extending to terminus.

This species is readily recognized by form of female spear, elongated basal bulb of esophagus, absence of spear in male, and rudimentary spicula and gubernaculum.

Host and distribution: Steiner found specimens inhabiting buds, stems, and leaves of strawberry plants, affected by "yellows" or "xanthosis," from California. Apparently the species is endoparasitic, although symptoms have not been defined or pathogenicity demonstrated.

Neotylenchus acutus Thorne, 1941

Morphology: ♀: 0.8 mm; a = 26; b = 4.4; c = 9; V = $^{60}83$

Transverse striae obscure, more distinct on subcuticle. Lateral field a smooth, refractive band about one-fourth as wide as body. Lateral sectors of cephalic framework narrow, with amphids located on outer contour of lips. Anterior portion of spear only about half as long as shaft. Basal knobs of spear very small. Corpus of esophagus cylindroid, tapering to a narrow isthmus. Basal portion of esophagus an extended gland with prominent nucleus. Intestine with narrow lumen and dense, thick walls. Ovary with oöcytes arranged in single file, sometimes forming a double flexure, an unusual occurrence in this genus. Male unknown, and females contained no spermatozoa (Fig. 10-1).

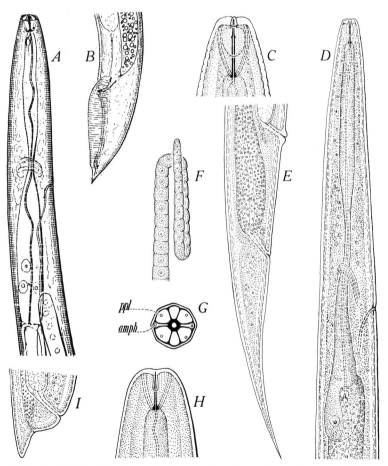

Fig. 10-1. *A, B—Neotylenchus abulbosus,* female neck and male tail. (*After Steiner.*) *C–F—Neotylenchus acutus,* head, neck, posterior portion of female, flexures of ovary, and face view. *H, I—Neotylenchus obesus,* head and posterior portion of female. (*After Thorne. Courtesy of Great Basin Naturalist.*)

Habitat: Frass of bark beetle, *Ips leconti* Swaine, from piñon pine, *Pinus edulis* Engelmn., near Tabiona, Utah.

Neotylenchus obesus Thorne, 1934

Synonym: *Iotonchium obesum* (Thorne) Filipjev & Stekhoven, 1941

Morphology: ♀: 0.8 mm; a = 10–16; b = 5–6; c = 20–50; V = 95–99
Obese body varying considerably in width. Spear 7 μ long, with very small knobs. Head rounded, with delicate framework in eight almost equal sectors. Esophagus with somewhat spindle-shaped corpus and narrow isthmus. Basal esophageal bulb generally obscured by pressure of ovary, which frequently extends to nerve ring. Oöcytes in multiple rows arranged about a rachis. Vulva sometimes almost terminal (Fig. 10-1).

Habitat: Small, pitlike lesions on alfalfa crowns, Greeley, Colorado, and potato field, Aberdeen, Idaho. It was not determined if the nemas were causal agents of the lesions. Perhaps they were merely mycelophagous.

Genus *Deladenus* Thorne, 1941

Diagnosis: Neotylenchinae. Esophagus joined to intestine by an obscure valvular apparatus immediately behind nerve ring. Esophageal glands extending in lobes over the intestine. A tiny, chamberlike opening sometimes present in corpus of esophagus where the submedian gland outlets are located. Vulva less than 10 per cent from terminus. Posterior uterine branch absent. Spicula and gubernaculum tylenchoid. Bursa almost enveloping tail. A small genus of four known species.

Type species: *Deladenus durus* (Cobb, 1922) Thorne, 1941
Synonyms: *Tylenchus durus* Cobb; *Anguillulina dura* (Cobb) Goodey, 1932; *Ditylenchus durus* (Cobb) Filipjev, 1936

Morphology: ♀: 1.0 mm; a = 30–50; b = 8–10; c = 25; V = ⁷⁰93
            ♂: 1.0 mm; a = 50; b = 8; c = 24; T = 65
Body rather cylindroid except at the tapering extremities. Striae about 1.5 μ apart. Lateral field elevated, consisting of six longitudinal elements. Deirids near latitude of excretory pore. Phasmids not seen. Amphid apertures porelike, located adjacent to vestibule entrance. A single papilla on each of the four rounded submedian lips. Cephalic armature in eight sectors, the lateral ones much reduced. Spear about 8 μ long, with distinct knobs. Corpus of esophagus with a fusiform swelling containing a tiny chamber into which the submedian salivary glands empty. Dorsal esophageal gland lobe four to six times as long as body width, containing one unusually large nucleus. Nuclei of submedian glands not observed. Excretory pore with heavily sclerotized tube. Intestinal lumen very narrow, twisted and convoluted in a most unusual manner. Ovary outstretched. Oöcytes at first in single file but soon arranged in four columns, forming a distended ovary. No rachis observed. Testis outstretched. Spicula and gubernaculum tylenchoid. Bursa enveloping tail except for a small part of the terminus.

Habitat and distribution: *Deladenus durus* probably feeds on the mycelia of fungi associated with decaying plant material and is not an obligate plant parasite. Cobb described the species from galls of chestnut oak, *Quercus prinus* L., near Lebanon Church Postoffice, Virginia. Other

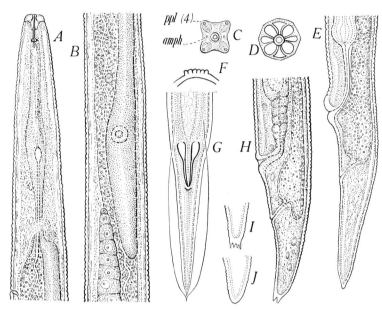

Fig. 10-2. *Deladenus durus. A, B*—Anterior portion of body. *C*—Face view. *D*—Basal plate of cephalic framework. *E, H*—Variations in posterior portion of female. *F*—Cross section of lateral field. *G*—Male tail. *I, J*—Variations in terminus of female. (*After Thorne. Courtesy of Great Basin Naturalist.*)

collections have been made from decaying fungus, *Pleurota* sp., near Payson, Utah; soil about alfalfa crowns, Manti and Murray, Utah, and Medford, Oregon; decaying potato tubers, Utah, Idaho, and Montana. Specimens from alfalfa crowns possessed longer necks and more posteriad excretory pores.

Subfamily Nothotylenchinae Thorne, 1941

Diagnosis: Neotylenchidae. Cephalic framework in six sectors. Corpus of esophagus cylindroid or with a fusiform swelling. Ovary outstretched. Posterior uterine branch present. Spicula and gubernaculum tylenchoid. In general form these nemas resemble members of the genera *Tylenchus* and *Ditylenchus.*

Type genus: *Nothotylenchus* Thorne, 1941

Diagnosis: Nothotylenchinae. Nemas so closely resembling *Ditylenchus* that determination under the highest powers of the microscope is always necessary.

Corpus of esophagus cylindroid or with a fusiform basal swelling. Basal esophageal bulb pyriform to cylindrical, joined to esophagus by a small but distinct cardia. Ovary outstretched, the oöcytes arranged in single file. Posterior uterine branch present. Spicula and gubernaculum ditylenchoid. Bursa extending to near middle of tail.

Type species: *Nothotylenchus acris* Thorne, 1941

Morphology: ♀: 0.9 mm; a = 33; b = 6.2; c = 15.5; V = ^{40}80
    ♂: 0.7 mm; a = 35; b = 6.5; c = 9.5; T = 48

Lip region about one-third as wide as base of neck. Tail conoid, ending in an abruptly pointed terminus. Lateral field marked by four incisures which occupy about one-fifth the body width. Deirids obscure, phasmids not seen. Spear slender, the tapering apical portion occupying only one-third its length.

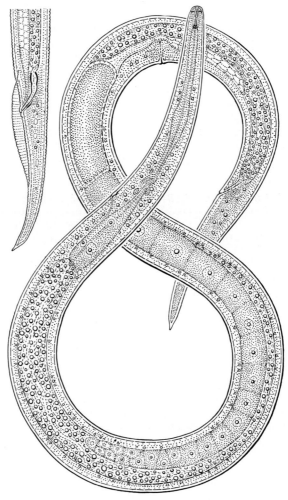

Fig. 10-3. *Nothotylenchus acris.*

Spear knobs well developed. Corpus of esophagus with a small, fusiform, valveless bulb. Esophagus lumen passing through ventral portion of basal bulb to a minute cardia. Anterior portion of oviduct forming a spermatheca. Ovary outstretched, the oöcytes arranged in single file. Posterior uterine branch two to three times as long as body diameter. Spicula and gubernaculum tylenchoid. Bursa finely crenate, rising about opposite anterior end of spicula and extending slightly past middle of tail.

Hosts and distribution: Soil about alfalfa crowns, Medford, Oregon; red clover roots, Redmond, Oregon; and sugar beets, Arvin, California. Nishizawa and Iyatomi (1955) found this species infesting strawberry plants in the nursery of the Shizuoka Agricultural Experimental Station, Japan. The nemas inhabit the axils and leaflets, with highest populations in the centers of the buds, where they apparently feed ectoparasitically on the plant tissues. Symptoms include twisting of young petioles, crimping of young leaves, and dwarfed condition of whole plant. Infested plants frequently produced several small lateral buds. Typical symptoms were produced by artificial inoculation into healthy buds by means of a capillary pipette. Distribution usually is through runner plants from infested mothers. Generally the nemas are within the plant tissues, not in soil. Havertz (1957) found *Nothotylenchus acris* living in roots of crested wheat grass in Utah.

Genus *Boleodorus* Thorne, 1941

Diagnosis: Nothotylenchinae. Cephalic framework in six sectors, the lateral ones much reduced in size. Spears of known species about 12 μ long, with prominent basal expansions which are more flangelike than rounded knobs. Corpus of esophagus with fusiform, valveless basal enlargement into which the submedian esophageal glands empty. Basal bulb of esophagus distinctly set off from intestine, to which it is joined by a well-developed valvular apparatus. Excretory duct with unusually strong sclerotization. Oviduct composed of several prominent cells, an anterior one forming a prominent spermatheca. Posterior uterine branch less than half as long as body width. Spicula and gubernaculum of the simple tylenchoid type. Bursa adanal, about twice as long as body width.

Type species: *Boleodorus thylactus* Thorne, 1941

Morphology: $\female$: 0.6 mm; a = 31; b = 5.5; c = 8.0; V = [36]61[1]

$\qquad$ $\male$: 0.5 mm; a = 33; b = 5.0; c = 7.2

Body arcuate, the female tail almost always ventrally hooked, male tail somewhat straighter. Bodies of fixed specimens always twisted until the heads and tails are seen from slightly submedian views. Striae about 1 μ apart near middle of body. Lateral field a refractive band about one-fifth the body width, bordered by two bright lines and bearing two other faint lines which mark the field into three equal spaces. Deirids slightly posterior to base of neck. Phasmids about one body width posterior to anus. Excretory tube so heavily sclerotized that frequently it forces the esophageal bulb out of alignment.

Cephalic papillae and amphids very obscure. Specimens stained intra-vitam with neutral red and gentian blue show that there apparently are 16 papillae, 6 grouped about the vestibule, 4 near the margins of the submedian lips,

and 6 very obscure ones near the base of the lip region.   Amphid apertures
minutely oval, located below contour of lips.   Amphidial tubes and pouches
best seen when stained with neutral red.   Cephalic framework strongly sclerotized.   Details of spear and esophagus typical of the genus.   Basal esophageal
bulb with a very large dorsal gland nucleus and two small submedian ones.

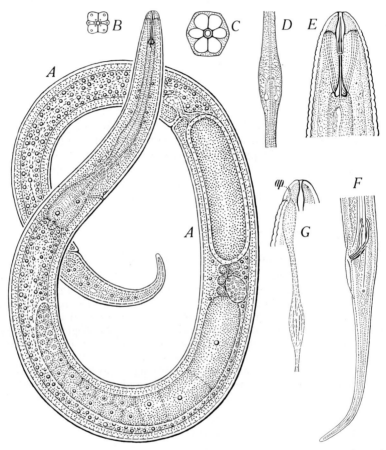

Fig. 10-4. *Boleodorus thylactus.* *A*—Female. *B, C*—Face view and cephalic
framework. *D*—Dorsoventral view of esophageal corpus, showing outlets of submedian esophageal glands. *E*—Head. *F*—Male tail. *G*—Amphidial system as
seen when stained by neutral red. (*After Thorne. Courtesy of Great Basin
Naturalist.*)

   Just after fertilization the spermatozoa are found in the lumen of the
oviduct, but soon they migrate to the fifth dorsal cell of the oviduct,
which enlarges to form a pouchlike spermatheca; hence the specific name
thylactus (pouch).   Testis single, outstretched.
   Boleodorus thylactus is one of the two known tylenchs with arcuate,

ventrally bent tail. The other species is *Tylenchus davaini,* which is about twice as long as *B. thylactus* and is easily recognized because of its size.

Hosts and distribution: This interesting species is found throughout the Western states and is known as far east as Wisconsin. Several thousand per pound of soil were found about the roots of declining celery near Pleasant Grove, Utah. Perhaps these nemas feed on root-hairs; if so, they may be of economic importance.

Genus *Thada* Thorne, 1941

Diagnosis: Small nemas with abnormally thick cuticle marked by deep striae. Cephalic framework in six sectors, the lateral ones being distinctly smaller. Esophagus with cylindroid corpus, slender isthmus, and definitely set off, elongate basal bulb. A caplike valvular apparatus joins it with the intestine. Ovary outstretched, the oöcytes in single file. Posterior uterine branch shorter than body width. Spicula arcuate, cephalated by an expansion. Gubernaculum thin, troughlike. Bursa adanal, narrow.

Type species: *Thada striata* Thorne, 1941

Morphology: ♀: 0.65 mm; a = 30; b = 6.0; c = 9.0; V = $^{37}71^2$

♂: 0.52 mm; a = 26; b = 5.2; c = 8.0; T = 48

Body practically cylindrical between vulva and base of neck. Lip region about one-fourth as wide as neck base. Tail uniformly conoid to blunt, rounded terminus. Cuticle marked by deep transverse striae which are coarser on the female than on the male. Lateral field marked by four refractive lines which at mid-body occupy one-third to three-fifths the body width. Amphid apertures porelike, located slightly dorsad on the outer contour of the lateral lips. Apparently only a single papilla on each submedian lip. Oviduct forming a spermatheca in its anterior portion. Testis reflexed a distance equal to one or two body widths.

Habitat: Desert soil about the roots of shadscale, *Atriplex conferticolia* (Torr. & Frem.) S. Wats., west of Utah Lake, Utah; and alfalfa crowns, Skull Valley, Utah.

Many specimens were somewhat deformed by slight swellings in the tail region, which may have been caused by some disease.

Thada cancellata Thorne, 1941

Morphology: ♀: 0.52 mm; a = 25; b = 5.4; c = 8; V = $^{20}66^2$

Cuticle marked by 155 to 175 deep transverse striae. At mid-body there are 16 longitudinal striae, the number decreasing toward the extremities. Lateral field marked by four deep incisures ending anteriorly and posteriorly as illustrated. Deirids prominent, located opposite basal esophageal bulb. Phasmids not seen. Spear exceedingly slender, its base obscured by muscle attachments until it was not possible to determine whether or not knobs were present Dorsal esophageal gland nucleus prominent, while the submedian are very small, with one apparently located near base of bulb. A distinct valvular apparatus present in anterior end of intestine. Ovary only four or five body widths long, the oöcytes arranged in single file. Anterior portion of oviduct serving as a spermatheca. Male unknown (Fig. 10-5).

Habitat: Sugar beet field, Fort Collins, Colorado.

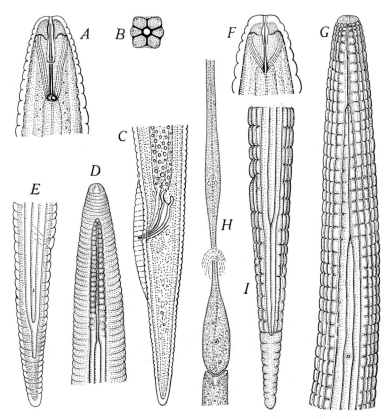

Fig. 10-5. *A–E—Thada striata,* head, face view, male tail, anterior portion of body, and female tail. *F–I—Thada cancellata,* head, anterior portion of body, esophagus, and posterior portion of female. *(After Thorne. Courtesy of Great Basin Naturalist.)*

Genus *Nothanguina* Whitehead, 1959

Diagnosis: Nothotylenchinae. Body plump, coiled, resembling that of *Anguina.* Cephalic framework in six sectors, the lateral ones somewhat larger than the submedian. Probably a single papilla on each submedian lip. Amphids on outer contour of lateral lips. Junction of esophagus and intestine an obscure muscular valve. Ovary single, outstretched or reflexed. Posterior uterine branch present. Bursa extending almost to the digitate terminus.

Type species: *Nothanguina cecidoplastes* (T. Goodey, 1934) Whitehead, 1959

Synonyms: *Anguillulina cecidoplastes* Goodey, 1934; *Anguina cecido-plastes* (Goodey) Filipjev, 1936

Morphology: ♀ : 1.2–2.0 mm; a = 13–18; b = 9–13; c = 18–32; V = 88–93
         ♂ : 0.9–1.3 mm; a = 16–23; b = 6–8; c = 13–17

Lip region low, flattened, about six times as wide as high, set off by a slight narrowing of the head contour. Spear 7 to 9 µ long, with small basal knobs. Dorsal esophageal gland aperture about 14 µ behind spear. Corpus of esophagus fusiform in region of submedian gland outlets. Ovary with double flexure, oöcytes arranged about a rachis. Spermatheca short, set off by sphincter cells.

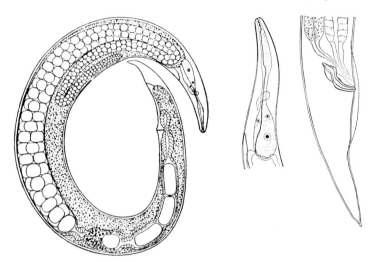

Fig. 10-6. *Nothanguina cecidoplastes.* Female, anterior end of female and male tail. *(After T. Goodey. Courtesy of Journal of Helminthology.)*

Posterior uterine branch present. Eggs 31 to 38 µ by 85 to 100 µ, segmented when deposited.

Male body fusiform, stout. Testis with single flexure, not reaching to esophagus. Spicula thickened, irregularly cephalated. Gubernaculum absent. Bursa rising just anterior to spicula and extending almost to the digitate terminus.

The general body characters of *Nothanguina* resemble those of *Anguina*, while the arrangement of the cephalic papillae and amphid apertures are more like those of *Ditylenchus*. The two known species, *N. cecidoplastes* and *N. phyllobia*, represent rather divergent types. The ovary of *N. cecidoplastes* contains multiple rows of oöcytes arranged about a rachis, and a gubernaculum is lacking, while in *N. phyllobia* the oöcytes are arranged in single file and the gubernaculum is present.

Goodey states that there are two larval stages, the first 0.53 to 0.66 mm long, the second 0.7 to 0.8 mm in length. Whitehead found that larvae probably moult once within the egg, then once after hatching to form the third-stage infective larvae. Apparently only one moult takes

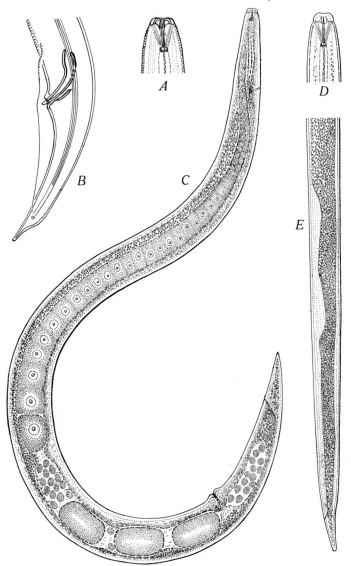

Fig. 10-7. *Nothanguina phyllobia.* *A*—Head. *B*—Male tail. *C*—Female. *D,* *E*—Head and portion of preadult. (*After Thorne. Courtesy of U.S. Department of Agriculture.*)

place in the host tissues when young males and females are formed, but this point was not definitely determined.

Type host: Galls produced on the leaves, stems, and flowers of *Bothriochloa pertusa* (Willd.) A. Camus, = *Andropogon pertusus* Willd.

Type locality: Collected by Venkatarayn from pastures in southern India and forwarded to T. Goodey

Nothanguina phyllobia (Thorne, 1934) n. comb.

Synonyms: *Anguillulina phyllobia* Thorne, 1934; *Ditylenchus phyllobius* (Thorne) Filipjev, 1936

In the original description the writer recorded the median esophageal bulb as "much reduced" and erroneously illustrated a small valve. This object actually was the refractive outlets of the submedian esophageal glands.

Morphology: ♀: 0.75–0.95 mm; a = 23; b = 8.3; c = 18; V = $^{75}82^8$

♂: 0.7–0.85 mm; a = 30; b = 7.4; c = 18; T = 85

Cuticle with excessively fine striae. Lateral field about one-tenth body width, marked by four bright lines. Lip region set off by a narrowing of the head contour. Cephalic framework in six sectors. Papillae and amphid apertures arranged as in *Ditylenchus dipsaci*. Labial striae not observed. Spear strongly knobbed, slightly longer than width of lip region. Corpus of esophagus cylindroid. Basal esophageal bulb obscure, crowded by the ovary. Ovary a single line of oöcytes except for a short section of multiplication. Spermatheca an elongate chamber. Posterior uterine branch extending two-thirds tne distance back to anus, frequently filled with spermatozoa. Eggs slightly longer than vulva body diameter. Female tail uniformly conoid, acute, with phasmids near beginning of terminal third.

Male more slender than female. Spicula slightly arcuate, somewhat cephalated, resting on a thin, troughlike gubernaculum. Bursa rising opposite anterior end of spicula and extending almost to the digitate terminus. Phasmids far back near beginning of digitate terminus.

Quiescent form. During the dry season the quiescent, preadults live over in dried leaves of the host. The young nemas average 0.62 mm in length and are 25 μ wide. Genital primordium translucent, no differentiation between sexes visible. Tail conical, with slightly rounded terminus. In a single leaf the population was estimated to be 842,000.

Details of the pathology are not known. Extensive hypertrophy and thickening and convoluting of infested leaves are obvious symptoms.

Type host: *Solanum eleagnifolium* Cav., the only known host

Distribution: Two small infestations were first found by H. R. Brisley near Camp Verde, Arizona, in 1922. Plants growing along ditch banks and in flooded areas were preferred. H. R. Reynolds (personal communication) reports colonies in the Salt River Valley west of Phoenix, Arizona, and in the Rio Grande Valley near Balmorhea and Weslaco, Texas. He notes that infestations develop after rains in July and August. One plowing destroyed the host and apparently eradicated the nemas.

Fig. 10-8. Leaves of *Solanum elaeagnifolium* infested with *Nothanguina phyllobia*. (*Specimens courtesy of H. W. Reynolds.*)

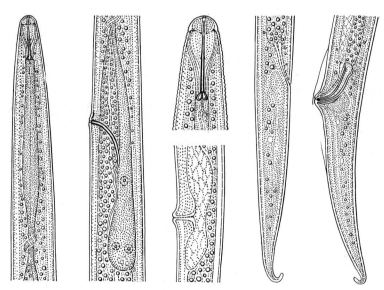

Fig. 10-9. *Halenchus fucicola.* (*Specimens courtesy of T. Goodey.*)

Tylenchus dipsaci var. *tobaensis* Schneider, 1937, may be a member of *Nothanguina*. This is an aquatic species found infesting *Potamogeton mucronatus* and *Myriophyllum spicatum* growing in Tobameer, Sumatra, Indonesia.

Genus *Halenchus* Cobb, 1933

Diagnosis: Tail elongate-conoid with hooked terminus. Corpus of esophagus cylindroid to fusiform without valvular median bulb. Esophageal glands extending dorsally over intestine in an elongated clavate lobe.

Type species: *Halenchus fucicola* (deMan and Barton, 1892) Cobb, 1933

Synonyms: *Tylenchus fucicola* deMan and Barton, 1892, in deMan, 1892; *Anguillulina fucicola* (deMan and Barton) T. Goodey, 1932b

Morphology: ♀: 1.3 mm; a = 40; b = 6; c = 11; V = 63
♂: 1.2 mm; a = 52; b = 6; c = 12

Body almost straight when relaxed by gradual heat. Cuticle marked by fine striae. Laterial field a plain band about one-eighth as wide as body, occasionally bordered by faint lines. Lateral cord conspicuous, about one-third body width. Longitudinal muscles may be mistaken for incisures by the uninitiated. Tail elongate, convex-conoid, ending in a hook which is bent both ventrally and to the left. Lip region hemispheroid without striae. Cephalic framework so obscure that even from a face view the six sectors can scarcely be distinguished. Amphid apertures at apex of lateral lips. Cephalic papillae four, one on the outer contour of each submedian lip. Spear 17 to 19 μ long, with moderately developed knobs. Muscles of spear extending forward and outward to the sclerotized sides of the labial framework. Esophagus with cylindroid or fusiform corpus devoid of a valvular apparatus. Esophageal glands extending dorsally over the intestine, forming a relatively huge, clavate lobe in which the three gland nuclei can usually be observed. Excretory tube heavily sclerotized and a conspicuous feature, more prominent than that of any other known tylench. Hemizonid and excretory pore adjacent, slightly elevated. Intestine with sparse, refractive granules. Ovary outstretched, oöcytes arranged in single file. Anterior half of uterine tube serving as a spermatheca in which numerous very large granular spermatozoa frequently are found. Spicula arcuate, cephalated. Gubernaculum simple, troughlike. Bursa rather narrow, rising slightly anterior to spicula and extending about two-fifths the tail length.

Host and distribution: *Fucus* (*Ascophyllum*) *nodosus* from east and west coasts of Scotland, and at mouth of Clyde River; Ayshire coast; and Port Erin, Isle of Man. Numerous specimens, determined by Cobb as this species, collected by the writer in 1930 near the Marine Biological Station, Woods Hole, Massachusetts. Small yellow or brown blotches on the bladderlike growths of the plant marked the nema colonies. No appreciable injury to the plants was evident.

The above emended description from specimens collected near the type locality on the island of Cumbrae, Scotland, and sent to the writer by T. Goodey.

Genus *Ecphyadophora* deMan, 1921

Diagnosis: Body very slender, without visible striae or lateral fields. Tails of both sexes ending in convex-conoid, truncated termini. Lip region rounded, with obscure sclerotization. From a face view the head is seen to be divided into six sectors. Amphid apertures appearing as tiny slits on the outer margin of the lateral lips. A single papilla apparently is present on each submedian lip, but the excessive smallness of the head makes accurate observations difficult. Spear tylenchoid, with well-developed knobs. Esophagus irregularly cylindroid, difficult to distinguish. Tarjan (1957a) determined from stained specimens that it bore an elongate lobe extending back beside the intestine. Nerve ring near middle of esophagus. Body ventrally narrowed at vulva, ovary prevulvar, outstretched. Posterior uterine branch about twice as long as vulva body diameter. Testis outstretched, spicula lineate, slightly curved. Bursa extending back as elongated flaps. Male body abruptly narrowed at anus.

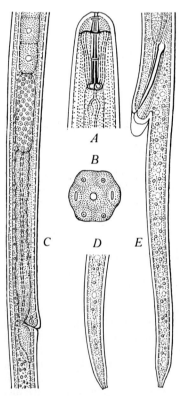

Fig. 10-10. *Ecphyadophora tenuissima.* A—Head. B—Face view. C—Reproductive region of female. D—Terminal portion of female. E—Posterior portion of male. (*Specimens courtesy of P. A. A. Loof.*)

Type species: *Ecphyadophora tenuissima* deMan, 1921

The single known species of this genus ranks among the most slender of nematodes and may easily be overlooked under the dissecting microscope. Relaxed specimens are practically straight. Tarjan reports that living nemas frequently assumed a multiple coil position. The following measurements are from Tarjan's data on specimens from Ruurlo, Netherlands. His specimens from Florida were somewhat shorter, with rather divergent proportions, as might be expected.

Ecphyadophora tenuissima deMan, 1921

Morphology: ♀: 1.0 mm; a = 159; b = 6.4; c = 10.8; V = ^{23}75

♂: 1.0 mm; a = 159; b = 6.0; c = 12.2; T = 24

General characters as set forth in the generic diagnosis. Most of the specimens illustrated by Tarjan possessed bluntly rounded tails, while in those observed by the writer the tails were truncate.

Habitat: About roots of various plants, Netherlands and Florida.

Subfamily PAURODONTINAE Thorne, 1941

Diagnosis: Basal esophageal bulb bearing a stemlike extension. Intestine often enveloping part, or even all, of the basal esophageal bulb. Ovary prevulvar, outstretched. Posterior uterine branch often absent. Spicula tylenchoid, bursa adanal or caudal. Body generally very dense in texture making observation of details difficult.

Type genus: *Paurodontus* Thorne, 1941

Diagnosis: Spear knobs symmetrical, or nearly so. Tails of both sexes acute or subacute. Bursa adanal. Only four species known.

Type species: *Paurodontus gracilis* Thorne, 1941

Morphology: ♀: 0.74 mm; a = 31; b = 7.2; c = 7.2; V = ^{54}76
♂: 0.65 mm; a = 35; b = 5.5; c = 6.5; T = 58
Transverse striae about 1.3 μ apart at their widest points. Lateral fields marked by four equally spaced incisures occupying about one-third the body width. Deirids and phasmids not observed. Vulva-anus distance about equal to tail length. Amphid apertures located on minute elevations at the apices of the lateral lips. A single papilla on each of the four submedian lips. Corpus of esophagus cylindroid, narrowing to the slender isthmus. Basal esophageal bulb elongated with a tubular valvular apparatus extending into intestine. A chamber surrounding the bulb apparently is formed by tissues from the anterior end of the intestine. Dorsal gland nucleus conspicuous, submedian nuclei obscure. Intestinal cells with distinct nuclei. Ovary outstretched, with oöcytes in single file. Anterior portion of oviduct forming a spermatheca. Posterior uterine branch about as long as body width. Spicula and gubernaculum simple, tylenchoid. Bursa slightly crenate, adanal.

Habitat: Soil about cotton roots, Tifton, Georgia.

Paurodontus densus Thorne, 1941

Morphology: ♀: 0.4 mm; a = 25; b = 5.7; c = 12; V = ^{55}82
Details of the body are largely illustrated in Fig. 10-11, *F–J*. Phasmids not observed. Deirids exceedingly small, located about opposite anterior end of esophageal bulb. Lateral lips much reduced, with amphid apertures at their apices. A single papilla on each submedian lip. Ovary outstretched, the oöcytes in single file. Oviduct not bearing a special branch like that of *Paurodontus apiticus.*

Habitat: Soil about roots of date palms, Indio, California.

Genus *Stictylus* Thorne, 1941

Synonym: *Sphaerulariopsis* Wachek, 1955

Diagnosis: Paurodontinae. Dorsal knob of spear much smaller than the ventrosubmedian ones. Terminus blunt, rounded. Bursa enveloping almost the entire tail. Six species known, most of them from the frass of bark beetles.

Type species: *Stictylus asymmetricus* Thorne, 1941

Morphology: ♀ : 0.8 mm; a = 22; b = 5.1; c = 27; V = ^{70}90

♂ : 0.8 mm; a = 27; b = 5.7; c = 23; T = 65

Female body generally assuming an arcuate form when relaxed by gradual heat. Lateral field marked by four lines, occupying a space one-fourth to one-third the body width. Lumen of esophagus at first lying against the elongated

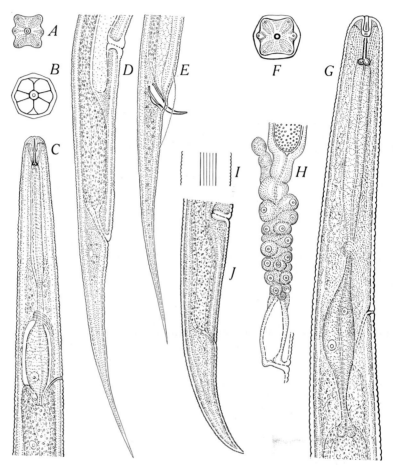

Fig. 10-11. *A–D—Paurodontus gracilis,* face view, basal ring of labial frame-work, neck, posterior portions of female and male. *F–J—Paurodontus densus,* face view, neck, uterine region, lateral field, and posterior portion of female. (*After Thorne. Courtesy of Great Basin Naturalist.*)

spear knobs. Corpus of esophagus fusiform. Basal bulb of esophagus ovoid to pyriform, with elongated stem extending into intestine. In certain specimens this stem was only one-fourth as long as that illustrated. Intestine packed with dense, coarse granules. Ovary outstretched in young females, while in older specimens one or two flexures were observed. Posterior uterine branch absent. Vulva and anus elevated.

Habitat: Soil about roots of desert plants near U.S. Field Station, Sacaton, Arizona.

Subfamily HEXATYLINAE Skarbilovitch, 1952

Diagnosis: Neotylenchidae. Basal portion of esophagus joined directly to intestine. Spear knobs slightly bifurcate, sometimes appearing as if six knobs instead of three are present; hence the generic name *Hexatylus*. Vulva near 90 per cent, ovary outstretched, the ova arranged in multiple rows about a

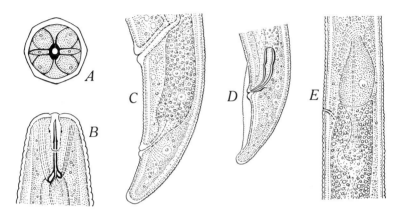

Fig. 10-12. *Stictylus asymmetricus.* *A, B*—Face and lateral views of head. *C*—Posterior portion of female. *D*—Male tail. *E*—Junction of esophagus and intestine. (*After Thorne. Courtesy of Great Basin Naturalist.*)

rachis. Males with tylenchoid bursa, spicula, and gubernaculum; very rarely observed.

Type genus: *Hexatylus* Goodey, 1926

Diagnosis: Esophagus base fused with intestine. Lumen of esophagus with distinct change of structure near base of corpus, where it becomes much wider, the walls heavier, and a muscular apparatus apparently is present. Pharynx slightly sclerotized, forming several minute guiding rings for spear. Cephalic framework divided into eight sectors, the lateral ones being somewhat narrower. Amphid apertures and four labial papillae near outer margin of lip region. A small genus of about six species.

Type species: *Hexatylus viviparus* Goodey, 1926
Synonym: *Iotonchium viviparum* (Goodey) Filipjev & Stekhoven, 1941

Morphology: ♀: 1.0–1.5 mm; a = 15–35; b = 5–7; c = 17–20; V = $^{70}89$
Marked variation in width is found between females which have not begun egg production and those which are approaching senility. Senile specimens sometimes shorter than younger specimens in the same collection. Lateral field marked by four refractive lines, the two outer ones being more prominent. Tissues of basal portion of esophagus somewhat less dense in structure than those of the intestine, to which they are fused. This basal portion includes a

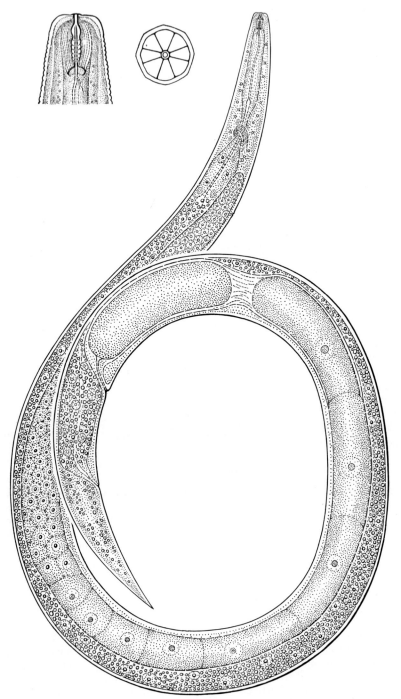

Fig. 10-13. *Hexatylus viviparus.* Head, basal ring of cephalic framework, and female.

number of nuclei, some of which appear identical to those of the intestine, while others probably correspond to the nuclei of the esophageal glands. Ovary often extending forward to nerve ring, the anterior half made up of hundreds of oöcytes grouped about a prominent rachis. Posterior portion a long tube in which the ova develop. Frequently larvae develop before eggs are deposited; hence the specific name *viviparus*. One colony from frass of a bark beetle in Utah contained numerous tylenchoid males.

Habitat and distribution: Described from decaying potato tubers and gladiolus corms, England. Colonies from the corms transferred to 2 per cent malt extract gave a growth of fungus mycelium on which the nemas throve and reproduced in great numbers. Reported from other localities in Europe and from various points in the United States. Usually found in decomposing potato tubers, alfalfa crowns, and other decaying plant tissues. Probably a typical mycelophagous species.

Chapter 11

Family HETERODERIDAE Skarbilovich, 1947

Subfamily HETERODERINAE Filipjev, 1934

Key to genera

1. Female a white saccate body with thin cuticle, eggs ejected into a mucoid mass about the posterior end; frequently gall-forming
   Meloidogyne Goeldi, 1887
   Female a tough, white saccate body, retaining most or all of eggs; not gall-forming... 2
2. Body becoming a brown cyst at maturity, vulva near terminus
   Heterodera Schmidt, 1871
   Body remaining white, vulva slightly posterior to middle of body
   Meloidodera Chitwood et al., 1956

Males are known only for *Meloidogyne* and *Heterodera,* and these are cylindroid with blunt, rounded tails devoid of bursae. Identification is best made from face views, which reveal the amphid apertures of *Meloidogyne* as elongate slits leading into pouchlike chambers in the lateral lips. In *Heterodera* the apertures are much shorter and their inner parts more tubelike. Occasionally a dorsoventral view of the head permits identification, when the pocketlike "cheeks" of *Meloidogyne* are visible. The posterior cephalids of male *Heterodera* and *Meloidogyne* are diagnostic in their location. Those of *Heterodera* lie opposite the middle of the spear, whereas in Meloidogyne they are opposite the spear base.

Meloidodera larvae closely resemble those of *Heterodera* but are readily distinguished by their large, easily observed phasmids. Larvae of both genera possess robust, strongly knobbed spears 20 μ long which differentiate them from the more slender, lightly knobbed spears of *Meloidogyne,* which average only 10 μ in length.

Cyst-forming nematodes, genus *Heterodera* Schmidt, 1871

During the 80 years following the discovery of the sugar beet nematode, *Heterodera schachtii* Schmidt, all the cyst-forming nematodes observed were generally included under that name. Although Liebscher (1890, 1892) had studied the form attacking peas and named it *H. gottingiana* and Wollenweber had observed differences in the form attack-

270

ing potatoes and named it *H. rostochiensis,* these names were not recognized because the authors failed to present diagnostic morphological characters by which the forms could be identified. Consequently these two species, as well as those attacking cereals and other plants, were all regarded as merely host forms of *H. schachtii.*

Because of this nomenclatorial confusion, the host lists of this era include all the plants on which any *Heterodera* was observed, and therefore a large part of these records are of doubtful value. This statement applies not only to the early records but also to those of Shaw (1915),

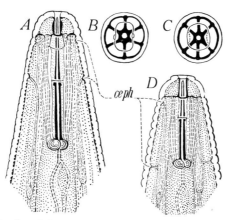

Fig. 11-1. *A, B*—Head and face view of *Heterodera schachtii. C, D*—Head and face view of *Meloidogyne hapla.*

Goodey (1933), Corder, Buhrer, and Thorne (1936), and Filipjev and Stekhoven (1941).

A voluminous and verbose literature had been built up on *Heterodera schachtii* during these years, but it was largely composed of repetitions and rehashes of the best early works and contained few new and worthwhile data. As Stift (1912) observed after attempting to review the many papers which had been written, "Here stand I, a poor fool, and am as wise as was before" (literal translation). But Stift did produce a good résumé of the work up to that time and assembled an extensive bibliography. Shaw (1915) gave us an outstanding and well-presented résumé in English of the pertinent European literature.

Morphology and Life History of *Heterodera*

Brown cyst: The genus *Heterodera* is unique among other nematode genera because of the unusual ability of the female cuticle to transform into a tough, brown, cystlike sac, protecting the eggs which have been formed within the body. This phenomenon constitutes one of the most outstanding instances of defensive adaptation found among the plant parasitic nematodes. Within this protective cyst the larvae may lie qui-

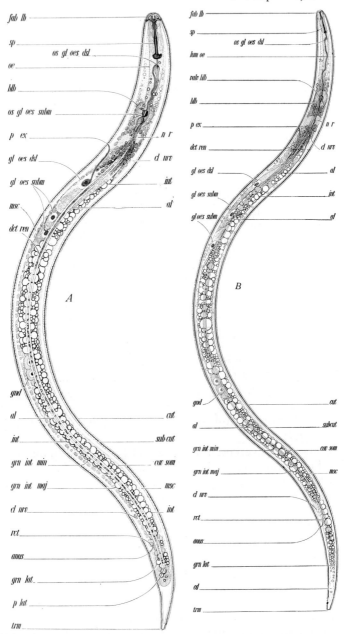

Fig. 11-2. *A*—Larva of *Heterodera schachtii,* the sugar beet nematode. *B—* Larvae of unidentified species of *Meloidogyne,* root-knot nematode. (*After Cobb. Courtesy of Nematology Section, U.S. Department of Agriculture.*)

escent for long periods when favorable host plants are not present or during times of unfavorable moisture and temperature conditions. Since the beginning and the end of the life cycle are associated with the brown cyst, it is fitting that we first investigate this interesting structure and follow the development of the larval nemas lying dormant therein.

Brown cysts are typically ovate to spheroid in form and usually range from 0.4 to 0.8 mm in length, with occasional extremes as small as 0.2 and as large as 1.1 mm, according to the species, the host, soil type, and growing conditions. Specimens are frequently found which have been deformed by pressure of roots or soil particles. Cyst walls decompose very slowly, with the result that the cysts accumulate year after year until an old infested field may have many billions per acre and as little as 10 g of soil from any part of it will usually contain one or more. The greater portion of these old cysts hold no eggs, while those developed during recent years will contain one or more to a full complement, which may number over 600 in large species like the sugar beet nematode.

Viewed externally, the cysts vary in color from light brown to dark reddish brown. The extreme outer layer presents a rugose surface composed of a network of zigzag or irregular ridges forming patterns which occasionally are distinctive of certain species. Just beneath this rugose pattern can usually be seen a field marked by minute punctations, generally without any definite arrangement, but occasionally in somewhat regular rows as in *Heterodera punctata*. Very small cysts containing fewer than twenty eggs usually have a thinner, lighter-colored cuticle which appears to be devoid of both rugose and punctate markings.

Transverse sections of the cyst wall of *Heterodera schachtii* show that it is built up of at least three layers; a very thin, rough outer layer formed by the rugose pattern, a thick exocuticle, and a somewhat thinner endocuticle. The exocuticle often presents an appearance of being columnar because of the radial markings, which apparently are associated with the punctations of the cuticle. These radial striae may actually be minute tubules through which the material is exuded to form the subcrystalline layer found on the females of certain species (Fuchs, 1911). The fibrous endocuticle sometimes appears to be made up of several layers. Ferris and Siegel (1957) demonstrated by electron microscopy that five distinct layers are present in the endocuticle of *H. rostochiensis*. Below these five layers is an indistinct, poorly defined layer which Wieser (1953) designated as the basal lamella.

An individual *Heterodera* passes through five stages in its development from the unsegmented egg to the adult female or male, and during this process it moults four times. True, we usually speak of the "brown-cyst stage," but this actually is the final form attained by a normally developing female at the completion of her life cycle and therefore does not constitute a sixth stage. Following is a brief account of these stages; should the reader desire more detailed information the works of Chitwood and Buhrer (1946) on *H. rostochiensis* and that of Raski (1950) on *H. schachtii* should be consulted.

Eggs. Female *Heterodera* produce fewer than 10 to more than 600 eggs which are two to three times as long as wide. Triffitt (1929) reported variations in width of 35 to 50 μ and in length of 75 to 125 μ, the average being 46 by 110 μ. When first formed, the egg is filled with undifferentiated granular material which often contains a visible nucleus. Segmentation in its various stages may be observed readily as the eggs are produced within the female, and frequently all stages are found in very recently formed cysts. Division follows the usual 2, 4, 8, 16, etc., series, but it very often is possible to see an intermediate stage of 3 as the egg passes from 2 to 4.

First-stage larva. This second stage in the life cycle develops from the segmented egg and its gross morphology usually is visible. In rare instances it is possible to observe moulting of the first cuticle within the egg as the larvae reaches the preparasitic or infective third stage. Eggs from mature cysts usually contain well developed third-stage larvae folded in loops within the tough membranous covering.

Preparasitic larva. Specimens of this third stage in the life cycle of *Heterodera* are most easily collected from the cysts, where they are found within the eggs or lying quiescent in the cyst cavity. During the growing season of their hosts they will often be found living free in the soil as they make their way about searching for roots in which to make their homes. A good portion of those present in a soil sample will be collected on the 200-mesh screen during processing.

Morphology: Length usually 0.4 to 0.5 mm, with occasional individuals as short as 0.3 mm and as long as 0.6 mm. The body is distinctly more robust and the spear more strongly developed than in *Meloidogyne* larvae. The very small phasmids immediately distinguish these specimens from *Meloidodera* larvae. The esophageal region is well developed, with strong median bulb and elongated basal glands extending back along the anterior end of the intestine. The genital primordium will be seen as a group of rather clear cells lying at the ventral side and slightly posterior to the middle of the body.

Entrance is made at any point on the root system, but tips of young roots appear to be preferred. In heavily infested soil it is not unusual for so many larvae to enter the roots that the young plant is severely stunted or even killed. This is especially true of the sugar beet nematode, which frequently kills the young plants before they reach the four-leaf stage. Beets which survive may be entirely covered by females and cysts at harvesttime.

Invading larvae take up a position parallel to the central cylinder in small roots, usually with the head pointing toward the plant. In larger roots they remain near the cortex. Giant cells are produced at the feeding point by a coalescence of cells near the heads of the larvae. The products of these cells nourish the nemas during their growth to maturity.

Fourth stage. The third-stage larvae soon moults and becomes somewhat cylindroid, about the same length as that of the original larva but much broader. During this period the genital primordium develops to an elongated mass of cells forming a "clear" area in the posterior third of the body. At this point in the life history the sexes cannot be differentiated, but as development proceeds the females become flask-shaped, while the male remains more or less cylindroid.

Female. From the flask form the female rapidly becomes more obese, breaks through the root cortex, and after two additional moults becomes an adult. In all species an elongated neck region remains embedded in the root tissues. The body becomes somewhat lemon-shaped in the *Heterodera schachtii* group and spheroid to pear-shaped in *H. rostochiensis* and its relatives. In lemon-shaped forms the vulva forms a terminal cleft, and the anus is located somewhat anterior to it on the dorsal side of the body. In the *H. rostochiensis* group the vulva and anus are both located on the rounded posterior portion of the body.

Male. When fully developed, the slender, active male completes the final moult and moves through the soil in search of the female. Frequently sugar beet nematode males are found in the gelatinous matrix surrounding the posterior end of the female. As many as four have been observed with one female. Sengbusch (1927) observed copulation of sugar beet nematodes on two occasions and found spermatozoa in most of the females examined. Males are very common in most species of *Heterodera,* but in certain species like *H. trifolii* they may be rare or unknown. Instances of males feeding on root tissues have not been recorded.

Emergence of Larvae from Brown Cysts

The factor or factors which influence the dormancy of *Heterodera* larvae are as yet unknown. Just why certain larvae within a cyst should hatch the first year while others remain 2, 4, 6, or even 10 years or more before emerging is a most baffling problem. Marcinowski (1909) suggested that plants secrete substances which diffuse through the soil and attract their nematode parasites. Baunacke (1922) conceived the idea that this substance might be used to stimulate the hatching of sugar beet nematode eggs and demonstrated that excretions secured by washing roots of beets did increase hatching of larvae. Numerous other substances and chemicals were tested without discovering anything of particular value or interest. Rensch (1924) attempted to isolate the stimulating substance and produced two compounds which increased rate of hatching. However, they did not have sufficient promise to justify continuing the work.

The problem of host stimulation and the manner in which nemas respond to root diffusates were well set forth by Steiner (1925). Citing a number of instances, he came to the conclusion that plant-infesting nematodes not only have the ability to recognize host plants but are able to distinguish the preferred one. He postulated that the active parts of root secretions are of rather simple chemical nature and that the element or elements which stimulate the larvae to hatch from the eggs are not the same as those which direct them to the roots. These elements are carried in soil water and are recognized by the nemas, which then proceed to the preferred roots. Discussing the possible methods by which nemas perceive these stimuli, Steiner offered the very plausible explanation that they are detected through the amphids. By means of these organs "the nema is led to its preferred host by some chemotaxic influence exerted by the plants." Apparently young, growing roots are the principal source of these secretions.

That nemas are capable of recognizing the root diffusates of their preferred hosts is indicated by the fact that weed hosts of the sugar beet nematode growing among sugar beets frequently are not attacked, while those in adjacent fields where sugar beets are not growing bear numerous females.

Thorne (1923) studied the emergence of sugar beet nematode larvae under actual field conditions and reported on data secured from twenty-one fields which had been in rotations without sugar beets 1 to 12 years. A total of 38,128 cysts were examined, and the data demonstrated that there was a continual emergence each growing season and that most of the population was hatched by the end of the sixth year. Emergence was especially heavy during the first year of the rotations, when it was estimated that more than half the larvae left the cysts, regardless of the crop grown.

Franklin (1938a) examined cysts of *Heterodera rostochiensis* from fields in Yorkshire, England. Those from a field only one year out of potatoes contained an average of 173.9 eggs per cyst, while from a field six years out of potatoes only 18.8 eggs per cyst remained. Yet in fields from Lincolnshire cysts from a one-year field contained only 75 eggs per cyst, while cysts from an eight-year field contained 24. Franklin attributes the differences in numbers of eggs per cyst in one-year fields to possible variation in cyst size. In the older fields crop histories might have had some bearing on the number of eggs remaining.

Perhaps the most exhaustive studies on the effects of cropping practices on the dormancy of *Heterodera schachtii* are those of Jones (1956). These were conducted in a large number of "microplots" (1/6,000 acre), and standard practices of fertilizing, sowing, cultivating, and harvesting were followed. Increase or decline of populations was determined by soil sampling. From the data secured it was possible to predict the number of years necessary to continue crop rotations when the various levels of infestation were definitely known. Den Ouden (1956) reported investigations on the influence of several host and nonhost plants on the hatching of *H. schachtii*. *Hesperis matronalis* was found to produce a very activating root excretion, yet was not attacked by nematodes. This biennial plant possesses a well-developed root system and appears to offer possibilities as an agent to reduce populations more rapidly and thus shorten the time required for crop rotations. Since this plant is a weed, certain precautions must be exercised to prevent it from becoming a pest in fields where it is introduced.

Root Diffusates

While working with potatoes Triffitt (1930) secured results which indicated that a water-soluble substance was produced by the roots which stimulated larvae to emerge from the cysts. Since that time other workers have found that leachings from preferred hosts usually produce similar responses when applied to the species of *Heterodera* under investigation. Diffusates are absorbed in water as it leaches through the soil about roots. These leachings may be collected and stored under refrigeration for future use, since the diffusates appear to be of a rather stable character.

Concentration of the hatching agent from potato-root leachings was first accomplished by Fassuliotis and Feldmesser (1952) when they divided the leachings into two fractions by freezing at 28 to 30°F for 40 hours. At this temperature one fraction was frozen, while the other was not. The unfrozen portion produced a greater rate of emergence of the larvae of the golden nematode of potatoes, *Heterodera rostochiensis,* than did the frozen portion, tap water, or unmodified potato-root leachings.

Fenwick (1952) found that activation of the larvae of *Heterodera rostochiensis* was decreased as the potato-root diffusate was diluted. Hague (1954) concentrated potato-root diffusate by vacuum distillation and determined that the most effective dilution of this concentrate was 1 to 16. Wallace (1956) made similar observations on the concentrate of sugar beet roots in activating larvae of *H. schachtii.*

Factors Influencing Emergence of Larvae

Wallace (1955) found that 25°C (77°F) is the optimum temperature for hatching larvae in the laboratory. Since field temperatures are not constant throughout the day, he conducted a series of experiments which demonstrated that 8 hours at 24°C followed by 16 hours at 15°C produced a marked increase in emergence.

Unfortunately experiments on the hatching of eggs of *Heterodera* must be carried out under conditions foreign to the natural habitat of the nemas. In fields they are surrounded by soil particles, among which circulate water, air, carbon dioxide, and other products, including attractive or unattractive exudates of living plant roots, decaying organic matter, and living soil organisms. When they are removed from this complex habitat of the soil atmosphere and brought into the laboratory, it is most remarkable that they respond as favorably as they sometimes do to the distilled water, root leachings, and other inorganic products to which they are exposed. Obviously, research of this type should be conducted under conditions which simulate as nearly as possible the natural habitat in which the nemas developed and in which they were lying quiescent when the soil was collected and brought into the laboratory.

Products which retard or inhibit the emergence of larvae from cysts have also been encountered: Morgan (1925) found that mustard inhibited the development of *Heterodera rostochiensis* cysts on potatoes when the two plants were grown together in pots. Triffitt (1930) confirmed these findings, although field trials failed to produce similar results. Wallace (1956) reported that concentrations of urea, sucrose, and sodium chloride above the 10^{2m} drastically inhibited the emergence of *H. schachtii* larvae. Thorne (1956) recorded that indol-3-acetic acid 1/50,-000,000 and theelin 1/1,000,000 both acted as hatching deterrents. Thorne and Fielding (unpublished data) demonstrated that hatching of sugar beet nematode larvae could be immediately stopped by adding the filtered extracts from a small sugar beet crushed in 100 ml of water.

Maturity of cysts had a direct bearing on larval emergence, those recently matured being much less activated by root diffusates than those which had been in storage for several months. There is always the problem of cysts which have been formed late in the season or when the host was destroyed at harvest. Many of these were immature females prematurely forced into the brown-cyst stage. As a result the eggs within them were either unsegmented or in various stages of segmentation, and differentiation was necessarily completed during dormancy. Just how long this process requires is not known, but Thorne (1956) found that under Utah conditions some eggs were still undergoing segmentation as late as mid-June, eight or nine months after cyst formation.

Occasionally cysts contain no viable eggs, perhaps because the female was not fertilized or because the host plant was harvested before eggs were developed in the ovaries. From outward appearances these cysts are perfectly normal; yet a small number of such nonviable cysts in an experiment will create serious errors in the hatching data. The only manner in which corrections for these aberrant cysts can be made is to open each one after the experiment and observe the contents.

Unfortunately, throughout the extensive research conducted on the hatching of larvae from the various species of *Heterodera* cysts, attention has been directed only to those larvae which actually emerge from the cysts, and little or nothing is recorded about the many which failed to emerge. In the field these quiescent individuals are of the greatest importance, because they are responsible for perpetuating the species through unfavorable periods when host plants are not present. Over a period of five or six years a cyst containing 500 larvae may gradually lose a portion of them each year during a crop rotation. If at the end of that time only a few larvae still remain within the eggs, they will be sufficient to reestablish a colony if a favorable host is again planted. Up to the present time no one has discovered any substance which will entice all the larvae to emerge from every cyst. No diffusate or other product has been applied to soil and appreciably reduced the number of eggs contained in the cysts.

Opening the cysts after an experiment is completed is always a most rewarding experience; those who have failed to do so have missed the most important part of their work. In some cysts every egg has hatched, and the larvae have emerged, while in rare instances none has hatched. In one sugar beet nematode cyst the writer found 625 fully developed larvae, which became active as soon as the eggshells were carefully ruptured. Occasional cysts contained 200 or 300 hatched larvae which apparently had been unable to escape because there were no openings in the cyst walls. Cysts containing dead eggs or larvae usually are filled with fungus mycelia, which occasionally bear sclerotia.

Saprophagous nematodes, *Acrobeloides bütschli, Eucephalobus oxyuroides, Panagrolaimus subelongatus,* and other species often inhabit the cysts. The beginner should not confuse these other species with *Heterodera* larvae (Thorne, 1928).

Cyst-collecting Techniques

Cysts are separated from soil by the usual Cobb sifting and gravity methods, with certain variations designed for this special problem. Egg-filled cysts from soil taken directly from the field usually sink to the bottom of the containers during the sifting process. Those which are empty or only partly filled with eggs float on the surface and accumulate around the side of the washing pans, together with similar-sized particles of organic matter. The following suggestions are offered to facilitate the recovery of cysts:

1. Pour the muddy liquid from pan to pan more rapidly than usual; otherwise egg-filled cysts may settle to the bottom and be discarded.

2. When pouring, slowly move the stream of water completely around the pan rim, and collect all floating residues clinging to the side.

3. Discard residues from the 10-mesh screen, but retain those from the 25-mesh, since oversize cysts sometimes are present.

4. Use extreme care in collecting all residues from the 50-mesh screen, since practically all the cysts will be assembled on it.

5. Very small cysts may pass through the 50-mesh screen; if detailed data are desired, use the 100-mesh also. Tiny cysts caught on this screen may contain only eight or ten eggs.

6. Scrape the floating residues from the beakers, transfer to a glass slide, add a few drops of water, and separate the cysts. If bubbles or foam interfere, spray lightly with 70 per cent alcohol from an atomizer.

7. Decant supernatant water, and examine settled residues, in which cysts filled with eggs will be found.

Techniques developed by Fenwick (1940) for the recovery and counting of cysts and their contents are especially useful if the project is on a long-time, large-scale basis and many thousands of cysts must be examined.

Soil samples collected during extensive surveys for the presence of *Heterodera* should be air-dried and processed by flotation. Large soil-washing machines developed by the Plant Protection Branch, U.S. Department of Agriculture, make it possible to process such samples rapidly; for large-scale operations machines of this type should be used.

Selection of Cysts for Experimental Purposes

Soil and roots from heavily infested plants should be secured at harvesttime if possible and immediately stored in a cool basement or cold room in a moist condition until needed. Cysts should be selected from those which sink during the screening process, as they are most likely to contain their full complement of eggs. Those which float usually have already lost a portion of the larvae by hatching or have been air-dried.

The practice of air-drying soil before processing injects a completely different element into the life cycle of the larvae. Under field conditions only a small portion of the cysts are ever exposed in the upper 2 inches of soil, where a similar drying occurs. Sometimes these floating residues are stored under refrigeration for several months or until needed for experimental work. One wonders that, after such treatment, any self-respecting larva would ever respond to root diffusates, extracts of plant tissues, or other organic and inorganic products to which it might be exposed.

Cysts for experimental purposes should not be collected from piles of soil at beet-loading dumps, potato-processing plants, or similar installations, because excess decaying organic material often heats and kills the larvae. Cysts from these sources may be filled with fungi and bacteria, which thrive on the dead larvae and eggs and decaying body contents of the females. Rarely, if ever, are living larvae within the cysts attacked by either fungi or bacteria.

Inspecting Fields by Cyst Flotation

Cyst flotation is a rapid and efficient method of determining if *Heterodera* are present in a field and, if so, how widespread they are. The process is relatively simple. Equipment consists of a water glass, a small wooden paddle about 6 inches long, and a few gallons of water. The glass is filled within an inch of the top, and small, dry pieces of surface soil are dropped into it and stirred with the paddle. Cysts move to the edge and float high on the side of the glass, where they are easily seen with the unaided eye, since their shiny brown color makes them conspicuous among other debris. The work is best done in bright sunlight, and the beginner should check the cysts with a small hand lens, since parts of the bodies of small beetles and tiny pieces of organic matter sometimes resemble cysts. It is always well to practice on known infested soil before going out into the fields. Differentiation between species in the field is not possible; so the method is more applicable to areas in which only one species of *Heterodera* is known, as in most sugar beet fields of the western United States.

Frequently farmers who purchase or rent land are interested in knowing if sugar beet nematodes are present. By zigzagging back and forth across the field and selecting pieces of dry soil at intervals of 20 or 50 feet it can soon be determined if there is any general infestation. If an infestation is found, a few samples in the immediate vicinity will soon disclose its approximate extent. Of course, minor infestations may be overlooked in such a survey, but the areas will be so small that little reduction in yield will result. Usually 30 or 40 minutes on a 10-acre field is sufficient to make determinations. With information on the crop history of the field during the past three to five years it is then possible to make recommendations on the advisability of planting sugar beets.

Identifying Species of *Heterodera*

The first species to be separated from the *Heterodera* complex by a detailed description was *H. punctata* Thorne, 1928a, a parasite of wheat from Saskatchewan, Canada. Triffitt (1929) made extensive measurements of cysts from sugar beets, oats, potatoes, hops, and mangolds and illustrated the great diversity in form and size found in each group, but diagnostic measurements were not apparent. Specimens collected from the same host in different localities exhibited great variations in size. Transfer from one locality to another indicated that soil conditions were contributing factors, with smaller cysts produced on heavy types. Males from different hosts varied in body length, but the spears and spicula were similar in size.

Goffart (1930a) used length/breadth ratios to separate cysts of the sugar beet, oat, and potato strains and found them significant, but failed to find important differences between cysts from three other hosts. O. Schmidt (1930) determined that the larvae of the sugar beet strain of *H. schachtii* averaged only 470 μ in length, while those from oats averaged 575 μ. On this basis he proposed that they be designated as *H. schachtii* subsp. *minor* and *H. schachtii* subsp. *major,* respectively. Franklin (1940) raised the latter to the specific rank of *Heterodera major,* = *H. avenae.* She noted that the distal ends of *Heterodera* spicula were distinctive in some instances. Those of *schachtii* are truncate and bidentate, those of *gottingiana* are tridentate, while in *avenae* they are pointed, twisted, or rolled in the distal third. Franklin (1951) assembled the best information available on eight species and two varieties of *Heterodera* in an excellent presentation which established a firm basis for future work.

Oostenbrink and den Ouden (1954), Cooper (1955), and Mulvey (1957) contributed information on diagnostic characters for certain members of the genus. Taylor (1957) assembled diagnostic observations together with the results of extensive original research to produce a key for the identification of cysts which is by far the most comprehensive and valuable publication on this difficult subject. With the aid of this key, cysts of typical form and cuticular markings can now be determined with a satisfactory degree of accuracy by one well informed on the *Heterodera,* but frequent odd-sized and aberrantly marked specimens often defy identification.

Jones (1950) found that the spicula of *Heterodera cruciferae, carotae,* and *trifolii* are bidentate as in *H. schachtii.* He also observed that the spicula of *H. humili, rostochiensis, punctate,* and *tabacum* have rather straight, pointed ends. While these characters are fairly constant, there are, nevertheless, occasional aberrant individuals.

Hirschmann (1956) described a pair of "hemizonidlike" organs located dorsally and ventrally near the middle of the heads of males and larvae of *Heterodera glycines* and *H. trifolii.* Later (1959) these were named "cephalids," and investigations revealed that they are present in all species of *Heterodera* and in certain other genera. Slender connective tissues lead in from the cephalids to glandlike organs adjacent to the esophagus just posterior to the spear. How these organs had escaped previous workers is a mystery, but the fact well illustrates the need of more critical morphological studies. Like the hemizonid, the cephalids probably are connected with the nervous system, as suggested by Chitwood (personal communication).

Mulvey (1957a) studied the oögenesis of the sugar beet nematode and found that the process is normal in this bisexual species, with two polar bodies being produced and the diploid number of chromosomes reduced during maturation. Nine bivalents were formed at meiosis, and at metaphase 1 the largest bivalent is about 1 μ long. Spermatozoa were extremely small and without tails, only one being observed in each oöcyte. The possibilities of variations in chromosome number among the various species of the genus may be well worth investigation as a means of identification. Ovaries were removed, fixed in an iron-mordant fixative to which a few drops of propionic orcein stain were added, and flattened under a cover glass for examination.

Males of the pear-shaped species, *Heterodera rostochiensis, punctata,* and *tabacum,* may be immediately distinguished by the fact that the hemizonid is adjacent to the excretory pore, while in *schachtii, cruciferae,* and related species the hemizonid is six to ten annules anterior to the excretory pore.

Many attempts have been made to separate the species of *Heterodera* on the basis of larval length, and for certain hosts in certain localities there may be diagnostic variations which can be used. However, a review of the literature indicates that wide variations for each species from different hosts and widely separated places render it almost impossible to select measurements which are of diagnostic value, as emphasized by Oostenbrink (1950). Taylor (1957) remarks that within a species the larvae may vary in length as much as 20 per cent.

Doubtless some of the variations recorded by different workers were due in part to methods of killing and fixation. Cold fixatives applied to living larvae cause obvious shrinkage, especially in the neck region, while if the larvae are first carefully relaxed by gradual heat, very little, if any, shrinkage occurs. Larvae hatched in the field under natural conditions are preferable to those secured by opening the cysts and applying pressure on the eggs.

A simple method of measuring consists in placing small numbers of larvae on a glass slide in a large drop of water, applying a cover slip, and measuring by means of a camera lucida before the water evaporates and pressure develops from the weight of the cover glass. A camera lucida sketch of 200 diameters gives lines about 80 to 120 mm long which are very satisfactory. If larvae are not perfectly straight, the curved lines may still be measured accurately, which is not possible with an ocular micrometer. If widths and other measurements are desired, a magnification of 500 diameters is preferable since under lower powers the width of a pencil mark on small measurements will have an appreciable effect on the actual distance.

Fenwick and Franklin (1942) made extensive statistical analyses of the lengths of 15,000 *Heterodera rostochiensis* larvae with special reference to factors which might influence the mean length. The larvae were relaxed by gradual heat before measuring. These workers found that potato varieties did not influence the mean length as much as did different plants from the same variety; that killing temperatures should be not over 80°C, or shrinkage will occur; that larvae soaked in distilled water gain considerably in length both before and after killing if liberated from the eggs mechanically. If liberated by means of calcium hypochlorite solution, they may shrink if there is a delay of more than 6 hours before measuring. A summary of one of their experiments is as follows:

> The mean length of 20 larvae from single cysts of *H. rostochiensis* from the potato, based on measurements of 20 larvae from each of ten cysts from each of five plants from each of seven varieties of potatoes (= 3,500 larvae) were such that in 95 per cent of the cases they fluctuated between 499.39 μ and 443.39 μ. A further computation showed that for a sample of such larvae, each of which came from a different cyst from a different plant, the standard deviation would be 22.79 μ, i.e. in 95 per cent of the cases the length would lie between 425.39 μ and 517.39 μ. This figure represents the best estimate that can be given of the mean length of larvae of *H. rostochiensis* prepared and measured in the manner described in this paper.

The Vulvar Cone in *Heterodera* Identification

Franklin (1939) observed that the vulvar regions of *Heterodera* were marked by hourglass or circular-shaped hyaline areas and that, just inside the cone, knoblike, dark brown objects often were present. Taylor (1952–1957, personal communications) and Oostenbrink and den Ouden (1954) called attention to the fact that these knoblike bodies were distinctive for *H. schachtii, H. avenae, H. glycines, H. trifolii,* and *H. galeopsidis.* Cooper (1955) reported observations on more than 2,000 vulvar cones and demonstrated that certain morphological features were of diagnostic value in species determination. He also proposed a system of nomenclature for the structures associated with the vulvar cone and divided the genus into two groups, Bullata and Abullata.

Mulvey (1959) published a detailed study of *Heterodera trifolii* and illustrated the structures described and named by Cooper. Usually these morphological details are visible only on mature cysts and not all specimens exhibit them in the typical manner. Nevertheless they are often useful for identification purposes (Fig. 11-6).

Further explanation of Cooper's terminology appears to be pertinent. The "hyaline parapets" forming the "vulvar bridge" are the thick muscular labia of the vulva as they appear after encystment. The "semifenestrae" are the thinner cuticular areas above and below the vulva through which larvae usually escape into the soil. They are best observed from a tail on end or from a lateral view of the cone. "Bullae" apparently are not homologous with caudal glands or other organs usually observed in nemas and must be regarded as specialized structures. Perhaps they secrete the mucoid substance which collects about the posterior end of certain *Heterodera* spp. into which eggs are often deposited. On rare specimens, droplets of this mucoid may be seen, apparently exuding from pores in the fenestra. This material forms an "operculum" (covering) which, as Cooper remarks, must be removed before the fenestra can be examined.

The "underbridge" is composed of muscle bands supporting the vagina. They extend right and left from the cervix to the body wall. Similar, less conspicuous bands anchor it dorsally and ventrally. These muscle bands and other tissues form a membranous, wall-like structure which prevents eggs from being forced into the body cone. From a dorsal or ventral view the vagina appears as a broad, sheaflike organ, as noted by Taylor (1957). Laterally it appears as a narrower muscular tube. An outstanding exception to this occurs in *Heterodera avenae*, in which there appears to be no muscular vagina, the entire cone area being occupied by a spheroid vaginal structure supported by a strong underbridge. A short valvular apparatus connects this structure to the vulva.

Sugar beet nematode, *Heterodera schachtii* Schmidt, 1871

Historical: Devastation of sugar beet fields in Europe during the last half of the nineteenth century was the dramatic prelude to widespread interest in sugar beet nematode. This interest stimulated search for other plant parasitic species which might be responsible for unexplained losses of various crops. Had it not been for the discovery of this pest, investigations of nematodes as causal agents of plant diseases would probably have been delayed for many years.

During the 1850s Herman Schacht observed fields in which the soil apparently had become exhausted, a condition known as *Rübenmüdigkeit,* or *beet weariness.* The condition was attributed to the fact that the fields had produced beets continuously without proper crop rotations. Beets from such fields were generally stunted and covered with hairy roots. On them Schacht observed small, white, lemon-shaped bodies, which he found to be the females of an undescribed species of nematode. In 1859 he published a short paper reporting his discovery. Schmidt (1871) named the pest *Heterodera schachtii*, and Strubell (1888) published a detailed morphological study of the species to which little has since been added.

Meantime, the governments of Germany, France, Austria, Russia, and other European countries fostered the growing beet sugar industry. This policy resulted in rapidly expanding acreages where beets were grown year after year until the crops failed. Shaw (1915) recounts the graphic description of the industry as given by Spiegler (1907):

> The beet industry was in its heyday in the seventies. Not satisfied with the land already under cultivation, the farmer plowed fertile meadows along the border of river and stream wherein to grow sugar beets. At this time, incredible as it may appear, beets were grown on the same land eight or ten years in succession and not seldom were yields of 20–27 tons obtained. . . . Finally such irrational conduct rapidly caused an increase in sugar beet pests, especially the nematode, thus rendering impossible further beet culture in those places.

Schacht, Kühn, Liebscher, and others in Germany demonstrated that the pest was unquestionably the causal agent of *Rübenmüdigkeit*. In France it was reported by Prillieaux (1879), in Finland by Warming (1879), in Holland by Chatin (1888), and in other countries in rapid succession. So numerous were the workers engaged on the problem that Shaw (1915) listed forty-five who had published papers by 1911, and this list is doubtless far from complete. The widespread distribution indicates that the nematode probably was indigenous to Europe and transferred from its native hosts to sugar beets when they were introduced. The rich tare soil which came from the beets when they were delivered at the factories was naturally returned to the fields. This provided an ideal means of distribution once the pest became etsablished in a locality.

The situation of the beet sugar industry in the western United States was similar to that in Europe when the writer began extensive surveys in 1918. The desert soils, unleached by rainfall, had been placed under irrigation and frequently produced excellent crops for 20 or 30 years in succession with no fertilizer other than barnyard manure. A field observed near Goshen, Utah, in 1923 produced 26 tons per acre from its twenty-sixth consecutive crop, and similar instances were not unusual. But during the 1920s the rapid distribution of sugar beet nematodes in tare soil returned to the farmers' wagons from the beet-unloading dumps finally brought to an end that memorable epoch in the beet sugar industry of the western United States. The most thorough job of distributing nematodes occurred in certain sections of California, where the waste water from sugar factories was pumped out over the fields for irrigation. In 1922 a two-weeks' survey was made of 14,000 acres of beet land adjacent to the Betteravia, California, sugar factory. During this time only two small clods of soil were examined by flotation that did not contain cysts of the sugar beet nematode.

West of the Rocky Mountains nematode damage was accompanied during the 1920s by invasions of the beet leaf hopper, *Eutettix tenellus* Baker, carrying the curly top disease. East of the Rockies leaf spot,

Cercospora beticola, became a serious problem along with the nematodes. Near the end of this decade competitive crops produced by the expanding dairy, canning, and vegetable industries cut heavily into beet acreage. These combined factors caused such drastic reductions in beet acreage that many factories were abandoned.

Representatives of the U.S. Sugar Plant Investigations (transferred in 1926 to the Division of Nematology) conducted an intensive educational campaign which reached into every locality in which sugar beet nematodes were known. Lectures illustrated with lantern slides and demonstrations of living nematodes projected on the screen were important features of this campaign, which was carried out with the cooperation of sugar companies and county agricultural agents. Programs of crop rotation and soil fertility were stressed, and these programs were put into effect by the beet growers, fieldmen, agricultural superintendents, and other officials of the sugar companies. Under the supervision of Asa C. Maxson, director of agricultural research for the Great Western Sugar Company, Denver, Colorado, crop-rotation records were maintained for every known nematode-infested field in the company territory. These were continued for over 20 years, and almost 4,000 fields were under observation when the work was abandoned in 1940—doubtless the greatest single project in nematology that has ever been organized.

Improved agronomic practices were put into effect throughout the industry. Commercial fertilizers were introduced to replenish the depleted phosphorus and nitrogen supplies, and disease-resistant varieties largely eliminated the losses from curly top and leaf spot. Old nematode-infested fields returned to production once in five or six years, with yields which frequently exceeded those which had been produced during the early years of the industry. In fact, some of the highest per acre yielding districts in the Western states are those which are most severely infested with sugar beet nematodes.

Morphology and biology: Female. The white or pale yellow females of the sugar beet nematode are easily observed with the unaided eye as they lie attached to roots. Typically they are lemon-shaped and usually vary from 0.5 to 0.8 mm in length, but some specimens may be smaller or larger. Many individuals diverge from the typical form. Usually the subcrystalline layer is a prominent feature, appearing as a white incrustation completely covering that part of the body protruding from the root. A mucoid mass extruded from the vulval region surrounds the posterior end and is covered with adhering soil particles. The subcrystalline layer and mucoid mass give the female protection from mononchs and other predators.

Eggs within the body may vary from less than 10 to over 600, with an average of 286 from 500 Utah specimens. Most females eject some eggs into the mucoid mass before encystment occurs. These may number from 1 to more than 200. They play an important part in the life history because they hatch immediately, enter roots, and produce another generation. Raski (1950) observed that eggs within mature females and newly formed cysts hatched immediately under favorable environmental conditions and completed the life cycle in about 30 days. Rapid multiplication through several generations in a season makes it possible for a relatively small population remaining after a rotation to increase to enormous numbers before the end of the growing season.

Cuticular markings of adult females and cysts are rugose, chaotic, short, zig-zag elements without order of arrangement. Head region annulated, the terminal annule almost round, surmounted by a squarish labial plate. Spear straight or slightly curved, averaging 26 μ in length and bearing ovoid basal knobs. Median esophageal bulb spheroid. Basal portion of esophagus extended in lobelike glands reaching back over intestine. In early stages of development the slender ovaries are coiled in the body cavity. As egg production proceeds, they completely fill the body. As Mulvey (1957) noted, the

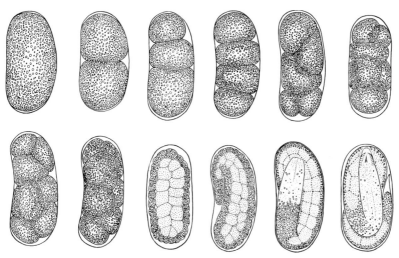

Fig. 11-3. *Heterodera schachtii.* Embryonic development from egg to moulting first-stage larva. (*After Raski. Courtesy of Phytopathology.*)

cervix is supported by a single band of muscles attached to the lateral regions. Vagina sheaflike from a dorsal view, ending in a deeply cleft vulva. Fenestrae average 45 μ long.

Male. The male begins to develop in much the same manner as the female. It first becomes an elongated, cylindroid body slightly shorter than the length of the original larva from which it was formed. The testis appears as a series of cells roughly arranged in rows, with the terminus reflexed. From the indefinite mass of cells and granules surrounding the testis the male body gradually takes form, finally appearing as an obese, wormlike organism flexed once within the cuticle. From this third stage the male elongates until it is flexed three or four times within the greatly expanded larval cuticle. It now possesses a well-developed spear with strong basal knobs and all other organs typical of nematodes of this sort. Development takes place in the root cortex, and after the final moult the male emerges into the soil.

In length the males usually range between 1.3 and 1.6 mm. Annules of the lip region, three or four, including the labial disc. Spear 25 to 28 μ long, with strong basal knobs. Lobes of esophageal glands extending back ventrally along the intestine. Testis single, outstretched; spicula bidentate, resting on a slightly arcuate, troughlike gubernaculum.

Larvae range from 450 to 500 μ in length, with a general average of about 460 μ as stated by Taylor (1957). However, under- and oversize larvae are not unusual, depending no doubt on the suitability of the host and on natural variation. Spear averaging about 25 μ in length, which usually is about the length of the hyaline portion of the tail.

Identification: Morphological differences between *Heterodera schachtii* and its close relatives are difficult to demonstrate. Taylor (1957) separates the

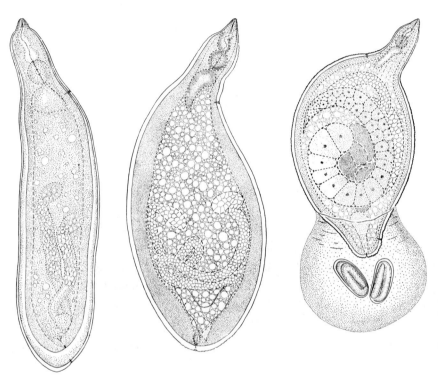

Fig. 11-4. *Heterodera schachtii.* Left to right, third-stage female larva moulting; fourth-stage female; adult female with egg-sac. (*After Raski. Courtesy of Phytopathology.*)

species on the basis of average larval lengths in microns: *schachtii,* 460; *glycines,* 484; *trifolii,* 502; *galeopsidis,* 518. While these measurements are no doubt diagnostic in most instances, the possibilities of variants within a species should not be overlooked. The muscle band supporting the cervix of *schachtii* is a single one, while the muscle bands of the closely related *trifolii* are furcate at their attachments on the body wall (Mulvey, 1957). This is an exceedingly difficult character to determine except on very favorable specimens. Franklin (1940) determined that the distal ends of the spicula are bidentate, a character which appears to be rather stable. However, males of other species also have bidentate spicula. The wide range of hosts for *H. schachtii* makes determination on the basis of hosts of doubtful value.

Host plants: As previously mentioned, the old host lists of *Heterodera schachtii* are so filled with errors that they are of little value. Jones (1950) and Raski (1952) published host lists based on our present knowledge of the several species of *Heterodera*. These were followed by the report of Winslow (1954) on his extensive investigations in England. This included ninety-eight species of host plants belonging to forty-

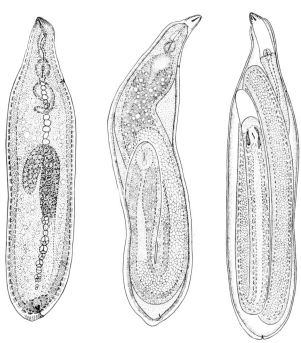

Fig. 11-5. *Heterodera schachtii.* Left to right, third-stage male larva; early fourth-stage male; fourth-stage male larva moulting. (*After Raski. Courtesy of Phytopathology.*)

eight genera representing nine families. Among these are practically all the species of *Beta* and *Brassica,* with numerous representatives from *Alyssum, Chenopodium, Rumex, Polygonum,* and other genera. Most of them are weeds commonly found in cultivated fields. Oostenbrink (1955), using his monocyst technique, produced mature cysts on thirty-six species of plants, many of which had been reported in the above-mentioned papers.

Obviously these lists do not include all hosts of *Heterodera schachtii.* Populations in different parts of the world have adapted themselves to different plants, and considerable variation doubtless will be found as more extensive studies are made. In the United States certain weeds have been found infested in one locality, while in nearby areas they are not attacked.

Host records should state specifically if cysts containing viable eggs were produced, because occasionally females will become well developed without producing embryonated eggs. Larvae of *Heterodera schachtii* are frequently found entering the tissues of plant roots which are not hosts, where they eventually die because the necessary giant cells do not develop.

Control: *Crop rotation.* A knowledge of host plants is essential in planning crop rotations. Fortunately cereals, corn, alfalfa, clover, pota-

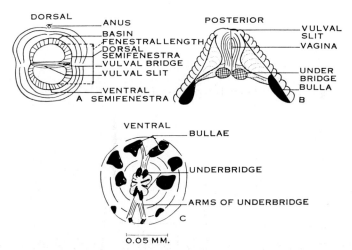

Fig. 11-6. Fenestrated cone of *Heterodera trifolii* cyst indicating positions of structures present. *A*—Posterior view of cone terminus. *B*—Dorsoventral view of cone. *C*—Anterior view of underbridge region. (*After Mulvey, Nematologica. Courtesy of E. J. Brill.*)

toes, tomatoes, and other important crops are not infested by sugar beet nematodes. After a rotation of three to five years, one normal crop of beets can be produced. In planning rotations four major points must be considered: (1) severity of infestation, (2) crops adapted to the field, (3) soil fertility, and (4) which crops will give a reasonable return for labor and investment and at the same time maintain or increase productivity.

Fields with only a few small infested spots can usually be kept in beet production by planting two years of peas, beans, potatoes, tomatoes, truck crops (except cabbage and related plants), small grains, or corn. Preferably the legumes should precede sugar beets. If one-fourth or more of the land is infested, the rotation should be extended to four or five years. For this purpose perennial crops like alfalfa, clovers, and pastures are excellent. But, if desired, the longer rotations can be made up of annual crops as listed above.

Small infested areas can sometimes be isolated and permanently removed from sugar beet production, and for this purpose perennials like alfalfa and pastures are preferable. Row crops are not recommended for this purpose because of the probability of moving infested soil to other parts of the field by machinery.

Control of weed hosts by cultivation during the rotation is essential. Otherwise they may enable the nematodes to maintain populations capable of causing severe damage when sugar beets are again planted.

Cultivated crops which are hosts of the sugar beet nematode include table beets, mangel-wurzels, cabbage, cauliflower, broccoli, Brussels

Fig. 11-7. Sugar beet field infested with *Heterodera schachtii*. Note how original infestation from beet dumped dirt was spread up and down rows by irrigation and cultivation and across field by harrowing and leveling. (*Photograph by E. G. Titus*, 1917. Interest in this field was responsible for the writer's entering nematology.)

sprouts, turnips, rutabagas, and radishes. When planted on infested land, they may be seriously damaged and any benefits derived from the rotation will be nullified.

When one satisfactory crop of sugar beets has been produced, the grower should not follow it with a second. During the one year of beets the large root systems enable the nematodes to increase tremendously, and severe loss to a second crop will occur. Reductions as great as 10 to 20 tons per acre are not unusual in such instances.

Maintenance of soil fertility is especially important when nematodes are present, because thrifty plants may make a good growth where undernourished ones will be killed. Barnyard and green manure are almost essential and frequently should be supplemented with commercial fertilizers containing nitrogen, phosphorus, and potash. Readily available fertility is especially desirable early in the season when the young

Fig. 11-8. Sugar beet infested with *Heterodera schachtii.* Note white females clinging to roots. (*Courtesy of Nematology Section, U.S. Department of Agriculture.*)

beets are becoming established. Early planting and proper cultural methods always pay good dividends.

Soil fumigation. Kühn (1881) determined that sugar beet nematodes could be killed in the field with carbon disulfide and other chemicals. But he remarked that it was impossible to exterminate them except by using quantities which would entail exorbitant expense, a statement which is just as true today as it was 80 years ago.

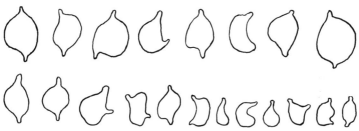

Fig. 11-9. Variations in size and form of sugar beet nematode cysts. Specimens secured from 1 pound of soil.

Sugar beet nematodes and other cyst-forming species are especially difficult to kill because the larvae are protected by both the eggshell and the cyst wall. Among the modern soil fumigants, dichloropropane-dichloropropene fumigants are especially effective in penetrating the cyst. When applied in an approved manner under proper soil and moisture conditions, they give good control, but for one year only. The standard application is 25 gallons per acre on soils having a moisture equivalent of 20 per cent or less, which costs approximately $40 (1959). To afford fumigation, the grower must produce 20 tons of beets per acre in order to make a profit. Another fumigant, 1,2-dibromo-3-chloropropane, is effective but so phytotoxic to young beets that under average conditions it must be applied one year prior to the beet crop.

Fig. 11-10. Body cones of *Heterodera schachtii.* *A*—Dorsoventral view showing sheathlike vagina suspended by underbridge. *B*—Lateral view showing dorsoventral segments of underbridge. *C*—Heads of second-stage larvae which have broken through the underbridge preparatory to escaping through the fenestra.

Oat cyst nematode, *Heterodera avenae* (Mortensen et al., 1908)
Filipjev, 1934

Synonyms: *Heterodera schachtii* var. *avenae* Mortensen, Rostop & Ravn, 1908; *Heterodera schachtii* subsp. *major* O. Schmidt, 1930; *Heterodera major* (O. Schmidt) Franklin, 1940

Historical: This species was first observed as a parasite of cereals in Germany by Kühn (1874), who regarded it as merely a form of *Heterodera schachtii.* It was so regarded until Mortensen et al. (1908) recognized it as a distinct form and named it *H. schachtii* var. *avenae.* Unfortunately these workers failed to give diagnostic morphological characters by which it could be identified. Wollenweber (1924) finally gave a brief statement on the form of the cysts which, combined with knowledge of the host, made identification possible. O. Schmidt (1930) observed that the larvae from oats were larger than those from sugar beets and designated the species as *H. schachtii* subsp. *major.* Franklin (1940),

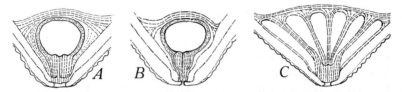

Fig. 11-11. *Heterodera avenae.* *A, B*—Dorsal and lateral views of body cone, showing spheroid vaginal chamber. *C*—Muscle system supporting inner cone structures, somewhat flattened. (*Specimens courtesy of H. Goffart.*)

not being aware of Wollenweber's paper, raised the subspecies to specific rank, which was later set aside by a ruling in favor of *H. avenae.*

Morphology and biology: Females usually vary between 0.55 and 0.75 mm in length and are about two-thirds as wide as long. Generally they are of the typical lemon-shaped form. The subcrystalline layer is a prominent feature of the female, sloughing off as the dark brown cyst is formed. Gelatinous exudations often are extruded from the vulval area, but eggs are rarely, if ever, deposited. On specimens from Europe and Canada the rugose cuticular pattern consists of zigzag, chaotic lines. On those from Australia there is a strong tendency toward a longitudinal arrangement except near the extremities. Underlying the rugose pattern the cuticle is marked by coarse, irregularly arranged punctations. Vulval cone of cyst conspicuous because of the spheroid, hyaline vaginal structure, which occupies almost the entire cone, forcing the bullae against the body wall and crowding them back near the fenestra. Oostenbrink and den Ouden (1954) illustrate a very short vulvar slit, less than one-half as long as the fenestra, and Mulvery (1957) gives the average length as 12.9 µ, which doubtless is too small to permit the deposition of eggs.

Head region annulated, somewhat hexagonal just behind the lip region. Labial disc quadrangular, slightly longer than wide. Six minute, rounded lips are visible from a face view. One especially favorable specimen bore what appeared to be circlets of four and six cephalic papillae. Amphid apertures beneath slight lateral bulges in the labial plate. Spear often curved slightly, averaging about 26 µ in length.

Males average 1.38 mm long according to Franklin (1951), and specimens from Canada correspond fairly well in size. However, those from Australia average only about 1.0 mm long. Lip region bearing five annules on the European and Canadian specimens, four on the Australian. Spear 26 to 29 μ long, with slightly rounded knobs. Spicula blunt or truncate, not dentate.

Larvae average 575 μ in length according to Franklin, and according to Schmidt, Putnam, and Chapman, 530 to 550, Goffart, 560, and Millikan, 430 to 490. Hyaline portion of larval tail 1½ times as long as spear.

Identification: Useful diagnostic characters are as follows: chaotic rugose pattern of cuticle; relatively large, irregularly spaced punctations; spheroid vaginal area occupying almost the entire cone; bullae crowded back near fenestra; vulva length 12.9 μ; absence of eggs in mucoid exudate; four or five annules in male lip region; spicula blunt or truncate; larvae 550 to 575 μ long; hyaline portion of larval tail 1½ times spear length; usually found infesting

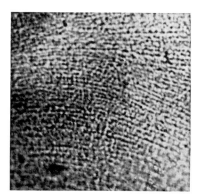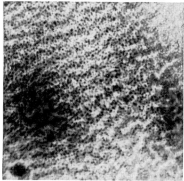

Fig. 11-12. Punctate pattern of cyst cuticles. *Heterodera avenae,* right, and *Heterodera rostochiensis,* left. *(After Franklin. Courtesy of Journal of Helminthology.)*

graminaceous plants, oats preferred. Australian specimens: rugose pattern often somewhat longitudinal; vulval cone less conspicuous; four annules on male lip region; larvae 430 to 490 μ long; wheat preferred host.

Adult females and cysts from Europe and Canada are morphologically very similar. Those from Australia have a longer neck and less developed vulval cone; as previously mentioned, the rugose pattern has a tendency to run in longitudinal lines; and the male lip region bears only four annules. Oats are the preferred host in Europe and Canada, with wheat and rye generally attacked to a slight degree, while wheat is most severely damaged in Australia. Doubtless this population represents a geographical variant which eventually may be set up as a distinct species.

Symptoms: Seedling plants may show injury as the fourth leaf appears with a slightly red tip. Roots are short, with multiple branches, giving a bunchy appearance, and often bearing small gall-like formations. As the season progresses, areas of sparse and stunted plants appear, often pale yellowish green in color. Damage is most severe during dry seasons.

Plants on fertile soil with abundant moisture may harbor heavy populations without visable injury. The weakened roots of infested plants are frequently attacked by soil fungi such as *Helminthosporum* sp., producing rots which often complete the destruction.

Hosts and distribution: *Heterodera avenae* has been reported from graminaceous plants almost exclusively, more than twenty species being recorded from the genera *Avenae, Bromus, Festuca, Hordeum, Lolium, Phalaris, Secale,* and *Triticum.* Records of *Chenopodium, Pisum, Sonchus,* and *Trifolium* probably represent small colonies in limited areas, since such divergent host adaptations are not unusual among *Heterodera* as well as other genera. However, these records may be, as Franklin suggests, due to contamination with an unrecognized species.

Distribution covers most of central and northern Europe and the British Isles. Putnam and Chapman (1935) reported it in Ontario, Canada, where it is now widely distributed. Millikan (1938) stated that the species had been known in South Australia since 1906. Franklin (1951) mentions a personal communication reporting its presence in Casablanca, Morocco.

Control methods: *Crop rotation.* Nongraminaceous plants for two or three years reduce average populations to a point where a profitable crop may be produced. Goffart (1932) suggests that root crops, clover, peas, and beans should be grown between oat crops. A few years in pasture will greatly reduce the numbers of nematodes, and then oats may be alternated with the crops mentioned. Millikan (1938) secured the best yields after three years of pasture, peas, and fallow in various sequences. Two years of fallow with one of peas or pasture gave the best yields, but such long periods of fallow are impractical.

Resistant varieties. Varieties of barley were studied by Nillson-Ehle (1920), who found Hannchen, Chevalier, Primus, and Schwannhals fairly resistant, with the character of resistance following Mendelian laws in crosses between varieties. Goffart (1932) found no cysts on the roots of Chevalier and Gold-X-Chevalier, although some larvae did enter the roots but failed to develop to maturity.

Millikan (1938), working with the populations preferring wheat, found that the oat varieties Mulga and Guyra were resistant. However, in Europe and Canada little or no resistance has been observed in oats, and even the Australian varieties were found susceptible.

Among the many wheat varieties which have been tested none has been found resistant to a degree to warrant planting on infested fields, although Millikan reported Sepoy as somewhat superior to Mogul and Free Gallipoli.

Pea cyst nematode, *Heterodera göttingiana,* Liebscher, 1892

Historical: Liebscher (1890) reported a disease of peas caused by a nematode which at first he thought to be *Heterodera schachtii.* After investigations of its morphology and host range he decided that it was a new species and named it *H. göttingiana,* since he had discovered it on the grounds of the Agricultural Institute at Göttingen. Goffart (1941) and Franklin (1951) made the principal contributions to our knowledge of the pest, which is well known in Germany and the British Isles.

Morphology and biology: Females are of the typical lemon-shaped type but inclined to be slightly more rounded than those of *Heterodera schachtii*. Subcrystalline layer absent. A gelatinous egg-sac is present, sometimes containing a few eggs which average about 110 by 50 μ, somewhat broader than those of *H. schachtii*. Females turn from white to brown without a yellow stage. Punctations of cuticle small and irregularly spaced. Rugose pattern coarse, with no definite arrangement. Bullae not present in vulval cone. Males average about 1.2 mm in length and resemble those of *H. schachtii* except that the termini of the spicula are tridentate.

Larval lengths are, as usual, variable. Liebscher gave the average as 462, Goffart as 456, and Franklin as 487 μ. No other distinguishing characters have been recorded.

Identification: Unless the host plant is known, identification of cysts is difficult. When a cyst is found developing on one of its typical hosts like peas or vetch, the absence of the subcrystalline layer is a good indication of the species. If males are available, the tridentate spicula provide a good diagnostic character.

Symptoms: Presence of nemas is indicated by stunted plants bearing yellow-green leaves which die early in the season. Infestations vary from small spots to entire fields, and sometimes the crop harvested is less than the seed sown. Nitrogen nodules rarely are formed in infested roots. Accompanying symptoms include a "foot rot," apparently produced by secondary fungi which invade the weakened roots.

Hosts and distribution: Liebscher in Germany found that all varieties of peas were infested. Oostenbrink in Holland tested 153 varieties, none of which showed evidence of possessing resistant qualities. Goffart worked on the same grounds as Liebscher and verified that the 8 species of *Vicia* which he reported were also hosts, and to these he added 6 more species. A few other hosts, *Ervum lens, Lathyrus circer, Circer arietinum,* four species of *Lupinus* and *Soja hispida,* = *Glycine hispida,* are known. Red and white clovers, broad beans, and alfalfa have not been attacked.

Probably this species also is generally distributed throughout Europe. The writer once received numerous cysts from sweet peas growing in a greenhouse in Chicago, Illinois. A similar collection was forwarded from Boise, Idaho. These records indicate that it probably was introduced with soil on bulbs or ornamentals imported from Europe.

Control: The wide range of nonhost crops available makes it a simple matter to arrange crop rotations of three years or more which will effectively reduce the populations to a point at which a satisfactory crop can be produced.

Soybean cyst nematode, *Heterodera glycines* Ichinohe, 1952

Historical: A disease of soybeans known as "yellow dwarf" was reported from Korea by Yokoo (1936) and from China (Manchuria) by

Nakata and Asuyama (1937). Ichinohe (1952) observed similar symptoms in Japan, discovered that the causal agent was an undescribed species of cyst-forming nematode, and named it *Heterodera glycines*. Winstead, Skotland, and Sasser (1955) reported it from North Carolina. Surveys revealed its presence in over 2,000 acres distributed through three counties. In 1956 the pest was discovered in western Tennessee. Extended surveys through 1959 have revealed its presence in more than 35,000 acres in North Carolina, Virginia, Tennessee, Kentucky, Missouri, Arkansas, Mississippi, and Illinois. This widespread distribution indicates long-standing infestations, and additional surveys will doubtless reveal the presence of this nematode in other areas where soybeans have been grown intensively. The species may be indigenous rather than introduced.

Morphology and biology: Females lemon-shaped, bearing the subcrystalline layer. They pass through a pale yellow stage before developing into a dark brown cyst. Rugose pattern a series of short, zigzag lines without order. Punctations of cuticle fine, irregularly arranged. As many as 200 eggs may be deposited in the egg-sac. Vulva averaging 49.7 μ (43 to 56) long. Bullae present.
  Males 1.3 mm (1.1 to 1.4) in length, closely resembling those of other *Heterodera*. Spear knobs massive, rounded. Cephalids located dorsally and ventrally near the sixth and eighth annules. Esophageal gland nuclei about one body width apart. Spicula bidentate. Hemizonid about six annules anterior to excretory pore.
  Second-stage larvae average 439.6 (373 to 490) μ long. Cephalids near middle of head. Spear knobs slightly rounded. Hemizonid adjacent to excretory pore. Dorsal esophageal gland opening 4.0 (3.3 to 5.2) μ behind spear base. About half of tail length occupied by the hyaline portion.
  Identification: The above descriptions are based on the work of Hirschmann (1956), which greatly simplifies identification of typical specimens if sufficient numbers in good condition are available. The characters which separate *Heterodera glycines* from *H. trifolii* were designated by Hirschmann as follows: larval lengths, based on five larvae from each of 30 cysts, average 439.6 μ compared with 496.6 for *trifolii*. Opening of dorso-esophageal gland 4.0 (3.3 to 5.2) μ behind spear, while in *trifolii* it is 7.3 (5.6 to 9.0) μ. Spear knobs of larvae somewhat rounded instead of forward-pointing as in *trifolii*.

Symptoms: Premature yellowing of the foliage on infested areas usually is the first obvious evidence of the presence of lethal populations of the nemas, but previous to yellowing it is possible to locate the areas by the reduced size and unthrifty-appearing plants.
  During years of abundant moisture and on fertile soil, soybeans may produce an almost normal crop while harboring enormous numbers of nematodes. This is especially true of crops following rotations. Under these conditions there is a tremendous build-up of the pest.
  Host plants: Known hosts of the soybean cyst nematode are limited to soybeans, *Glycine max,* snap beans, *Phaseolus vulgaris,* annual lespedeza, *Lespedeza stipulacea,* hemp sesbania, *Sesbania macrocarpa,* white lupine, *Lupinus albus,* henbit dead nettle, *Lamium amplexicaule,* and vetch, *Vicia sativa.*

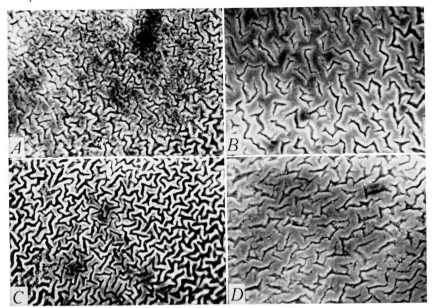

Fig. 11-13. Rugose patterns of cysts. *A, B—Heterodera glycines*, small and large cysts. *C, D—Heterodera trifolii*, small and large cysts. *(After Hirschmann. Courtesy of Helminthological Society of Washington.)*

Control: Rotations with nonhost plants should extend through four or five years. These will reduce populations to a point where one satisfactory crop of soybeans can be produced. Plowing two or three times during hot dry periods will be beneficial if practical. Soil fumigation is impractical because of high cost compared with the relatively low value of the crop.

Clover cyst nematode, *Heterodera trifolii* (Goffart, 1932)
Oostenbrink, 1949

Synonym: *Heterodera schachtii* var. *trifolii* Goffart, 1932

Hirschmann (1956) made a thorough investigation of the morphology of this species, and the following data are largely from her work:

Morphology and biology: Females are practically identical to those of *Heterodera glycines* in form and size through all stages of development. They pass through a distinctive pale yellow phase as the brown-cyst stage develops. Subcrystalline layer present in young females. Cyst cone prominent. Bullae present. As many as 200 eggs may be deposited in the gelatinous egg-sac.

Males are rare and have been reported only by McBeth (1938) and Franklin (1939). Those from Utah were 0.63 to 0.98 mm long, while Franklin's specimens from England were 1.32 mm. Cephalic annules four or five. Spicula bidentate as in *Heterodera schachtii*.

Larvae 502 (490 to 504) μ long according to Franklin, while Hirschmann reports them as 497 (443 to 547) μ. Spear 25 to 29 μ long, with forward-pointing knobs. Dorsal gland opening 5.6 to 9.0 μ behind spear, the average being 7.3.

Identification: The average size of the larvae constitutes the most satisfactory diagnostic character, and the position of the esophageal gland outlet is especially valuable in distinguishing the larvae from those of *Heterodera glycines,* as demonstrated by Hirschmann. Fenestrae considerably larger than those of *H. schachtii* (Fig. 11-13).

Symptoms: In Europe there frequently is marked injury to white clover. Plants become unthrifty, wilt during warm periods, and eventually die. In the United States injury to white clover is usually limited to small areas, if visible at all. However, Allison (1957) reported damage to both white and Ladino clover in North Carolina.

Hosts and distribution: Records of hosts are variable, but *Trifolium repens* and *T. pratense* appear to be generally infested. Goffart found that *T. incarnatum, Phaseolus vulgaris, Vicia villosa,* and *V. narbornesis* were also hosts. Franklin added *V. sativa* and *Pisum sativum* but failed to infest *Phaseolus vulgaris* and *T. incarnatum.* Franklin also reported *Rumex crispus, R. nemorosa, Stellaria media, Isatis tinctoria, Brassica alba* (very lightly), and *Beta vulgaris* (very lightly) infested. Raski and Hart (1953) added *Sesbania macrocarpa* and carnation, *Dianthus caryophyllus.* Hastings and Bosher (1952) worked with two populations which did not attack the same hosts. One followed closely the usual host trends and also attacked *Medicago* and *Lathyrus.* The other population appeared to behave more like *Heterodera göttingiana* but attacked certain species of *Trifolium* and *Phaseolus.* Mankau and Linford, working with a population from Illinois, tested twenty-seven varieties of soybeans, *Glycine max.* They found that mature cysts with eggs were produced on two varieties, Dunfield and Earlyana. Stained roots revealed that larvae had freely entered all species.

Heterodera trifolii is widely distributed in Europe and is known in British Columbia, Canada. In the United States it has been found in North Carolina, Illinois, Wisconsin, Utah, Idaho, and California. Usually it is associated with white clover in lawn and pastures. The species probably is indigenous to both Europe and North America.

Brassica cyst nematode, *Heterodera cruciferae* Franklin, 1945

Brassicas and other cruciferous plants were known as hosts of the sugar beet nematode early in the history of the pest, and the literature is replete with references. That one population of *Heterodera* was specific to crucifers was not known until Franklin (1945) described it as *H. cruciferae.*

Morphology and biology: Female somewhat more rounded than that of *Heterodera schachtii* but still definitely lemon-shaped. Subcrystalline layer present. Cuticular punctations irregular. As many as 200 eggs may be deposited in the gelatinous egg-sac. Rugose pattern (California specimens) irregular, lacelike, with small open spaces between the lines. Bullae not present. No yellow phase as the female becomes a brown cyst.

Males average 1.2 mm long, slightly less than those of *Heterodera schachtii*. Cephalic annules four or five. Spear 25 μ long. Spicula tridentate.

Larvae average 418 μ, considerably smaller than those of *Heterodera schachtii* but otherwise very similar.

Identification: Tangible morphological characters are difficult to describe, but the more rounded female, open-network rugose pattern, and shorter larvae are good indications of the species. Host-range studies like those of Raski (1952b) are almost essential for accurate identification.

Symptoms: Franklin records reports that Brussels sprouts, kale, cabbage, and similar crops may be severely damaged in spots or over entire fields, the infestation causing the usual decline and dying plants.

Control: Rotations with noncruciferous plants for three or more years should be sufficient to give one good crop. Soil fumigation with dichloropropene fumigants should be practical in high-yielding cabbage and cauliflower fields.

Hemp nettle cyst nematode, *Heterodera galeopsidis* (Goffart, 1936) Filipjev and Stekhoven, 1941

Synonym: *Heterodera schachtii* var. *galeopsidis* Goffart, 1936

Morphology and biology: Females are more rounded and have a lower cone than those of *Heterodera schachtii*. They pass through a yellow stage as they become cysts. Subcrystalline layer well developed. Punctations of cuticle irregular. According to the figure of Oostenbrink and den Ouden (1954) the vulva is about 60 μ long, slightly greater than the length of the fenestra, and twice the length of the vulva of *H. schachtii*. A gelatinous egg-sac is extruded, but only the largest females deposit eggs. Larvae average 485 μ long according to Goffart, while Jones gives 521 μ. Males not reported.

Identification probably can best be made from characters of the vulvar cone. Host tests doubtless would be more satisfactory when possible. The species is of no known importance other than being a nuisance in the identification of cysts of similar form.

Host plants and distribution: Goffart found this species in Germany as a parasite of hemp nettle, *Galeopsis tetrahit*. Investigations by Jones (1950) and Franklin (1951) in England extended the host range to *G. speciosa*, *G. pyrenacia*, *Stellaria media*, *Saptonaria vaccaris*, *Saptonaria officianalis,* and *Veronica agrestis,* with rare cysts on red clover, red beets, and mangolds.

Hop cyst nematode, *Heterodera humuli* Filipjev, 1934

Morphology and biology: Filipjev based the species on morphological characters mentioned by Voigt (1894) and Triffitt (1929), supplemented by Franklin's observations.

The small females range from 0.4 to 0.7 mm in length and average about twice as long as wide. Vulva located on a low, inconspicuous cone. Subcrystalline layer present. Cuticle punctations fine and irregular. Gelatinous extrusions frequently present, but eggs rarely deposited in them. Males about 1.0 mm long, with unusually large spears 27 to 31 μ long. Larvae 390 to 400 μ long, being among the smallest of all *Heterodera*.

Identification: The most striking features of this species appear to be the elongated cysts, small larvae, and long spears of the males.

Hosts and distribution: Voigt (1894) reported a *Heterodera* attacking hops in Germany, and the following year Percival observed them in England. Subsequently several records came from hop-growing areas of southern England and from Europe. The species has also been found on hemp, *Cannabis sativa*. Franklin succeeded in transferring specimens from hops to the nettles *Urtica diorca* and *U. urens*. Actual damage to crops is questionable.

Fig cyst nematode, *Heterodera fici* Kiri'anova, 1954

This little known species was described by Kiri'anova as a parasite of the ornamental fig palm in Russia. Sher and Raski (1956) reported it from *Ficus elastica* in Riverside and Yolo counties, California, where it is present in several orchards and nurseries. Cysts from which the following data were secured were collected by D. J. Raski from Mission figs in Yolo County. Females and cysts are difficult to detect when attached to the rough root-cortex.

Morphology and biology: Cysts almost spheroid in many instances, 0.6 (0.4 to 0.7) mm long and 0.5 (0.3 to 0.6) mm wide. Fragments of subcrystalline layer still attached to many cysts. Cuticle punctations minute, irregular. Rugose markings are zigzag lines, usually not closely spaced and forming a lacy pattern near mid-body. Mucoid egg-sac occasionally present; one contained upward of 100 embryonated eggs. Vulva forming a deep cleft on a low cone with a fenestra pattern much like that of *Heterodera schachtii*. Very fine rugose markings present on fenestra. Bullae present.

Larvae (25) 370 (330 to 420) μ long. These were released by slight pressure on the eggs. Spear 23 μ long, with forward-pointing knobs. Hyaline portion of tail occupying two-fifths of tail length, slightly longer than spear.

Identification: The small spheroid cysts with low vulval cones and short larvae are fairly diagnostic. When they are found in association with the few known hosts there is ltttle question as to their identity.

Hosts: Raski found that *Ficus elastica* and *F. carica* were attacked, but no other associated plants, a limited host range being thus indicated.

Control: Heavily infested trees appeared to show no appreciable injury, but the many dead roots indicated considerable damage to the root systems. Clean nursery stock should be used when establishing new orchards.

Polygonum cyst nematode, *Heterodera weissi* Steiner, 1949

Morphology: Adult females and cysts averaging 0.6 mm in length and about two-thirds as wide as long. Flaky subcrystalline remnants present on females and newly formed cysts. Cuticle bearing a network of transverse meandering ridges with connecting branches which form rhomboidal markings. Coarse, irregular, granular punctate markings conspicuous. Vulvar cone tapering to a narrow fenestral area. Fenestrae so constricted that larvae may not make their exit through them. Small egg-sacs often present, but eggs not observed; they

probably cannot be extruded because of the narrow fenestra. Underbridge high above the short vaginal structure. Bullae not observed. Cysts apparently do not persist for more than one year, since they are not commonly found where extensive colonies are present.
Males 1.0 to 1.5 mm long. Lip region with five annules and labial disc. Spear 26 μ long, with strong, sloping knobs. Dorsal esophageal gland outlet 6 μ behind spear. Esophageal gland lobes about twice as long as body width. Hemizonid adjacent to, or one to three annules anterior to, excretory pore. Spicula slightly arcuate, tapering, obscurely bidentate.

Hosts and distribution: This species is known to attack only *Polygonum pennsylvanicum* and other species of the genus. Found in Virginia and neighboring states and in the upper Mississippi Valley, with colonies as far north as southern Wisconsin.

Carrot cyst nematode, *Heterodera carotae* Jones, 1950

This species was reported by Jones from the Chatteras area on the Isle of Ely, England, where heavy infestations produced spots of sparse and poor carrots in a number of fields. Foliage on those areas were marked by a reddish tinge, which, however, is a symptom usually present on carrots when the roots are damaged by any agent.

Morphology and biology: Females lemon-shaped, somewhat more slender and smaller than those of *Heterodera schachtii*. Large, mucoid egg-sacs are produced, into which many eggs are extruded. Transformation to the brown cyst is made without a yellow stage. Subcrystalline layer present. Cuticular punctations irregular. Jones does not mention the rugose layer. Males 1.0 mm long. Spicula bidentate. Larvae average 453.8 μ in length.
Hosts are limited to cultivated and wild carrots, and this fact should permit control by crop rotation, but the length of such rotations has not been reported.
Identification: The close resemblance to *Heterodera schachtii* makes determination by host tests almost mandatory.

Hosts and distribution: Only cultivated and wild carrots were found infested, as mentioned above.

Cactus cyst nematode, *Heterodera cacti* Filipjev and Stekhoven, 1941

This species was first collected by Adam (1932), who classified it as a race of *Heterodera schachtii* living on cacti. Goffart (1936) made further investigations, but he, too, considered it as *H. schachtii*. It remained so classified until elevated to specific rank by Filipjev and Stekhoven. Southey (1957) summarized the limited information available and reported results of extensive tests on cacti in England. He found that every species investigated was susceptible. These included twenty-nine species belonging to fifteen genera, most of which originated in Spain and Italy. G. Minz (personal communication) states that he has occasionally collected *H. cacti* from cacti imported into Palestine. Most records are from greenhouse and nursery stock. Injury to plants rarely is evident, even when roots are severely infested.

Morphology: Females are rather distinctive because the bodies usually are almost spherical, sometimes being wider than long. A thin subcrystalline layer is present on newly formed cysts. Outer layer of cyst grainy-appearing instead of punctate, according to Taylor (1957). Rugose layer near middle of cyst is marked by straight or wavy lines which are occasionally broken by short oblique or vertical lines. Females pass through a golden-yellow or orange stage before becoming dark brown cysts. Gelatinous egg-sac not observed. Vulva with delicate, transparent margins, its length being equal to the width of the rather round fenestra area.

Filipjev and Stekhoven state that the *male* spear is 26 to 29 (28) μ long, and the spicula are described as having truncate points.

Larvae 426 to 630 (485) μ long. Knobs of larval spear convex anteriorly; hyaline portion of tail usually shorter than spear.

Since cacti usually are propagated from cuttings, the most simple method of control lies in starting new plants in uninfested soil.

Golden nematode of potatoes, *Heterodera rostochiensis* Wollenweber, 1923

Synonyms: *Heterodera schachtii* forma *solani* Zimmermann, 1927; *Heterodera schachtii* subsp. *rostochiensis* (Woll.) Kemner, 1929

Historical: During the campaign against sugar beet nematode in Germany, Julius Kühn observed a cyst-forming nematode attacking potatoes. He recorded it among his many notes (1881), thinking it was *Heterodera schachtii*. The problem remained unrecognized until Zimmermann (1914) definitely established the fact that what he thought to be *H. schachtii* was a serious parasite of potatoes. In Scotland, Massee (1913) had already reported it as a common parasite of potatoes. During the following decade it became widely known in England as the potato root eelworm. Other European countries soon found the pest within their borders, and Cannon (1941) found it on Long Island, New York. A possible explanation of the original source of the pest was offered when Bazah de Segura (1952) reported it from Peru, the home of the potato. The most recent extension of its range is by virtue of a report on nematodes from Israel, where it has been found by Minz (1956).

Wollenweber (1923) observed that cysts from potatoes were pear-shaped, instead of lemon-shaped, and that the larvae were slightly shorter than those from sugar beets. After investigating its morphology he decided that this was a species different from the one attacking beets. He proposed the name *Heterodera rostochiensis* since he had found it in the vicinity of the city of Rostock, Germany. Unfortunately this specific name was not accepted by the numerous workers, and the species continued to be known as *H. schachtii*, although it occasionally was called the potato form or strain. It was not until the excellent work of Franklin (1940) that *H. rostochiensis* became recognized as a valid species. Even since that date there are occasional references under the name *H. schachtii*. The common name "golden nematode of potatoes" was proposed by Chitwood (1944).

The impact of the golden nematode on the world's potato industry was no less spectacular than that of *Heterodera schachtii* on the beet sugar industry. Each infested country invested heavily in what proved to be futile efforts to stem the tide of the rapidly spreading menace, since the pest had already been widely distributed through infested seed. An almost entirely new generation of nematologists was recruited to investigate the many phases of the problem. A complete roster of those engaged would doubtless include more than 200 names. Among the most outstanding individuals we find Zimmermann, Wollenweber, and Goffart in Germany; Massee and Gemmell in Scotland; Filipjev in the U.S.S.R.; Triffitt, Franklin, Fenwick, Jones, Ellenby, and Peters in England; Carroll and McMahon in Ireland; Kemner and Ahlberg in Sweden; Oostenbrink in the Netherlands; van den Brande in Belgium; and Chitwood, Mai, Buhrer, Feldmesser, and Betz in the United States. As research workers gave their attention to this "new" pest, numerous publications appeared, an unusually large portion of them being of good quality.

Some countries initiated regulatory measures to prevent introduction of infested potatoes into clean areas, as recorded by Chitwood (1951). Germany required crop rotations before planting potatoes on infested land. The Netherlands, Denmark, Sweden, and Ireland prohibited the growing of potatoes on known infested fields. Norway, Sweden, Italy, and the U.S.S.R. placed embargoes on potatoes from infested areas. Perhaps the most intensive regulatory campaign to control the pest is that of the United States government, cooperating with the various states through the Section of Domestic Quarantines. Intensive surveys were begun on Long Island soon after the golden nematode was discovered there. These have been extended from year to year, occasional additional infestations being discovered each season. Hundreds of thousands of soil samples have been collected and processed during nation-wide surveys without finding additional infestations.

Sources of survey samples are fields, warehouses, storage cellars and bins, grader dirt, soil on diggers and other machinery, bags, baskets, and other containers. Chitwood (1951) records an instance in which 5 gallons of soil, containing 32,000 cysts, were secured from a tractor which had been operating in a heavily infested field. In another case, 180 cysts were found in the soil on a floor where a worker had changed his shoes.

From a financial standpoint the golden nematode has demanded far greater expenditures than any other nematode problem. In the United States more money is being spent on this project than on all other plant parasitic nematode programs combined. Total expenditures for golden nematode control and research by counties, states, and the Federal government have doubtless passed the 10-million-dollar mark (1958). No estimate is available on the amounts appropriated by other countries, but they have probably spent a comparable amount. In the United States the pest appears to have been held in check. But in most European countries there has been a gradual dissemination until in some instances major portions of potato-producing areas are now infested.

Morphology and biology: Females of *Heterodera rostochiensis* are generally spheroid, except for the protruding neck. They measure between 0.5 and 0.8 mm in length. The usual under- and oversized and aberrantly formed individuals are always present. The subcrystalline layer is present on young females, and small specimens may retain it even after becoming cysts. However, it is thinner and more friable in texture than that of *H. schachtii* and *H. avenae* and generally disappears by the time the cyst is removed from soil. Occasionally small fragments are found clinging to the walls of large cysts. Rugose layer marked by elongated, somewhat zigzag lines which usually are parallel with the body axis. On the posterior fourth of the body there is little semblance of order in their arrangement. Cuticle marked by transverse rows of minute punctations, creating a somewhat striated appearance. The rounded posterior part of the body bears a circular, clear fenestral area, and near it can usually be discerned the very small anal opening. No gelatinous egg-sac is produced, and all eggs are retained within the body. Various workers have commented on the fact that different soil types and even different potato plants may have considerable influence on size of cyst (Fig. 11-12).

Males average about 1.0 mm long. Lip region marked by 6 to 8 annules. Spear with rounded knobs. Testis one. Spicula pointed. Cephalids 8 to 10 annules behind lip region. Hemizonid adjacent to excretory pore. Ellenby (1954) found males more numerous under high population conditions.

Larvae are generally 440 to 460 μ long. Hyaline portion of tail equal to spear length.

Fig. 11-14. *Heterodera rostochiensis* females on potato roots. (*Photograph by H. H. Lyon. Courtesy of Department of Plant Pathology, Cornell University.*)

Identification: Diagnostic characters are usually rather definite, because the females are spheroid, while those of *Heterodera punctata* and *H. leptonepia* are more elongated. The rugose layer distinguishes it from *punctata*, which has none. The larval width, a = 22, separates it from *leptonepia*, a = 39. From *tabacum* it is distinguished by the relatively longer distance between the vulva and anus, 3.1 to 7.2 times the fenestra diameter compared with 1.0 to 1.9.

The life history of *Heterodera rostochiensis* follows rather closely the general pattern of the genus. Most workers have stated that a first moult

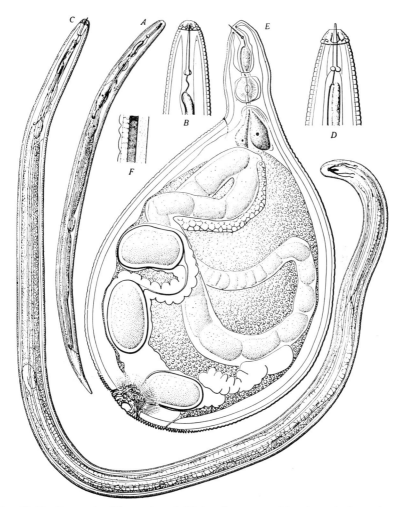

Fig. 11-15. Stages in life cycle of *Heterodera rostochiensis.* *A*—Second-stage larva. *B*—Head of larva. *C*—Male. *D*—Head of male. *E*—Female. *F*—Section of cuticle. (*After Chitwood. Courtesy of Helminthological Society of Washington.*)

does not occur in the egg, but Hagemeyer (1951) found that a first moult does occur there. Therefore, it is the second-stage larvae which emerge from the egg, and only three moults occur within the host root. Entrance is usually made near the tip of a root, but other portions, and even tubers, are sometimes entered. The usual giant cells are produced, and the females break through the cortex and remain attached by the neck and head, while the male enters the soil and searches out the female. The life cycle requires from five to seven weeks, depending on moisture, temperature, and other factors. Only one generation is produced each year. In the absence of host plants, larvae may remain in the cysts for seven or eight years, perhaps longer. Even when potatoes are planted all the larvae do not hatch that season. Many remain dormant within the eggs protected by the cyst.

Symptoms: Injury appears when young potato plants have utilized the stored food in the seed and must depend on their own roots for sustenance. Under conditions of severe infestation, plant growth is checked, and wilting occurs during hot parts of the day. Eventually the plant makes a very poor growth or dies. When visible injury occurs, it is confined not to individual plants but to a spot in the field, the size depending on the age of the infestation and opportunities for dispersion. Old, widespread infestations may involve an entire field and a loss of 25 to 50 per cent of the crop. Greater losses have occasionally been reported. Roots of injured plants are short and brown, have numerous branches, and usually present an appearance of general deterioration. Symptoms may vary from year to year, depending on growing conditions and fluctuations in populations. Potatoes following a crop rotation usually grow thriftily and produce a "normal crop." Yet by the end of the season they will carry great numbers of females and cysts developed from eggs which managed to lie dormant during the rotation period.

Host plants: All known varieties of potato, *Solanum tuberosum,* and tomato, *Lycopersicon esculentum,* are severely attacked by the golden nematode. Eggplant, *S. melongena,* was added to the list of susceptible crops by Fassuliotis and Feldmesser (1954). Ellenby (1954) reported tests with about 1,300 forms of more than 60 cultivated and wild species of *Solanum.* Among this vast collection a diploid species, *S. vernei,* and four lines of *S. tuberosum* subsp. *andigem* were found to have marked resistance, the other forms all being susceptible. These resistant types are now being used for potato-breeding work in Great Britain, the Netherlands, and the United States. All known common species of Solanaceae are susceptible. The only susceptible plant outside the family is snapdragon, *Antirrhinum majus* (Franklin, 1951). It will be most interesting to learn if varieties resistant to a population of *Heterodera rostochiensis* in one locality will also be resistant to populations in other areas. Considerable variation can be expected in colonies which may have been separated from parent colonies for long periods of time. Jones (1957) has already reported that certain biotypes have appeared which are able successfully to infest certain resistant varieties.

Control: Crop rotation was the first recommendation made for control of golden nematode on a field basis (O'Brien and Prentice, 1930). After expenditures of millions of dollars on research this remains the only practical method of combating the pest. Fortunately the limited host range among crop plants, potatoes, tomatoes, and eggplant gives the grower a wide range of crops from which he may select. Under average conditions it should be possible to keep 15 to 20 per cent of the farm in potato production, provided that proper cultural and fertility programs are followed.

Soil fumigation with dichloropropene-dichloropropane fumigants should give satisfactory control, but this method depends on high yields and prices to make it economically feasible. To date (1958) fields fumigated for potato production have been largely on a small experimental basis. On the vast acreages of clay, muck, and peat soils there is no possibility of fumigation because of exorbitant costs. Unless more efficient soil fumigants or other control methods are developed, the care-free days of unlimited consecutive potato crops are doomed whenever the golden nematode appears in the field. Tomatoes grown in greenhouses are the one crop which has sufficient value to justify fumigation, but the acreage is very limited.

Early varieties of potatoes usually suffer less injury than do late types, as noted by Carroll and McMahon (1935) in Ireland, and by Chitwood and Buhrer (1946) in the United States. The early Irish Cobbler makes a good growth when weekly mean temperatures are 50 to 55°F, when nematode activity is still restricted. Green Mountain makes its major growth at 59° and is more severely attacked. Gemmell (1943) found that cysts from certain British varieties were smaller and less numerous, a fact that indicates a difference in their host efficiency and susceptibility. Selection of varieties combined with time of planting should supplement any control program if maximum results are to be secured.

Grass cyst nematode, *Heterodera punctata* Thorne, 1928

Areas of reduced growth in wheat fields were observed by R. C. Russell in Saskatchewan, Canada, in 1926 and were found to be infested with a cyst-forming nematode which was described as *Heterodera punctata* by Thorne (1928a).

Morphology and biology: Females average 0.52 mm long and are pear-shaped, with a thick but friable subcrystalline layer which does not persist on the cysts. Cysts contain an average of 78 eggs, Franklin's specimens 125. Cuticle marked by transverse lines of coarse punctations but bearing no rugose layer. Perineal sections reveal that the vulva and anus are located on conspicuous clear areas almost equal in size. Six minute spheroid lips arranged about the labial disc.

Males 0.9 to 1.3 mm long, with lip region marked by five striae. Labial papillae apparently four, with slightly oval amphidial apertures adjacent to the oral opening. Under each annule the subcuticle is marked by two refractive dots when observed in profile. Excretory pore about two body widths posterior to latitude or nerve ring. Hemizonid adjacent to excretory pore. Spicula slightly arcuate with tapering, rounded points. Phasmids almost terminal.

Larvae 350 to 470 μ long from Canada, 520 μ from England. Spear about 20 μ long, basal knobs rounded. Lateral fields marked by two refractive bands. Anus very obscure.

Identification: Among pear-shaped, *Heterodera, H. punctata* is distinguished by the lines of coarse cuticular punctations, absence of a rugose layer, and the anal region, which is almost as large as the vulvar fenestra.

Specimens collected in June included a complete series of both males and females in all stages of development, while in August all were mature cysts filled with embryonated eggs. Probably one generation occurs in each season.

Hosts and distribution: Baker (1945) found *Heterodera punctata* in Alberta, Canada. Franklin (1938) collected cysts from roots of grasses, *Agrostis stolonifera* L. and *A. tenuis* Sibth., in Hertfordshire, England. Oostenbrink (1950) records it from the Netherlands. However, Oostenbrink (1959, personal communication) stated that it is doubtful if the England and Netherland species is the same as that from Canada.

Tobacco cyst nematode, *Heterodera tabacum* Lowns. & Lowns., 1954

This close relative of *Heterodera rostochiensis* was found parasitizing tobacco near Hazardville, Connecticut, in 1951.

Morphology and biology: Females ovate to spheroid, 0.46 to 0.69 mm long; at first white, then passing through a yellow stage as the brown cyst is formed. Lip region with three prominent annules. Cuticular punctations obscure, usually forming transverse rows near middle of body. Rugose pattern near middle, with a longitudinal trend of short irregular segments. Anus small, located only 1.0 to 1.9 times the fenestra diameter from the vulva.

Males 0.7 to 1.4 mm long. Lip region with six annules in addition to the labial disc. Spear 24 to 27 μ long with strong rounded knobs. Hemizonid adjacent to excretory pore. Striae about 2 μ wide near middle of body. Sub-cuticle striae duplex. Spicula slightly arcuate, tapering, and bluntly pointed. Tail 0.2 to 3.6 μ long.

Larvae 410 to 527 μ long. Lip region with four annules and the labial disc. Spear 22 to 26 μ long with rounded knobs. Lateral field marked by four incisures. Phasmids slightly anterior to middle of tail.

Identification: Differs from *Heterodera rostochiensis* in the slightly shorter male tail; shorter distance from spear base to esophageal gland outlet, 2.0 to 5.5 compared with 5.1 to 10.9; female lip region with three annules compared with two; vulva-anus distance 1.0 to 1.9 times fenestra width compared with 3.1 to 7.2 (Granek, 1955). Differs from *punctata* in cyst form and cuticular markings and from *leptonepia* in the more robust larvae.

Hosts: Host tests revealed that *Heterodera tabacum* did not mature on potato but did on *Solanum nigrum, S. dulcamara, S. integrifolium, S. rostratum,* and tomato, *Lycopersicon esculentum.* All these species are also hosts of *H. rostochiensis.* Thus these two *Heterodera* spp. share these five hosts to a limited degree but do not interchange on their principal hosts, which are tobacco and potatoes.

Appreciable yield reduction in tobacco has not been observed even though some infestations must have been of long standing. In pot experiments a slight decrease in height and weight of plants was produced by infestations of 820 larvae per gram of soil. Marked reduction in height and weight was evident when 3,278 larvae per gram of soil were present. Populations of these magnitudes probably will not develop under average field conditions, which doubtless accounts for the absence of visible field symptoms.

Heterodera leptonepia Cobb and Taylor, 1953

Three cysts of this species were collected from soil carried on potatoes in ship's stores, apparently originating in Callao, Peru, an indication that they probably came from fields in that vicinity.

Morphology: Cysts light brown, rounded posteriorly as in *Heterodera rostochiensis*. Vulval opening round and much larger than the very small anus. Rugose pattern in lines extending from neck to near vulva, where they are interrupted by an irregular pattern. Punctations minute, arranged in closely spaced lines at right angles to cyst axis.

Larvae 567 (520 to 600) μ long, more slender than those of any other *Heterodera* sp., a = 39; b = 2.7; c = 9.1. Spear about 18 μ long, with anteriorly convex knobs. Dorsal esophageal gland outlet 12 μ behind spear. Hyaline portion of tail longer than spear.

Identification: Longitudinal lines of the rugose cyst pattern and unusually slender larvae constitute diagnostic characters.

Host unknown.

Chapter 12

Root-knot nematodes, genus *Meloidogyne* Goeldi, 1892

Root-knot nematodes were considered to be a single species until Chitwood (1949a) definitely identified five species and one variety. Previously they had generally been known under the name *Heterodera radicicola* (Greef, 1872) Müller, 1884. This later was replaced by *H. marioni* (Cornu, 1879) Goodey, 1932. The majority of literature citations will be found under these two names. Other infrequent designations are: *Anguillula marioni* Cornu, 1879; *A. arenaria* Neal, 1889; *A. vialae* Lavergne, 1901; *H. javanica* Treub, 1885; *Tylenchus arenarius* Cobb, 1890; *Meloidogyne exigua* Goeldi, 1892; *Oxyurus incognita* Kofoid and White, 1919; *Caconema radicicola* Cobb, 1924; and Berkeley (1855) referred to them as "Vibrios." Of the above species names, Chitwood retained *arenaria, javanica, exigua,* and *incognita*.

Field symptoms and identification: Infested plants usually are conspicuous because of their reduced, unthrifty growth and a tendency to wilt during warm days. When nematode populations are very high, young seedlings may be killed over large areas without a trace of gall formation appearing on the roots. In such instances examination under the microscope will reveal that frequently the young roots are encrusted with dozens of females attached by their heads and with their egg masses covered by adhering soil particles.

Suspected plants should be carefully lifted with a trowel or shovel and their roots examined for gall formation. If galls are visible, there is little doubt that one or more species of *Meloidogyne* are present. Because of these conspicuous, gall-like symptoms, these nemas have been observed and recorded more frequently than other groups which often are of equal or greater economic importance. Galls carefully split with a knife blade or scalpel will reveal the pearly-white females, which may be removed for examination with or without a hand lens or with a dissecting microscope. These females are typically elongate-pyriform, but wide variations occur, some being almost spherical, while others from tough, woody roots may be of various abnormal forms. Gall formation and crop damage in warm, long-season parts of the world are generally much more conspicuous than in the colder, short-season areas.

Females on cereals, potato, and other comparatively nonsucculent roots usually are attached only by their anterior ends. Their protruding bodies are covered with the gelatinous matrix into which eggs are deposited.

312

Actually, more females probably develop in this manner than within galls, and this fact makes detection difficult unless roots are examined under the dissecting microscope. Tubers, bulbs, rhizomes, and certain roots may carry considerable numbers of females without producing the characteristic symptoms. These can be detected only by cutting during inspection. Light infestations may very easily be overlooked. Seed potatoes frequently carry many females without exhibiting the characteristic wartlike growths by which they are generally recognized. The position of the female in a potato tuber is usually marked by a small brown spot. This brown spot is formed by a group of cells in contact with the egg mass. This gelatinous material apparently is toxic to the cells, which turn brown but do not decay. Because of these many non-gall-forming types of infestation, the name "root-knot" is actually something of a misnomer.

Root-knot nematode injury is usually associated with, and accentuated by, certain plant parasitic fungi which find the weakened root-tissues favorable for their development. A typical example is that recorded by Sasser, Lucas, and Powers (1955) of the relationship between nematodes and black shank of tobacco. Plantings were made of strains selected for resistance to black shank, *Phytophthora parasitica* var. *nicotiana* Tucker. Some were inoculated with both root-knot nematodes and black shank, others with black shank only. Three weeks after planting 75 to 100 per cent of the plants inoculated with both root-knot and black shank were dead. Among those inoculated with black shank only, there was a mortality of 0 to 30 per cent. Control plants and those inoculated with root-knot only were not attacked by black shank. *Meloidogyne incognita, M. incognita acrita,* and *M. javanica* were the nemas used in these experiments.

Host ranges: Until recent years all *Meloidogyne* (root-knot) host records have been grouped together, since only one species was recognized. Therefore, it is useless to discuss or record the hundreds of plant species which have been reported. Any plant may be suspected as a potential host for one or more species, and only testing under local conditions, as done by Sasser (1954), will enable the nematologist intelligently to plan crop rotations for control purposes. Possible exceptions to the necessity of such testing procedures are those instances in which local obervations have already been made and verified under actual field conditions.

Life cycle of *Meloidogyne*: Eggs of *Meloidogyne* are elongate ovate bodies about twice as long as wide. They are usually found in the gelatinous egg-sac surrounding the posterior end of the female. Those recently deposited are filled with a mass of undifferentiated granular material which, in the first stage of development, divides into 2 cells, each containing a nucleus. Each of these cells divides, making 4, with often a 3-cell stage when the division is not simultaneous. Then follow the 8, 16, 32, and succeeding stages, which eventually lead to the formation of a larva. The number of cells necessary to produce a larva has not been determined. There appears to be no diagnostic value in either lengths or widths of eggs, which range from 30 to 60 by 75 to 113 μ, the average being 33 to 42 by 78 to 97 μ. Variations of these magnitudes may be found among eggs of a single collection.

Egg production. The number of eggs produced by one female on a preferred host may reach 1,998, as recorded by Tyler, but the average is probably between 200 and 500. On unfavorable hosts only occasional females may produce eggs, and frequently these number fewer than 10.

Larva. This slender, wormlike organism is found coiled within the egg. Occasionally it is possible to see the very thin cuticle cast off during the first moult still clinging to the anterior end. Probably all larvae make their first moult within the egg, but this point has not been definitely established. At this stage the spear, median bulb of the esophagus, excretory pore, and intestine are easily visible. When hatched from the egg, the young nema is known as the preparasitic larva and is capable of moving through the soil to its host, which it doubtless locates by means of the amphids.

Preparasitic larva. The smallest preparasitic larvae recorded by Chitwood were those of *Meloidogyne exigua,* which ranged in length from 281 to 337 μ. However, he remarked that the material was in poor condition, which may have had some effect on lengths of the specimens. Largest larvae were those of *M. arenaria,* which ranged from 450 to 490 μ. Spear length is near 10 μ for all species (Fig. 11-1).

Larvae hatched from eggs produced within the gall usually move to nearby portions of the root, establish themselves, and repeat the life cycle. Thus it is generally possible to find all stages from larvae to adults in a single gall. When root-tissues have been so severely damaged that further habitation is impossible, only the exhausted carcasses of the old females remain. Larvae from the eggs of females protruding from the roots move through the soil to other locations, either on the same plant or on adjacent ones. Many females develop near the cortex and frequently force their eggs out into the soil, where the larvae hatch and migrate to suitable roots.

Linford (1939) made extensive observations on the movements of *Meloidogyne* larvae by means of root-observation boxes. He found that when they were introduced about the roots of young *Portulaca oleracea* L. plants, they rapidly made their way to the growing points, just behind the root-caps, where penetration most frequently was made. Puncture of the cell wall required several minutes' work while the larva thrust its spear into it as often as three or four times per second until an opening was finally made and the larva entered the root. Other larvae were immediately attracted to the wound, and frequently mass penetration resulted.

Linford also observed that roots injured while forcing their way between sand crystals or by other means were immediately attacked by larvae attempting to enter through the wounds. A very interesting observation in this work was that roots of the same plant varied in attractiveness, many larvae congregating about one while another nearby was left unnoticed. Similar observations were made on the roots of Whippoorwill cowpeas, *Vigna sinensis* Endl, *Amaranthus gracilis* Desf., *Cyperus rotundus* L., and other plants. Roots of *Erigenon, Euphorbia,* and *Panicum* appeared highly resistant. Unfortunately the species of *Meloidogyne* used in this work is not known, since it preceded identification of the various species.

Upon entering roots the larvae immediately establish themselves or move back a short distance until they find a suitable location, usually near the central cylinder. However, it is not unusual for larvae to enter large roots, rhizomes, and tubers at any desired point.

Formation of giant cells. After the larva is established, feeding begins, and giant cells are formed from which the larva derives its food. Linford (1937a) observed that giant cells are developed under stimulation of a persistently repeated cycle which includes (1) puncture of the cell wall by the spear of the larva, (2) injection of esophageal gland secretions into the cell, and (3) sucking out only a portion of the cell contents.

Female development. Once the giant cells are functioning, the female larva rapidly develops into an obese, spindle-shaped body. According to Christie and Cobb (1941) the original larval cuticle expands to a remarkable degree as the individual becomes flask-shaped, with the pointed terminus projecting posteriorly. Third- and fourth-stage cuticles are also produced without a moult, and not until gonads begin to develop does the final moult occur. At this time the second-, third-, and fourth-stage cuticles are moulted simultaneously.

Male development. During the development of the fourth stage, differentiation between the sexes takes place. The female becomes an elongated pear-shaped body, while the male appears as a slender, rather cylindrical, active nema possessing a strong spear and a bluntly rounded tail devoid of a bursa. While males do frequently appear, it is not definitely known that they are ever necessary to reproduction. Tyler (1933) demonstrated that reproduction readily occurs without the presence of males, and colonies descended from a single larva were successfully carried through as many as twelve generations. In such instances the female gonad produces spermatozoa which are stored in a seminal receptacle. These fertilize the eggs which subsequently are developed by the ovary, a process known as "syngonism" which was observed by Maupas (1900) and discussed and illustrated in detail by Cobb (1918).

Tyler's work indicated that males rarely develop in large primary galls; in one instance she found only 9 among 1,201 females. In secondary galls they were numerous, and in one example 26 were found with only 20 females. This increase in numbers of males was correlated with declining vitality of the host. Occasionally "nests" of males were found in overcrowded roots. Frequently many males were only half as long as normal ones, a condition which often is observed among *Meloidogyne hapla* from strawberry roots.

Numbers of generations. In tropical countries there appears to be a continuous series of life cycles, with generations overlapping one another throughout the year. However, numbers of generations are dependent on favorable moisture and temperature conditions and desirability of hosts. In temperate zones limited numbers of generations may develop, especially in semiarid areas. During winter months larvae disappear from the soil, and survival apparently is through eggs only. An exception to this statement is discussed later with reference to *Meloidogyne hapla.*

Histology of infestation and gall formation: The exemplary work of Christie (1936) presents a most thorough and detailed account of the method of attack by larval nematodes and histology of gall formation. Studies were made on very young tomato seedlings sprouted in sand and inoculated under conditions by which the actual age of the gall could be determined to within 24 hours. Entrance was made near the root-cap, where the larvae were placed, after which many of them moved to positions behind the growing point. Usually the larvae pushed their way between the cells, but in other instances they broke their way through them, especially in the apical meristem and the region close behind it. Along the central cylinder they generally moved between the cells. They usually became permanently established with their heads buried in the pleurome.

The first reaction to the entrance of the larvae was hypertrophy of the cortical cells, even those at some distance from the point of entry. Sometimes cells of the pericycle and endodermis lying near the path of the larvae also showed slightly hypertrophy. One larva did not stop the growth of the root, but when several entered, growth stopped within 24 hours. When this happened, there was an absence of cap cells and other cells near the tip of the root appeared to cease dividing. Growth of the central cylinder stopped abruptly, and parenchyma cells of the cortex showed some hypertrophy. Apparently the parasite stopped all mitotic activity in the apical meristem.

Giant cells usually originated in the pleurome adjacent to the head of the larva. For the first 48 to 60 hours the effect of parasitism appeared only to stop cell differentiation. At the end of that period some cells began to enlarge, and division of the nuclei took place. Gradually the cell walls disappeared, and the protoplasmic contents of the cells coalesced to form giant cells. In tomato, giant cells usually began their development in the vascular system and were composed of several cells. But occasionally they appeared in the cortex, where larvae became established. The many nuclei observed in giant cells probably represent the nuclei of the cells composing them. In 4- to 5-day-old cells nuclei near the head of the parasite were especially conspicuous. During the first 10 to 20 days, giant cells increased rapidly by invading the surrounding tissues; then the invasion gradually ceased and appeared to stop at the end of 40 days. Each root-gall usually contained four to six giant cells. Doubtless considerable deviation from the above schedule of development will be found among the species of *Meloidogyne* on their many hosts and under varying conditions of temperature and moisture.

Gall development: A layer of small parenchyma cells, originating from the pericycle, surrounds the central cylinder, and from it outgrowths form lateral roots. Some tracheids are interrupted, but others pass around the giant cells. Development of the xylem elements is interrupted, especially where the body of the nematode extends into the cortex. As the gall develops, other elements are formed from the cells of the surrounding parenchyma and the resulting xylem is composed of short, irregular elements. During early gall development, cells of the cortex increase greatly in size in order to contain the rapidly expanding internal tissues. In the final stages they proliferate rapidly to produce the rugose, massive enlargements so typical of *Meloidogyne* infestation.

Distribution of *Meloidogyne:* Actual travel by preparasitic larvae probably amounts to a few feet each year as they move to the roots of the nearest host plant. General distribution over fields or from one field to another is effected by machinery, water, the feet of animals, seedling plants and nursery stock, or any other agency by which infested soil and plant material is moved from one point to another. Dispersal over long distances occurs through the movement of nursery stock, seedling plants, tubers, rhizomes, and other plant material, especially when soil is transplanted, as with balled trees and shrubbery.

Occasionally the origin of some isolated infestation can definitely be traced to introduction through infested plant or soil material. Widespread infestations may stem from such introductions, but there is always the possibility that the species may have been indigenous to the area and that it has merely transferred from its original native hosts to cultivated plants.

Field control of root-knot nematodes: *Crop rotation.* Usually rotation cannot be recommended for root-knot nematode control because of wide variations in hosts of the several species. Former host lists under the names *Heterodera radicicola* and *H. marioni* included observations on all species and are, therefore, worthless. However, there are many instances in which successful rotations have already been determined by field and experimental evidence. In these specific localities where successful control has been achieved they may still be recommended. If each situation is properly evaluated on information available from the local county agent, the state experiment station, and leading farmers, there will generally be a possibility of utilizing certain crops to reduce populations to a point where good yields can be produced.

Mixed populations of two or more species of *Meloidogyne* frequently complicate a situation, and in such instances the development of satisfactory rotations may be more difficult, yet possible of solution. A typical example of such a local problem is that of Kern County, California, which has previously been mentioned. This county generally has a mixed population of cotton root-knot nematode, *M. incognita acrita,* and the peanut nematode, *M. arenaria.* After three years alfalfa is severely damaged by *M. arenaria* and is plowed up. Cotton follows for two years, during which *M. incognita acrita* builds up lethal numbers, and the field is then reseeded with alfalfa. Frequently potatoes are planted in January and February and harvested as "new potatoes" in April and May before the second generation of nematodes develops and attacks the tubers. In this manner the farmers of this region can successfully control both species of *Meloidogyne* and still produce profitable crops.

Alfalfa, cotton, tobacco, corn, cereals, and other field crops will produce satisfactory yields on land in which a considerable number of nematodes are present. In the same field, carrots, beets, Irish and sweet potatoes, and other root crops for human consumption will be infested to a degree which will make them unmarketable. Vegetables are often successfully produced in warmer areas during the winter months, when nemic activity is retarded. These are followed by more resistant field crops which thrive during the summer. Cereals and corn are generally infested to only a slight degree, and, if properly used in rotations, they generally aid in reducing root-knot populations. However, the value of any rotation may be largely nullified unless weed hosts are eliminated.

It must be borne in mind that under field conditions the root-knot problem is frequently complicated by the presence of other endo- and ectoparasitic nemas. Unless these other species are included in evaluating the problem, it is a very simple matter to be misled into making recommendations for certain cropping procedures which will result in failures.

The entire host problem of *Meloidogyne* must be completely reevaluated on the basis of each of the several species in the various localities in which they occur. Until this reevaluation is made, definite recommendations for specific crop rotations cannot in many instances be offered. A typical example of populations within a species possessing host preferences is that of *M. javanica,* which Sasser (1954) observed producing galls on *Lycopersicon peruvianum* in Maryland; yet Sauer and Giles (1957) in Australia found that this plant was not attacked. Sasser's excellent work and that of the committee testing species of *Lycopersicon* for root-knot resistance (A. L. Taylor, chairman, 1955) set a pattern for further intensive investigations in this very important field.

But before venturing into extensive experiments, the worker is cautioned first to demonstrate that the species of *Meloidogyne* with which he is working will successfully reproduce and maintain colonies on its preferred hosts under the prevailing conditions. Otherwise, negative results are of little or no value, because the nemas may not have been given a favorable opportunity to complete their life cycles. Of special importance is the necessity, when galls are not observed, to determine if females are attached to the roots, as so frequently happens. For critical examination the roots should be stained with lactophenol–acid fuchsin, as outlined by McBeth, Taylor, and Smith (1945).

Observations on local farming practices will frequently reveal that a certain crop sequence will give satisfactory control, as cited for the alfalfa-cotton rotation in the San Joaquin Valley of California. Much will depend on the crops grown and the species of *Meloidogyne* present. Mixed populations of two or more species greatly complicate the problem. Production of potatoes, carrots, and other edible root crops usually is exceedingly difficult, especially in temperate, short-season areas.

Fallow. Dry fallow with two or three deep plowings during the hot summer months gives excellent control of root-knot in succeeding winter vegetable crops. This method is applicable only to long-season, high-temperature regions like the Imperial Valley of California and the Rio Grande Valley of Texas.

Time of planting. In long-season, warm-climate regions certain crops may be planted during the winter months and harvested before injury occurs in the spring. The potato industry of the San Joaquin Valley of California is based on this method of farming. Plantings are made early in the year and harvested before June without visible infestation. If allowed to remain a month or two longer, the entire crop would be unsalable.

Soil fumigation. Recommended applications of standard soil fumigants give satisfactory control if applied in the approved manner. Root residues containing nemas should be removed or allowed to decay before applications are made. Otherwise large numbers of nemas may escape, the fumigation being thus partly nullified.

Root-knot nematode resistance in plants: Resistance in plants was reported in 1899 by Boquet de la Gyre, who found *Coffea liberica* to be less susceptible to root-knot than *C. arabica* and recommended grafting the latter upon the former. Lavergne (1901) observed that European varieties of grapes, *Vitis vinifera,* were very susceptible to root-knot, *Anguillula vialae,* but that American hybrids were resistant. Similar observations on grapes were made by Bessey (1911). The same varieties were resistant to the mealy bug, *Phylloxera,* which was so destructive to the vineyards of France. Weber and Orton (1902) demonstrated that the Iron variety of cowpea is practically immune to root-knot and wilt, *Neocosmospora vasinfecta, = Fusarium oxysporum* f. *bracheiphilum* (E. F. Smith) Snyder & Hansen, while other varieties were very susceptible. Shamel and Coby (1907) while working on tobacco breeding found a strain which was resistant to root-knot. Since these early records were made, the literature is replete with references to resistance in various plants, but, unfortunately, in most instances the identities of the species of *Meloidogyne* involved are not known, and therefore data are frequently contradictory. Early investigators were not cognizant of the fact that female *Meloidogyne* frequently are located externally on roots and do not form galls. Because of this fact many early records of resistance are of questionable value.

Little is known of the morphological or physiological characters of plants which may be responsible for such resistance. Steiner (1925) suggested that host "resistance" was based on certain mechanical or chemical factors which actually prevented the nemas from entering the roots, while host "immunity" enabled certain plants to make growth despite the presence of invaded and galled roots. As an example of resistance, he quoted from an unpublished paper by E. H. Arzberger, who found that the roots of resistant Iron and Brabham cowpeas possessed better-developed cork layers; the walls of the cork cells were more suberized; and the mechanical tissue of the cortex was more uniformly distributed. Susceptible varieties contained more starch in the cortex, and cells containing starch were more remote from the periphery.

Christie (1949) emphasized the fact that all nematode resistant plants are not necessarily resistant for the same reason and cited experiments in which alfalfa roots were readily entered by one species of root-knot nematode which only rarely entered the roots of lantana. He also called attention to the fact that, while peanuts are resistant to most species of *Meloidogyne,* they are susceptible to *M. hapla* and *M. arenaria* and that similar observations have been made on such highly resistant plants as *Crotalaria spectabilis* and marigolds.

Christie also referred to the work of LaPage (1937) on animal parasites in which three criteria of resistance were recognized:

> (1) Failure of the nematode to live inside the host or its early death in it. (2) Decrease in its production of eggs and larvae. (3) Inhibition of its growth or development, so that . . . the adults require longer to mature and do not live so long when they are mature, sometimes being stunted and smaller.

He stated that these criteria apply to the *Meloidogyne* group and probably to all sedentary plant parasites.

Susceptible plants respond readily to the stimulation of salivary gland secretions and produce large galls of comparatively healthy tissues in which the nemas thrive and no decay occurs until late in the season. In resistant plants necrotic areas develop at the point of invasion, and larvae fail to survive. Under good growing conditions and moderate degrees of infestation tomatoes made an almost normal growth. Under similar circumstances peach, pepper, cotton, and okra were severely damaged. These data indicated that with these plants there was an incompatibility between host and parasite which was detrimental to both. Cross sections of resistant marigold roots demonstrated that giant cells had failed to develop after six to eight days, a fact resulting in the death of the invading larvae.

Reynolds (1955) found that, of ten varieties of alfalfa tested, only two selections, African and Narragansett, were not seriously damaged by *Meloidogyne javanica* and *M. incognita acrita.* Oddly enough, Nemastan, the alfalfa which is immune to the stem nematode, *Ditylenchus dipsaci,* was the one most susceptible to both species of *Meloidogyne.* Reynolds also records that *M. javanica* does not damage cotton in Arizona.

Generally the activities of *Meloidogyne* are confined to the roots of their hosts, but occasionally specimens are found in stems and leaves. Apparently such instances occur under conditions of exceedingly heavy infestation when the larvae migrate to the upper portions of the plant in an effort to find a more suitable habitat. Tomatoes have been observed in which the nemas had penetrated 2 or 3 inches up along the base of the stems and reproduction was proceeding in the usual manner. African violets, *Saintpaulia* var., frequently carry larvae in the stems and leaves, which are used for propagation, and in this manner the new plants become infested immediately. Steiner, Buhrer, and Rhodes (1934) found huge galls extending above the soil on the stems of *Rhunbergia* spp., and smaller galls in similar locations on *Rheum rhaponticum* and *Begonia* spp.

Linford (1941) successfully inoculated stems, petioles, mid-ribs, and other parts of tomatoes by using volcanic black sand to hold suspensions of root-knot larvae on them. In one week galls began to develop and colonies were carried through several generations. He also found stems and young leaves of Whippoorwill cowpeas very susceptible to such transplanted larvae.

Byars (1914a) appears to have been the first successfully to culture root-knot larvae on aseptic root-tissues. Linford (1937) observed the feeding of larvae on root-tissues in nutrient solution. Later (1939) he demonstrated that they were readily attracted to pieces of green pineapple leaf, tomato petiole, green stems of *Crotalaria juncea* and *Portulaca oleracea,* and similar portions of many other plants. Pieces of plant tissues in nonaseptic cultures soon began to decay but remained attractive to larvae for several days. Mature pineapple stems became more attractive as they decayed, and even cork attracted larvae after two days' exposure when the tissues became darkened. Linford remarks that perhaps it was this attractiveness of decomposing leaf and stem tissues which had an important bearing on the development of root-knot nematodes, and the temporary benefit of applying organic matter, as demonstrated by Linford, Yap, and Oliveira (1938).

Identifying Species of *Meloidogyne*

Diagnostic morphological characters by which the species of *Meloidogyne* could be distinguished were unknown until Chitwood (1949a) determined that the posterior ends of females bore rather distinctive arrangements of striae about the vulva-anus areas. These striae proved to be characteristic for the different "populations" with which he was working, and for them he proposed the trite name of "perineal patterns." With these as diagnostic characters he established five species and one variety of the genus.

Perineal patterns constitute the most reliable specific characters, and every nematologist must become familiar with them if he plans to work with members of this genus. However, certain variations occur among specimens of each species, and if the first patterns examined do not fit into the type description, it may be necessary to examine ten or more before a "trend" toward a certain pattern may be established. When only one or a few specimens are available, it may be difficult, if not impossible, to make a satisfactory decision. Concerning this problem of

variants Chitwood wrote, ". . . twice we have encountered individual
females in which the perineal pattern on one side of the body was that
of *Meloidogyne incognita* and on the other side it was in one instance
M. incognita acrita and in the other case *M. javanica.*"

The possibilities of variants within a species were well illustrated by
Allen (1952). He produced many females from a single egg-mass of
Meloidogyne incognita acrita and found individuals with patterns which
more closely resembled those of other species. Dropkin (1953) worked

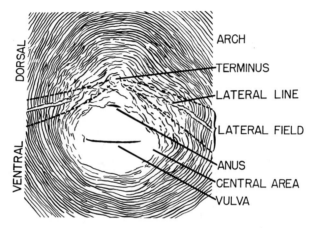

Fig. 12-1. Perineal pattern of *Meloidogyne javanica*
showing nomenclature of the various parts. (*Adapted
from Taylor, Dropkin, and Martin. Courtesy of Phytopathology.*)

with populations derived from a single larva and found that ". . . patterns are less variable in single larva families of *M. acrita* than in populations of mixed ancestry; in *M. arenaria* no differences could be demonstrated." Sasser (1954) and Taylor, Dropkin, and Martin (1955) made
additional contributions to our knowledge of these perineal patterns in
the various species. The reader is urged to study all five of the above-
mentioned papers and thus become more intimately acquainted with
the variations which may be anticipated. There is always the possibility
of mixed populations, and in these instances even more patterns may
have to be examined before the two or more species can be segregated.

Obviously we cannot expect to find identical patterns, but diligent
study of permanent slides should eventually enable a skilled worker to
identify accurately upward of 90 per cent of the groups of patterns examined. Identification of individual patterns may be somewhere between 60 and 80 per cent. In plain words, identification of *Meloidogyne*
spp. is not a task for the casual observer. The beginner should have preliminary identifications verified by someone well informed on the genus.

Preparation of Permanent Slides of Perineal Patterns

Permanent reference slides of perineal patterns are a necessity and should be prepared with utmost care. Specimens fixed in hot lactophenol with acid fuchsin stain are preferable. This fixative tends to separate the granular body contents from the cuticle, and stain facilitates locating the perineal patterns. Formalin-preserved material is least desirable because it often is almost impossible to clean the granular body material from the cuticle. When working with fresh, unpreserved material, first pierce the cuticle in the anterior end of the body with a sharp eye knife to relieve body pressure.

Select a well-developed specimen, and transfer it to a drop of lactophenol solution or water on a piece of celluloid. Photographic film is very satisfactory and does not turn the delicate edge of the knife. Cut off the posterior third of the body, and press out body contents. Cut away the edges of the cuplike piece of cuticle, leaving only a small, almost flat piece bearing the perineal pattern. This operation should be completed under the higher powers of the dissecting microscope. Unless trimming is carefully done, pressure lines may form and interfere with identification when the cover glass is applied. Complete cleaning by using a dental pulp file to hold down the pattern while brushing away the granular material with a finely pointed bamboo splinter. Transfer the pattern to a drop of desiccated glycerin, and repeat the process until at least a half-dozen patterns are ready. Mount in desiccated glycerin, carefully arranging the patterns near the center of the drop with three pieces of very fine glass rod for supports. Apply cover glass, tack down, and finish with a substantial ring as outlined in Chapter 3 under Microscopic Techniques.

Taylor, Dropkin, and Martin (1955) recommend first fixing the specimen, puncturing it near the anterior end with a sharp blade, transferring it to a glass slide, and cutting off the posterior end. This portion is then placed upside down, a cover glass carefully lowered on it, and a drop of lactophenol solution run under the edge. It is then ready for examination or, if desired, ringed in as a permanent slide. Mounting a considerable part of the body often involves difficulties in securing suitable light transmission for accurate identification purposes. Making a permanent mount of a single specimen is wasteful of time and materials when ten or a dozen can just as easily be placed on one slide.

When ample material is available, Taylor and Dropkin suggest placing a number of galls in a blendor and reducing them to pulp; then the portions bearing perineal sections may be selected and prepared for mounting. It is always advisable to retain bulk collections in 5 per cent formaldehyde for future reference of any questionable material or until identification has been accomplished.

Unfortunately we do not have descriptive terminology for perineal patterns which is sufficiently accurate and lucid to justify a key to species.

Nor are there consistent diagnostic values in number of labial annules, spear length, position of excretory pore, location of phasmids, or other characters by which species can be determined. Therefore, representative photographs or tracings have been selected for each species. These are supplemented with a brief statement of the more important characteristics of each.

Genus *Meloidogyne* Goeldi, 1892

Synonym: *Caconema* Cobb, 1924

Diagnosis: Heteroderinae with marked sexual dimorphism. Female a white, saccate spheroid to elongate-pyriform body with elongated neck. Cuticle marked by fine transverse striae which, in some species, are interrupted on the lateral fields by narrow incisures which are most often visible near the posterior end. Vulva and anus terminal, surrounded by cuticular striae which form diagnostic perineal patterns. Lip region bearing six minute lips on which papillae and amphids have not been observed. Spear more slender than that of larva or male, bearing strong basal knobs. Median esophageal bulb strongly developed, followed by a short isthmus. Basal bulb expanding into large, flattened lobes reaching back over anterior end of intestine, and containing three large esophageal gland nuclei. Ovaries two, convoluted about the spacious body cavity, consisting of hundreds of developing oöcytes arranged in tandem except in short zones of multiplication near the distal ends. Spermatheca pouchlike, with cellular walls.

Male cylindroid, wormlike, with neck tapering to the strongly sclerotized head region. Lateral fields marked by four incisures extending from near middle of the neck to blunt, rounded terminus, which is devoid of a bursa. Deirids not observed; phasmids often difficult to see, usually located slightly anterior to latitude of anus. Lip region bearing prominent lateral lips, or "cheeks," which contain the amphidial pouches. Amphid apertures slitlike, close to oral opening, visible only from a face view (Fig. 11-2). Spear with strongly developed basal knobs. Esophagus with a well-developed median bulb followed by a slender isthmus which joins the three elongate glands forming the basal bulb extending along anterior end of intestine. Excretory pore and hemizonid near latitude of nerve ring. Testes one or two. Body generally twisted through an arc of 90° until the head and spicula are seen more from a dorsoventral view. Populations frequently contain no males, and Tyler (1933) demonstrated that reproduction by syngonism frequently occurs.

Type species: *Meloidogyne exigua* Goeldi, 1887

Coffee root-knot nematode, *Meloidogyne exigua* Goeldi, 1892

Morphology: The well-formed arches are moderately low and flattened, while the coarse ventral striae are frequently broken. Lateral areas marked by numerous folded and broken striae which sometimes form pairs of whorls opposite the anus.

Type host: *Coffea* sp.
Type locality: Province of Rio de Janeiro, Brazil
Distribution: Chitwood redescribed this species from specimens collected by E. A. Arzburger from coffee plants in the New York Botanical

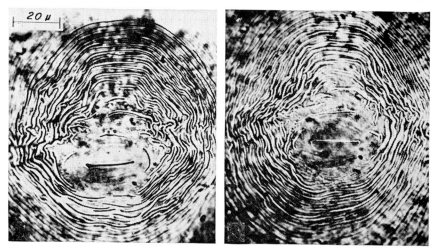

Fig. 12-2. *Meloidogyne exigua* perineal pattern. *(After Taylor, Dropkin, and Martin. Courtesy of Phytopathology.)*

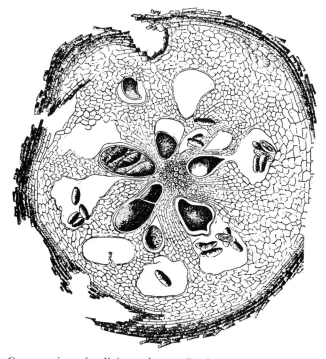

Fig. 12-3. Cross section of gall formed on coffee by *Meloidogyne exigua*. *(After Goeldi.)*

Garden in 1926. Goeldi's description was deficient in many respects, and the exact identity of the species with which he worked must await more extensive collecting in the type locality.

Javanese root-knot nematode, *Meloidogyne javanica* (Treub, 1885)
Chitwood, 1949a

Synonym: *Heterodera javanica* Treub, 1885

Morphology and biology: The lateral lines of this species are distinct incisures cutting through the striae of the perineal pattern so that few or no striae extend unbroken from the dorsal to the ventral sector. In some instances these lines extend completely across the pattern just above the anus, although

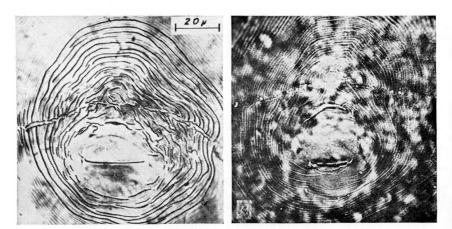

Fig. 12-4. *Meloidogyne javanica* perineal patterns. *(After Taylor, Dropkin, and Martin. Courtesy of Phytopathology.)*

a distinct whorl frequently is present at the body terminus. Usually the arch is low and rounded, but occasionally specimens have high, narrow arches. Ventral striae smooth, usually unbroken. Male with three postlabial annules on lip region; testes two. Males rare, but intersexes (males with rudimentary or well-developed vulva) are numerous.

Type host: Sugar cane, *Saccharum officinarium*
Type locality: Cheribon and Bogor, Java
Hosts and distribution: Inconspicuous galls are formed on sugar cane, but on other hosts they may be well developed. Root-knot resistant Yunnan, Lovell, and Shalil peach root-stocks are attacked, and a number of other hosts have been reported from various localities in the United States: lima beans, Florida, Georgia, and Texas; garden balsam, *Impatiens balsama*, Los Angeles, California; potatoes, cabbage, and broccoli, Florida; carnations from a greenhouse, New York. Chitwood found that "population 11C" recorded by Christie and Havis (1948) was

Meloidogyne javanica. Records from Australia, Europe, Israel, and South Africa indicate a cosmopolitan species.

Northern root-knot nematode, *Meloidogyne hapla* Chitwood, 1949a

Morphology and biology: Distinct punctations usually are present at the body terminus just above the anus, a character not found in any other known species. Lateral lines may be marked by only slight irregularities in the striae, or the striae of the dorsal and ventral sectors may meet at a slight angle along the lines. Arch low, somewhat rounded. Ventral striae frequently extended laterally to form "wings" on one or both sides, the symmetry of the perineal pattern thus being broken. Striae of both sectors smooth or slightly wavy.

Males with one or two testes. Frequently certain colonies of *Meloidogyne hapla* have no males, while in others they are numerous. In some instances,

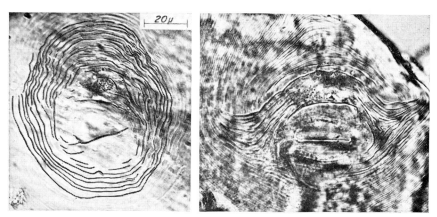

Fig. 12-5. *Meloidogyne hapla* perineal patterns. *(After Taylor, Dropkin, and Martin. Courtesy of Phytopathology.)*

especially in strawberries, there are miniature males which may be only half the usual length.

Generally infestations of *Meloidogyne hapla* are characterized by numerous small galls, although large galls are formed on potato tubers and, rarely, on sugar beets and other succulent roots.

Allen (1939, unpublished report) found young female *Meloidogyne* overwintering on roots of dandelion, *Taraxacum officinale,* near Reno, Nevada. Since *M. hapla* is the only species known in that locality, it appears safe to assume that this was the form observed. In Wisconsin the larvae of *M. hapla* enter the young roots of strawberries in September and October and develop into third-stage females. In this form they pass through the winter months, when temperature often drops to 10 to 25°F below zero and soil freezes to a depth of 4 feet. With the advent of spring growing temperatures the females mature and complete their life cycle.

Type host: Green Mountain variety potato
Type locality: Bridgehampton, New York

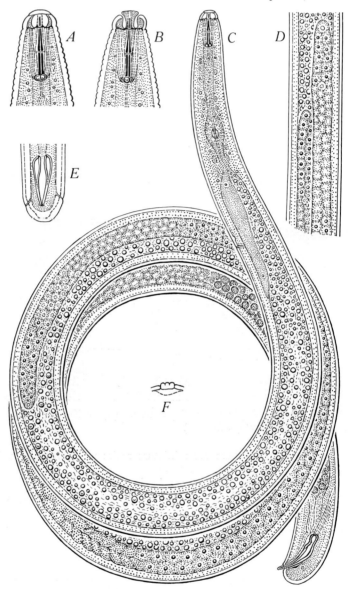

Fig. 12-6. *Meloidogyne hapla.* *A*—Head, lateral view. *B*—Head, dorsoventral view showing amphid pockets. *C*—Male with one testis. *D*—Portion of male from same colony with two testes. *E*—Ventral view of male tail. *F*—Cross section of lateral field. (*Specimens courtesy of M. W. Allen.*)

Hosts and distribution: The name "northern root-knot nematode" is something of a misnomer, for the pest is distributed throughout the United States. This species is the one most often found in potato tubers, although it frequently appears in seedling tomato, celery, and other

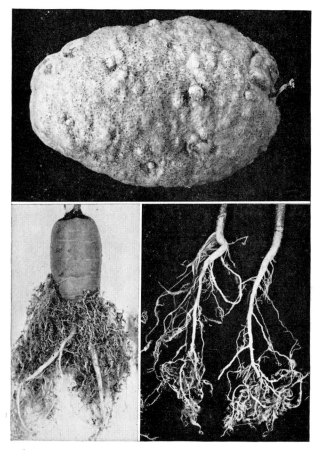

Fig. 12-7. *Meloidogyne hapla* gall formation on Burbank Russet potato, carrot, and tomato seedlings.

plants as well as in nursery stock. Either the species has been widely distributed by means of seed potatoes and other plant material, or else it is a native and has transferred from the original hosts to our cultivated crops.

Meloidogyne hapla has also been reported from various countries in Europe, Asia, Africa, and Australia. Apparently it is a cosmopolitan species.

Peanut root-knot nematode, *Meloidogyne arenaria* (Neal, 1889)
Chitwood, 1949a

Synonym: *Anguillulina arenaria* Neal, 1889

Morphology and biology: Numerous short, disordered striae occur near the lateral lines where the dorsal and ventral striae meet. Arch rather low and rounded except when the ventral striae are extended to form wings. Perineal patterns of this species most closely resemble those of *Meloidogyne hapla* but never have the punctate markings above the anus. All males observed had two testes.

Obviously Neal worked with more than one species of root-knot nematodes in Florida. Among them was one which produced severe galling on peanuts, and this Chitwood described to represent Neal's species *arenaria*.

Type host: Peanut
Type locality: Archer or Lake City, Florida
Hosts and distribution: Sasser (1954) found that the species also attacked watermelon, wheat, barley, corn, and *Lycopersicon peruvianum;*

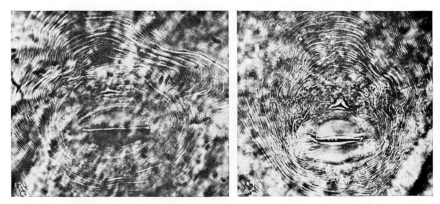

Fig. 12-8. *Meloidogyne arenaria* perineal patterns. *(After Taylor, Dropkin, and Martin. Courtesy of Phytopathology.)*

these findings indicate that the host range is much wider than the name implies and that crop rotations must be carefully worked out before they can be recommended. Records from Europe, South Africa, and Israel suggest that *Meloidogyne arenaria* is a cosmopolitan species.

Thames root-knot nematode, *Meloidogyne arenaria thamesi*
Chitwood, 1952

Morphology: According to the photographs of the perineal patterns (Taylor et al.), the arch is higher and more pronounced than in *Meloidogyne arenaria*. There is also a tendency for the lateral lines to be more developed, and these are bordered near the body terminus by numerous short, irregular lines. The dorsal gland orifice of both sexes lies only 3 μ behind the spear base, compared with 4 to 7 μ in *M. arenaria.* If the morphological characters are as pronounced as the photographs indicate, specific rank for this form would have been more fitting.

Type host: Ramie, *Boehmeria utilis*
Type locality: Canal Point, Florida
Records from Germany and South Africa indicate a world-wide distribution.

Southern root-knot nematode, *Meloidogyne incognita* (Kofoid and White, 1919) Chitwood, 1949a

Synonym: *Oxyuris incognita* Kofoid and White, 1919

Morphology: Perineal pattern somewhat oval, with a high, irregular arch composed of closely spaced wavy lines. Interior portion of the arch above anus marked by numerous zigzag and broken striae which sometimes form a whorl. There is little evidence of lateral lines, but along these areas both the dorsal

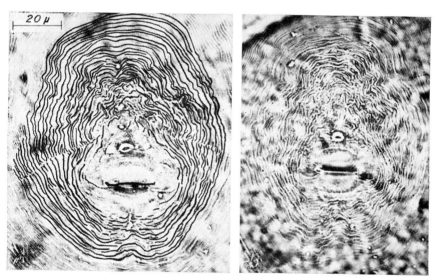

Fig. 12-9. *Meloidogyne incognita* perineal patterns. (*After Taylor, Dropkin, and Martin. Courtesy of Phytopathology.*)

and ventral striae have a tendency to become forked. Often there are short transverse striae extending from the inner striae toward the vulva. Males produced from the eggs of a single female had either one or two testes.

Kofoid and White based their diagnosis on eggs recovered from faeces of soldiers at Camp Travis, Texas, and various other army units in New Mexico, Arizona, and Oklahoma. Sandground (1923) observed that these eggs were similar to those of root-knot nematodes. Chitwood applied the name *Meloidogyne incognita* to the predominant species found in those states.

Type host: Probably a parasite of carrots eaten by man
Type locality: El Paso, Texas
Distribution: Chitwood suggested that this species probably is native to the southern United States and subtropical islands of America. Massive galls are formed on Yellow Globe onions and cotton, but none on peanuts or Yunnan or Shalil peach roots. An extensive host range is

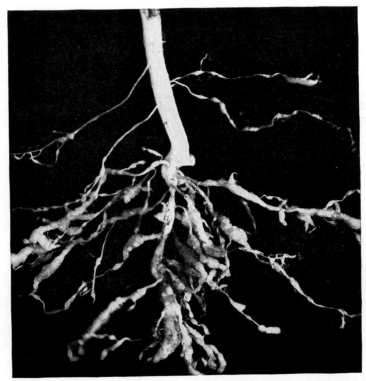

Fig. 12-10. *Meloidogyne incognita* galls on roots of young cucumber plant. (*Courtesy of G. F. Weber, Department of Plant Pathology, University of Florida.*)

indicated by records of celery and peppers in Florida; lima beans, New Jersey; cotton, Arizona; rye, Maryland; and cactus, Cadereyta, Mexico. Reports from England, South Africa, and Israel indicate world-wide distribution.

Cotton root-knot nematode, *Meloidogyne incognita* var. *acrita* Chitwood, 1949a

Morphology and biology: Compared with *Meloidogyne incognita*, the variety *acrita* is distinguished by the higher, more perfectly formed arch of the perineal pattern and the widely spaced, coarse striae of which it is largely composed. However, it resembles the type species in that center striae of the arch above the anus are fine and wavy, with a few zigzag lines interspersed. Along the lateral lines there is the same tendency for some dorsal and ventral striae to be forked. Males with either one or two testes.

Only small galls are produced on cotton, and a major portion of the females protrude from the roots, depositing their eggs into gelatinous masses forced into the soil, where they become encrusted with soil par-

Fig. 12-11. *A*—Third consecutive year of cotton in field infested with *Meloidogyne incognita acrita*. Note irregular distribution of severely damaged areas. *B*—First-year cotton following three years of alfalfa. *C*—Recently cut alfalfa. *(Photograph by M. A. Lindsay, 1940. Lloyd Frick Farm, Arvin, California. First aerial photograph of a nematode-infested field.)*

ticles. These females and egg-masses are easily overlooked unless examined under a dissecting microscope. This is especially true of very young plants, which may be killed by the thousands without a trace of gall formation. Suitability of the host has a marked influence on egg production. Guayule, *Parthenium argentatum*, is readily attacked, but most females fail to complete development. A small portion produce only five to twelve eggs each, compared with several hundreds produced on cotton. Chitwood states that galls on tomatoes are massive, with eggs ejected into the plant tissues.

Type host: Sea Island cotton, *Gossypium barbadense*
Type locality: Tifton, Georgia

Hosts and distribution: Hosts cover a wide variety of plants. Sasser (1954) recorded reproduction on thirty-nine of sixty species and varieties of plants tested. Known distribution in the United States includes practically all cotton-producing states and areas considerably north of this belt. Reports from England, South Africa, and Israel indicate a cosmopolitan species.

Very frequently it is difficult to determine if specimens belong in *Meloidogyne incognita* or *M. incognita acrita,* and certain workers have expressed doubts of the advisability of separating the two forms.

Meloidogyne inornata Lordello, 1956

Morphology: Lordello states that this species is so closely related to *Meloidogyne incognita* that the perineal patterns are of doubtful diagnostic value. The most important character is the male lip region, which is made up of only one broad labial annule, while that of *M. incognita* has three annules. Excretory pore about two spear lengths behind lip region, while that of *incognita* is only slightly more than one length. Larvae with four or six incisures in lateral field.

Type host: Soybean, var. Abura

Type locality: Estacao Experimental Central do Instituto Agronimico, Campinas, state of São Paulo, Brazil

When grown in the Campinas region of São Paulo, the soybean variety La 41-1219 is highly resistant to this species. In the Baru region,

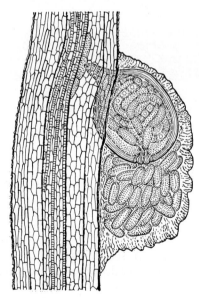

Fig. 12-12. *Meloidogyne incognita acrita* female on young cotton root.

Fig. 12-13. *Meloidogyne brevicauda* perineal pattern. *(After Taylor, Dropkin, and Martin. Courtesy of Phytopathology.)*

rather far from Campinas, this same variety is severely infested by *Meloidogyne incognita*. This host difference between the two species constituted an important factor in Lordello's justification of a new species.

Meloidogyne brevicauda Loos, 1953

Morphology: Perineal pattern most outstanding of all species and easily identified. The high, wide arches are arranged in a rectangular pattern with widely spaced striae. Only traces of lateral lines sometimes visible. Lips of both sexes prominently lobed and unlike those of other species. Male tail short, rounded; hence the name *brevicauda*.

Type host: Tea, *Thea sinensis*
Type locality: Talawakelle, Ceylon

Genus *Meloidodera* Chitwood, Hannon, and Esser, 1956

Diagnosis: Heteroderinae. Females pyriform, resembling those of *Heterodera rostochiensis* group and most *Meloidogyne*. Cuticle white, tough, does not become yellow or brown at maturity. Cuticle marked by plain striae, with internal rows of punctations parallel to annules. Vulva much farther forward than in *Heterodera* and *Meloidogyne*. Spears of females and larvae resembling those of *Heterodera*. Eggs retained in female.

Larvae resembling those of *Heterodera* in general form. Head with three annules and a labial disc. Phasmids conspicuous, as wide as one of the caudal annules.

Male unknown.

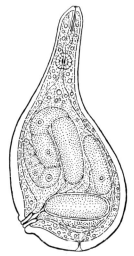

Fig. 12-14. *Meloidodera floridensis* female and larval tail. (*Specimens courtesy of J. L. Ruehle.*)

Type species: *Meloidodera floridensis* Chitwood, Hannon, and Esser, 1956

Morphology: Characters of the genus. Female 0.5 to 0.8 mm long, 0.22 to 0.4 mm wide. Lip region with three (perhaps four) annules. Neck occupying 20 per cent of body length. Spear 35 to 37 μ long. Dorsal gland orifice about 5 μ posterior to spear base. Median esophageal bulb ovate. Excretory pore slightly posterior to median bulb. Esophageal glands extending in lobes over anterior end of intestine. Anus subterminal. Vulva-anus distance 90 to 300 μ; phasmids, 30 to 40 μ posterior to anus. Eggs 115 to 118 by 55 μ. Oviparous.
Larva: 0.5–0.6 mm; a = 26–29; b = 6.4–7.1; c = 8.4–10
Spear length 27 to 29 μ, with strong basal knobs. Esophageal glands extending ventrally past anterior end of intestine. Phasmids less than one-third distance from latitude of anus to terminus. Hyaline caudal portion 25 to 35 μ.

Habitat: Roots of southern slash pine, *Pinus elliottii* Englm.

Chapter 13

Family CRICONEMATIDAE Thorne, 1943

Diagnosis: Tylenchoidea. Cuticle usually strongly striated, with annules sometimes divided into retorse scales or spines. Anterior portion of esophagus and median bulb fused into one large, muscular bundle surrounding base of spear when it is retracted. Spear strongly developed except in males, in which it is reduced or absent. Vulva near posterior end. Ovary single, outstretched, except in Dolichodorinae, in which two ovaries are present. Bursa present or absent. Ectoparasites of plants.

Type subfamily: CRICONEMATINAE Taylor, 1936

Nemas of this group were allocated to various genera until Taylor (1936) monographed the group and established Criconematinae, assigning the species to *Criconema, Procriconema,* = *Hemicycliophora,* and *Paratylenchus.* He added the genus *Criconemoides* to accommodate several species which obviously did not belong in other genera. So carefully was Taylor's work done that no changes have been made other than additions of new genera and species.

Taylor considered *Criconema* as the end product of an evolutionary process which produced the genus from *Hoplolaimus* through species of the genera *Dolichodorus, Paratylenchus, Hemicycliophora,* and *Criconemoides.* He regarded *Dolichodorus* as an intermediate form between Tylenchinae and Criconematinae. With the discovery of *Belonolaimus* this theory of relationship was strengthened, and the Chitwoods (1950) erected the Subfamily Dolichodorinae and placed it under Criconematidae. In this evolutionary process Taylor listed the following steps:

(1) Lengthening of the stylet in relation to the distance from the oral opening to the valve of the middle esophageal bulb with consequent changes in the position of the esophageal canal when the stylet is not protruded. (2) Disappearance of the sharp line of demarcation between the anterior portion of the esophagus and the middle bulb. (3) Shortening of the isthmus of the esophagus. (4) Change from an amphidelphic to a prodelphic condition. (5) Reduction or disappearance of the bursa. (6) Decrease in length of body in relation to its diameter with consequent reduction in number of annules and increase in their size. (7) Development of cuticular spines. As some of these changes appear to be gradual and others abrupt, tracing them aids in drawing dividing lines separating subfamily and generic groups.

Taylor cited one especially convincing bit of evolutionary evidence from *Criconemoides mutabile:* immature forms of this species possess spines on the annules, while they are absent in adults. There is also a fairly complete series illustrating spine development. This begins with the narrow segments of *Criconema squamosum,* followed by the short, retorse triangular plates of *Criconema octangulare.* Then come the elongate-triangular spines of *Criconema cobbi,* and the series ends with the elaborately fringed spines of *Criconema civellae.*

Key to subfamilies and genera of Criconematidae

1. Slender nemas 1.5 to 3.0 mm long, a = 50 or less.........Dolichodorinae 3
   Robust nemas less than 2.0 mm long, a = 35 or more................... 2
2. Cuticle finely annulated, basal bulb well defined........Paratylenchinae 4
   Cuticle coarsely striated, basal bulb reduced..............Criconematinae 5
3. Lateral field with three or four incisures....................*Dolichodorus*
   Lateral field with only a single line.......................*Belonolaimus*
4. Females active nemas...................................*Paratylenchus*
   Female sessile...*Cacopaurus*
5. Annules divided into retorse scales or spines...................*Criconema*
   Annules plain... 6
6. Body without a sheathlike cuticle.......................*Criconemoides*
   Body with a sheathlike cuticle................................... 7
7. Stylet knobs sloping backward, males with bursa.........*Hemicycliophora*
   Stylet knobs anteriorly cupped......................*Hemicriconemoides*
   Indefinite genus, male only known, cuticle coarsely striated, stylet and esoph-
   agus degenerate.......................................*Macroposthonia*

Subfamily Criconematinae Taylor, 1936

Diagnosis: Cuticle marked by deep striae which form conspicuous annules. These either may be plain or may bear scales or spinelike retorse projections. Longitudinal ridges and incisures rarely present. Stylet greatly elongated. Median bulb of esophagus enlarged, fused with procorpus. Isthmus often wide and continuous with basal bulb. Cardia hemispheroid to cylindroid. Females frequently with sheathlike extra cuticle. Males usually with distinct lateral fields. Bursa present or absent.

Type genus: *Criconema* Hofmänner and Menzel, 1914
The four genera comprising this subfamily usually present diagnostic characters which very definitely separate them. However, within the genera, identification of species is difficult in many instances, and extensive collections are essential before determination can be accomplished.

Genus *Criconema* Hofmänner and Menzel, 1914

Criconemas probably are among the most bizarre of all soil-inhabiting nemas. They are readily distinguished by their small, plump bodies, which may be covered with minute particles of organic matter adhering to the spines. Their movements are slow and sluggish. The cuticle resists decay, and frequently the body "shell" is found intact after all internal organs have disintegrated. Usually only small numbers appear in collections. Demonstrations of pathogenicity have not been made. Chitwood (1957) described two new species and presented a key to all species described up to that time. The following discussion of *Criconema* is largely from Taylor's monograph:

Diagnosis: Criconematinae. Body stout, fusiform. Female length six to twelve times body width. Annules 50 to 150, very coarse, divided into retorse scales or flattened spines. Lip region a discoid annule, usually set off by constriction. Spear elongated, with broad, forward cupped knobs. Basal portion of esophagus cylindroid, with little trace of an isthmus. Procorpus and bulb of esophagus combined in a broad, fusiform, muscular bundle surrounding base of spear. Vulva in posterior fifth of body. Ovary outstretched. Male more slender than female, known only for *Criconema squamosum*. Spear lost during moulting. Bursa and gubernaculum not present.

Type species: *Criconema guernei* (Certes, 1889) Hofmänner and Menzel, 1914

Synonyms: *Eubostrichus guernei* Certes; *Hoplolaimus guernei* (Certes) Menzel, 1917; *Jota guernei* (Certes) Micoletzky, 1925

Morphology: 0.4 mm; a = 12
No other measurements given, and description is inadequate. Certes states that there are six parallel rows of triangular spines on the body, but it seems more probable that eight were present. About 100 annules shown in illustration. Position of vulva, anus, and internal organs not recorded.

Criconema octangulare (Cobb, 1914) Taylor, 1936

Synonyms: *Iota octangulare* Cobb, 1914; *Hoplolaimus octangularis* (Cobb) Menzel, 1917

Morphology: ♀: 0.4 mm; a = 8; b = 3.6; c = 14.3; V = 85
Annules 65 to 75. Throughout most of the body each annule is divided into eight scalelike plates which project slightly backward. Excretory pore at nineteenth annule. Lip region a discoid cupped annule with six perioral elevations on which papillae are located. A deep constriction sets this annule off from the following one, which is rounded anteriorly. Stylet 63 μ long, extending through 12 annules. Esophageal lumen coiled in anterior end of esophagus, which is broadly expanded and embraces the basal portion of the spear. Nerve ring near base of short, cylindroid portion of esophagus. Vulva on twelfth

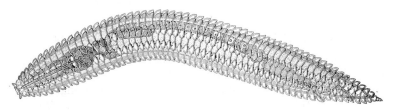

Fig. 13-1. *Criconema octangulare.* (*After Cobb.*)

annule from terminus. Ovary extending forward to near base of esophagus, sometimes with a short flexure. Anus at seventh annule from terminus.

Habitat: Dismal Swamp, Virginia. Forest soil, Door County, Wisconsin.

Criconema cobbi (Micoletzky, 1925) Taylor, 1936

Synonym: *Jota cobbi* Micoletzky, 1925

Morphology: ♀: 0.28–0.38 mm; a = 7.3; b = 3.1; c = ?; V = $^{60}83$
Body with 61 to 64 annules. First labial annule somewhat cupped, discoid. Second annule narrower than first, crenate around its border. Cuticle near mid-body with 16 rows of plain, triangular, backward-pointing plates or spines. Anteriorly some of the annules may bear 20 to 24 shorter, blunter spines. Posteriorly the spines are slenderer and sharper. Spear occupying one-fourth to almost one-third body length, 69 to 96 μ long. Esophagus extending only a distance of about 4 annules from base of spear, the isthmus and base being cylindroid. Nerve ring, excretory pore, and hemizonid not observed. Intestinal granules small, sparse. Ovary outstretched, sometimes reaching to base of esophagus, with oöcytes arranged in single file. Vulva on twelfth annule from terminus.

Habitat: Described by Micoletzky from sphagnum moss, Gribsee-Moor, Denmark. The above description and Figure 13*A* (page 340) from specimens collected by J. W. Seinhorst from forest soil near Wageningen, Netherlands.

Criconema civellae Steiner, 1949

Morphology: ♀: 0.38 mm
Other measurements not available. The illustration, Figure 13*B*, presents most of the morphological details essential to identification. Annules 58 to 62. Four parallel series of projecting scales. Each scale bears a fringe of four to six outward-pointing spines. Labial annule discoid, with an elevated perioral ring. Stylet 68 μ long, extending through about 9 annules.

Habitat: Florida, from soil about roots of *Citrus grandis,* which is named as type host.

Ring nematodes, genus *Criconemoides* Taylor, 1936

Ring nematodes are widely distributed about roots of many plant species, as is evident from survey reports of Chitwood (1949), Graham (1955), Machmer (1953), and numerous other workers. Unfortunately, most of these records do not give specific names. Orchards, vineyards, brambles, shrubbery, and perennial ornamentals frequently harbor large populations. Forest trees and shrubs, grasslands, and pastures are favorable habitats. Although the nemas obviously are ectoparasites, demonstrations of pathogenicity have not been made.

Diagnosis: Criconematinae. Annules plain, with occasional anastomosis, except numerous in *Criconemoides sphaerocephalum.* Lip region usually with 2 differentiated annules, although the framework may extend back through

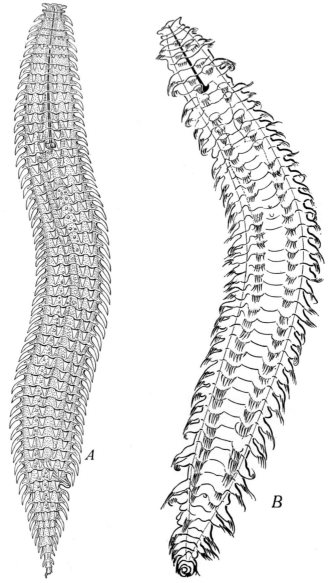

Fig. 13-2. *A—Criconema cobbi. B—Criconema civellae. (B, after Steiner. Courtesy of Florida State Department of Agriculture.)*

3 or 4 annules. Four sublateral lobes, sometimes arranged about labial disc. Amphid apertures elongate, located at margin of labial disc. Spear strongly developed, with massive, forward-pointing knobs. Anterior esophagus expanded, surrounding base of spear. Isthmus reduced, often obscure and fused with small basal bulb. Vulva 5 to 10 annules anterior to terminus, except to 13 in *C. crotaloides*. Location of anus difficult to determine. Ovary outstretched, the oöcytes generally arranged in tandem. Males with four lines in lateral field, spicula straight to slightly arcuate. Bursa rather narrow, enveloping most of tail.

Type species: *Criconemoides morgense* (Hofm. & Menz., 1914) Taylor, 1936

Criconemoides differs from *Criconema* by the absence of cuticular plates and spines in adults. It does not have the sheath cuticle of *Hemicycliophora* and *Hemicriconemoides*. Males are distinctive because of their straight or slightly arcuate spicula and well-developed bursa. About twenty-five species have been described, but diagnostic information is inadequate for several of them. Only some of the better-known representative forms are included herein. A complete key to species was presented by Raski (1952a) and emended (1958a) to include all species described up to that time.

Measurements of b and c values in species descriptions have usually been omitted because they are not of diagnostic value. Position of vulva is expressed in annules distant from the terminus rather than in per cent of body length.

Criconemoides morgense (Hofmänner and Menzel, 1914) Taylor, 1936

Synonym: *Criconema morgense* Hofmänner and Menzel, 1914

Morphology: ♀: 0.57 mm; a = 11–12

Annules 110 to 115, not retorse. Tail conoid to a sharp point. Stylet 73 μ long, extending through 16 annules. Vulva at eighth annule anterior to terminus. This species appears to belong in the *crotaloides* group, as indicated by its distinctly expanded lip region and sharp tail.

Habitat: Mud at mouth of Morges River; moss at Vevey, Lake Geneva; and littoral zone, Lake of Lucerne, Switzerland.

Criconemoides xenoplax Raski, 1952a

Morphology: ♀: 0.4–0.6 mm; a = 8.1–13.6; b = 3.1–4.8; c = 23–56; V = 90–95

♂: 0.5–0.6 mm; a = 23–28; b = ?; c = 12–15; T = 28–35

Annules 87 to 114. Labial annule cupped, with four conspicuous sublateral lobes arranged equidistantly about the oral disc. Raski figures the disc as being variable in form. Head sclerotization massive, extending through third annule. Spear 71 to 86 μ long. Isthmus slightly narrower than basal portion of esophagus. Excretory pore on twenty-fifth to thirty-fifth annule. Ovary 45 to 80 per cent of body length, outstretched. Anus 4 to 8 annules anterior to terminus.

Male body cylindroid, with lateral fields marked by four incisures. Head rounded, without annules or lips. Pharynx cup-shaped. Spear absent. Spicula

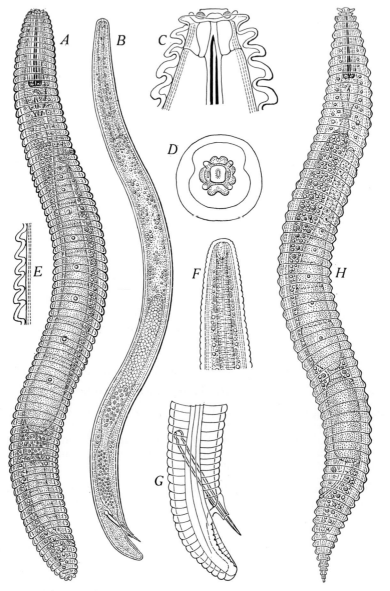

Fig. 13-3. *Criconemoides xenoplax.* *A*—Female. *B*—Male. *C, D*—Head and face views. *E*—Male head. *F*—Detail of cuticle. *G*—Male tail. *H*—*Criconemoides crotaloides.*

straight, 38 to 43 μ long, resting on a short, flat gubernaculum. Spicula sheath conspicuous, protruding, with refractive posterior side. Tail ventrally bent. Bursa narrow, extending from near terminus to a point about opposite cloacal opening. Incisures extending along bursa to near terminus. Larvae with longitudinal cuticular markings.

Hosts and distribution: Collected from soil about roots of grape, walnut, plum, and native plants at many points in California, and also from Idaho Springs, Colorado, and two points in New York. The illustrations (page 342) from specimens collected near Corvallis, Oregon, by H. J. Jensen. The spear of this specimen is only 56 μ long, considerably shorter than that of type, and probably represents a geographical variation. Other body characters correspond well to those of type.

Criconemoides annulifer (deMan, 1921) Taylor, 1936

Synonyms: *Hoplolaimus annulifer* deMan, 1921; *Criconema annulifer* (deMan) Micoletzky, 1925

Morphology: ♀: 0.47–0.55 mm; a = 10–11
Annules 58 to 61, exclusive of head. Labial annules slightly narrower and thinner than basal cephalic annule, setting off the very characteristic head. Stylet 100 to 108 μ long, extending through 11 annules, slender, with thin basal knobs. Isthmus slightly narrower than basal portion of esophagus. Vulva at sixth to ninth annules from terminus. Anus at third to fourth annules (Fig. 13-4A to D).

Habitat: Forest soil near Breda, and a municipal park of Bergen op Zoom, Netherlands. The figures (page 343) from specimens collected by J. W. Seinhorst from forest soil near Goeree, Netherlands. The spear of this specimen is only 72 μ long and extends through only seven annules.

Criconemoides sphaerocephalum Taylor, 1936

Morphology: ♀: 0.3–0.4 mm; a = 9–10
Body arcuate, cylindroid except at extremities. Annules 64 to 72, not retorse, a large portion of them with breaks along the lateral field and frequent anastomosis. Thus, there is a semblance of a lateral line in zigzag pattern. Lip region composed of 2 plain annules, the anterior one slightly cupped about a low, rounded labial disc. Spear 54 to 60 μ long, with strongly developed knobs, extending through 9 to 14 annules. Anterior portion of esophagus more than half as wide as neck. Isthmus more distinct than is usual in the genus. Basal bulb pyriform, one-third as wide as neck. Cardia hemispheroid. Excretory pore near seventeenth annule. Vulva at fourth or fifth annule from terminus. Ovary outstretched to near base of esophagus, sometimes reflexed a distance equal to body width. Eggs 24 by 72 μ. Spermatheca present at anterior end of uterus, filled with sperms (Fig. 13-4C, D).

Habitat: Described by Taylor from specimens coiled about roots of grass, island of Trinidad, British West Indies. The accompanying figures from specimens found in pasture soil near Goeree, Netherlands, by J. W. Seinhorst.

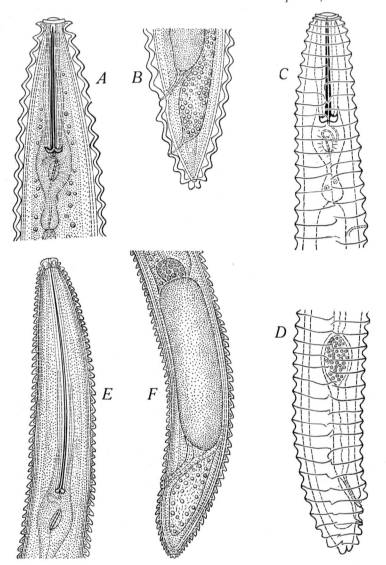

Fig. 13-4. *A, B—Criconemoides annulifer. C, D—Criconemoides sphaerocephalum. E, F—Criconemoides macrodorum.*

Criconemoides macrodorum Taylor, 1936

Morphology: ♀: 0.3 mm; a = 10–11

Body slightly arcuate, bearing 102 to 110 retorse annules on which anastomosis occasionally occurs. Neck convex-conoid to narrow lip region, which is set off by the usual 2 differentiated annules, the anterior one being rounded without any trace of lips. Stylet curved, 95 to 110 μ long, with relatively small, rounded knobs, much smaller than those of any other known *Criconemoides*. Isthmus continuous with basal bulb. Vulva near twelfth annule from terminus. Ovary outstretched. Tail convex-conoid, with very retorse annules, ending in a buttonlike knob with a minute point. Males not observed, but a spermatheca filled with spermatozoa in one specimen indicated that they exist (Fig. 13-4E, F).

Habitat: Described by Taylor from leaf mould in a woods near Alexandria, Virginia. The accompanying illustration from specimens collected in forest soil near Goeree, Netherlands. The very close similarity to Taylor's specimens is rather remarkable, considering how long the populations have probably been separated.

Criconemoides crotaloides (Cobb, 1924) Taylor, 1936

Synonym: *Iota crotaloides* Cobb, 1924

Morphology: ♀: 0.7 mm; a = 11; b = 4.7; c = 19; V = $^{66}87$

Annules 57 to 72, rounded in contour, not retorse, with occasional anastomosis. First annule of lip region wider than the second, somewhat cupped, with six low, rounded lips about the oral opening. Amphid opening under border of labial disc. Stylet 90 to 100 μ long, with strong, cupped knobs. Isthmus continuous with contour of basal bulb. Ovary outstretched, oöcytes arranged in single file except for a region of reproduction about eight cells long. Tail conoid, the annules decreasing in size to a minute pointed terminus. The specimen illustrated by Cobb apparently had lost the terminal annule (Fig. 13-3H).

Habitat: About roots of forest trees and shrubs, Wasatch Mountains, Utah, at elevations between 4,700 and 9,500 feet. Widely distributed in very small numbers. A specimen from Goeree, Netherlands, had only fifty-one annules, and the vulva was on the eleventh annule from the terminus.

Sheath nematodes, genus *Hemicycliophora* deMan, 1921

Synonym: *Procriconema* Micoletzky, 1925

DeMan's description of *Hemicycliophora* was based on a single male which was so unlike females of the genus that Micoletzky (1925) did not recognize their relationship. Accordingly, he described females under a new genus, *Procriconema*, with *P. membranifer* as type. To this genus he transferred a species which he had formerly (1913) described as *Tylencholaimus aquaticus*. Taylor accepted *Procriconema* as a valid genus in his monograph on Criconematinae. It was not until Loos (1948) in Ceylon discovered associated males and females that the relationship between *Hemicycliophora* and *Procriconema* was solved. This resulted in *Procriconema* becoming a synonym.

Taxonomy of the genus was revised when Tarjan (1952) assembled descriptions of the six species already described and added another one. He reproduced the original illustrations and gave a key to species. The writer (1955) published descriptions and figures of fifteen new species. This extensive collection demonstrated that the posterior portion of the body varied from filiform to hemispheroid and that numerous other characters were of use in specific diagnoses. Raski (1958) and Luc (1958) added four and three new species, respectively. Observations on life cycle were made by Paetzold (1958) and Van Gundy (1959).

Economic importance of *Hemicycliophora* was first reported by Steiner (1942, printed 1949) when *Procriconema, = Hemicycliophora* sp., was observed attacking slash pine seedlings, *Pinus caribaea* Morlet, near Oulustee, Florida. Groups of nemas attached by spears and heads to root-tips were obviously responsible for stunting of root growth. Tarjan (1952) built up populations of *H. parvana* on celery grown in pots in a greenhouse but did not make observations on root conditions. Several other workers reported the nemas about roots of various plants but did not determine if they were causal agents of damage.

Extensive injury to roots was not observed until Van Gundy (1957) found *Hemicycliophora* sp. associated with gall-like terminal growths on roots of rough lemon, *Citrus limonia* Osbeck, near Mecca, California. Galls stained in hot acid fuchsin lactophenol revealed that about 90 per cent had 1 to 150 *Hemicycliophora* attached to each root-tip. Nemas were not seen on other parts of roots. Gall formation appeared to be due to increase in parenchyma cells. Approximately 50 of 5,000 two- to four-year-old rough lemon seedlings and rough lemon budded to Marsh grapefruit were found infested. Raski (1958) described the species as *H. arenaria,* and subsequent research is reported under that heading.

Diagnosis: Criconematinae. Body 0.4 to 2.0 mm long, bearing a loosely fitting fifth cuticle. Cuticle with 200 to 400 coarse, rounded striae, which in *Hemicycliophora membranifer, H. penetrans,* and *H. oostenbrinki* are marked by longitudinal striae. Female lateral fields usually simple, without markings, sometimes with zigzag lines. Faint patterns beneath the cuticle occasionally observed. Head rounded or truncate, with 2 or 3 obscure annules surmounted by a labial disc. Amphid apertures at margin of labial disc. Cephalic framework well sclerotized. Spear slender, elongated, extending through 25 to 40 annules. Basal knobs of spear well developed, sloping posteriad. Median bulb and anterior portion of esophagus fused into a huge swelling which surrounds the spear base and in which the esophageal lumen is coiled when the spear is retracted. Isthmus short, well defined. Basal bulb pyriform, with three large gland nuclei usually visible. Excretory pore and hemizonid near anterior end of intestine. Ovary outstretched, with oöcytes arranged in single file except for a short region of reproduction. Vulva a transverse slit, with a tube leading out through the sheath cuticle. Spermatheca spheroid, present in bisexual species, absent in monosexual forms. Intestine extending into tail, with obscure rectum and anus, which often cannot be observed.

Males much slenderer and shorter than females. Sheath cuticle absent. Spear lost at last moult. Pharynx and esophagus degenerate, obscure. Testis outstretched. Spicula sickle-shaped, rarely a U or straight. Bursa well developed, adanal.

Type species: *Hemicycliophora typica* deMan, 1921

Hemicycliophora is immediately recognized by the sheath cuticle and sloping spear knobs. This sheath is the fifth cuticle, which becomes loose from the body when a sixth cuticle is formed beneath it. Previously the sheath was presumed to be the fourth cuticle. This process is well presented by Van Gundy (1959) in his discussion of the life cycle of *H. arenaria*.

It is interesting to note that the hemizonid is conspicuous on bisexual species, while on monosexual forms it is either missing or very obscure. This may indicate that there is some connection between this organ and the sexual processes (Thorne, 1955).

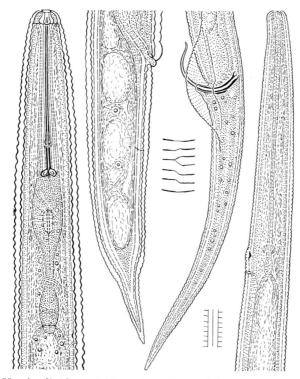

Fig. 13-5. *Hemicycliophora typica.* Anterior and posterior portions of male and female, and lateral fields of female and male. (*After Thorne. Courtesy of Helminthological Society of Washington.*)

Hemicycliophora typica deMan, 1921

Morphology: ♀: 1.2 mm; a = 20; b = 6.0; V = ^{52}84

  ♂: 1.0 mm; a = 34; b = 6.2; c = 5.1; T = 42

Female body with 256 to 280 annules. Lateral fields marked by occasional anastomosis and angles in the annules. Sheath fitting body rather loosely. Lip region rounded, without annules, but 2 are present on the sheath. Spear averaging about 95 μ long, extending through 19 to 26 annules. Isthmus somewhat longer than usual, expanding slightly to the clavate basal bulb. Excretory pore and hemizonid near anterior end of intestine. Intestinal cells vacuolated, their nuclei small. Uterus with prominent spermatheca. Body slightly contracted ventrally at vulva. Anus 14 to 17 annules anterior to terminus. Tail convex-conoid, then conoid to sharp terminus.

Male cylindroid except near extremities. Cuticle finely annulated. Lateral fields marked by three lines forming two bands extending from near head to middle of tail. Lip region slightly expanded, obtuse. Spear lost at last moult. Pharynx sometimes appearing as a small chamber. Esophagus a slender tube without bulbs, with nerve ring near its base. Excretory pore opposite base of esophagus. Hemizonid slightly anterior to excretory pore, marked by a slight elevation of the cuticle. Spicula semicircular, with thin, curved gubernaculum. Bursa broad, about three times as long as body width. Tail tapering gradually to a slightly rounded terminus.

Habitat: Widely distributed in the Netherlands. Frequently the first plant parasitic nematode to cause damage in crops on new *polders* (lands reclaimed from the ocean) according to Oostenbrink (1959, personal communication). Paetzold found large numbers of this species while investigating the salt pits in central Germany near Langenbogen and Artern. A study of male development revealed that the well-developed larval spear was lost with the fourth moult.

Hemicycliophora epicharis Raski, 1958

Morphology: ♀: 0.9 mm; a = 22–27; b = 6.0; c = 11.0–15.1; V = $^{30-62}$85

  ♂: 0.67 mm; a = 31; b = ?; c = 8.8; T = 33–35

Female with 164 annules, with occasional anastomosis on lateral fields. Sheath very thick, fitting loosely about body. Lip region bluntly rounded, bearing 2 annules. Spear 83 μ long, extending through 16 annules. Hemizonid obscure. Excretory pore about 4 annules posterior to beginning of intestine. Spermatheca prominent feature of uterus. Vulva with long, overlapping fold extending through sheath. Tail convex-conoid to blunt terminus.

Male cylindroid, tapering at extremities. Lateral field marked by four lines. Lip region well set off, spheroid, without annules. Esophagus degenerate. Hemizonid prominent, two annules anterior to excretory pore. Spicula semicircular, with sheath bearing a hamate posterior process. Gubernaculum thin, 9 μ long. Bursa broad, about three times as long as body width.

Hemicycliophora epicharis resembles *H. brevis,* from which it is distinguished by the longer spear and single line in lateral field of *H. brevis.*

Hemicycliophora epicharis is distinguished from *H. typica* by fewer annules, blunter tail, and shorter spear.

Habitat: Soil about roots of cajeput, *Melaleuca leucadendra* L., near Lakeland, Florida.

Fig. 13-6. *Hemicycliophora typica* damage to carrots. *(Photograph by K. Kuiper. Courtesy of M. Oostenbrink.)*

Hemicycliophora arenaria Raski, 1958

Morphology: ♀: 0.9 mm; a = 20–26; b = 4.9–5.1; V = $^{39-69}90$
♂: 0.5–0.7; a = 26–38; b = ?; c = 9.3; T = 27–46

Female body with 172 annules, which are unbroken on the lateral fields. Sheath closely fitted to body. Lip region rounded, bearing 2 annules. Spear 85 μ long, extending through 20 annules. Excretory pore on thirty-fifth annule, near base of esophagus. Hemizonid not observed. Body with ventral constriction at vulva which is located 18 annules from the broadly rounded terminus. Spear slightly longer than tail.

Male slender, cylindroid except at extremities. Cuticle finely annulated. Lateral fields marked by four lines. Lip region hemispheroid. Spear absent. Esophagus degenerate, obscure. Excretory pore and hemizonid near base of esophagus. Spicula semicircular, with sheath bearing a hamate process on distal posterior edge. Gubernaculum only 6 μ long. Bursa broad, three times as long as body width. Tail tapering uniformly to small, rounded terminus (Fig. 13-7).

Hemicycliophora arenaria is the only one of the rounded tailed species for which males are known.

Host and distribution: Rough lemon root-stock, *Citrus limonia* Osbeck, and various herbaceous plants, Mecca, California.

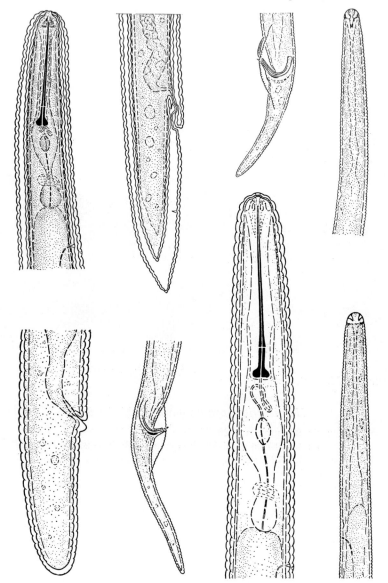

Fig. 13-7. Above—*Hemicycliophora epicharis.* Below—*Hemicycliophora arenaria.* (*After Raski. Courtesy of Helminthological Society of Washington.*)

Life history: Van Gundy (1959) made the first detailed life history of a *Hemicycliophora* while studying this species and its parasitism on rough lemon root-stock. Disease symptom, the enlargement of terminal and lateral root-tips, which resembled small knobs, was produced by an increased cell division. Nuclei of cells in the area showed hypertrophy, this fact suggesting secretion of one or more enzymes by the nemas. Rough lemon seedlings were inoculated with 250 nemas and

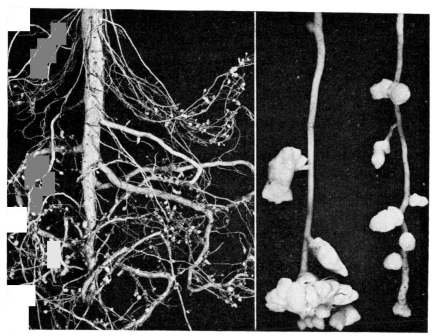

Fig. 13-8. Citrus roots bearing galls formed by feeding of *Hemicycliophora arenaria.* *(After Van Gundy. Courtesy of Helminthological Society of Washington.)*

grown for five months at 30°C. At the end of this period they were 35 per cent smaller than uninoculated checks. Nematodes increased at the rate of 1 to 640 during this time.

Females deposited eggs in depression slides, and these were incubated in moisture chambers at 28 to 30°C. Hatched larvae were removed to other slides and observed every 24 hours. Water on the larvae was changed every three days. Tomato seedlings were planted in soil in half-pint paper cups and 100 one-day-old larvae added to each cup. These were kept at 30°C in a temperature tank. Additional observations were made in petri dishes containing water agar and sterile tomato seedlings.

The first larval moult occurred within the egg, and then followed the usual second, third, and fourth moults, culminating in the development of adult females and males. A period of feeding was necessary between each moult. At this point it was discovered that the females developed a sixth cuticle beneath the fourth-stage moult (fifth cuticle), which formed the sheath. Previously this sheath had been presumed to be the last larval cuticle.

Males did not produce a sixth cuticle. Isolated females deposited eggs from which hatched normal larvae, an indication that males are not essential to reproduction. The life cycle was completed in 15 to 18 days at 28 to 30°C. Detailed observations and measurements of the entire life history are recorded by Van Gundy (1959).

Hemicycliophora gracilis Thorne, 1955

Morphology: ♀: 1.3–1.7 mm; a = 27; b = 6.1; V = $^{40}81$

Body with 341 to 390 annules. Sheath fitting loosely about body. Lateral field marked by two lines, which are obscure on many specimens; between them

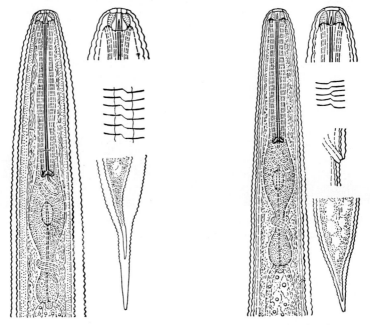

Fig. 13-9. Left, *Hemicycliophora gracilis*. Right, *Hemicycliophora similis*. *(After Thorne. Courtesy of Helminthological Society of Washington.)*

the annules frequently present angular joints. Lip region rounded, with 2 large annules. Spear extending through about 30 annules, averaging 110 μ long. Basal esophageal bulb clavate. Excretory pore about one body width posterior to esophagus base, its tube leading back about five body widths to join the renette cell on the right side of the body. Hemizonid not seen, absent, or very obscure. Ovary sometimes reaching to median esophageal bulb. Uterus without spermatheca. Vulva 70 to 80 annules anterior to terminus. Body slightly contracted ventrally posterior to vulva. Eggs averaged 30 by 100 μ. Anus very obscure, 20 to 30 annules behind vulva.

This species is distinctive because of the two lines in the lateral field, rounded lip region, and convex-conoid tail.

Habitat: Soil from stream bank, Broad Run, Virginia; peach orchard, Michigan; pine barrens, New Jersey; grass sod, Raleigh, North Carolina; and about gladiolus corms, Grants Pass, Oregon.

Hemicycliophora similis Thorne, 1955

Morphology: ♀: 1.1 mm; a = 23; b = 5.6; V = ^{51}79

Annules 290 to 307. Sheath fitting snugly about body. Lateral fields plain, without markings other than occasional anastomosis of annules. Lip region rounded, bearing 2 annules. Spear averaging about 80 μ long, extending through 23 to 34 annules, its length one-half the vulva terminus distance. Isthmus narrow. Basal bulb pyriform. Excretory pore opposite anterior end of intestine. Hemizonid not observed. Uterus without spermatheca. Vulva located at ventral contraction, 48 to 66 annules anterior to terminus. Tail convex-conoid (Fig. 13-9).

Females of *Hemicycliophora similis* closely resemble those of *H. typica* but lack the spermatheca and prominent hemizonid. It was while comparing the females of these two species that the absence of a hemizonid was noticed in the monosexual form. Examination of other species corroborated this observation. Luc has made similar observations in African species.

Habitat: Grass sod, Uintah Mountains, Utah; alfalfa field, Yerington, Nevada; peach orchard, California; greenhouse soil, Denver, Colorado; and grass sod, Quebec, Canada.

Hemicycliophora obesa Thorne, 1955

Morphology: ♀: 1.1 mm; a = 14; b = 5.0; V = ^{42}84

Sheath fitting loosely about body. Annules 259 to 279. Lateral field plain. Lip region rounded, bearing 2 annules. Stylet about 120 μ long, extending through 32 annules. Excretory pore and hemizonid slightly posterior to base of esophagus. Uterus with well-developed cell which is reminiscent of the spermatheca of *Boleodorus*. However, it did not contain sperms, and males are unknown. Possibly it is a spermagonium similar to that described for certain *Helicotylenchus*. Vulva located at a slight ventral contraction of the body. Anus not seen. Tail slightly convex-conoid to blunt terminus.

Hemicycliophora obesa is distinctive because of its robust body, form of tail, and spermatheca-like uterine gland.

Habitat: Soil about alpine plants, Brighton, Utah.

Hemicycliophora rotundicauda Thorne, 1955

Morphology: ♀: 1.2 mm; a = 23; b = 5.1; V = ^{49}87

Body cylindroid, with 255 to 275 annules. Sheath closely fitting body. Lateral field without markings. Lip region rounded, with 2 broad annules. Spear two-thirds as long as vulva-anus distance, slightly arcuate, extending through 20 annules, knobs rounded. Anterior esophagus almost as wide as body cavity; basal bulb clavate, almost twice as wide as isthmus. Hemizonid not observed. Nerve ring at anterior end of basal bulb. Body not ventrally contracted at vulva. Second-stage larvae with elongate-conoid tail which becomes shorter with each succeeding moult until the adult terminus is hemispheroid (Fig. 13-10).

This species is distinctive among the cylindroid forms because of its larger size and form of lip region.

Habitat: Soil about roots of a conifer, Echo Lake, Mount Evans, Colorado.

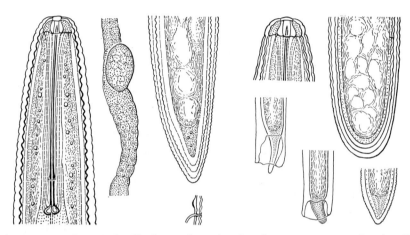

Fig. 13-10. Left, *Hemicycliophora obesa;* head, tail, excretory pore, hemizonid, and uterus with spermatheca. Right, *Hemicycliophora rotundicauda;* tails of first, second, and third larval stages and head and tail of adult female. (*After Thorne. Courtesy of Helminthological Society of Washington.*)

Hemicycliophora penetrans Thorne, 1955

Morphology: ♀: 1.0 mm; a = 25; b = 6.0; V = $^{51}83$

♂: 0.8 mm; a = 28; b = 6.2; c = 7.3; T = 31

Body with 256 to 280 annules. Sheath fitting loosely about body. Longitudinal lines mark the cuticle, about 20 being present at mid-body. Two more prominent lines bordering lateral field, forming a series of rectangular blocks. Lip region rounded, bearing 2 obscure annules. Labial disc about one-third lip width. Spear extending through 20 to 24 annules, averaging about 80 μ long. Basal esophageal bulb slightly clavate or continuous with isthmus. Uterus with prominent spermatheca. Vulva 41 to 53 annules anterior to terminus.

Male practically cylindrical, marked by fine striae. Lateral fields bordered by two conspicuous lines with a plain narrow band between them. Lip region rounded, slightly expanded, without annulation. Pharynx with slightly sclerotized walls which sometimes appear to form an open chamber. Spear lost at last moult. Esophagus degenerate, only a slender tube remaining. Hemizonid three or four annules anterior to excretory pore, usually marked by a slight elevation of the cuticle. Intestinal cells vacuolated, almost devoid of granules. Spicula bent to a U form, the distal portion carried outside the body. In two

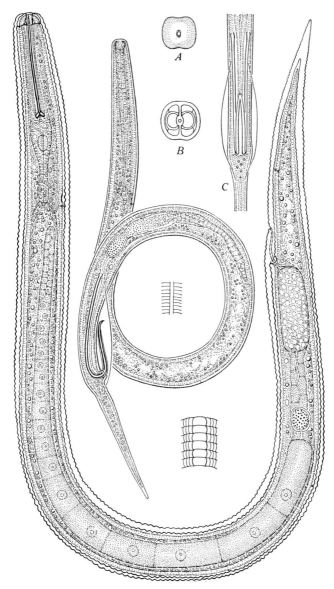

Fig. 13-11. *Hemicycliophora penetrans. A*—Labial disc. *B*—Cephalic framework. *(After Thorne. Courtesy of Helminthological Society of Washington.)*

instances part of the spicula was broken off. This usual development of the spicula is apparently nature's way of achieving copulation through the long vulval tube. Bursa broad, three or four times as long as body width, folded ventrally, and protecting the spicula when moving.

Hemicycliophora penetrans is distinctive among the longitudinally striated forms by the unusual form of the spicula, the broad head, and the slender basal esophageal bulb.

Habitat: Several hundred specimens, including many males, from rice and corn plots, Experiment Station, Bogor, Java.

Subfamily DOLICHODORINAE Chitwood and Chitwood, 1950

Diagnosis: Criconematidae? Slender nemas with cylindroid bodies 1.5 to 3.0 mm long, assuming an almost straight pose when relaxed. Cuticle distinctly striated. Lateral fields a single groove (*Belonolaimus*) or three to four incisures (*Dolichodorus*). Lip regions usually set off by constriction, bearing 8 to 10 annules. From a face view the lip region is somewhat quadrangular, with indentations, or clefts, on the dorsal, ventral, and both lateral sides. Spears unusually long, varying from 80 to 150 mm. Basal portion of esophagus a bulb with cardia (*Dolichodorus*) or extended in lobes with obscure muscular valve (*Belonolaimus*). Ovaries two, outstretched; bursa caudal.

Type genus: *Dolichodorus* Cobb, 1914
Dolichodorus was included with Tylenchinae of doubtful position by the writer (1949). The same year *Belonolaimus* was described, and those who saw members of the two genera immediately recognized important similar morphological characters common to both: general body form; quadrangular head with dorsal, ventral, and lateral indentations; similarity of four sublateral lips; arrangement of amphid apertures and cephalic papillae; elongated stylets; criconemoid anterior esophagus; two outstretched ovaries; intestine extending into tail cavity with rectum attached ventrally, annules extending around terminus, bursae caudal. Lateral fields of *Dolichodorus* are marked by three or four deep incisures, while in *Belonolaimus* there is only one. The only important supergeneric character separating the two genera is found in the development of the esophagus base. *Dolichodorus* has a definite basal bulb and cardia, while in *Belonolaimus* the esophagus is extended in long lobes, and junction with the intestine is through an obscure muscular valve.

Loof (1958) abandoned the Subfamily Dolichodorinae, returned *Dolichodorus* to Tylenchinae, and transferred *Belonolaimus* to Hoplolaiminae. He based these actions on form of the lip region, differences in lateral field, coarsely annulated cuticle, terminal annulations, and basal esophageal lobes. Study of several species has convinced the writer that the Chitwoods were justified in establishing Dolichodorinae. Global collecting will probably reveal that these two genera represent two subfamilies of a family group intermediate between Tylenchidae and Criconematidae.

Awl nematodes, genus *Dolichodorus* Cobb, 1914

Diagnosis: Dolichodorinae. Slender nemas 2.0 to 3.0 mm long. Cuticle strongly striated. Lateral fields marked by three incisures, the bands between them usually being aerolated. Lip region set off by constriction, bearing 8 to 10 annules. Amphid apertures of *Dolichodorus heterocephalus* on outer margin of lateral lips, while on *D. obtusus* they are at the edge of the wide labial disc. Spears slender, 80 to 150 μ long, with prominent knobs. Esophagus with conspicuous median bulb and elongate basal bulb, joined to intestine by a well-developed cardia. Hemizonid posterior to excretory pore. Ovaries two, outstretched. Postanal intestinal sac present. Male with lobed, caudal bursa.

Type species: *Dolichodorus heterocephalus* Cobb, 1914

Morphology: ♀: 2.2–2.7 mm; a = 50–60;
b = 10–12; c = 28–35;
V = $^{26}5_{426}$
♂: 1.8–2.4 mm; a = 54–60;
b = 8–10; c = 32–37;
T = 42–60

Lateral fields marked by three incisures which form two bands of elongate tilelike elements extending from near the neck to a short distance anterior to the tail. Posteriorly the two outer lines disappear, and the center one forms a deep cleft in which the phasmid is located. This cleft is similar to that of *Belonolaimus,* which extends the entire body length. From a face view the head is seen to be somewhat flattened dorsoventrally. Labial disc circular. Lateral sectors much larger than sublateral, with amphid apertures located near margin of head. A single papilla located on each sublateral sector, rather close together on the dorsal and ventral indentations of the head. Spear 83 to 95 μ long, with strong, sloping knobs. Median bulb two-thirds as wide as body cavity. Isthmus as long as neck width, with nerve ring near its base. Ex-

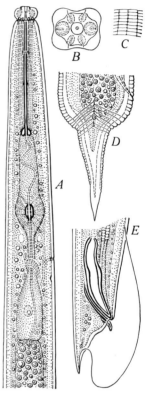

Fig. 13-12. *Dolichodorus heterocephalus.* *A*—Neck region. *B*—Face view. *C* —Pattern of lateral field. *D, E*—Female and male tails.

cretory pore about opposite nerve ring. Hemizonid 10 to 15 annules behind excretory pore. Basal esophageal bulb elongate-pyriform, with lumen located in the ventral sector. Cardia very small, pyriform. Intestine with very coarse refractive granules, extending into tail cavity, with rectum attached to ventral side. Ovaries outstretched. Tail irregularly conoid to acute terminus or convex-conoid, then spicate. Spicula massive, slightly arcuate. Gubernaculum more than half as long as spicula, with protrusile reflexed portion. Phasmid near terminus. Bursa adanal, rising slightly anterior to spicula to a broad lobe formed by a deep cleft adjacent to the terminus. From a dorsoventral view the terminus is located in a tiny cleft between the ends of the bursa.

The above description is from specimens collected by V. G. Perry near Sanford, Florida. Cobb reported a single male from Douglas Lake, Michigan. No other collection has been made in Northern states, and possibly this male represents an accidental transfer of a specimen from one collection to another.

Hosts and distribution: *Dolichodorus heterocephalus* is typically an inhabitant of wet, sandy soils in Florida. No doubt it has transferred from roots of native plants to those of cultivated crops.

Tarjan, Lownsberry, and Hawley (1952) first demonstrated pathogenicity of *Dolichodorus heterocephalus* on celery plants in 5-inch pots. These were inoculated with a mixed population of which 70 per ecnt were awl nemas. Plants receiving 1,000 nemas were visibly reduced in size by the end of the third week. At the end of the experiment, roots from these plants weighed only about one-fourth as much as those from controls. Populations of 500 per plant reduced weights to about one-half those of controls. Secondary roots of inoculated plants were generally stubby, and fine feeder roots were severely reduced in numbers. Experiments indicated that this species is a factor in "red root" disease of celery.

Damage under field conditions was first noted by Perry (1953) near Sanford, Florida. Yield of one large celery field was reduced more than 50 per cent. Injury was observed soon after seedlings were planted, when large areas showed no apparent growth. Examination revealed that root growth was practically nonexistent. After these field observations, Perry demonstrated under controlled conditions that pure populations of awl nemas produced severe stunting on celery, corn, bean, and tomato plants and moderate injury on pepper. Perry also found that the nemas ". . . may prevent seed from germinating by penetrating the seed coat to feed on and devitalize the embryo." He determined that the nemas fed not only on root-tips but also along the sides of roots and even at the base of the hypocotyl.

Infestation of Chinese water chestnuts, *Eleocharis dulcis* (Burm. f.) Henschel, was noted by Tarjan (1953). Damage was evidenced by unthrifty areas in plantings which produced undersized corms. Pathogenicity demonstrations were secured by planting in crocks and inoculating with awl nematodes. Plants receiving 750 and 1,500 nemas per crock suffered a two-fifths reduction in root weight compared with controls.

Control: Standard applications of D-D and EDB soil fumigants when properly administered give satisfactory control under field conditions.

Dolichodorus obtusus Allen, 1957a

Morphology: ♀: 1.9–2.7 mm; a = 35–45; b = 6.2–8.7; c = 45–65;
V = $^{20-16}51-60^{15-22}$

♂: 1.8–2.6 mm; a = 36–46; b = 6.7; c = 47–51; T = 38

Cuticle marked by four incisures, the outer bands marked by transverse striae. Lip region set off by a slight constriction, bearing seven or eight annules. From a face view the labial plate found to be somewhat hexagonal and much wider than that of *Dolichodorus heterocephalus*. First annule of lip region six-lobed, the remainder with four broad, rounding depressions, making the head some-

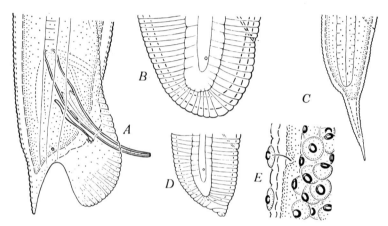

Fig. 13-13. *Dolichodorus obtusus. A, B*—Male and female tails. *C*—Larval tail. *D*—Preadult tail. *E*—Parasites. (*Adapted from Allen. Courtesy of Helmintho-logical Society of Washington.*)

what quadrangular. Amphid apertures beneath lateral margins of labial plate. Papillae not observed. Female spear 132 to 136 μ long, that of male 120 to 138 μ. Spear knobs slightly cupped. Esophagus typical of genus. Hemizonid located about eight annules posterior to excretory pore. Reproductive systems typical of genus. Female tail hemispheroid, with short postanal sac. Male tail concave-conoid to acute terminus. Bursa caudal, with wide posteriad projecting flaps formed by a deep cleft in the posterior margin. Spicula slightly arcuate. Gubernaculum slightly cephalated, the distal portion in three parallel pieces. The two lateral pieces may be homologous with the titillae of *Hoplolaimus*.

Young specimens of *Dolichodorus obtusus* have convex-conoid tails very similar to those of adult *D. heterocephalus*. Terminus of preadult slightly digitate.

A considerable portion of the specimens were parasitized by *Duboscqia penetrans* or a closely related organism.

Host and distribution: Soil about roots of *Arctostaphylos manzanita* Parry collected 10 miles south of Montello, Napa County, California.

Sting nematodes, genus *Belonolaimus* Steiner, 1949

Diagnosis: Dolichodorinae. Body elongate-cylindroid, straight when relaxed. Lateral field a single incisure when viewed in cross section. Lip region with 8 or 10 annules, set off by constriction in known species. However, on certain undescribed forms the lip region is not set off. From a face view the lip region is observed to be quadrangular, with four rounded lips formed by deep indentations on the dorsal, ventral, and lateral sectors. Labial disc circular. Amphids out near head contour, deep in the lateral clefts. One conspicuous papilla observed on each sublateral lip. Spear 100 μ long or more, with well-developed knobs. Basal part of esophagus extending in lobes back over anterior end of intestine. Junction of esophagus and intestine an obscure muscular valve. Hemizonid anterior to excretory pore. Ovaries two, outstretched. Testis single, outstretched. Bursa enveloping tail.

Type species: *Belonolaimus gracilis* Steiner, 1949

The first sting nematode, *Belonolaimus gracilis,* was reported by Steiner in 1942, but his paper was not published until 1949. Several species of this genus are present in Florida and probably will be found in other Southeastern states. However, it is generally agreed by workers in the region that *B. longicaudatus* Rau (1958) is most widespread and doubtless is the species which has been under observation in most instances, rather than *B. gracilis.* Because of this confusing state of affairs, discussions on host plants, damage to crops, and control methods will be largely dealt with under the generic group, rather than by each species.

Hosts and distribution: Brooks and Christie (1950) and Christie (1951) reported *Belonolaimus* (doubtless *longicaudatus)* causing injury to strawberries and certain vegetable crops in the vicinity of Plant City, Florida. Christie determined that feeding took place near the root-tip and along the sides of small roots, causing some necrosis and brown tips. Owens (1951) described the pathology of sting nemas on peanuts and noted injury to cotton, corn, and soybeans near Holland, Virginia.

Christie, Brooks, and Perry (1952) made demonstrations of pathogenicity on young sweet corn, celery, and strawberry plants in the Sanford, Florida, area, proving the economic importance of the species. They also found evidence of feeding on bean, beet, cowpea, crab grass, *Digitaria* sp., and possibly pepper. Cabbage, cauliflower, lettuce, and endive were not appreciably injured. Soil fumigation gave satisfactory control when administered in row applications for strawberry and as complete coverage on celery and sweet corn.

Graham and Holdeman (1952) found large areas in South Carolina cotton fields which were severely damaged by sting nemas (*Belonolaimus longicaudatus* as indicated by their illustrations). Injured roots exhibited dark, shrunken lesions along the root-axis and at the tip. Sometimes lesions girdled the roots, which were thus caused to break off. Similar injury was observed on soybean and cowpea roots. In corn there was a proliferation of roots above the injured areas. Field symptoms were the usual decline and dying of small plants, with retarded growth of those remaining. Pathogenicity tests in the greenhouse gave typical

symptoms on cotton, corn, soybean, cowpeas, strawberries, and sweet potatoes. Tobacco was not attacked and may be used in rotations for
control. Holdeman and Graham (1953) reported on the host relationship of thirty-four species and varieties of crops and weeds.

Belonolaimus gracilis Steiner, 1949

Morphology: ♀: 2.15 mm; a = 52; b = 10; c = 19.2; V = 52

♂: 1.7 mm; a = 52; b = 9; c = 14.7

Characters of the genus as presented above. Lip region set off by deep constriction, bearing about nine annules. A face view shows the head to be four-

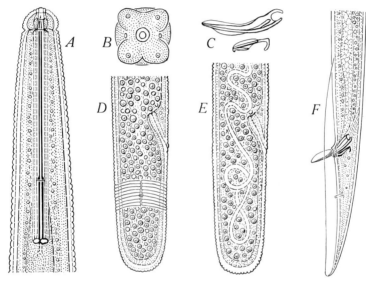

Fig. 13-14. *Belonolaimus gracilis.* *A, B*—Anterior end and face view of female.
C—Spiculum and gubernaculum. *D*—Female tail; note intestine extending into
caudal cavity. *E*—Female tail; note lateral canals coiled in body cavity. *F*—
Male tail. (*Specimens courtesy of G. F. Rau.*)

lobed, with deep lateral grooves in which the amphid apertures are located.
These grooves are in alignment with the lateral body lines, which extend to the
lip region. Labial disc a prominent feature. Spear 157 μ long, with strong,
rounded knobs. Esophageal lumen convoluted in procorpus when spear is retracted. Median bulb spherical, more than half as wide as neck. Nerve ring
almost adjacent to median bulb. Hemizonid adjacent to excretory pore. Basal
portion of esophagus extended in a broad lobe. Junction of esophagus and intestine an obscure muscular valve. Intestine extending into tail cavity, with
rectum attached ventrally. Ovaries outstretched, with spermatheca. Phasmids
of both sexes slightly anterior to middle of tail. Male tail enveloped by bursa,
which rises anterior to spicula.

Belonolaimus gracilis is distinguished from *B. longicaudatus* by the
shorter tail, longer spear, and greater relative width.

Hosts and distribution: Slash pine, *Pinus caribaea* Morelet, Ocala, Florida, and longleaf pine seedlings in forest nurseries in other parts of the state. According to Rau, *Belonolaimus gracilis* has a very limited distribution.

Belonolaimus longicaudatus Rau, 1958

Morphology: ♀: 2.0–2.6 mm; a = 56–75; b = 7.3–9.9; c = 14.5–18;
V = 46–54
♂: 1.6–2.1 mm; a = 54–76; b = 6.3–8.1; c = 12.9–16.9

Lateral field marked by a single deep incisure extending from base of lip region to near terminus. Lip region set off by constriction, with deep lateral grooves aligned with those in the lateral field. In these grooves, near the margin of the head, the amphid apertures are located. Dorsal and ventral indentations less conspicuous than lateral. From a face view the lip region is of the typical quadrangular form, with four rounded sublateral lips, on each of which is a single conspicuous papilla. Labial disc low, rounded. Spear 107 to 115 μ long, with well-developed, rounded knobs. Median esophageal bulb more than

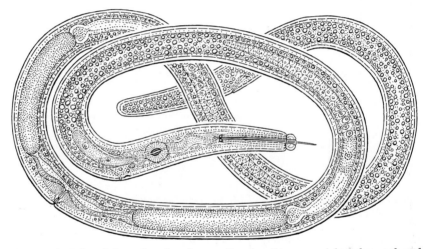

Fig. 13-15. *Belonolaimus longicaudatus.* Species almost straight when relaxed, not coiled as illustrated. (*Specimens courtesy of V. G. Perry.*)

half as wide as neck. Isthmus shorter than neck width, with nerve ring adjacent to bulb. Esophageal glands lobelike, extending over anterior end of intestine. Excretory pore about one neck width behind median bulb. Hemizonid slightly anterior to excretory pore. Vulva a transverse slit. Ovaries outstretched, each uterus containing a spermatheca. Intestine extending into tail, with rectum attached to ventral side. Tail four to five times as long as anal body diameter. Male with caudal bursa extending from slightly anterior to spicula to terminus. Phasmids about one-third distance from cloaca to terminus, located at base of bursa.

Belonolaimus longicaudatus is distinguished from *B. gracilis* by the slenderer body, shorter spear, and longer tail.

Rau records finding *Belonolaimus longicaudatus* about the roots of thirty plant species.

Subfamily PARATYLENCHINAE Thorne, 1949

Diagnosis: Female an active migratory endoparasite (*Paratylenchus*) or sessile and obese (*Cacopaurus*). Cuticle finely annulated. Lateral fields marked by minute incisures. Female spear strong to slender and elongated; male spear reduced or lost at last moult. Esophagus with expanded anterior bulbous portion, slender isthmus, and well-developed basal bulb. Ovary single, usually outstretched, with or without spermatheca. Bursa absent.

Type genus: *Paratylenchus* Micoletzky, 1922
Paratylenchinae are among the smallest plant parasitic nemas. None is known to exceed 0.5 mm, and many are less than 0.3 mm in length. But their minute size is compensated for by the huge populations which develop on favorable hosts. Sifting and gravity methods give only a partial recovery, since the nemas easily pass through the finest screens.

Pin nematodes, genus *Paratylenchus* Micoletzky, 1922

Diagnosis: Paratylenchinae. Female body plump, ventrally arcuate. Vulva usually between 80 and 85 per cent. Males more slender than females. Lateral field marked by minute incisures. Female spear with well-developed knobs, male spear reduced or lost at last moult. Lateral membranes present at vulva. Bursa absent.

Type species: *Paratylenchus bukowinensis* Micoletzky, 1922
Previous to Micoletzky's description of *Paratylenchus bukowinensis,* deMan (1880) had described a species as *Tylenchus macrophallus* from a meadow in the Netherlands. T. Goodey (1934a) recognized the species as a *Paratylenchus* and transferred it to that genus. At that time Goodey was working with an exceedingly variable population from a meadow in England which led him to believe that all species were synonyms of *P. macrophallus.* As a result he designated this species as type of the genus. As Oostenbrink (1953) pointed out, Goodey probably had at least three species in the complex which he studied. The form which he illustrated as *P. macrophallus* did not possess a posterior rudimentary uterine branch. Therefore, *P. bukowinensis* remains the type species.

Paratylenchus macrophallus is a bisexual species closely resembling *P. hamatus.* The principal differentiating character is found in the acute tails of both sexes, those of *P. hamatus* being bluntly rounded. Oostenbrink collected extensively in the Netherlands but failed to find specimens corresponding to those described by deMan. He also failed to secure specimens described by Goodey as *P. macrophallus.* However, he found three "strains" among his Netherlands material and also described *P. goodeyi,* a new species. Oostenbrink's summary of diagnostic features of the ten described species was the first attempt to bring members of the group together so that they could be properly evaluated and identified.

Thorne and Allen (1950) described *Paratylenchus hamatus* and presented a thorough morphological study. Details of head structure, amphid apertures, cephalic papillae, and lateral vulval membranes were illustrated.

Jenkins (1956) described *Paratylenchus projectus* and assembled a key to twelve species described at that time. This was a decided advance in identification procedure, but taxonomy of the genus remains very difficult. Many species have been inadequately described and illustrated. Certain species may be bisexual, and yet males have not been collected. Three types of species are involved:

1. Bisexual forms in which the male has a well-developed spear: *Paratylenchus macrophallus* deMan, 1880; *P. hamatus* Thorne & Allen, 1950; and *P. goodeyi* Oostenbrink, 1953

2. Bisexual species in which the spear is lost at last moult: *Paratylenchus besoekianus* Bally & Reydon, 1931; *P. elachistus* Steiner, 1949; *P. minutus* Linford, 1949; *P. dianthus* Jenkins & Taylor, 1956; *P. audriellus*, *P. aciculus*, and *P. aculentus* all of Brown, 1959

3. Monosexual species or bisexual forms of which males have not been collected: *Paratylenchus bukowinensis* Micoletzky, 1922; *P. nanus* and *P. anceps* Cobb, 1923a; and *P. curvitata* van der Linde, 1938

The following variations are found in *Paratylenchus* with respect to the type of uterus: (1) species in which a true spermatheca is present in the uterine tract; (2) those with a modified uterine cell forming a small spermatheca adjacent to the oviduct; (3) forms in which a modified uterine cell functions as a spermagonium similar to that described for certain *Helicotylenchus*.

Immature *Paratylenchus* often occur in great numbers and may not be recognized by those unacquainted with the group. Usually they lie immobile in a semicircular position. These probably are second- or third-stage larvae without spears. Intestinal granules generally are arranged in bands between vacuolated areas. When once identified, they are easily recognized even under lower powers of the dissecting microscope.

Frequently there are marked differences in length and body proportions between recently moulted young females and mature, egg-producing adults. These variations may be 10 to 30 per cent, with even greater ranges in *Paratylenchus goodeyi*.

Paratylenchus bukowinensis Micoletzky, 1922

Morphology: ♀: 0.39 mm; a = 20.5; b = 4.3; c = 16.8; V = $\frac{32}{84}$
Body moderately plump, tapering rapidly at both ends. Cuticle marked by two fine incisures. Spear 26 μ long, with small knobs. Anterior portion of esophagus almost as wide as body cavity, suddenly constricted to a narrow isthmus leading to a pyriform basal bulb. Excretory pore opposite basal bulb. Ovary outstretched. A posterior uterine branch present. Body uniformly conoid to a blunt, slightly digitate terminus.

Habitat: Roots of grass by Pruth River, Czernowitz (Chernovtsy), West Ukraine.

Paratylenchus bukowinensis is immediately distinguished by the posterior uterine branch and slightly digitate terminus. Micoletzky overlooked the valve of the median bulb, but other characteristics leave no doubt that his species was what we now recognize as a *Paratylenchus*. He also overlooked the vulval membranes, as did all workers before *P. hamatus* was described and the membranes illustrated.

Paratylenchus minutus Linford, 1949

Morphology: ♀: 0.24–0.31 mm; a = 16–24; b = 3.4–4.1; c = 12–18;
V = 80–84
♂: 0.22–0.27 mm; a = 22–27; b = 3.5–4.1; c = 12–19

Cuticle finely annulated, with narrow lateral fields marked by four faint incisures. Head obtusely rounded. Body with marked ventral constriction at vulva. Female stylet 16 to 21 μ long, with strong knobs. Stylet absent in male. Spermatheca present. Postvulvar uterine branch not present. Spicula slender, nearly straight, 16 to 19 μ long, almost equal in length to the short tail. Female tail ventrally arcuate, terminus subacute, sometimes slightly subdigitate.

Type host: Pineapple, *Ananas comosus* (L.) Merr.
Type locality: Wahiawa, Oahu, Hawaii

Paratylenchus minutus is distinctive among the bisexual non-spear-bearing male species by its small size and four lines in the lateral field. Females and males are found in about equal numbers.

Biology: Observations by Linford, Oliveira, and Ishii (1949) on this species constitute our first accurate information on *Paratylenchus* as plant parasites. Specimens in large numbers were found attached to host roots by their spears and were stained and photographed successfully. Populations of 100 or more per gram of soil about pineapple roots were frequently observed, two lots yielding over 900 per gram. Extractions were made through fine-textured paper towel in a Baermann funnel, because practically all specimens passed through the finest screens. Roots carefully dug and washed gave up to 23,800 per gram, or over 570 per centimeter of length.

No apparent correlation existed in fields between numbers of nemas and vigor of plants. Very heavy populations were often found about roots of strong plants, as might be expected, since vigorous-growing plants provided more roots on which the nemas increased. Lower populations on less vigorous plants would naturally be expected. However, it was not possible to determine the extent of pathogenicity under field conditions.

Parasitism was heaviest in the young mature zone of roots. This fact was determined by microscopic examination of living roots, as described by Linford (1942a). Nemas seemed attracted to the piliferous zone. Larvae and females fed by inserting their stylets into epidermal cells or root-hairs. Pulsation of the sucking bulb was observed for periods of over one hour, followed by periods of rest. Even after long feeding from one cell or a group of cells no definite pathological effects could be detected. Ectoparasitic feeding appeared to be the rule; yet stained tissues sometimes contained females, young, eggs, and a few males within epidermal cells or between cortical cells. These may have entered through wounds made by sand crystals or other agencies.

Nemas from fields which had been plowed several times and thoroughly dried appeared to have escaped serious injury. Soil samples from these fields with a wilting point of 27 per cent contained 30.7 per cent moisture when brought into the laboratory. Drying at 20 per cent gave little reduction in numbers, but at 16.3 per cent larvae and males were slightly reduced. A few females survived at 7.2 per cent, but none remained alive at 6.3 per cent. Therefore, dry field fallow would have little influence on populations, especially those living at a depth of 18 inches or more.

Distribution and hosts: Linford et al. found *Paratylenchus minutus* in many fields on Oahu and in a single field from Molokai. On Maui the nema was taken from roots of mixed vegetation at elevations of 4,100 to 6,700 feet above sea level. Continued surveys during the past decade have extended the range to many other areas in the Hawaiian Islands.

Host tests were conducted with twenty-five economic plants and weeds, and all were found susceptible.

Paratylenchus hamatus Thorne and Allen, 1950

Morphology: ♀: 0.35–0.40 mm; a = 17; b = 4.3; c = 15; V = ^{50}84
♂: 0.35–0.40 mm; a = 24; b = 5.1; c = 13; T = 34

Body marked by rather coarse striae which are interrupted on the lateral fields by four incisures occupying about one-fourth the body width. Lip region rounded, continuous with body contour, hexagonal in form when seen from a face view. Labial plate with amphid apertures located at its margin and four submedian papillae. An outer circlet of six papillae is located well below the lip-region contour. Cephalic framework lightly sclerotized, with tubular pharynx forming faint guiding rings. Female spear averaging 28 μ long, with well-developed basal knobs. Dorsal esophageal gland opening about 8 μ behind spear. Median bulb almost as wide as body cavity, with strongly sclerotized vulvular apparatus. Isthmus slender, expanding slightly to join the pyriform basal bulb. Cardia conoid. Excretory pore and hemizonid opposite anterior end of basal bulb. Intestine packed with moderately sized, uniform granules. Vulva a transverse slit, with lateral membranes. Ovary outstretched, with oöcytes in single file except for a short region of multiplications. Eggs 12 to 16 μ by 40 to 53 μ. Spermatheca present in uterine tract. Body tapering uniformly past the vulva through the slightly arcuate tail to a small, rounded terminus.

Male more slender than female, with spear only 18 μ long. Median bulb of esophagus elongate-ovoid, with a narrow valve; basal bulb pyriform. Testis outstretched, the spermatocytes in single file. Excretory pore and hemizonid opposite base of esophagus. Spicula slightly arcuate, cephalated. Gubernaculum thin, troughlike. Sheath surrounding spicula with posterior hooked process. Cloacal region slightly cupped, giving the impression of a narrow bursa when viewed from a subdorsal angle. Details of male tail as illustrated.

Type host: Fig, *Ficus carica*
Type locality: Near Planada, California

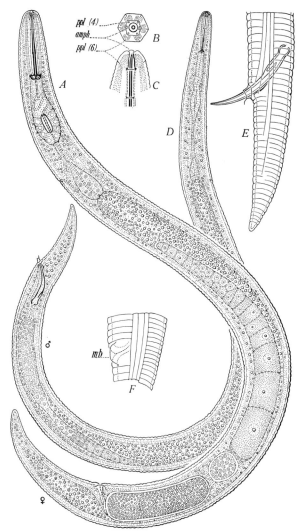

Fig. 13-16. *Paratylenchus hamatus.* *A*—Female. *B, C*—Face and lateral views of head. *D, E*—Male. *F*—Vulvar region. (*After Thorne and Allen. Courtesy of Helminthological Society of Washington.*)

Biology: *Paratylenchus hamatus* is an ectoparasite associated with "leaf drop" of White Adriatic and Calimyrna figs. Soil and roots from infested trees were sent from California to Salt Lake City, Utah, and numerous nemas were still attached to the smaller roots when they arrived. Infested roots were somewhat swollen, and their cells were enlarged and spongy. Activity of the growing point had apparently been checked and the roots prevented from functioning in a normal manner. Symptoms began with leaves turning a lighter green, and this condition gradually became more pronounced until they died and fell. Fruit was undersized and generally fell with the leaves. Slow decline of the trees accompanied by dieback of twigs and small limbs eventually developed. Symptoms may have been aggravated by inadequate irrigation during the hot summer months. However, high nematode populations almost invariably accompanied the leaf drop and decline symptoms. Erratic distribution through orchards indicated that the nemas had been introduced with infested nursery stock.

Nemas from samples collected in August were almost all immature forms, while those secured in March after the winter rains contained abundant adults of both sexes. Populations from various samples ranged from 6 to over 3,000 per pound of soil. Because of heavy losses during the screening process, it is doubtful if these numbers represent even half of those present.

Lownsberry et al. (1952) found *Paratylenchus hamatus* severely infesting celery in Connecticut, and under greenhouse conditions the pest demonstrated marked pathogenicity.

Paratylenchus goodeyi Oostenbrink, 1953

Morphology: ♀: 0.26–0.5 mm; a = 11–46; b = 11–26; c = 11–21; V = 44–64
♂: 0.36 mm; a = 33; b = 3.9; c = 10.5

Female body unusually obese at maturity, while recently moulted individuals are rather slender. Annules of cuticle varying from 1 μ in young females to 2 μ on the distended bodies of mature specimens. Lateral fields marked by four incisures. Neck tapering rapidly to a pointed lip region which is marked by several fine annules. Spear 48 to 56 μ long, with strong basal knobs. Median esophageal bulb almost filling neck cavity. Isthmus narrow, with nerve ring at anterior end. Basal bulb pyriform. Excretory pore opposite nerve ring. Lateral vulval membranes present. Ovary outstretched, extending to base of esophagus, with oöcytes arranged in single file except for a short region of multiplication. Eggs 22 to 25 by 38 to 55 μ. Spermatheca present. Posterior uterine branch absent. Anus frequently not visible. Annules between vulva and terminus 44 to 64. Terminus variable in form.

Male slender, cylindroid except at extremities. Head tapering to a pointed lip region. Spear 15 μ long, with small knobs. Esophagus obscure, degenerate. Spicula almost straight, slightly cephalated. Sclerotized anal sheath present. Gubernaculum thin, troughlike.

Type habitat: Grass turf under a pear tree in a lawn
Type locality: Arnhem, Netherlands

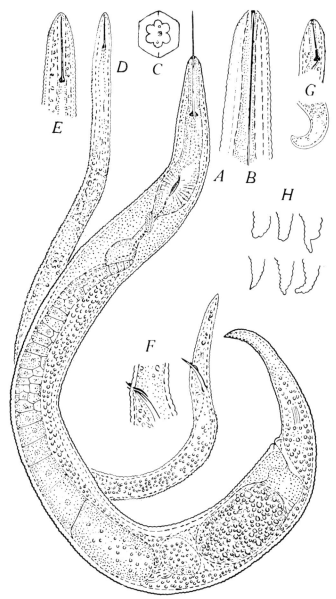

Fig. 13-17. *Paratylenchus goodeyi.* *A*—Female. *B, C*—Lateral and face views of head. *D*—Male. *E*—Male head. *F*—Anal sheath. *G*—Larval head and tail. *H*—Caudal variations. (*After Oostenbrink. Courtesy of Tijdschrift over Plantenziekten.*)

Paratylenchus goodeyi is distinctive because of its long spear, pointed lip region, and greatly distended body when mature. Young nematologists should note the wide variations in size and body proportions between recently moulted females and "dowagers," as Alex Baker calls them. These variations emphasize the importance of valid morphological characters over statistical analysis of measurements in species determination. This species and *P. audriellus* represent a group with slender, flexible spears which are very different from the strong spear types previously discussed.

Paratylenchus audriellus Brown, 1959

Morphology: ♀: 0.34 mm; a = 18–23; b = 3.1–4.4; c = 11–19; V = 82
♂: 0.33 mm; a = 25–30; b = ?; c = 10–13; T = 41

Female body cylindroid except near head and posterior to vulva. Lateral fields marked by four bright lines extending from near head to terminus. Lip region rounded, with six obscure lobes which are visible only from a face view. A minute papilla on each submedian lip. Spear slender, flexible, 48 to 55 μ long, with small rounded knobs. Median bulb spindle-shaped. Isthmus slender, with nerve ring near anterior end. Basal bulb broadly pyriform. Excretory pore near middle of isthmus. Gonad of immature female about ten times as long as body width. Vulval membranes present. Body tapering posteriorly to an arcuate tail which terminates in a clawlike process. Male body cylindroid, tapering anteriorly to a rounded lip region. Esophagus indefinite. Spicula slightly arcuate, with sclerotized cloacal sheath. Larva with well-developed spear 48 μ long. Terminus clawlike.

Habitat and distribution: Soil about roots of white birch, *Betula papyrifera* Marsh, 2 miles south of Orleans, Ontario, Canada; also about roots of beech, *Fagus grandiflora* Ehrh., Isle d'Orleans, Quebec; quaking aspen, *Populus tremuloides* Michx., near Dwyer Hill, Ontario; and pin cherry, *Prunus pennsylvanica* L., near Haliburton, Ontario.

Paratylenchus audriellus is immediately distinguished from other species with slender spears by the clawlike caudal process.

Paratylenchus aculentus Brown, 1959

Morphology: ♀: 0.26 mm; a = 21; b = 2.6; c = 11; V = 72
♂: 0.31 mm; a = 24; b = ?; c = 12

Female body tapering gradually to a rather broad, rounded lip region. Posteriorly it tapers from near vulva to an obtuse, slightly arcuate tail. Lateral field marked by two bright lines, with a third faint one between. A face view shows the lip region to be composed of six obscure lobes. Spear 54 to 62 μ long, flexible, with well-defined knobs. Median bulb with a very strong valvular apparatus. Excretory pore opposite valve. Isthmus very slender, then expanded to a pyriform basal bulb. Deirids observed in latitude of median bulb. Vulva without lateral membranes. Ovary only about three times as long as body width. Numerous spermatozoa present in the broad uterine chamber. No posterior uterine branch present.

Male cylindroid without spear. Tail blunt, slightly arcuate. Lateral field with three incisures. Spicula almost straight, acute. Anal sheath not observed on the single male collected (Fig. 13-18).

Habitat and distribution: Soil about roots of grass near Mayberries, Alberta, and Gatineau Park, Quebec, Canada.

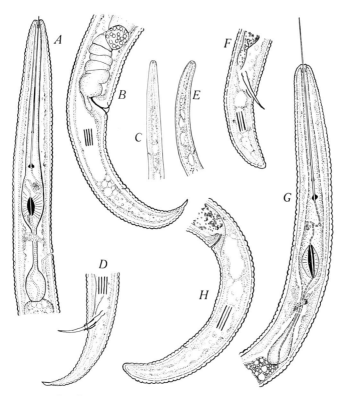

Fig. 13-18. *Paratylenchus audriellus.* *A, B*—Anterior and posterior portions of female. *C, D*—Same parts of male. *Paratylenchus aculentus.* *E, F*—Anterior and posterior portions of male. *G, H*—Corresponding parts of female. (*Adapted from Brown. Courtesy of Canada Department of Agriculture.*)

The elongated spear, anterior position of excretory pore, absence of vulval membranes, and well-developed larval spear indicate a possible relationship to *Cacopaurus.*

Genus *Cacopaurus* Thorne, 1943

Diagnosis: Paratylenchinae. Female body obese, immobile, generally distorted in form, attached to host by unusually long spear. Female annules ornamented by minute tubercules. Vulva near terminus. Ovary single. Phasmids a scutellumlike area. At senility the female forms a brownish-yellow empty case which remains attached to the root. Excretory pore far forward, opposite median bulb or even to base of spear. Males slender, active, losing spear at last moult. Both males and females about equal in length to fourth-stage larvae, from which they developed. Male cuticle with plain striae. Cloacal region a shallow depression, with outer margins sometimes appearing as a narrow bursa when seen from a subdorsal view. Testis one.

Type species: *Cacopaurus pestis* Thorne, 1943

Cacopaurus is distinguished from *Paratylenchus* by the obese, distorted female body, tubercules on annules of cuticle, large phasmid areas, and sessile type of parasitism. Second- and third-stage larvae of *Cacopaurus* have well-developed spears, while those of *Paratylenchus* have no spears. Males of both genera may lose their spears at the last moult, and both have similar spicula, gubernacula, and testes.

Cacopaurus pestis Thorne, 1943

Morphology: ♀: 0.20–0.26 mm; width 35–43 μ

♂: 0.25–0.29 mm; a = 30; b = 3.5; c = 11; T = 37

Characters of the genus. Body sometimes straight but usually curved, arcuate, or folded. Cuticle with striae about 1 μ apart near middle of body. Annules ornamented by minute, refractive elements. Lateral fields marked by three lines extending from near middle of neck to terminus, each line composed of two rows of minute cuticular elements. The lateral field widens near the tail to an ovate field on which the cuticular elements are irregularly arranged. Beneath this field is a circular organ reminiscent of the scutellumlike phasmids of *Hoplolaimus*. Phasmids apparently are certain minute refractive points from which fibrous ducts lead inward to the scutellumlike organs.

Lip region with six obscure lips visible only from a face view. Labial papillae and amphids so minute as to be visible only on the most favorable specimens. First two annules adjacent to lips somewhat hexagonal, not marked by refractive elements. Cephalic framework very obscure, with small sclerotized structures surrounding the vestibule. Spear very slender, flexible, 40 to 110 μ long. Esophageal lumen convoluted between spear and median bulb, especially when spear is retracted. Median bulb with strongly sclerotized valvular apparatus. Isthmus slender, with nerve ring near middle. Basal bulb broadly pyriform. Intestine with unusually large refractive granules, usually arranged in groups which mark the positions of the few intestinal cells. Rectum and anus practically invisible on most specimens.

Gonad consisting of a broad, spacious chamber from which the uterus leads forward. Ventral uterine cell adjacent to ovary, forming a conspicuous spermatheca. Ovary with two flexures in neck region, with cap cell sometimes located near lips. Eggs huge when compared with size of body, deposited before segmentation.

Male body more slender and uniformly cylindroid than that of female. Coarse annules of cuticle not ornamented. Lateral field marked by three faint lines. Deirids conspicuous, about opposite anterior end of intestine. Testis consisting of a cap cell followed by two large spermatogonia. About eight spermatocytes usually present, from which many spermatids develop. Spicula elongate, curved, cephalated. Gubernaculum thin, slightly curved, troughlike. Margins of cloacal area sometimes appearing as narrow bursae.

Larvae 0.2 to 0.25 mm long; width 10 to 13 μ. Body widest near base of neck. Spear 40 to 65 μ long, well developed even in youngest larvae. Tail uniformly conoid to slightly blunt terminus. As larvae develop, neither males nor females make more than a slight increase in length; in fact, during certain periods they become even shorter than the larvae. At least three moults occur

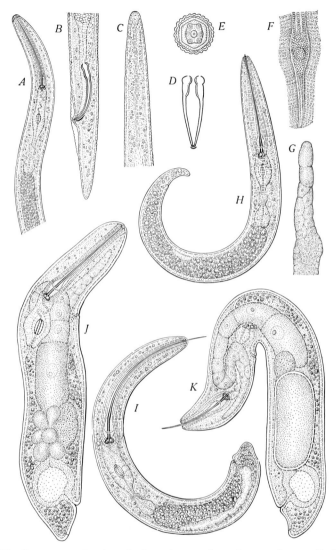

Fig. 13-19. *Cacopaurus pestis.* *A*—Anterior portion of young larva. *B*—Posterior portion of male, slightly subdorsal view with bursa in profile. *C*—Anterior portion of male. *D*—Spicula and gubernaculum, ventral view. *E*—Female head *en face*. *F*—Cuticular pattern on posterior portion of female. *G*—Anterior portion of testis. *H*—Developing female larva. *I*—Female just after last moult. *J*—Adult female showing structure of oviduct and spermatheca. *K*—Adult gravid female. (*After Thorne. Courtesy of Helminthological Society of Washington.*)

after leaving the egg, and each time the spear is retracted from the root and can be seen attached to the cuticle beside the anterior end of the developing larva.

Biology: When the female larva inserts its spear into the root, it first assumes an arcuate form and then gradually becomes obese. During feeding and moulting the spear greatly develops, sometimes occupying half the body length. The larva probably does not move far, if at all, from the point where it begins feeding. The tail becomes shorter and more bluntly rounded; striae and lateral fields become visible, and the annules begin to develop minute refractive elements.

Cacopaurus pestis appears to have a very simple life history. Collections made in May contained larvae and females in all stages of development, and this fact indicates that there is a series of overlapping generations as in most other plant parasitic nemas. Eggs are deposited adjacent to the roots, and upon hatching the sluggish-moving larvae immediately begin feeding. Frequently several females are found in a group, the progeny of a single mother. They may be located on the root surface, beneath a bark scale, or in tiny, pustulelike masses overlying small pits in the root-cortex.

Root sections show that epidermal cells are punctured and the salivary secretions injected. The cells become two to three times their normal size and secrete a substance which distends their walls until they rupture. The resulting exudate wells up about the nema, and apparently it is upon this that it feeds, and not on the original cell contents. As additional cells are ruptured, a small pit may be formed in the root-epidermis and the nema becomes completely covered by the exudate. Larvae produced from eggs deposited in this mass probably begin feeding there and then attack the walls of the pit. As these cells break open, the larvae force their way into them and thus cause minute scales of bark to form. In some instances apparently the nemas do not attack cells but live on the exudate produced by other members of the colony. As the colony increases in size and the nemas penetrate deeper into the epidermal tissues, they may almost reach the underlying parenchyma cells. Perhaps they do reach this point, the result being immediate death of the root. This possibility may account for the quantities of dead roots collected on soil screens when samples from infested trees are examined.

Males were not observed feeding, and intermediate stages were not found. Consequently, it is assumed that they pass through the usual series of moults and lose their spears with the last one, as do other members of the Family Criconematidae.

Special techniques: Small species like *Cacopaurus pestis* pass through the usual soil screens. Such nemas may be successfully processed by carefully rinsing soil from the roots and then rubbing them briskly between the fingers in a small amount of water. If the roots are infested, the brown cases and numbers of larvae will be found, together with males and developing females of all stages. Specimens attached to roots are best seen under direct illumination from a bright lamp used with the higher powers of the dissecting microscope.

Distribution: Known only from one walnut orchard near Santa Clara, California.

Cacopaurus epacris Allen, 1950

Morphology: ♀: 0.24–0.32 mm; a = 7–8; b = 2.6–3.6; c = 16–20; V = 86
Young ♀: 0.28–0.29 mm; a = 13; b = 2.9; c = 19; V = 83
♂: 0.24–0.30 mm; a = 19; b = 4.0; c = 12

Female body obese, straight, curved, or bent in various forms. Annules plain, not ornamented. Lateral fields marked by four incisures extending from neck

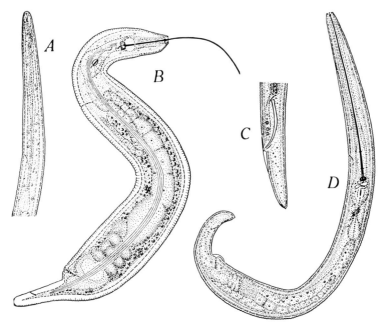

Fig. 13-20. *Cacopaurus epacris. A*—Male neck region. *B*—Adult female. *C*—Male tail. *D*—Young female. (*After Allen. Courtesy of Helminthological Society of Washington.*)

region to vicinity of anal opening. Spear slender, flexible, 82 to 98 μ long, with strong, rounded basal knobs. Median esophageal bulb variable in position, according to extrusion or retraction of the spear. Isthmus less than half as long as neck width. Basal bulb elongate-pyriform, usually obscured by ovary and intestine. Excretory pore opposite basal bulb. Ovary reaching into neck region, with double flexure. Uterus with thick-walled cells, the anterior ventral one differentiated into a spermatheca. Body suddenly constricted behind vulva to a cylindroid tail ending in a blunt, rounded terminus.

Male body tapering gradually through neck to rounded lip region. Spear absent. Esophagus degenerate, obscure. Spicula slightly arcuate. Gubernaculum a tiny, curved plate. Margin of cloacal depression sometimes giving appearance of a very narrow bursa. Terminus bluntly rounded, sometimes subdigitate.

Body of young female tapering through anterior half to the rounded lip region. Spear sometimes 100 μ long, similar to that of adult. Position of esophagus dependent on extrusion of spear, very compact when retracted or elongated when extruded. Excretory pore anterior to base of spear when it is retracted. Immature gonad about five times as long as body diameter. Vulval membranes present.

Larvae 0.20 to 0.26 mm long, width 22 μ. Body cylindroid. Spear 42 μ long. Esophagus one-third body length. Excretory pore slightly posterior to nerve ring. Tail conoid to blunt terminus. A small mucro sometimes present.

Type host: California black walnut, *Juglans hindsii* Jepson
Type locality: Near Visalia, Tulare County, California

Cacopaurus epacris combines certain characteristics of both *C. pestis* and *Paratylenchus*. The vulval membranes indicate that these organs are not of generic diagnostic value, as they were previously believed to be. The well-developed spear of the larva and obese female body point toward a relationship with *Cacopaurus*. Obviously, this species lies midway between *P. audriellus* and *C. pestis*. Thus we have an almost complete series from one genus to the other, and the dividing point appears to be fixed on the obese, distorted female body.

Chapter 14

Family TYLENCHULIDAE Raski, 1957

Diagnosis: Females saccate, males slender. Spears of females and larvae well developed, not over 15 μ long, with strong basal knobs. Esophagus with large, fusiform median bulb, narrow isthmus, and pyriform basal bulb. Ovary with flexures, occupying a major portion of body cavity. Spears of males reduced or absent. Bursa not present. Obligate plant parasites.

Type subfamily: TYLENCHULINAE Skarbilovich, 1947

Members of the Family Tylenchulidae are obligate plant parasites. The most well-known species is the citrus nematode, *Tylenchulus semipenetrans,* which is one of our most destructive and economically important nemic pests. Specimens of this group have doubtless been overlooked on many occasions because of their small size. Unless extreme care is exercised in root examination, these minute forms are not seen. The delicate bodies are easily crushed by dissecting instruments, and considerable skill is required to remove them from root-tissues. All too frequently the anterior portion of the body is broken off and remains in the root. Fixed plant material usually is preferable, because specimens do not "explode" when the pressure of root-tissues is released during dissection. Gentle rubbing of the roots together often will dislodge the bodies, but the anterior ends may remain in the tissues surrounding them. Males may not be recognized in soil screenings because they are so inconspicuous. Because of their small size a large portion is almost certain to pass through the finest mesh screens and be lost.

Key to genera of Tylenchulidae

1. Excretory pore at 30 per cent or more, male stylet present............. 2
   Excretory pore within range of esophagus, male stylet absent............ 3
2. Excretory pore at 50 per cent or more, lip region rounded......*Tylenchulus*
   Excretory pore between 30 and 45 per cent, lip region with circumoral elevation
   Trophotylenchulus
3. Female spheroid, vulva subterminal.......................*Sphaeronema*
   Female elongated, obese, vulva ventral...................*Trophonema*

Subfamily TYLENCHULINAE Skarbilovich, 1947

Diagnosis: Excretory pore located 30 per cent or more from anterior end. Male stylet present, fragile.

Type genus: *Tylenchulus* Cobb, 1913

377

Diagnosis: Tylenchulinae. Marked sexual dimorphism present. Females obese, variable in form, usually protruding from roots. Excretory pore slightly anterior to vulva. Male slender, with fragile spear. Bursa absent. Excretory pore near 55 per cent from anterior end.

Type species: *Tylenchulus semipenetrans* Cobb, 1913

Historical: This species was first observed by J. R. Hodges, horticultural inspector of Los Angeles County, California, while inspecting orange trees in 1912. Hodges informed E. E. Thomas, Citrus Experiment Station, Riverside, California, who immediately began research on the problem. Cobb (1913) published a preliminary report, including a morphological description and diagnoses of the new genus and species. Within six months, Thomas had found specimens on citrus from Alabama and Florida. Cobb (1914b) published a more detailed account of the morphology and life history and reported finding the pest on citrus roots from Florida, Spain, Malta, Palestine, Australia, and South America.

Thomas (1913, 1923) continued investigations of *Tylenchulus semipenetrans* and its relation to citrus growth. Definite demonstrations of pathogenicity were secured under controlled conditions in a lath house and in orchards. In one experiment 1,240 trees, one half of them infested with the nematode, the other half not infested, were grown under controlled conditions. Without exception, the uninfested trees made a better and more normal growth than the infested trees. Among many hundreds of severely infested trees examined, not one was found to be in good condition.

Experiments with carbon disulfide, mercuric chloride, formalin, potassium cyanide, and other chemicals failed to show any promise. Hot-water treatment of infested roots, severe pruning, and cultural methods also were ineffective. Thomas found a *Fusarium* associated with the nemas and demonstrated that it produced no signs of injury on uninfested roots.

Following the work of Thomas, little or no attention was directed to the problem in California until 1939, when J. C. Johnston, Citrus Experiment Station, became interested in the widespread slow decline and dieback of the citrus orchards of the state. The writer cooperated by making soil and root examinations, and of over 100 samples from various parts of the state only one was found free of *Tylenchulus semipenetrans*. By that time, reduced yields and undersized fruit had become a serious problem in many areas. However, the futility of attempting control by agronomic practices or other methods discouraged research, and little attention was directed toward solving the problem.

A similar attitude apparently prevailed in other parts of the world, and no records were published until Carvalho (1942) reviewed the problem in Argentina. Gutierrez (1947) continued the work in Argentina and described the first moult within the egg. He also noted two types of larvae which he thought might be males and females, but as Van

Gundy (1958) remarks, Gutierrez probably was comparing third-stage males with second-stage females.

California revived interest in citrus nematode and began intensive studies at the Citrus Experiment Station in 1947, with R. D. Baines in charge. Possibilities of resistance were explored by extensive host studies of all available types of citrus and their botanical relatives. Direct control methods with modern soil fumigants were investigated, as will be outlined later.

Research departments of the Shell Chemical Company and The Dow Chemical Company recognized the growing menace to the citrus industry and invested heavily in possible soil fumigants and methods of application.

Morphology and biology: Van Gundy (1958) reported detailed studies on the life history and morphology of *Tylenchulus semipenetrans*. His work corroborated the previous findings of Cobb and Gutierrez and added several new details. The following discussion on life history is largely from his work:

> Females are most frequently found on thick, stunted rootlets to which a layer of soil particles is clinging. These particles are held in place by a gelatinous mucus secreted by the females. This mucus and the attached soil doubtless protects them from predators and other natural enemies. It also forms a protective covering for the masses of eggs which are deposited. Careful removing of the incrustation reveals the distorted females clinging to the roots with heads and necks buried in the cortical layer. Difficulty is usually experienced in releasing specimens without breaking off the anterior end.
>
> Females range from 0.35 to 0.40 mm long with variable saccate body which usually is ventrally bent in the vulvar region just anterior to the short, blunt tail. Excretory pore unusually well developed, ending in a conspicuous pore located just anterior to vulva. Ovary usually with two flexures, reaching to the esophageal region. Eggs average $33 \times 67 \ \mu$, deposited before segmentation. Usually only one egg is observed in the uterus at one time.
>
> Larvae hatched under laboratory condition in from twelve to fourteen days, the first moult having occurred before hatching. Van Gundy found that two types of larvae emerged from the eggs. One was shorter and wider than the other and from them mature males developed within one week without feeding. The longer, more slender individuals failed to develop unless they fed on a root and these became females. Of the total larvae observed, twenty-six per cent became males.
>
> Second stage male larvae usually are formed before emerging from the egg mass and range in length from 0.28 to 0.34 μ. Stylet and esophagus well developed. Excretory pore located slightly behind middle of body where it remains during succeeding moults. At this stage two clear areas are present in the posterior third of the body, marking the points where the testis and cloacal opening will eventually be found.
>
> As the third moult of the male approaches, movement gradually ceases and the basal portion of the spear disappears, usually in 24 to 28 hours

after hatching. Upon emerging from the moult the third stage male larvae range from 0.25 to 0.30 mm in length, slightly less than the second stage larvae. The genital primordium now is four to eight celled and the anal or cloacal area more conspicuous.

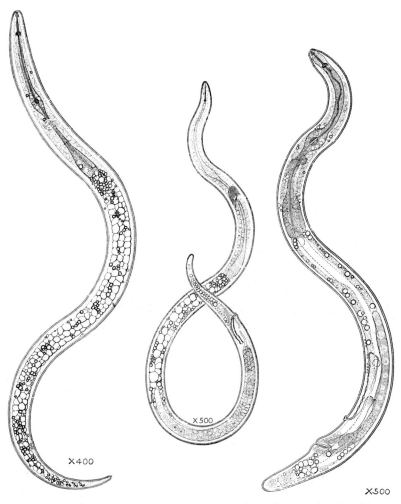

Fig. 14-1. *Tylenchulus semipenetrans.* Larva, male and young female. Note posterior position of excretory pore. *(After Cobb. Courtesy of U.S. Department of Agriculture.)*

The fourth stage male increases in length to 0.26 to 0.33 mm, the testis and spicula are visible but the stylet remains indistinct. From this stage the adult male emerges as a slender nema 0.30 to 0.41 mm long. The stylet is indistinct and only 11 μ long, and the esophagus is degenerate. The well-developed testis filled with sperms occupies about 36 per cent of the body length.

Second stage females required about fourteen days to locate and feed on epidermal root cells and develop until ready for moulting. During the period of searching for a feeding position, 25 to 50 larvae congregated under fragments of cortical tissue, soil particles, or organic fragments. Rarely were they found in unprotected locations on roots. They ranged in length from 0.30 to 0.36 mm long, the genital primordium consisted of two cells, and the esophagus was better developed. This is the stage most frequently found when soil samples are examined, and in which they may live over when host roots are not present. Baines found them alive in soil stored at 59°F for two and one-half years, but only after two and one-half months when stored at 91°F. Arnold White, Assistant County Agent, Santa Barbara, California, collected soil where a citrus planting had been removed over three years previously and in it the writer found hundreds of second stage larvae. Many of them were practically transparent and showed little signs of life, but a considerable number were well filled with

Fig. 14-2. *Tylenchulus semipenetrans* females attached to citrus root. (*After Cobb. Courtesy of U.S. Department of Agriculture.*)

dense, refractive granules and appeared to be in normal, active physical condition.

The third and fourth stages end in a shorter immature female which exhibits a longer esophagus and a distinct vulval cleft from which an immature gonad of four cells extends forward. At this point the last cuticle is moulted and the young female emerges. The length now varies from 0.25 to 0.36 mm. Spear well developed, 13.5 μ long. Esophagus comprising almost half the body length. Vulva a deep transverse slit. Excretory pore very prominent, less than one body width anterior to vulva. Tail slightly convex-conoid dorsally, ending in a blunt terminus. Anus and rectum apparently absent. Fourth stage females and young females were present twenty-one days after roots were inoculated.

Within a week young females had penetrated to the pericycle of the root and were from three-fourths to fully enlarged. The complete life cycle from egg to egg required six to eight weeks.

A most interesting point in Van Gundy's observations was the fact that hand-picked second-stage larval females developed and reproduced on citrus roots in the absence of males. Both male and female larvae were produced by these unfertilized individuals. He adds that preliminary work indicates that sex ratios may be influenced by fertilization or lack of fertilization.

Many of the measurements secured by Raski and Gutierrez were somewhat smaller than those given by Cobb. This difference may have been due to a difference in accuracy of equipment used in making measurements or to the different host plants of the populations studied. However, the variations are not sufficiently great to be of significance in identification.

Symptoms: During early days of the citrus industry in the United States, plantings throve and produced excellent yields for 20 to 40 years before injury from nematodes became evident. Apparently nema populations in nurseries were low because trees and the surrounding soil were frequently removed, carrying most of the nemas with them. Growth of young trees in the clean, fertile soil was so rapid that root systems developed faster than the nemas increased. Not until there was competition for fertility and moisture between roots and between trees did the nemas overtake root production and begin to check top growth.

The first indication of injury is a reduction in terminal growth. This is followed by a general appearance of reduced vigor, accompanied by yellowing and dying of leaves and twigs. The trees are not killed but maintain life on a limited scale and produce a reduced crop of inferior fruit.

Young nursery stock planted on infested land may begin to show yellow leaves, defoliated twigs, and small fruit within 5 or 10 years. If such trees are used as replants immediately after infested trees have been removed, they may fail to survive the first year. Symptoms will vary considerably in different plantings, depending on soil fertility, moisture, and agronomic practices.

Hosts: Baines, Clark, and Bitters (1948) reported that eighty-one species and varieties of the genus *Citrus* were found to be susceptible to *Tylenchulus semipenetrans*. Several other plant species of related genera are known to be infested. The reader is referred to their work for detailed information.

Species of related genera which Baines and his coworkers failed to infest were Uganda powder flask fruit, *Balsamocitrus dawei* Stapt; wampee, *Claucenea lansium* (Lour.) Skeels; jasmin orange, *Murraya paniculata* (L.) Jack; Chinese box orange, *Severinia buxifolia* (Poir.) Ten.; and three of twenty selections of trifoliate orange, *Poncitrus trifoliata* (L.) Raf. Possibilities for selection and breeding of resistant root-stocks appear to be limited.

Among the hosts which have been reported are three which were rather unexpected: olive, *Olea europaea* L.; grape, variety Emperor, *Vitis vinifera* L.; and lilac, *Syringia vulgaris* L.

Distribution: Moving of infested nursery stock is the most common means of carrying citrus nemas, and this doubtless has been responsible for the rapid dissemination of the pest from one continent, country, or locality to another. Citrus trees are usually transported "balled," with roots and soil held together by burlap or other packing, an ideal method of moving nemas as well as trees.

Random observations by occasional investigators indicate that *Tylenchulus semipenetrans* is now distributed in practically all citrus-growing regions of the world. Additions to early records already cited are Brazil, South Africa, Egypt, Spain, Palestine, U.S.S.R., Ceylon, Java, Thailand, China, Australia, and the Philippine and Hawaiian Islands.

More intensive surveys have been made in the United States, and the distribution of the pest is better known than in other countries. Baines (1950) found 90 to 95 per cent of the citrus groves of southern California infested, with widespread infestations in other parts of the state. Reynolds and O'Bannon (1958) reported that more than half the plantings surveyed in Arizona were infested. As early as 1940 Godfrey (personal communication) observed the pest in the Rio Grande Valley of Texas, where it probably is widely distributed. Findings during the burrowing nematode survey in Florida revealed it in the principal citrus-producing areas.

Aggregate losses doubtless place *Tylenchulus semipenetrans* as one of the most economically important nemic pests in the United States because of the reduced yield and quality of the fruit. Fortunately the citrus-juice industry has provided a market for the great quantities of undersized fruit from infested trees. Otherwise losses would have been far greater than they are at present.

Control: Clean nursery stock is desirable, but trace infestations may be overlooked in most careful inspections. Trees should be purchased from reputable nurserymen, preferably those who thoroughly fumigate the soil in which seedlings are produced.

Fumigation of fields from which infested orchards have been removed is a very difficult and expensive process. Baines, Foote, and Martin (1957) used various fumigants at different rates on varying soil types. Typical of their results were those where 120 to 180 gallons of D-D per acre were applied on fine sandy loam. Good control was secured to a depth of 6 feet, but below that point the nemas escaped. Five months after treatment lemons were planted. Four years later roots in the 4- to 6-foot depth were infested. In no instance was eradication achieved. However, increased growth and production of trees on heavily fumigated plots were so superior that fumigation was deemed worthwhile.

Reynolds and O'Bannon (1958) conducted field-scale soil-fumigation control experiments with living citrus in Arizona. Three blocks of thirty-, thirty-one-, and thirty-six-year-old grapefruit on sour orange rootstocks were selected. These were known to be moderately to heavily infested with *Tylenchulus semipenetrans*. Emulsifiable 1,2-dibromo-3-chloropropane (DBCP) was added to approximately 5 inches of irrigation water. Rates used were 2, 3, 4, 5, 6, and 10 gallons per acre, equivalent to 17.3, 25.8, 34.4, 43, 51.6, and 86 pounds of active ingredient. Adjacent untreated rows were used as checks.

Counts of nemas from soil samples were made before application and at periods of 2 to 15 months afterward. In the 6-gallon experiment no nemas were found alive after 2 months, compared with 10,000 in the check. In the same orchard the 2-gallon application showed 60 nemas in the soil sample, representing a control of 99.4 per cent. In all other plots the kill ranged from 99.7 to 99.9 per cent. Since even the 10-gallon application did not accomplish eradication, future treatments probably will be necessary as the populations again build up to dangerous numbers.

Effective control was secured throughout the rows, regardless of the distance from the point where DBCP was added to the irrigation water. No symptoms of phytotoxicity were observed on any plot. Hedging (machine trimming of treees) and selective pruning resulted in more rapid tree recovery.

Tylenchulus mangenoti Luc, 1957a

Morphology: ♀: 0.33–0.41 mm; a = 2.6; b = 2.7; c = 15; V = 71–87
            ♂: 0.33 mm; a = 27; b = ?; c = 6.5; T = 32

Female body broadly reniform. Phasmids, deirids, hemizonid, and lateral fields not seen. Lip region irregularly lobed from pressure of the host tissues. Stylet 13 to 15 μ long, with rounded knobs. Median esophageal bulb massive, abruptly narrowed to a slender isthmus which joins the almost spheroid basal bulb. Rectum and anus visible. Excretory pore at 51 to 61 per cent of body

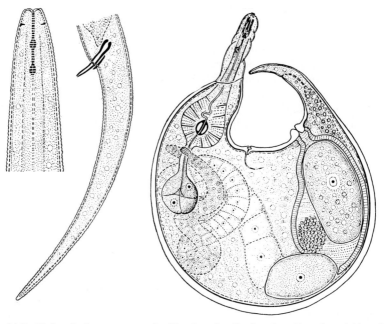

Fig. 14-3. *Tylenchulus mangenoti.* Head and tail of male. Female. (*After Luc, Nemotologica. Courtesy of E. J. Brill.*)

length. Ovary extending forward to region of esophagus, reflexed twice. Oöcytes of terminal fourth of ovary arranged in two lines, then in single file to the uterus. Eggs 59 to 64 by 29 to 32 μ.

Male slender, cylindroid. Stylet much reduced, bearing small, ovate knobs. Esophagus degenerate, its structures obscure. Testis with spermatocytes in multiple rows. Spicula almost straight, slightly cephalated. Tail uniformly conoid to fine, rounded terminus.

Larvae 0.28 mm long, with well-developed spear. Excretory pore at 57 to 62 per cent from anterior end. Similar to general body characteristics of larvae of *Tylenchulus semipenetrans*.

Tylenchulus mangenoti is distinctive because of the female body form, the well-developed rectum and anus, and the elongated, tapering male tail. Luc suggests that the rectum and anus of other members of the Tylenchulidae may be present and functional, although very difficult to observe.

Host and habitat: Roots and rhizomes of *Dorstenia embergeri* G. Mangenot. Institut d'enseignement et de recherches tropicales d'Adiopodoume, I. D. E. R. T. near Abidjan, Ivory Coast, Africa.

Genus *Trophotylenchulus* Raski, 1957

Diagnosis: Tylenchulinae. Sexual dimorphism present. Females obese, spiral; males slender. Lip region with circumoral elevation in females and larvae. Stylet well developed. Esophagus tylenchoid with conspicuous median bulb. Anus apparently not functional. Female excretory pore near 33 to 44 per cent, even farther back in larvae. Ovary with flexures, extending into region of esophagus. Oviparous, one egg at a time present in uterus, deposited in mucoid mass surrounding vulva. Male tail elongate-conoid with bluntly rounded terminus. Male spear reduced. Spicula almost straight except for distinct angle near distal end. Bursa absent.

Type species: *Trophotylenchulus floridensis* Raski, 1957

Trophotylenchulus is distinctive because of the obese, ventrally arcuate, coiled female body, circumoral elevation, and position of the excretory pore. The genus appears to stand intermediate between *Tylenchulus* and *Trophonema*.

Trophotylenchulus floridensis Raski, 1957

Morphology: ♀: 0.44 mm; a = 5.3; b = 2.4; c = 18.6; V = $^{57}80^{1.5}$

♂: 0.41–0.58 mm; a = 32–41; b = ?; c = 7.6–9.9; T = 27–41

Characters of the genus as presented above. Female body obese, tapering rapidly and uniformly to the extremities. Lip region conoid, surmounted by a minute, discoid, circumoral elevation. Stylet 15 μ long, with strong, sloping basal knobs. Median esophageal bulb elongated, fusiform. Isthmus very slender, expanding slightly to join the pyriform basal bulb. Nerve ring at base of median bulb. Ovary with two flexures, extending forward into neck region. Spermatheca present. Eggs almost one-fourth as long as body. Posterior uterine branch short or absent. Anal opening obscure, marked by slight elevation of cuticle, perhaps not functional. Tail arcuate, bluntly rounded.

Male body cylindroid, tapering toward extremities. Lip region hemispheroid, apparently without annulation. Circumoral elevation not present. Spear 11.5 μ long, with basal knobs reduced to slight swellings. Esophagus degenerate, obscure. Hemizonid immediately behind latitude of nerve ring, its width equal to that of two annules. Spicula with distal angle, spicule sheath present. Bursa absent.

Larvae 0.45 μ long. Lip region conoid, with circumoral elevation similar to that of female. Spear 15 μ long, with rounded knobs. Hemizonid just posterior to latitude of nerve ring. Anus obscure, probably not functional.

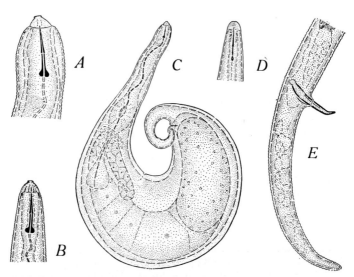

Fig. 14-4. *Trophotylenchulus floridensis.* *A*—Female head. *B*—Head of larva. *C*—Female. *D, E*—Head and tail of male. (*After Raski, Nematologica. Courtesy of E. J. Brill.*)

Hosts and distribution: Roots of *Quercus falcata* Michx., near Winter Haven, Florida; also *Magnolia* sp. near Lake Alfred, and persimmon, *Diospyros* sp., Lake County, both localities in Florida.

Subfamily SPHAERONEMATINAE Raski and Sher, 1952

Diagnosis: Tylenchulidae. Female body subspherical. Cuticle thick, sometimes with well-defined reticulate pattern. Vulva subterminal. Male without spear. Esophagus degenerate, obscure. Bursa absent.

Type genus: *Sphaeronema* Raski and Sher, 1952

Raski and Sher first placed Sphaeronematinae in Criconematidae because the males closely resembled those of *Paratylenchus*. The vulvar membranes are also reminiscent of that genus. Obviously, *Sphaeronema* represents a form midway between Criconematidae and Tylenchulidae. Extensive collecting will doubtless reveal other intermediate forms of the series.

Sphaeronema Raski and Sher, 1952

Diagnosis: Sphaeronematinae. Larvae with strongly developed spear. Cephalic framework hexaradiate. Female subspherical, with well-developed spear. One or two obscure annules near lip region. Esophagus strongly developed. Ovary single. Uterus large, spheroid. Spermatheca present. Male slender, without spear, definite esophagus, or bursa. Spicule sheath present.

Type species: *Sphaeronema californicum* Raski and Sher, 1952

Morphology: ♀: 0.13–0.20 mm; vulva subterminal

♂: 0.40–0.47 mm; a = 33–45; b = ?; c = 12–15; T = 20–30

Characters of the genus as outlined above. Female with elongated neck of variable form due to pressure of host tissues. Cuticle 9 μ thick, marked by a conspicuous reticulate pattern, assuming vague cross lines near and on lips of

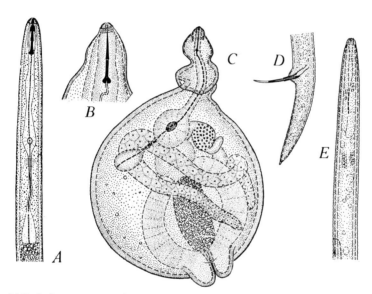

Fig. 14-5. *Sphaeronema californicum.* *A*—Neck region of larva. *B*—Female head. *C*—Female. *D, E*—Tail and neck region of male. (*After Raski and Sher. Courtesy of Helminthological Society of Washington.*)

vulva. Cephalic framework delicate, obscure. Spear 14 to 20 μ long, with small sloping knobs. Esophagus well developed, with large, spheroid median bulb, very slender isthmus, and ovoid basal bulb. Excretory pore about opposite median bulb. Ovary coiled about body cavity. Vulvar membranes small, obscure. Anus and phasmids not observed. Females prior to last moult without protruding vulva and reticulate cuticle pattern.

Male cylindroid, tapering toward extremities. Annules of cuticle very narrow. Lateral field not marked by definite lines. Lip region set off by slight constriction. Cephalic framework delicate, obscure in face view. Spear absent. Esophagus degenerate. Excretory pore 66 to 99 μ from anterior end. Hemizonid slightly posterior to excretory pore. Spicules 19 to 21 μ long, slender, slightly arcuate. Spicule sheath conspicuous. Bursa absent.

Larvae: 0.39–0.47 mm; a = 25–31; b = 3.3–4.4; c = 11

Body cylindroid except at extremities. Annules obscure. Cephalic framework well sclerotized, hexaradiate. Amphid apertures visible as minute pores from a face view. Spear 14.4 to 16.7 μ long, with well-developed, sloping basal knobs. Esophagus tylenchoid, with nerve ring near base of median bulb. Excretory pore opposite nerve ring. Anus obscure. Terminus bluntly rounded, variable in form.

Hosts and distribution: Roots of California laurel, *Umbellularia californica* Nutt., shore of Tomales Bay, near Iverness, Marin County, California; near sea level. Also from roots of *Arctostaphylos* sp. near Pyramid Ranger Station, El Dorado County, California; elevation 5,500 feet.

Sphaeronema minutissimum Goodey, 1958a

Morphology: ♀: 0.101–0.129 mm; width about 66 μ.

Body spheroid, with elongated, irregular-shaped neck and head due to pressure of host tissues. Cuticle about 4 μ thick, with no surface markings. Lip region with circumoral elevation. Cuticle thickened behind lip region. Median esophageal bulb spheroid, located within the body. Isthmus short, expanding to join the elongate-pyriform basal bulb. Entire digestive system indefinite. Vulvar lips practically continuous with body contour. Uterus thick-walled, spheroid. Ovary apparently made up of only a few cells, practically filling body cavity. A spheroid egg filled the uterine cavity. Male unknown.

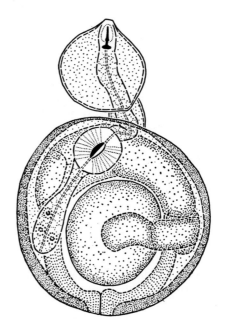

Fig. 14-6. *Sphaeronema minutissimum* female. (*After J. B. Goodey, Nematologica. Courtesy of E. J. Brill.*)

Larvae (newly hatched): 0.296–0.338 mm; a = 29; b = 3.6; c = ?
Lip region with elevation similar to that of female. Stylet 12 to 13 μ long,
with strong basal knobs which are convex anteriorly and flat posteriorly, a
most unusual form. Median bulb about midway in the neck. Excretory pore
about one body width behind bulb.

Habitat: Roots of *Citrus* sp., Pasar Minggu, near Djakarta, Java, Indonesia. Associated with *Tylenchulus semipenetrans*.

The body form of *Sphaeronema minutissimum* indicates relationship
to the genus in which it is placed. However, the circumoral elevation is
more like that of *Trophotylenchulus*.

Trophonema Raski, 1957

Diagnosis: Sphaeronematinae. Sexual dimorphism present. Females obese,
spiral. Males slender. Females with tylenchoid esophagus; median bulb fusiform, filling neck cavity; isthmus short, slender; basal bulb pyriform. Stylet

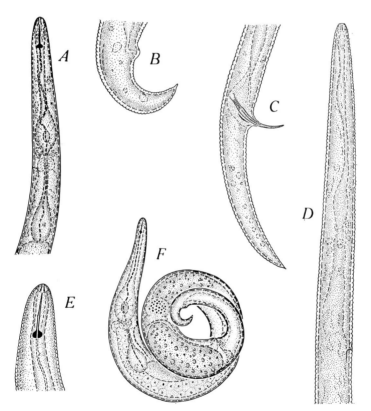

Fig. 14-7. *Trophonema arenarium.* *A*—Neck region of larva. *B*—Female tail.
C, D—Tail and anterior portion of male. *E*—Female head. *F*—Female. (*After
Raski. Courtesy of Helminthological Society of Washington.*)

fairly strong, with well-developed, rounded knobs. Ovary single. One egg present at a time, oviparous, deposited in a mucoid mass. Body tapering rapidly posterior to vulva. Tail arcuate. Anus and rectum obscure, probably not functional. Male tail acute, bursa absent. Spicula arcuate, slightly cephalated.

Type species: *Trophonema arenarium* (Raski, 1956) Raski, 1957
Synonym: *Sphaeronema arenarium* Raski, 1956
Trophonema differs from *Sphaeronema* principally in form of female. Raski also listed the reticulate cuticle and protruding vulvar lips as differentiating characters, but these do not hold true for *S. minutissimum.*

Trophonema arenarium (Raski) Raski, 1957

Morphology: ♀: 0.45–0.58 mm; a = 10–16; b = 3.3–4.5; c = 12–18; V = 74–80
♂: 0.43–0.57 mm; a = 30–44; b = ?; c = 8–10; T = 24–39

Characters of the genus. Female body tapering uniformly both ways from its widest point, which is about two body widths anterior to vulva. Lip region with definite annulation. Labial framework slightly sclerotized. Stylet 14 μ long, with strong, rounded knobs. Excretory pore at level of nerve ring. Hemizonid about two annules wide, immediately anterior to excretory pore. Spermatheca present. Ovary usually extending to median bulb, reflexed once or twice. Posterior uterine branch very short or absent. Anus obscure, located on a slight elevation, perhaps not functional. Tail ventrally coiled, tapering to a minutely rounded terminus.

Male cylindroid except at extremities. Lip region without annulation. Stylet absent. Esophagus indefinite. Excretory pore 107 μ from anterior end. Hemizonid two annules wide, immediately anterior to excretory pore. Spicules curved, 22 μ long. Gubernaculum a simple plate 5 μ long. Spicule sheath prominent. Lateral fields, phasmids, and deirids not observed.

Larvae: 0.32–0.40 mm long; a = 21–29; b = 3.1–3.7; c = 10.1

Body slender, usually assuming a coiled position in fixative. Lateral field not observed. Stylet 12 to 14 μ long, with well-developed knobs. Median esophageal bulb filling body cavity. Nerve ring surrounding the narrow isthmus near anterior end. Excretory pore opposite nerve ring. Tail conoid, ventrally arcuate with minutely rounded terminus.

Host and habitat: Roots of salt bush, *Juncus leseuri* Boland. Dillon Beach, Marin County, California.

Chapter 15

Superfamily APHELENCHOIDEA Fuchs, 1937

Historical: Bastian (1865) established the genus *Aphelenchus* to receive the species *avenae, parietinus, pyri,* and *villosus.* A type species was not named, but later, 1905, in a letter to Stiles and Hassall, he designated *A. avenae.* This was a rather unfortunate choice, because *A. avenae* and its relatives comprise only a small segment of the species in the superfamily. About a dozen additional species were described up to the year 1900. After that date many others were recorded until about seventy-five were listed under the generic name *Aphelenchus.* The majority of these have since been transferred to *Aphelenchoides* and other genera.

The first record of an economically important plant parasitic species is that of *Aphelenchus* (now *Aphelenchoides*) *fragariae* Ritzema Bos, 1891. This was the beginning of a series of controversial specific names based largely on host relationships. These are now generally recognized as synonyms of *A. fragariae* and *A. ritzema-bosi,* as outlined in the section on Bud and Leaf Nemas of the genus *Aphelenchoides.*

Fischer (1894) established the first new genus of the group when he described *Aphelenchoides* with *A. kuehnii* as type. Unfortunately, Fischer's work was overlooked until Steiner (1932) brought it to attention, as recounted in the section on *Aphelenchoides* on page 403. About forty species have since been transferred to this genus from *Aphelenchus.* To these have been added many new species and several additional transfers until over seventy species are now included.

Micoletzky (1922) established the subgenus *Chitinoaphelenchus* to include *Aphelenchus ritzema-bosi, A. cocophilus,* and certain other plant parasitic species. All these have since been transferred to *Aphelenchoides.* At the same time, Micoletzky erected the subgenus *Paraphelenchus* for *Aphelenchus* (*Paraphelenchus*) *pseudoparietinus* and similar species which possess a definite basal esophageal bulb. In 1925 he raised *Paraphelenchus* to full generic status.

T. Goodey (1923) assembled pertinent information on the known plant parasitic species of *Aphelenchus* and later (1928) made a complete review of all species described up to that time. In this review Goodey placed numerous inadequately described species in synonymy instead of leaving them as species *inquirendae.*

391

Cobb (1928) suggested the genus *Pathoaphelenchus*, which included the species for which Micoletzky had proposed the subgenus *Chitinoaphelenchus*. Cobb also proposed two subgenera, *P.* (*Pathoaphelenchus*) for plant parasites which are now in *Aphelenchoides* and *P.* (*Schistonchus*) for a species found associated with *Blastophaga psenes* (L.), an insect which pollinates figs.

Goffart (1930) published an excellent review of the plant parasitic species, together with detailed information on their biology, distribution, and control. A comprehensive review of the literature was an especially important part of this work.

The most varied forms of Aphelenchoidea were those revealed by Fuchs (1930, 1931, 1937) during his studies of the nemic parasites and associates of bark beetles. Four new genera and four subgenera were described, and three of the latter are now recognized as valid genera. Further investigations of beetle fauna by Wachek (1955) produced two additional genera, and Rühm (1956) added two more.

The superfamily now includes an extremely varied group of nemas, among which are obligate plant parasites, mycophages, predators, and insect parasites and associates. One mycophagous species has been found associated with deteriorating mushroom beds. Certain plant parasitic species are of economic importance because they attack crop plants, especially ornamentals. Little is known of the feeding habits of many species, and some of them no doubt merit intensive investigation.

Identification: Diagnostic details of lateral fields, stylets, cephalic armature, esophageal structures, and gonads are usually best observed on living specimens. Lateral fields are most distinct on those killed in cold formaldehyde solution. Many of these important morphological characters are frequently obscured during fixation and processing into glycerin, balsam, or other permanent mounting media.

Diagnosis: Tylenchida. Dorsal esophageal gland outlet in lumen of median bulb anterior to valve. Stylet plain or with basal thickenings, rarely with conspicuous knobs. Female with single anterior outstretched ovary. Posterior uterine branch often well developed in bisexual species and serving as a reservoir for spermatozoa, while in monosexual forms it generally is rudimentary and collapsed. Males without bursa except in *Aphelenchus* and *Metaphelenchus*. Gubernaculum present only in *Aphelenchus*, *Metaphelenchus*, *Paraphelenchus*, and *Schistonchus*.

Type family: APHELENCHIDAE (Fuchs, 1937) Steiner, 1949

Diagnosis: Lateral field marked by 6 to 14 fine incisures at mid-body. Males with slightly curved spicula and gubernaculum. Bursa present or absent. Spear plain without basal thickenings. Basal portion of esophagus consisting of an elongate bulb containing the gland nuclei or extended in lobes which reach back over anterior portion of intestine.

Two other families have been established: Aphelenchoididae (Skarbilovich, 1947) Paramanov, 1953, includes the plant parasites, mycophages, and certain genera of insect parasites and associates. The taxonomy of this group is involved because of the numerous genera and subgenera which have been established with inadequate diagnoses. Sphaerularidae (Filipjev, 1934) Skarbilovich, 1946, comprises a group of internal parasites of insects in which the median esophageal bulb is missing. However, outlets of the esophageal glands remain in relatively the same positions as those of other members of the superfamily. Frequently the female body and reproductive system are so profoundly altered in form that the specimens are scarcely recognizable as nemas.

Outline of the superfamily Aphelenchoidea

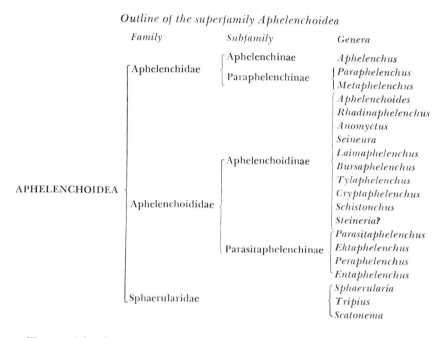

Type subfamily: APHELENCHINAE Stekhoven and Teunissen, 1938

Diagnosis: Aphelenchidae. Basal portion of esophagus extended in long lobes containing the gland nuclei. Males with costate (ribbed) bursa similar to those of the genus *Rhabditis*.

Type genus: *Aphelenchus* Bastian, 1865

Key to subfamilies and genera of Aphelenchidae

1. Esophagus ending in lobes extending back over intestine....Aphelenchinae
A single genus...*Aphelenchus*
Esophagus ending in a definite basal bulb.............Paraphelenchinae 2
2. Female tail conoid-elongate, often mucronate; males without bursa
....*Paraphelenchus*
Female tail short, bluntly rounded, not mucronate; males with bursa
....*Metaphelenchus*

The wisdom of establishing these two subfamilies is most questionable. *Metaphelenchus* bears a bursa similar to that of *Aphelenchus* and a basal esophageal bulb like that of *Paraphelenchus*. The importance of these two morphological characters is problematical.

Genus *Aphelenchus* Bastian, 1865

Synonym: *Isonchus* Cobb, 1913a

Diagnosis: Aphelenchinae. Lateral fields marked by 6 to 14 minute incisures. Spicula slightly arcuate, resting on a simple, almost straight gubernaculum. Bursa well developed, with supporting ribs similar to those of *Rhabditis*. Male phasmid located in lateral field near terminus. Female tail blunt, rounded, with terminal phasmids. Spear without basal thickenings. Esophageal lobes usually located dorsally, extending back over anterior end of intestine. Hemizonid usually present, three to eight annules posterior to excretory pore. Ovary and testis outstretched, rarely with terminal flexure. Posterior uterine branch serving as a storage reservoir for spermatozoa in bisexual species; in monosexual forms it is rudimentary and collapsed.

Type species: *Aphelenchus avenae* Bastian, 1865

The nomenclature of this genus was well discussed by Steiner (1931). Bastian established the genus without a type species, but later (1905), in a letter to Stiles and Hassall, he designated *Aphelenchus avenae* as type. This was rather unfortunate, since *A. avenae* is syngonic and males are rarely seen.

Members of the genus *Aphelenchus* occur in almost any soil sample taken from the rhizosphere of plants. Frequently they are found inhabiting the crown, leaf sheaths, root-cortex, and other parts, where they appear to be feeding on the cell contents of living tissues. Christie and Arndt (1936) recorded *A. avenae* as being associated with lesions of the hypocotyl and other tissues of seedling cotton plants. Sometimes specimens penetrated into healthy cells, where they might be presumed to feed. Linford (1939) observed that colonies of *A. avenae* were not attracted to root-tips of seedling plants, as were *Meloidogyne* sp., *Pratylenchus pratensis,* and *Rotylenchus multicinctus*.

Numerous specimens are often found in decaying potato tubers, dying alfalfa crowns, dump dirt at sugar beet loading stations, and similar decomposing organic material. Because of this type of habitat, they have generally been classed as saprophagous. However, Christie and Arndt found them feeding on a fungus, *Neurospora sitophila,* and were able to see the stylet action as the nema punctured the hypha and withdrew the contents. Since fungi are associated with decaying organic material, it appears plausible that the nemas feed on them instead of decomposition products. Rhoades and Linford (1959) controlled root rot caused by *Pythium arrhenomanes* by adding 125,000 *Aphelenchus avenae* to a 6-inch pot in which corn seedlings were growing. *Pythium* lesions were invaded, but not healthy roots in which *Pythium* was absent. These findings indicated that this population of *A. avenae* is a beneficial mycophagous form which, when present in great numbers, may aid in control of fungus diseases of roots.

Length of esophageal gland lobes may vary considerably in specimens within a collection or in collections from various geographical areas. Rare individuals may have no development of the esophageal lobes and may resemble *Metaphelenchus*. Occasionally lateral incisures appear as minute, wavy lines, especially on living specimens as they move about under slight pressure of a cover glass.

Specimens of *Aphelenchus* are most interesting when observed under slight pressure. As the nema progresses, one may observe tiny droplets of fluid ejected from the phasmids. These droplets dissolve almost instantly and are lost to view. In this manner the nemas probably leave scent trails by which they locate one another as they travel through the soil.

There has been a general tendency to consider most described species of *Aphelenchus* as synonyms of *A. avenae*. However, there are certain species with definite diagnostic characters when they are properly evaluated, as emphasized by Steiner (1931, 1942). Specimens in the writer's collection indicate that *A. macrobolbus, A. solani,* and *A. agricola* are valid species. Proper evaluation of the number of lines in the lateral fields, position of hemizonid in relation to excretory pore, type of posterior uterine branch, and other diagnostic characters make definite diagnoses possible.

Aphelenchus avenae probably is a cosmopolitan species. Specimens from the Western states and from Wisconsin and Illinois appear to be very similar to those collected by J. B. Goodey in England and forwarded to the writer. The posterior uterine branch of American specimens usually is shorter, varying from one to three times as long as the body diameter. The broad lateral field with ten to twelve incisures is a very constant diagnostic character.

Species of *Aphelenchus* appear to belong to three groups: (1) monosexual species with collapsed posterior uterine branch and no hemizonid; (2) monosexual species with collapsed uterine branch and hemizonid present; (3) bisexual species in which the posterior uterine branch is an elongate pouch serving as a reservoir for spermatozoa, hemizonids well-developed on both sexes. These groups resemble those observed in *Hemicycliophora* by the writer (1955) and Luc (1958).

Aphelenchus avenae Bastian, 1865

Morphology: ♀: 0.85 mm; a = 28; b = 8.3; c = 28; V = 70–78
♂: 0.76 mm; a = 28; b = 5–6; c = 25–31

Lateral field marked by 10 or 12 incisures. From a face view the lip region is somewhat hexagonal, with amphid apertures at apices of lateral lips. One obscure papilla usually is visible on each of the submedian lips. Cephalic framework indistinct except for the refractive, sclerotized hexaradiate oral armature. Excretory pore opposite nerve ring. Hemizonid well developed, three or four annules posterior to excretory pore. Esophageal gland lobes usually extending about four body widths over anterior end of intestine. Ovary outstretched, the oöcytes arranged in single file. Posterior uterine branch rudimentary, collapsed, three to four times as long as body diameter. Female tail blunt, rounded, slightly longer than anal body diameter. Phasmids almost terminal. Male with broad bursa supported by four pairs of ribs, of which one pair is just anterior to anal region and the other three grouped near the terminus. Spicula slightly arcuate, slender. Gubernaculum almost straight, about one-third as long as spicula.

The above measurements are from T. Goodey (1951). He observed two males among several hundred females living on agar and made sure

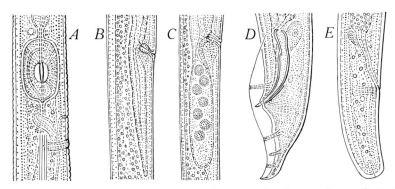

Fig. 15-1. *A, B—Aphelenchus avenae* esophageal and vulvar regions. *C, D, E— Aphelenchus radicicolus* vulvar region, male and female tails. (*Specimens of A. avenae courtesy of J. B. Goodey. A. radicicolus courtesy of T. J. Graham.*)

that they were functional but did not record copulation or presence of spermatozoa in females. One male was present in the collection forwarded to the writer by J. B. Goodey in 1958. Examination of the females failed to reveal spermatozoa in the uteri. The rudimentary, collapsed posterior uterine branch is very different from that present in bisexual species.

Aphelenchus agricola deMan, 1876, has not been retained as a synonym of *A. avenae,* as previous workers have classed it. Specimens from Europe in the writer's collection indicate that species other than *A. avenae* are present. Extensive collecting in the type locality may reveal that the synonomy was an error.

Aphelenchus radicicolus (Cobb, 1913a) Steiner, 1931

Synonym: *Isonchus radicicolus* Cobb, 1913a

Morphology: ♀: 0.93 mm; a = 28; b = 6.4; c = 23; V = $^{41}75^7$
         ♂: 0.75 mm; a = 30; b = 5.7; c = 22; T = 52

Lateral fields marked by 12 fine incisures which are reduced in numbers at the extremities. Lip region low, rounded, continuous with body contour. From a face view the amphid apertures and four submedian papillae are usually visible. Labial framework well sclerotized. Spear 17 μ long, devoid of basal swellings. Median bulb elongate, completely filling neck cavity. Isthmus 1½ times as long as body width, with nerve ring near its base. Excretory pore slightly anterior to nerve ring. Hemizonid six annules posterior to excretory pore, occupying a space equal to three or four annules. Deirids easily observed, about opposite nerve ring. Esophageal lobes 3 to 4 times as long as body width. Ovary outstretched, the oöcytes arranged in two lines throughout most of its length. Spermatheca about twice as long as body width, containing about 25 or 30 spermatozoa when filled. Posterior uterine branch a broad pouch 3 to 4 times as long as body width, often containing spermatozoa. Tail about twice as long as anal body diameter. Phasmids subterminal. Male with broad bursa rising anterior to proximal ends of spicula and completely enveloping tail. The bursa is supported by four pairs of ribs, the anterior one about opposite the anal region, the other three on the posterior half of the tail, as illustrated. Phasmids near the terminus, very difficult to observe. Testis half as wide as body, with multiple rows of spermatocytes. Spicula slightly arcuate, somewhat cephalated. Gubernaculum plain, about half as long as spicula (Fig. 15-1).

Cobb's brief diagnosis is hereby emended. His statement relative to the lateral field "Wing single" was obviously an error when considered from the standpoint of our present knowledge of that portion of the anatomy. Cobb also mentioned five pairs of bursal ribs but illustrated only four, the same number as found in present collections from the type vicinity.

Habitat and distribution: Cobb's specimens came from soil about roots of cotton collected near Springfield, South Carolina. The above description is from specimens collected by T. W. Graham near the Pee Dee Experiment Station, Florence, South Carolina, and other points in that state. Other collections came from a citrus grove, Sanford, Florida, and bean and sugar beet fields near Indio and Chino, California, respectively. Some males in a group from Weslaco, Texas, had only two or three pairs of bursal ribs. Other characters appeared identical to those of specimens from South Carolina. Steiner (1931) figured specimens from South Africa with males very similar to the type. However, at that time he recorded them as *Aphelenchus avenae,* in which classification all similar species had been grouped.

Aphelenchus eremitus n. sp.

Morphology: ♀: 0.9 mm; a = 30; b = 7; c = 37; V = $^{70}8_{19}$
♂: 0.9 mm; a = 33; b = 6.4; c = 30; T = 50

Lateral field marked by eight incisures near mid-body. Neck tapering rapidly until lip region is one-third as wide as body at base of neck. A face view reveals the lip region as obscurely hexagonal, with six approximately equal sectors. Amphid apertures and four submedian papillae usually visible. Cephalic framework lightly sclerotized except for the refractive oral armature. Spear 14 μ long, devoid of basal enlargements. Median bulb slightly fusiform. Isthmus only about as long as median bulb, with nerve ring surrounding it near the middle. Excretory pore about one neck width posterior to median bulb. Hemizonid six annules posterior to excretory pore. Esophageal lobes about twice as long as body width. Ovary outstretched, with oöcytes arranged in

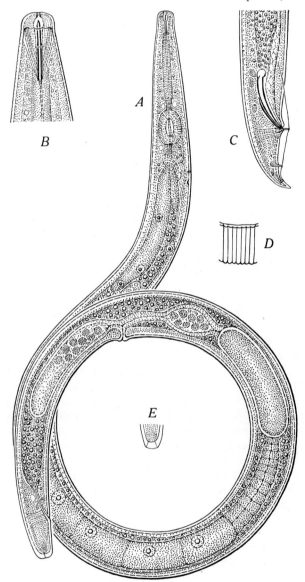

Fig. 15-2. *Aphelenchus eremitus.*   *A*—Female.   *B*—Head.   *C*—Posterior portion of male.   *D*—Lateral field.   *E*—Dorsal view showing terminal phasmids.

single file. Uterus with fusiform spermatheca in which several spermatozoa are usually present. Posterior uterine branch a broad pouch about three times as long as body width, serving as a storage reservoir for spermatozoa which are about 3 μ in diameter. An egg was 22 by 53 μ. Female tail obtuse, slightly longer than anal body diameter. Phasmids practically terminal. Spicula slightly curved, cephalated. Gubernaculum about half as long as spicula. Bursa rising about opposite proximal ends of spicula and extending to terminus. Three pairs of bursal ribs, one about opposite anus, the other two as illustrated. Phasmid in lateral field near terminus.

Habitat: Soil about roots of desert plants in southern Utah and northern Arizona and in cultivated field, Modesto, California.

Aphelenchus eremitus is readily distinguished from *A. radicicola* by number of lines in the lateral fields.

Genus *Paraphelenchus* (Micoletzky, 1922) Micoletzky, 1925

Synonym: *Aphelenchus (Paraphelenchus)* Micoletzky, 1922

Historical: The first description of this genus was based on numerous females collected from several sites in Austria. No males were observed, and the species was assumed to be parthenogenetic. Micoletzky (1925) collected a single male in Denmark and raised the group to generic rank, doubtless because of the spicula form, presence of a gubernaculum, and arrangement of the caudal papillae. At this time he called attention to similar males described by Maupas (1900) and deMan (1921) which had been identified as males of *Aphelenchus agricola* deMan, 1884. It is doubtful if these males belonged with the parthenogenetic females.

The great variations in length and body proportions recorded by Micoletzky indicate that more than one species was present. This may be assumed because he was prone to lump together all forms which resembled each other.

Diagnosis: Paraphelenchinae. Lateral fields marked by numerous incisures. Lip region continuous with head contour. Spear without basal knobs. Basal portion of esophagus an elongated bulb containing the gland nuclei. This bulb is joined to the intestine by an obscure muscular valvular apparatus. Hemizonid adjacent and posterior to excretory pore. Ovary outstretched. Posterior uterine branch short and collapsed in monosexual species, while in bisexual forms it becomes an elongate, pouchlike reservoir in which spermatozoa are almost always present. Spicula simple, slightly arcuate, pointed, resting on a plain, troughlike gubernaculum. Male tail bearing three to five pairs of conspicuous submedian papillae. Tails of both sexes frequently mucronate.

Type species: *Paraphelenchus pseudoparietinus* (Micol., 1922) Micol., 1925

Morphology: ♀: 0.4–0.9 mm; a = 25–26; b = 4.1–6.3; c = 14–24; V = 68–78

Characters of the genus as outlined above. Nine incisures are illustrated in the lateral field a short distance anterior to the tail. Basal plate of cephalic framework well sclerotized. Distance from anterior end to valve of median bulb slightly less than that from valve to base of esophagus. Excretory pore one body width posterior to median bulb. Posterior uterine branch two to three times as long as body diameter. Males unknown, and spermatozoa not observed in the uteri; therefore, the species is presumed to be parthenogenetic. Tail slightly arcuate dorsally, ending in a blunt, mucronate terminus. The nine lines of the lateral field appear to be the most outstanding diagnostic character.

Habitat: Soil about roots of numerous species of plants from several localities in Austria.

Paraphelenchus myceliophthorus Goodey, 1958

Morphology: ♀: 0.6–0.8 mm; a = 22–34; b = 4.1–6.6; c = 13–24; V = 71–78
♂: 0.56–0.8 mm; a = 23–32; b = 3.9–5.9; c = 14–30; T = 47

Lateral fields marked by six incisures occupying about one-third the body width near its middle. Head continuous with neck contour, without striae. Six rather uniform lips visible from a face view. Amphid apertures and papillae not observed. Stylet about 16 μ long, without basal knobs. Nerve ring adjacent to the ovate median bulb. Excretory pore opposite ring. Excretory tube connected directly with a gland lying adjacent to anterior end of intestine. Gonad outstretched, with oöcytes arranged in one or more rows. Uterus forming a long spermatheca in which numerous spermatozoa are present. Posterior uterine branch extending two-thirds distance to tail, forming a storage reservoir for spermatozoa. According to Goodey's figure the female tail length equals about three times the anal body diameter. Phasmids terminal. Mucro absent in adults but present on preadult larvae. Males numerous. Spicula slightly curved, 28 μ long. Gubernaculum almost straight, 13.5 μ long. One pair of submedian papillae about opposite anal region, a second pair near middle of tail, and two pairs near terminus, one subventral, the other subdorsal. A single ventromedian preanal papilla present.

This species is distinctive because of the six lateral incisures, absence of caudal mucro, elongate uterine spermatheca, well-developed posterior uterine branch, and presence of numerous males which obviously are functional.

Type host: Mycelium of *Agaricus hortensis* Cooke, the cultivated mushroom

Habitat: Mushroom compost, West Chiltington, Sussex, England.

Family APHELENCHOIDIDAE (Skarbilovich, 1947) Paramanov, 1953

Diagnosis: Aphelenchoidea. Intestine joined directly to median bulb. Esophageal glands extended dorsally in long lobes parallel with anterior end of intestine. Nerve ring encircling anterior ends of intestine and esophageal glands. Female tails elongate-conoid to filiform, rarely bluntly rounded. Male tails ventrally arcuate, with two or more pairs of submedian caudal papillae. Spicula massive, arcuate, often with prominent ventral apophysis. Bursa and gubernaculum absent.

Type subfamily: APHELENCHOIDINAE Skarbilovich, 1947

Diagnosis: Aphelenchoididae. Lip region amalgamated, the individual lips only slightly set off even from a face view. Stylet with narrow lumen, especially in the anterior portion, where it frequently is almost invisible. Median esophageal bulb spheroid or somewhat ovate. Male submedian caudal papillae only slightly elevated above body contour.

Type genus: *Aphelenchoides* Fischer, 1894

The Subfamily Aphelenchoidinae includes a diverse group of plant parasitic, mycophagous, and predatory nemas which are difficult to define. The situation was complicated by Rühm (1956) when he established the Subfamily Parasitaphelenchinae embracing four genera of insect associates. In many respects these four are allied to insect associates of Aphelenchoidinae, and only an intensive study of thousands of speci-

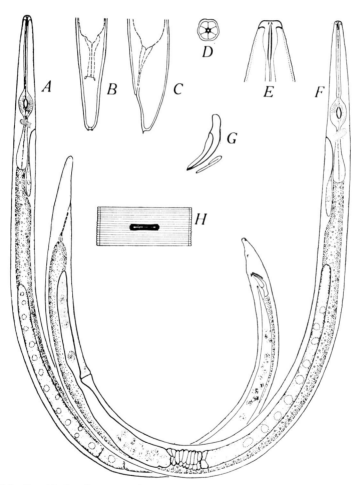

Fig. 15-3. *Paraphelenchus myceliophthorus.* *A*—Male. *B, C*—Female tail, ventral and lateral views. *D*—Basal cephalic framework. *E*—Head. *F*—Female. *G*—Spiculum and gubernaculum. *H*—Vulvar region. (*After J. B. Goodey, Nematologica. Courtesy of E. J. Brill.*)

mens by a qualified nematologist will clarify the taxonomy. To simplify the present taxonomy, the writer recognizes as genera the several subgenera set up by Fuchs (1937) and Rühm (1956). Since none of their specimens was permanently mounted on slides and preserved for future studies, someone must eventually assume the task of securing similar specimens and properly organizing the taxonomy.

Key to subfamilies and genera of Aphelenchoididae

1. Spear with narrow, obscure lumen; male caudal papillae obscure, only slightly elevated..................................Aphelenchodinae 2
   Spear with relatively broad lumen; male caudal papillae elevated, conspicuous...Parasitaphelenchinae 11
2. Lip region with sclerotized labial disc......................*Anomyctus*
   Lip region without sclerotized disc.................................. 3
3. Spear with trifurcate base...............................*Schistonchus*
   Spear base not trifurcate... 4
4. Male tail with sclerotized, spadelike terminus........................ 5
   Male tail without spadelike terminus................................. 6
5. Cephalic framework massive, sclerotized..............*Rhadinaphelenchus*
   Cephalic framework not massive, sclerotized............*Bursaphelenchus*
6. Female tail with pronglike tubercules.................*Laimaphelenchus*
   Female tail without pronglike tubercules............................. 7
7. Tails of both sexes elongate-conoid or filiform, acute............*Seineura*
   Tails of both sexes shorter, conoid, blunt or mucronate............... 8
8. Spear length equal to lip-region width, strongly knobbed...*Tylaphelenchus*
   Spear length distinctly greater than lip-region width, plain or with small knobs, rarely strongly knobbed..................................... 9
9. Body length under 0.5 mm.. 10
   Body length greater than 0.6 mm......................*Aphelenchoides*
10. Spear short, with well-developed knobs.................*Cryptaphelenchus*
    Spear elongate, slender, without knobs.......................*Steineria*
11. Lips prominent, petaloid... 12
    Lips amalgamated, obscurely defined.............................. 13
12. Spicula distally arcuate, not fused together..............*Ektaphelenchus*
    Spicula only slightly curved, fused together...........*Parasitaphelenchus*
13. Females with prominent saccate vaginal glands...........*Entaphelenchus*
    Females without saccate vaginal glands..................*Peraphelenchus*

Genus *Aphelenchoides* Fischer, 1894

Synonyms: Subgenus *Chitinoaphelenchus* Micoletzky, 1922; *Pathoaphelenchus* (Cobb, 1927) Steiner, 1932

Diagnosis: Aphelenchoidinae. Cuticle marked by fine transverse striae. Lateral fields with two, three, or four lines or incisures. Lip region not striated. Six amalgamated lips, slightly hexagonal when seen from a face view. Amphid apertures minute, at apex of lateral lips. A single papilla usually present on each of the four submedian lips. Labial framework hexaradiate, lightly sclerotized except for refractive spear guide at oral aperture. Esophageal glands in long lobes extending back over intestine. Hemizonid posterior to excretory pore. Ovary outstretched, with oöcytes arranged in tandem or multiple rows. Posterior uterine branch short and collapsed or forming an elongate reservoir for spermatozoa. Males without bursa or gubernaculum. Two or three pairs of ventrosubmedian papillae usually present. Phasmids excessively small and difficult to observe, usually subterminal. Tails of both sexes conoid to blunt or pointed terminus, often mucronate, never filiform.

Type species: *Aphelenchoides kuehnii* Fischer, 1894
Cobb (1927) established *Pathoaphelenchus* as a subgenus of *Aphelenchus*. Steiner (1931) elevated *Pathoaphelenchus* to generic rank and designated *P. parietinus, = Aphelenchus parietinus,* as type. However, Steiner (1932a) found Fischer's description of *Aphelenchoides kuehnii* and decided that this species was a synonym of *A. parietinus*. Since *Aphelenchoides kuehnii* had been designated type of *Aphelenchoides,* this action made *A. parietinus* type of *Aphelenchoides.*

Franklin (1955) clarified the identity of *Aphelenchoides parietinus* in a most satisfactory manner when she redescribed the species from specimens collected from the type host in the type locality. These specimens indicated that females are only about two-thirds as long as those of *A. kuehnii* and more robust and that males do not occur in *A. parietinus*. Thus it is apparent that *A. kuehnii* is not a synonym of *A. parietinus* and must be recognized as the type of the genus, as Fischer designated. *Aphelenchoides* now includes about eighty named species.

Aphelenchoides kuehnii Fischer, 1894

Morphology: ♀: 0.7 mm; a = 32; b = 11; c = 15; V = $^{34}75$
♂: 0.6 mm; a = 33; b = ?; c = ?
Fischer's illustration of the female shows a nema similar in body form to Franklin's drawing of *Aphelenchoides parietinus*. Lip region set off by a distinct expansion, one-half as wide as the neck at the median bulb. Stylet 14 μ long, with very distinct basal knobs, constituting an outstanding characteristic of the species. Median bulb 14 by 12.5 μ. Excretory pore only half a body width behind median bulb. Ovary outstretched, the oöcytes arranged in single file. Posterior uterine branch indefinitely illustrated. Body tapering posteriorly to the uniformly conoid, slightly arcuate tail, which ends in a moderately sharp terminus. Fischer makes no mention of a terminal mucro. Male slenderer and slightly shorter than female. Tail ventrally bent into a hooklike form, with slightly rounded terminus. Bursa not present. Spicula 18 μ long, massive, arcuate.

This species is especially distinctive because of the relatively broad lip region, strongly knobbed spear, and very arcuate, massive spicula. It appears to resemble *Aphelenchoides megadorus* Allen, 1941, with its broad head and massive spear, which are much more developed than those of *A. parietinus* and similar species. Collections from the type locality and emendation of the diagnosis are desirable.

Habitat: Associated with *Tylenchus gulosus* Kuhn, 1889, = *Pratylenchus* sp., in roots of clematis, *Clematis jackmani,* Halle, Germany.

Aphelenchoides megadorus Allen, 1941

Morphology: ♀: 0.5 mm; a = 31; b = 8.3; c = 22.7; V = $^{30}72^8$

Striae near lip region 1.1 μ wide, while those near middle of body are 1.7 μ. Lateral fields one-fifth body width, marked by three incisures. Cephalic region set off by constriction and expansion, with hexaradiate framework. Radial elements of framework double. Amphid apertures and four submedian papillae visible from a face view. Pharynx heavily sclerotized, triquetrous in cross section. Spear 17 μ long, with massive knobs, the largest of any known aphelench. Anterior portion of spear very slender, with well-developed guiding apparatus. Esophageal glands extended dorsally in very slender lobes three to five body widths long. Intestine at first a slender tube without granules until after it passes through nerve ring. Cells of intestine 16 in number, polynucleate. Ovary very short, with oöcytes arranged in single file. Eggs half as wide as body and 3½ times as long as wide. Posterior uterine branch 2 to 3 times as long as body width, collapsed. Phasmids not observed. Tail bluntly rounded, without mucro. Male unknown, and gravid females contained no spermatozoa.

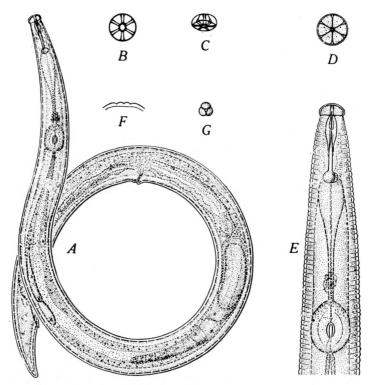

Fig. 15-4. *Aphelenchoides megadorus. A, B*—Head and face views. *C*—Region of esophageal glands. *D*—Female. *E, F*—Ventral and lateral views of tail. (*After Allen. Courtesy of Helminthological Society of Washington.*)

Habitat: Soil about desert plants west of Utah Lake, Utah. Several specimens were infested with a sporozoan parasite, probably *Duboscqia penetrans* Thorne, 1940.

Aphelenchoides parietinus (Bastian, 1865) Steiner, 1932

Synonyms: *Aphelenchus parietinus* Bastian, 1865

Fourteen additional species have been declared synonyms by Micoletzky (1922), T. Goodey (1951), and Steiner (1932). These inadequately described forms should be maintained as species *inquirenda* until specimens are again collected in the type localities and descriptions emended. Micoletzky also established fifteen forms, subforms, and varieties of *Aphelenchus parietinus* which are unrecognizable and must be declared *numen nudum*.

Historical: Bastian's original collection came from yellow lichen, *Xanthoria* (formerly *Parmelia*) *parietina*. Only females were recorded, and his description and figures were most inadequate. Throughout the years, *Aphelenchoides parietinus* has frequently been mentioned, and certain writers have reported males. Variations in length and body proportions indicate that numerous species have been involved in these reports. The following description is from Franklin (1950) and well illustrates the manner in which old, inadequate diagnoses should be emended and validated from specimens collected in type localities.

Morphology: ♀ : 0.45 mm; a = 26; b = 7.8; c = 13.8; V = 68
Lateral field marked by four incisures which are reduced in numbers at the extremities. Annules near mid-body 1.0 to 1.3 μ wide. Lip region set off by distinct expansion. Cephalic framework lightly sclerotized, divided into six equal sectors. Spear with basal thickenings which scarcely can be termed knobs. Median bulb almost as wide as body cavity. Nerve ring close to median bulb, encircling anterior end of intestine and ducts of esophageal glands. Excretory pore opposite nerve ring. Esophageal gland lobes extending dorsally a distance equal to about four times body width. Ovary outstretched, the oöcytes in single file. Eggs about four times as long as wide. Posterior rudimentary uterine branch not collapsed, extending about halfway to anus. Sperms not observed either in uterus or in posterior uterine branch. Tail arcuate-conoid to mucronate terminus.

Habitat: A common inhabitant of yellow lichen, where it is assumed to feed on the fungal constituent, according to Franklin. It was also found on the green foliose lichen, *Cladonia fimbriata* var. *simplex*. Colonies were established on fungus growing in agar, and in one instance females, eggs, and larvae were observed after three months. No males were observed.

Aphelenchoides parietinus is representative of a group of rather robust nemas which usually are less than 1.0 mm long. They inhabit soil and frequently are found associated with decaying plant tissues both above and below the surface. Occasionally they are found as plant parasites, e.g., *A. blastophorus*. More frequently they inhabit healthy tissues of higher plants without apparent pathogenic effects. Often they feed on the mycelia of fungi, and one species, *A. composticola,* is a serious parasite of mushroom beds. Christie and Arndt (1936) found that cotton seedlings sometimes produced blind buds and distorted foliage when grown in soil heavily infested with *A. parietinus.* Roots of young plants were yellowish, an indication that the nemas had been feeding on the cortical cells. However, lesions were not developed.

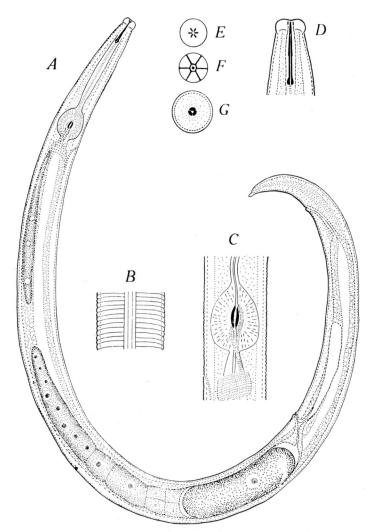

Fig. 15-5. *Aphelenchoides parietinus.* *A*—Female. *B*—Lateral field. *C*—Region of median esophageal bulb. *D*—Head. *E*—Framework about oral opening. *F*—Basal cephalic framework. *G*—Cross section through base of spear. (*After Franklin, Nematologica. Courtesy of E. J. Brill.*)

Aphelenchoides blastophora Franklin, 1952

Morphology: ♀: 0.7–0.9 mm; a = 32–47; b = 10.2; c = 16–21; V = 68–74
        ♂: 0.7–0.9 mm; a = 35–47; b = 9.5; c = 14–19

Lateral fields marked by four incisures. Lip region set off by a distinct expansion. Faint amphidial apertures on the lateral lips and probably two faint papillae on each submedian lip are visible from a face view. Stylet averaging 17 μ long, with small, well-defined basal knobs. Median bulb elongated. Nerve ring and excretory pore one body width posterior to median bulb. Esophageal gland lobes extending back three or four times body width. Ovary outstretched, with oöcytes arranged in single file. Uterus with a spermatheca twice as long as body width, containing several elongated spermatozoa. Posterior uterine branch an elongate pouch extending halfway back to anus, serving as a reservoir for spermatozoa. Eggs about twice as long as body width. Female tail uniformly conoid to a single mucron. Male tail arcuate, bearing three pairs of obscure papillae, the first pair near the anal region, the second near middle of tail, and the third near the terminus. Spicula arcuate, the dorsal limb bearing a curved terminus.

Aphelenchoides blastophora belongs in the *parietinus* group. It is distinctive because of its bisexuality, length, and width. Its width and simple terminal mucro differentiate it from the *fragariae* group.

Biology: *Aphelenchoides blastophora* is a parasite of scabiosa on which it lives both as an ecto- and endoparasite. Franklin found numerous specimens in damaged buds and florets. Often twenty to fifty nemas of all ages were in a leaf axil. Stained sections of infested tissues indicated that about equal numbers were inside and outside the plant. Most of those living endoparasitically were in tissues surrounding the lower part of the mid-rib, with very few in the lamina. Diseased plants often darker green. Florets failed to develop in severely infested inflorescences. Leaves distorted, twisted, and puckered, and mid-ribs thickened. In January and February some nemas were in small living leaves of the center of the crown, but most remained in the dead leaves.

Franklin experienced no difficulty in demonstrating pathogenicity by adding suspensions of nemas from infested to young plants. No other species of plants were found to be hosts except teasle, *Dipsacus fullonum*.

Distribution: Scabiosa plantings near Leicester and four other localities in England.

Franklin's careful work on *Aphelenchoides composticola* and *A. blastophora* sets a good standard for others to follow in evaluating and describing the numerous species belonging in the *A. parietinus* group.

Timber nema, *Aphelenchoides xylophilus* Steiner and Buhrer, 1934

Morphology: ♀: 0.9 mm; a = 62; b = 11.5; c = 26; V = 74
        ♂: 0.8 mm; a = 50; b = 10; c = 24

Structure of lateral fields not recorded. Lip region knoblike, set off by deep constriction. Amphid apertures and four submedian papillae visible from a face view, arranged in the usual manner. Stylet 1½ times as long as lip-region width, bearing minute thickenings at its base. Median bulb elongate, with

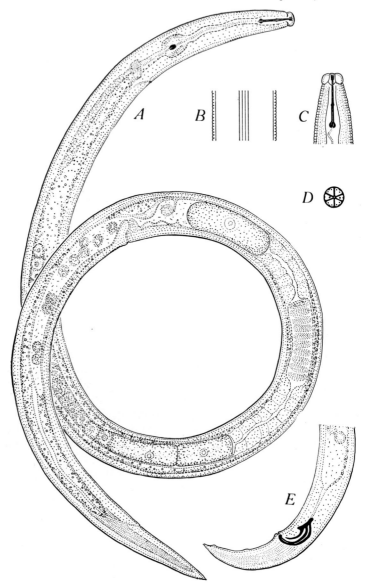

Fig. 15-6. *Aphelenchoides blastophorus.* *A*—Female.   *B*—Lateral field.   *C*—Head.   *D*—Face view.   *E*—Male tail.   (*After Franklin.   Courtesy of Annals of Applied Biology.*)

valve in posterior half. Esophageal gland lobes arranged in a series extending dorsally over intestine, about 85 μ long. Excretory pore about opposite nerve ring. Female and larval tails blunt, rounded. Male tail arcuate, with somewhat hooked terminal portion. One pair mammiform submedian papillae in anal region, and two pairs near middle of tail, one pair being subdorsal, an unusual occurrence in aphelenchs. Spicula with prominent ventral apophysis, somewhat mitten-shaped. A small gubernaculum present, another rare occurrence in this group.

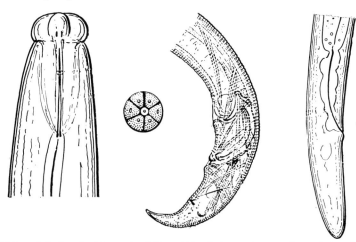

Fig. 15-7. *Aphelenchoides xylophilus.* Head, face view, male and female tails. *(After Steiner. Courtesy of U.S. Department of Agriculture.)*

Habitat and distribution: The species was first observed in 1929 in wood from longleaf Louisiana pine, *Pinus palustris* Mill., originating in Orange, Texas. Small numbers of females, males, and larvae were present in and about streaks caused by blue-stain fungus. These emerged from the tissues after soaking in water. Later, numerous specimens were established on plates of a brown fungus, probably of the genus *Trichosporium,* collected in the vicinity of Bogalusa, Louisiana. These came from a log attacked by a bark beetle of the genus *Ips.* A third collection near Fairfax, Virginia, came from *Pinus echinata* Mill. killed by *Dendroctonus frontalis* Zimm., another species of bark beetle.

Apparently the nemas are distributed by bark beetles and feed on wood-inhabiting fungi. In some respects this species resembles members of the genus *Bursaphelenchus.* There is no known economic importance arising from its association with the blue-stain fungi.

Bud and leaf nemas of the genus *Aphelenchoides*

Bud- and leaf-infesting species of *Aphelenchoides* include all but one of the known major plant parasites of the family, the other being *Rhadinaphlenchus cocophilus.* They are both ecto- and endoparasitic as observed by Franklin (1950). Ectoparasitism is frequent in plant crowns, leaf axils, or inflorescence where the nemas are protected by folded or juxtaposed tissues. Endoparasitism is most often found in leaves, especially succulent types like those of *Begonia* or *Saintpaulia*. In general morphology the species resemble other members of the genus except for their more slender, cylindroid bodies. The one tangible diagnostic character is the position of the hemizonid in relation to the excretory pore. This organ lies eight or ten annules behind the pore in bud and leaf species except *A. ritzema-bosi*. In other species it is posteriorly adjacent to the pore.

Bud and leaf nemas were first collected in 1889 by Miss E. A. Ormerod near Kent, England, and forwarded to Ritzema Bos in the Netherlands for identification. From this material he described (1891) two species, *Aphelenchus fragariae* and *A. ormerodis*, both of which were later transferred to *Aphelenchoides*. *A. fragariae* is now a well-known plant parasitic species. *A. ormerodis* is best regarded as species *inquirendum*, because proper diagnostic characters were not presented. It was a more robust form somewhat resembling *A. parietinus*, with which it has been synonymized by certain workers.

Of the twelve names which have been applied to bud and leaf nemas, eight are now recognized as synonyms of the remaining four. This synonymy resulted from the fact that species names were assigned to certain host populations without accompanying diagnostic morphological characters. Diagnostic characters are resolvable only in favorable specimens skillfully examined under the highest powers of the microscope. Among those who have contributed to solving the taxonomic problems of the group are Marcinowski (1909), Goffart (1930), Steiner (1932), T. Goodey (1933), Junges (1938), and Franklin (1950). The final adjustments in taxonomy were made by Allen (1952a) after studying over two thousand specimens collected from many parts of the world over a period of 15 years. The following key to species is largely from Allen:

Key to species of bud and leaf nematodes

1. Lip region expanded, wider than adjacent head, four lines in lateral field. . 2
   Lip region not expanded, two lines in lateral field . . . . *fragariae*
2. Length of posterior uterine branch five or more times body width 3
   Length of posterior uterine branch less than four times body width . . . *besseyi*
3. Tail bluntly rounded, bearing a single terminal spine . . . . *subtenuis*
   Tail with peglike terminus bearing four small mucrones . . . . *ritzema-bosi*

Spring crimp nematode

Aphelenchoides fragariae (Ritzema Bos, 1891) Christie, 1932

Synonyms: *Aphelenchus fragariae* Ritzema Bos; *Aphelenchus olesistus* Ritzema Bos, 1893; *Aphelenchoides olesistus* (Ritzema Bos) Steiner, 1932; *Aphelenchus olesistus* var. *longicollis* Schwartz, 1911; *Aphelenchoides olesistus* var. *longicollis* (Schwartz) Goodey, 1933; *Aphelenchus pseudole-*

sistus Goodey, 1928; *Aphelenchoides pseudolesistus* (Goodey) Goodey, 1933

Morphology: ♀: 0.45–0.8 mm; a = 45–60; b = 9–11; c = 12–22;
V = $^{41-22}64-71^{11-18}$

♂: 0.48–0.65 mm; a = 46–63; b = 9–11; c = 16–19; T = 44–61

Body slender, cylindroid, tapering near extremities. Lateral field a narrow band occupying about one-seventh of body width, marked by two lines. Lip region almost continuous with head contour, not marked by striae. Labial framework delicate, obscure, except for hexaradiate oral armature. Stylet slender, 10 μ long, with small but distinct knobs. Nerve ring about one body width behind median bulb, encircling both intestine and esophageal gland ducts. Excretory pore opposite nerve ring. Esophageal glands extending about five body widths posterior to median bulb. Anterior portion of intestine a slender tube crowded ventrally by esophageal gland lobes. Ovary outstretched, the oöcytes arranged in single file. Posterior uterine branch an elongated pouch serving as a reservoir for spermatozoa. Tail tapering uniformly to an abruptly conoid, acute terminus. Male tail slightly curved when relaxed, bearing three pairs of ventrosubmedian papillae. First pair slightly postanal, second pair near middle of tail, and third pair near terminus.

Aphelenchoides fragariae is distinctive because of the very slightly set-off lip region, two lines in the lateral field, and tapering tail with abruptly conoid, pointed terminus.

The above measurements and most of the descriptions are from Allen, who ably discusses the several synonyms of *Aphelenchoides fragariae*. His collections from strawberry, Croft lily, bird's-nest fern, daffodil, violets, and begonia indicated that the only differences in these populations were in size, and size is not consistent within any one population. Position of excretory pore and length of posterior uterine branch were as variable within populations as between populations.

    Hosts: *Aphelenchoides fragariae* has been well known because of its association with strawberries. Actually it is a polyphagous form with a wide range of hosts. Most of these have been recorded under the synonym *A. olesistus*, which has been studied extensively because of its importance as a parasite of ferns and other ornamentals. Goffart (1930) listed over sixty species, representing more than forty genera of flowering plants. These included well-known groups like *Anemonae, Begonia, Chrysanthemum, Coleus, Primula, Ranunculus, Saintpaulia,* and many others.

    Crossman and Christie (1936) made a complete survey of hosts and recorded 179, of which 45 were known in the United States. Each host is listed under its accepted scientific name accompanied by the common name, if any. The nema involved in each instance is recorded under the original name for which it was reported, *Aphelenchoides olesistus, A. ritzema-bosi, A. subtenuis,* and *A. ribes,* all of which they considered as synonyms of *A. fragariae*. Host ranges of different populations from various plants in widespread geographical areas are almost certain to

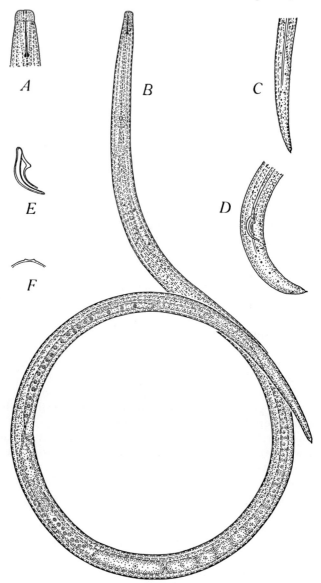

Fig. 15-8. *Aphelenchoides fragariae.* *A*—Head.   *B*—Female.   *C*—Female tail.
D—Male tail.   *E*—Spiculum.   *F*—Cross section of lateral field.   (*After Allen.
Courtesy of Helminthological Society of Washington.*)

be extremely variable. Only careful research in each locality will reveal which species of nema is present and the plants involved.

Aphelenchoides fragariae as a parasite of strawberries

Biology: In strawberry plants the nemas generally congregate about the plant crown, where they live as ectoparasites in buds and leaflets of the growing point or in leaf axils. Movement from one point to another or from plant to plant is dependent on a film of moisture from rain, dew, or high humidity. Runner plants from infested mothers usually are also infested unless they are produced during dry periods when a moisture film is not present. Occasionally specimens are found within leaf tissues. Eggs are deposited in the axils or within leaves, and mature adults develop from them in about 14 days according to Goffart (1930). Populations may vary from several thousand per plant during humid periods to fewer than 100, under dry conditions.

In Europe *Aphelenchoides fragariae* is associated with "cauliflower disease" and "red plant" of strawberries. In the United States it is recognized as the causal agent of "spring dwarf," or "crimp," of strawberries. Cobb (1891) referred to it as "strawberry bunch" after reading the papers of Ritzema Bos.

Cauliflower disease: This was the disease first observed by Miss Ormerod and identified by Ritzema Bos (1889). The nemas were presumed to be the causal agent of the disease until Crosse and Pitcher (1952) determined that cauliflower disease symptoms occurred only when the nemas were associated with a bacterium, *Corynebacterium fascians* (Tilford) Dowson. Their detailed studies indicated that typical cauliflower symptoms developed only on plants inoculated with eelworms and the strains of *C. fascians,* C6 and C1. However, it was clearly shown that the nemas were essential in producing all variations of the disease symptoms. They also stated: "The eelworm probably functions as a vector, transporting the bacterium to the meristematic regions of the crown, which, because of their tight enclosure within the stipules, are normally inaccessible to it. It is also possible that the eelworms' ectoparasitic mode of feeding may in some way favor the activity of the bacterium."

Symptoms: Infestation results in stunted plants with deformed stems, leaves, and flowers. In advanced stages the severely stunted, fasciated plants somewhat resemble a tiny cauliflower. T. Goodey (1933) states that the flowers are especially affected, with leaflike parts reduced to scales. There may be an enormous development of the calyx, accompanied by greatly enlarged sepals. Petals may be lacking or, if produced, are smaller than sepals and greenish in color. Stamens are deformed and receptacle so reduced that fruit cannot be formed. Plants may be found which exhibit stages varying from extreme cauliflower type to types with moderate or minor infestation.

It was while working with *Aphelenchoides* that Ritzema Bos first conceived the idea that nemas injected a salivary secretion into the plant cells and that this product caused hypertrophy of the tissues.

Fig. 15-9. Strawberry (variety Corvallis) with "spring dwarf" produced by *Aphelenchoides fragariae.* (*Courtesy of H. J. Jensen, Department of Botany and Plant Pathology, Oregon State College.*)

Red plant: Principal symptoms are deformed and reduced growth of buds, stems, leaves, and flowers. Leaves may be crinkled and fruit stems have only one or two flowers. Only a few varieties like Royal Sovereign, Lexton's King George, and Duke show red symptoms in their foliage; hence the name is somewhat misleading. Ball, Mann, and Staniland (1927) found that affected plants may bear both normal and diseased sections of the crown.

Spring dwarf, or crimp: This is typically a strawberry disease of early spring in the North Atlantic states. It was first recorded from Massachusetts and Maryland. As in red plant, the symptoms are stunting and deforming in various stages of severity of buds, leaves, and flowers. Red coloration of foliage has not been recorded, but otherwise the two diseases are very similar, if not identical. Christie (1938) transferred plants from Massachusetts to North Carolina and found that the nemas persisted through two years. Typical symptoms developed, but they appeared much earlier in the season.

Spring dwarf also occurs in both wild and cultivated strawberries on the Pacific coast from central California north through Oregon and Washington. Severe damage frequently occurs, as recorded by Raski and Allen (1948).

Control: *Soil fumigation:* Many strawberry growers now consistently practice soil fumigation before planting. Applications of standard fumigants often are double those usually recommended for control and almost achieve eradication of all ecto- and endoparasitic nemas. Two- to sixfold increases in yields after fumigation are not unusual.

Clean plants: Many nurseries now advertise certified plants from fumigated fields. These should be used, especially after the expense of fumigation.

Roguing: Plantings with small infestations may be rogued with good results if care is exercised in removing infested plants and adjacent soil to a depth of 2 or 3 inches.

Systemic sprays: Raski and Allen (1948) applied 15 per cent wettable Parathion powder at the rate of 0.45 pound of Parathion per 100 gallons of water. Application was made under 200 pounds pressure. Three weeks after spraying samples of fifteen buds from sprayed and unsprayed plots were examined. Sprayed buds averaged 108 nemas per bud, while those from unsprayed plants averaged 498. While it was evident that Parathion was toxic to the nemas, it was also apparent that even under heavy pressure the chemical failed to reach nemas in tightly folded buds and leaves. Two applications did not appreciably increase the kill. Addition of spreader to the solution was also ineffective.

Warm water: Numerous investigators have attempted to control *Aphelenchoides* spp. by submersion in water at various temperatures. These experiments have resulted in conflicting data, for different species of the genus were involved. A typical example is that of Christie and Crossman (1935), who recognized four "strains" of *A. fragariae* in their extensive experiments. Fifty specimens in each of twenty-five lots were placed in small test tubes submerged in a water bath at eight different temperatures. Populations of *A. fragariae* from strawberry and begonia reacted in a rather similar manner. Another strain from North Carolina strawberries, *A. besseyi,* required much higher temperatures. A fourth strain from chrysanthemum, *A. ritzema-bosi,* was killed by temperatures intermediate between those necessary for *A. fragariae* and *A. besseyi.* The importance of species identification is emphasized by this work.

Nemas within plant tissues require longer periods of submersion owing to the time required to bring plants up to desired temperatures. This time factor also varies with size and number of plants. Preheating of large quantities of plants is necessary; otherwise the desired temperature will not be maintained for the full length of time required for an effective kill. From a practical standpoint, warm-water treatment generally is applicable only on small lots of valuable breeding stock. Even under the most carefully controlled conditions some nemas may escape in tightly folded buds.

Aphelenchoides fragariae as a parasite of ferns and other plants

Ritzema Bos (1893) found a fern, *Asplenium* sp., infested by nemas which he named *Aphelenchus olesistus*. According to Goodey (1933) the same species probably had been observed in England on begonia leaves as early as 1890. Klebahn (1891) also had mentioned a species of *Aphelenchus* found in the leaves of *Asplenium bulbiferum* in Germany. During the following four years numerous records were made of *Aphelenchus olesistus* in ferns and scores of other ornamentals. These were well discussed by Goffart (1930), who stated that, in many instances, species other than *Aphelenchus olesistus* may have been involved.

Marcinowski (1909) stated that *Aphelenchus olesistus* might be the same as *Aphelenchoides fragariae,* and Steiner (1932) declared it a synonym. However, the synonym was not generally accepted until Franklin (1950) published results of her extensive host-transfer experiments and morphological studies. Allen's careful studies of the morphology finally produced the necessary diagnostic characters for accurate identification.

FERNS

Biology: The nemas move about on the plant in a film of moisture and enter the leaves through the stomata. Here they set up localized zones of infestation causing brown or black markings which may vary in size and pattern with different fern species. Goffart concluded that the nemas do not penetrate far from the point of entrance, and for this reason spots or bands on leaves frequently are widely separated.

Control: The only practical method of control lies in destruction of infested plants, accompanied by thorough cleaning up and denematizing of contaminated soil by steam or fumigants before introduction of clean stock.

CROFT LILY

This flower, commonly known as "Easter lily" in the United States, was found infested with nemas in Washington state early in 1944. Specimens collected by W. D. Courtney were identified as *Aphelenchoides olesistus, = A. fragariae,* by J. R. Christie. Similar collections made in Oregon at approximately the same time were recorded by McWhorter, Elmsweller, and Brierly (1944). In their publication the nema was reported as the causal agent of bunchy top and dieback. Courtney's survey of Washington (1945) showed that the pest was already widespread in both greenhouse and field plantings throughout the lily-growing areas. In Oregon, McWhorter also found numerous infestations, and by patho-

Fig. 15-10. Croft lily (left) infested with *Aphelenchoides fragariae*. Normal plant right. (*Courtesy of W. D. Courtney, Nematology Section, U.S. Department of Agriculture.*)

genicity tests he demonstrated (1945) that typical symptoms could be produced in about four weeks.

Symptoms: First indications of infestation are yellow to bronze leaves which soon droop, become blackish brown, and eventually die. The stem becomes stunted, infested buds fail to produce flowers, and death of the plant may follow. Because of these symptoms the disease was formerly known as "dieback." Presence of the nema is readily determined by shredding or blending infested tissues and processing the fragments in a funnel through screens or by immediate examination.

Control: Light infestations of scattering plants can be materially reduced by careful roguing. Brierly, Smith, and McWhorter (1947) recommended that bulbs from infested lots be held for one hour at 110°F in a solution of 1 pint commercial formaldehyde to 30 gallons of water. After treatment bulbs should be dipped in an approved fungicide to guard against bulb and root rots.

BELLINGHAM HYBRID LILIES

Jensen and Caveness (1954) secured good control with the above warm-water method. After treatment the bulbs were dipped in Spergon (5 ounces of 25 per cent wettable powder to 3 gallons of water) to prevent secondary rots.

Practical control was also achieved with two or three applications of foliar spray consisting of 1 quart of Systox in 100 gallons of water. Eradication was apparently achieved with warm water at 118°F for one hour and Systox sprays, 1 gallon to 100 gallons of water. However, these severe treatments resulted in considerable plant injury.

BEGONIA

The thick, succulent leaves of begonias are especially adapted to endoparasitism by *Aphelenchoides fragariae*. The extensive, dark-colored lesions frequently involve a large portion of the leaves.

VIOLET

Schwartz (1911) described a disease of violets caused by *Aphelenchus olesistus longicollis,* = *Aphelenchoides fragiariae*. A spectacular type of injury was produced in which often all portions of the plant were deformed and stunted and sometimes a large gall bearing numerous abortive buds and leaves appeared. In general this injury resembled cauliflower disease of strawberry, and one might expect to find an associated bacterium similar to that described for strawberry.

General symptoms exhibited by the many hosts vary from leaf spotting to deformed buds, shortened leaf and flower stems, and imperfect flowers. Severe infestation of the crown may prevent growth of any type and cause death of plants, especially those which are very young. Suspected infestations may be determined by isolating the specimens by dissection, Baermann funnel, blending, and screening. Combinations of these methods may be used, depending on the equipment at hand. Unless one is well trained in working with the group, it is always advisable to have identifications verified by a specialist. Otherwise, one may add another erroneous identification to the many already recorded.

Production of Bud and Leaf Nemas on Fungus Cultures

Bud and leaf aphelenchs are generally recognized as obligate plant parasites. However, it is possible to rear certain species on fungi growing on culture media, as outlined by Christie and Crossman (1936). This was accomplished under the following conditions: "(a) Presence of a suitable fungus, (b) A comparatively dry culture with only a thin film of moisture over the surface of the agar, and (c) Absence of bacteria." Best results were secured with *Alternaria citri,* but other species would probably be suitable.

Colonies of *Aphelenchoides besseyi* from North Carolina were maintained for eight months and built up ample populations for experimental purposes. *A. fragariae* from Massachusetts survived but reproduced only enough to maintain the population and did not produce large numbers. *A. ritzema-bosi* failed to survive.

Inoculations were made by introducing the nemas around the bud at the base of the leaf petioles. When only one or two nemas per plant were used, a drop of water was placed between the small unfolding leaves and the nemas transferred to it by means of a bamboo pick.

Later Christie (1938a) demonstrated pathogenicity of these colonies by producing typical symptoms on pot- and field-grown plants. In one field experiment concentrated lots of nemas were introduced into the crowns of thirty-six varieties of strawberries and all were found susceptible.

Christie's successful method of establishing colonies of *Aphelenchoides besseyi* was achieved by preparing agar in the following manner:

A. Extract 15 g of cornmeal in 750 ml of water, and filter.
   Add water to filtrate to make 500 ml.
   Add:
      2.5 g malt extract.
      7.5 g sucrose.
      20 g agar.
B. 500 ml plant nutrient solution.
   1 ml concentrated lactic acid.

To avoid hydrolysis, autoclave A and B separately, and combine just before pouring the plates.

Inoculation with fungi usually was made two days before introducing the nemas. To avoid bacterial and fungal contamination, the nemas were sometimes treated with 1 to 2,000 mercuric chloride solution. First a small quantity of water was poured over the plate from which the nemas were to be transferred. After 5 or 10 minutes this was poured into a centrifuge tube and processed for 2 or 3 minutes at a moderate speed. Most of the water was then drawn off, the nemas being left in a few milliliters at the bottom of the tube. The mercuric chloride solution was then introduced and allowed to stand for 30 minutes, and it was then centrifuged and the excess drawn off. The nemas were washed twice by adding sterile water, centrifuging, and drawing off the supernatant fluid. Specimens of *Aphelenchoides besseyi* from North Carolina survived the process in good condition, while those of *A. fragariae* from Massachusetts seemed to be less resistant.

By means of a similar method, Todd and Atkins (1958) established large colonies of *Aphelenchoides besseyi*, as cited later in the section on white tip of rice.

Summer crimp nematode of strawberries and white tip of rice

Aphelenchoides besseyi Christie, 1942

Synonym: *Aphelenchoides oryzae* Yokoo, 1948

Morphology: ♀: 0.62–0.88 mm; a = 38–58; b =9–12; c = 15–20;
        V = $^{43-33}66-72^{4-8}$
      ♂: 0.44–0.72 mm; a = 36–47; b = 9–11; c = 14–19; T = 50–65

Lateral field occupying one-fourth of body width, marked by four incisures.
Lip region expanded, wider than adjacent neck. Lips without annulation.
Cephalic framework delicate, with refractive hexaradiate oral armature. Spear
10 μ long, with moderate-sized basal knobs. Nerve ring one body width behind
median bulb. Excretory pore anterior to nerve ring. Esophageal gland lobe
extending five body widths behind median bulb. Intestine joined to esophagus
immediately behind median bulb. Ovary relatively short, with oöcytes arranged
in several lines. Posterior uterine branch two to four times as long as body
width, narrow, usually not containing spermatozoa. Tail tapering, conoid.
Terminus bearing four mucrones arranged in a shape somewhat that of a star.
Male tail curvature about 180° when relaxed. Three pairs of ventrosubmedian
papillae present, the first being about adanal. Spicula curved, with a slight
basal process. Terminus bearing four variably arranged mucrones.

Aphelenchoides besseyi is distinctive because of the four incisures of
the lateral field, slightly expanded lip region, short posterior uterine
branch, anterior position of the excretory pore, and four mucrones on
the terminus.

Summer dwarf of strawberries

Aphelenchoides besseyi was named in honor of E. A. Bessey, who observed it attacking strawberries in the Southeastern states as early as
1901, according to Christie and Stevens (1933). Doubtless, it had been
prevalent for many years previous to that time. Plakidas (1928) studied
the disease, named it "dwarf," but failed to determine that nemas were
the causal agents. Brooks (1931) made further investigations, identified
the nemas as *A. fragariae,* and named the disease "crimp" because of the
bud and leaf symptoms. The work of Christie and Crossman (1935,
1936) and Christie (1938) indicated that the nemas attacking strawberries
in the Southeastern states were different from those in the Northeast,
which produced a disease known as "spring dwarf," or "crimp," as previously recorded. Christie found that plants transferred from North
Carolina to Massachusetts developed characteristic symptoms in July and
August of the first year, but the populations disappeared during the two
following years. After more critical morphological studies Christie (1942)
established the species *A. besseyi* for the form causing summer dwarf in
the southeastern United States. This diagnosis was emended by Allen
(1952a).

Symptoms: Plakidas (1928) states that the leaves of infested plants are
deformed and reduced in size. Petioles are short and leaflets rather
elongated in comparison with their width. Leaves are often unsymmetrical, usually crinkled, with margins cupping upward in young leaves,
downward in older ones. In extreme cases leaves are merely rudimentary
and make no growth. Older leaves are slightly greener than normal and
more shiny. Petioles, veins, and underside of leaflets are often reddish
purple. Infested leaves are distinctly more brittle than normal ones.
If the main bud is killed, the plant may fail to produce more leaves and

often dies. In some instances, adventitious buds develop to perpetuate a deformed, weak plant.

Mother plants with summer dwarf usually transmit the disease to all daughter plants, although occasionally a few individuals are not infested. Root systems remain normal unless top growth is greatly reduced or destroyed. Plakidas states that the Klondike variety is almost always infested, with losses of 10 to 20 per cent unless careful roguing is done.

Distribution: The range of *Aphelenchoides besseyi* on strawberries now extends along the Atlantic coast from Florida to Maryland. Numerous infestations have been reported from states as far west as Arkansas, Missouri, and Oklahoma. Infested plants doubtless have been, and will continue to be, reponsible for this widespread dissemination.

White tip of rice

Dastur (1936) published an account of a widespread rice disease in the Central provinces of India, where it had reached epidemic proportions in 1934. His detailed account of the symptoms and description of an *Aphelenchoides* sp. associated with them leaves little, if any, doubt as to the nema involved. In Japan Yoshii (1946) reported a similar disease of rice, also associated with a nema, which he mentioned as *Aphelenchoides oryzae* Yokoo, 1946. However, Yokoo did not publish the description until 1948. Cralley (1949) reported finding a nema similar to that described by Yokoo associated with white tip of rice in Arkansas. This disease caused severe losses in Arkansas, Louisiana, and Texas during the decade 1935 to 1945. Timm (1955) reported its presence in East Pakistan. Identification of the species as *A. besseyi* was made by Allen (1952).

Biology: *Aphelenchoides besseyi* is carried beneath the hull of the rice kernel in a quiescent, immature, usually preadult stage. In this state the nemas may lie dormant as long as 23 months. Since only an average of five or six nemas are present in each seed, there is no apparent damage to the young plant. When the seed is planted and sprouts, the nemas revive and move to the growing points of the leaves and stems, where they feed ectoparasitically. Apparently, most eggs are deposited in leaf axils or in panicles, and several generations occur each season. Reproduction follows plant growth, and the nemas move upward as leaves and tillers develop. Movement from one part of the plant to another is restricted to periods when a film of moisture is present following rain, dew, or high humidity. Finally, many members of the colony find their way into the panicles, and some eventually become located inside the hulls.

Nature of the injury to plant tissues has not been determined. Probably it consists in cell destruction by puncturing, injection of salivary secretions, and withdrawal of the contents. This conclusion is indicated by the brown necrotic lesions which appear after feeding has taken place on the leaf tips, in leaf axils, and in the deformed tissues of the panicles.

Symptoms: Rice varieties show different reactions to the parasite. Leaf tips of susceptible varieties may be white or yellow for an inch or two. Later these areas become brown or black as necrosis sets in. Tips of developing leaves may be twisted and wrinkled. The flag leaf may be twisted about the panicle until it interferes with development. General stunting of the plant accompanies leaf injury. Panicles are shorter and spikelets reduced in number. Terminal tissues of the panicles are severely reduced and produce small deformed kernels. Maturity of panicles is delayed, and secondary panicles may arise from lower nodes if the panicle is sterile.

Control: *Resistant varieties.* Dastur observed that certain varieties were less affected than others during the epidemic in Chatisgarh District in 1934. Practically every plant in every field of Ludka was diseased, while Gurmatria and Chinoor showed very little damage. Jordon (1935) recognized white tip as a problem in rice breeding but failed to determine the causal organism. During the following years he and numerous other workers found that certain varieties and selections reacted in varying degrees to white tip. Atkins and Todd (1959) reported that, in their extensive three-year tests, yields were reduced 17 per cent in susceptible varieties but only 7 per cent in resistant ones. Varieties like Early Prolific and Blue Rose were especially susceptible, while Bluebonnet 50, Fortuna, Texas Patna, and others were very resistant.

Goto and Fukatsu (1956) found that field experiments demonstrated important differences in resistance of varieties in the Tokai-Kinki region of Japan. Among twenty varieties tested, Tosan 38 showed no symptoms of white tip during three years of testing. Other varieties showed different degrees of resistance, while some were most susceptible. These workers found that specimens of *Aphelenchoides oryzae* from susceptible varieties were larger than those from resistant. They also demonstrated that certain varieties supported populations of *A. oryzae* without developing white tip symptoms.

Warm-water treatment. Cralley (1949) reported good control of white tip in greenhouse tests by immersing seed in water at 52 to 53°C for 15 minutes. Other workers used certain variations of Cralley's method, including presoaking. Todd and Atkins (1959) reviewed the several methods and advised 15 minutes at 55 to 61°C without presoaking. Since only limited quantities of seed can be processed in this manner, the method is of value only in denematizing small lots of valuable seed used for experimental purposes or for foundation stock. Ample supplies of certified seed are now generally available for commercial field plantings. In the United States the use of certified seed has almost eliminated the pest from a large portion of its range.

Seeding methods. Cralley (1957) found that rice seeded in water was much less severely infested than that drilled and flooded, or drilled and flooded when 3 or 4 inches high. Probably the quiescent nemas revive when immersed, begin moving about, leave the seed, and are lost in the water before the seeds sprout.

Methyl bromide. Tests by Todd and Atkins and other workers have demonstrated that methyl bromide is an effective nematicide. However, germination was reduced if the moisture content of the seed was more than 14 per cent. None of the many treatments gave complete kill without serious injury to the seed.

Artificial propagation of nemas. Todd and Atkins (1958) developed large colonies of *Aphelenchoides besseyi* under laboratory conditions. Erlenmeyer flasks were partly filled with unhulled rice seed to which a small amount of water was added. The flasks were then plugged with cotton and sterilized. Infested seeds were placed in 1 to 1,000 mercuric chloride for three to five minutes and then washed in a 1 to 5 solution of Clorox (sodium hypochlorite). This step partly sterilized the seed without injury to the nemas. About ten of the seeds were then introduced into each flask, where they germinated, but soon dried. Fungi, usually *Alternaria, Curvularia, Helminthosporium,* or *Fusarium,* soon developed, and on these the nemas increased to many thousands, often forming lacy patterns on the sides of the flasks. Nemas produced in this manner were a satisfactory inoculum for experimental work.

Chrysanthemum foliar nematode

Aphelenchoides ritzema-bosi (Schwartz, 1911) Steiner, 1932

Synonyms: *Aphelenchus ritzema-bosi* Schwartz; *Tylenchus ribes* Taylor, 1917; *Aphelenchus ribes* (Taylor) Goodey, 1923; *Aphelenchoides ribes* (Taylor) Goodey, 1933; *Aphelenchus phyllophagus* Stewart, 1921

Morphology: $\female$: 0.77–1.2 mm; a = 40–54; b = 10–13; c = 18–24;
$$V = {}^{33-48}66-75^{14-17}$$
$\male$: 0.71–0.93 mm; a = 31–50; b = 10–14; c = 16–30; T = 35–64
Lateral field about one-fourth as wide as body, marked by four incisures. Lip region conspicuously expanded. Spear 12 μ long, with distinct knobs. Nerve ring 1½ body widths behind median bulb. Hemizonid six or eight annules posterior to excretory pore. Esophageal glands four times as long as body width. Excretory pore about 1 body width behind nerve ring. Anterior end of intestine a slender tube, joining the esophagus immediately behind bulb. Oöcytes arranged in two or more lines. Posterior uterine branch an elongated pouch, usually containing spermatozoa. Tail uniformly tapering to a peglike point armed with four small mucrones. Male tail curvature about 180° when relaxed by gentle heat. Three pairs of ventrosubmedian papillae arranged in the usual manner. Spicula simple, arcuate, the ventral shaft only about one-third as long as the dorsal.

Aphelenchoides ritzema-bosi is distinctive because of the following combination of characters: large size, four incisures in lateral fields, prominent expanded lip region, position of excretory pore well behind nerve ring, hemizonid posteriorly adjacent to excretory pore, multiple rows of oöcytes, and four small mucrones on the peglike terminus. Terminal mucrones of both males and females vary considerably in size and form. Curvature of male tails occasionally is more or less than the 180° arc. However, male tail form is indicative of the species but should

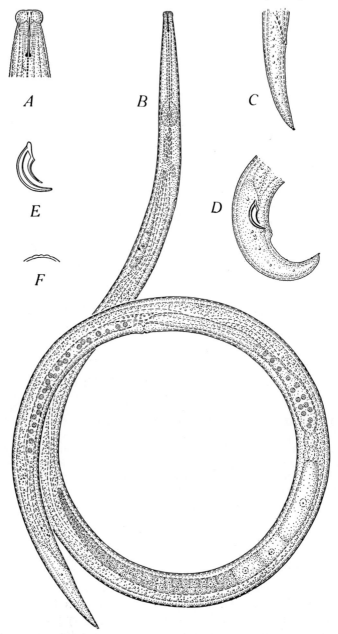

Fig. 15-11. *Aphelenchoides ritzema-bosi.* *A*—Head. *B*—Female. *C*—Female tail. *D*—Male tail. *E*—Spiculum. *F*—Cross section of lateral field. (*After Allen. Courtesy of Helminthological Society of Washington.*)

be used only in conjunction with other more reliable characters. The above description is largely from Allen.

In many reports this species has doubtless been confused with *Aphelenchoides fragariae* because of overlapping host ranges. Allen examined specimens from chrysanthemum, gooseberry, gloxinia, strawberry, lupine, *Campanula, Mimulus,* and *Saintpaulia* from the United States and chrysanthemum, strawberry, and black currant from England. There were variations in size and body proportions between the different populations. However, within populations there also were variations which gave overlapping measurements between the various groups. Host specificity did not constitute a diagnostic characteristic.

Historical: The first records of nemas infesting chrysanthemums appeared in 1890. Halstead in New Jersey and an anonymous writer in *Gardeners' Chronicle* in England both observed damage and determined that nemas were present. During the following two decades numerous reports indicated that they were widespread both in Europe and in the United States. Usually they were recorded as *Aphelenchus olesistus* or *A. ormerodis.* Marcinowski (1909) made numerous attempts to control infestations with chemicals, none of which were satisfactory. She also immersed plants in water at various temperatures for 1 to 10 minutes and found that 5 minutes at 50°C (122°F) gave satisfactory control.

Schwartz (1911) recognized that typical nemas from chrysanthemums were different from those found in strawberry and fern and named the species *Aphelenchus ritzema-bosi.* Stewart (1921) made a detailed morphological study of the species and differentiated it from *A. fragariae* and *A. olesistus.* He then wrote a description and applied the name *A. phyllophagus,* unaware of the work of Schwartz. Goffart (1928, 1930) made extensive investigations of the biology, host range, and symptoms on the various plants. Voss (1930) made additional studies on the biology and produced good illustrations of internal and external symptoms. Voss also made observations on movement of nemas in films of moisture on the plant. However, he decided that they moved against the flow of waterdrops, a theory which Wallace (1959) found untenable.

Biology: *Aphelenchoides ritzema-bosi* is an endoparasitic species most frequently found in leaves, but often in buds, growing points, and even outer layers of stems. In the Temperate Zone the nemas overwinter in dormant buds and growing points in the crown, becoming active as soon as plant growth begins. The first stems may become dwarfed, the plant thus being forced to produce other stems. Usually a good portion of these make a fair growth, but during moist periods the nemas migrate up the stems in films of water and make their way to the leaves. Here they enter through the stomata and live in the intercellular spaces of the mesophyll, where they apparently feed on the cells and cause them to break down and become discolored. First symptoms appear as spots on the underside of the leaves, which soon become brown and then black. In early stages numerous small spots are present, since leaf veins confine each colony to a relatively small area. Later the entire leaf becomes involved, dies, and falls to the ground, carrying large numbers of nemas with it. When moisture is present, the nemas move from the leaves to the crowns, remaining in the soil no longer than necessary. As infestation progresses upward, growing points and flower buds may be invaded and severely damaged. Brown (1956) reports an instance in which the nemas were carried in seeds of annual aster. In greenhouses, infestation is largely from colonies living in the crown, and it attacks new shoots as they are produced. From plant to plant the nemas may move by crossing of branches or leaves falling into the beds. The entire life cycle is about 14 days under average conditions of moisture and temperature, according to Stewart.

Control: *Top cuttings.* Christie and Crossman (1942) found that 72.6 per cent of plants from crown shoots were infested. However, among plants produced from top cuttings only 2 per cent were infested. Top cuttings are not so satisfactory as shoots for commercial production, but

Fig. 15-12. Chrysanthemum leaves infested with *Aphelenchoides ritzema-bosi*. Center leaf not infested. (*Photograph by E. H. Herrling. Courtesy of Department of Plant Pathology, University of Wisconsin.*)

they do offer an opportunity to secure relatively clean stock for foundation plantings. Top cuttings should be selected from plants growing under dry conditions; otherwise, small numbers of nemas may have worked up the stems through the moisture film.

Warm water. Marcinowski's recommendation to immerse plants in water at 50°C (122°F) for 5 minutes is still a standard treatment. Christie (1959) also advises 44.4°C (122°F) for 30 minutes. The longer treatment would be more certain to ensure exposure at the proper temperature for lethal effects. Goodey advises immersing only the aerial portions of rooted cuttings, the roots being kept wrapped in damp cotton to prevent drying while handling. Foliage was sometimes killed, but new leaves were soon produced. Unrooted cuttings did not survive treatment. Goodey also found that root-stocks could be denematized in a similar manner after all soil had been washed off.

Parathion. Dimock and Ford (1949) accidentally discovered that Parathion applied to chrysanthemums for mite control also controlled *Aphelenchoides ritzema-bosi,* which was severely infesting the plants. After additional experiments they announced (1950) that best results were obtained with 0.25 pound of active wettable powder to 100 gallons water. When this mixture was applied at weekly intervals, nearly perfect control was secured with four applications. Thorough dispersal of spray over the foliage is essential. More nemas would probably be on the surface during periods of high humidity, and they would then be more vulnerable to Parathion.

Sanitation. Thorough cleaning up and burning of all infested plant material are essential in all control programs. Soil fumigation or steam sterilization of greenhouse beds should follow the cleanup operation.

Resistant varieties. Molz (1909) reported 5 varieties of chrysanthemums which were not attacked. However, Goffart (1930) tested about 100 varieties and found that there were differences in susceptibility but that all were infested to some degree. Varieties with large blooms appear to be more susceptible than those with small flowers.

Aphelenchoides subtenuis (Cobb, 1926) Steiner and Buhrer, 1932a

Synonyms: *Aphelenchus subtenuis* Cobb; *Aphelenchoides hodsoni* Goodey, 1935

Morphology: ♀: 0.87–1.15 mm; a = 44–57; b = 12–17; c = 24–28; V = $^{44-58}7_0{}^{12-16}$

♂: 0.87–0.95 mm; a = 57–68; b = 12–14; c = 21–28; T = 62–70
Lateral field marked by four incisures. Lip region set off by distinct expansion. Labial framework delicate. Spear 11 μ long, with small but distinct knobs. Nerve ring about one body width behind median bulb. Excretory pore slightly anterior to region of nerve ring. Esophageal gland lobes extending back over intestine about five times body width. Oöcytes arranged in tandem. Posterior uterine branch reaching halfway to tail, often serving as a storage place for spermatheca. Female tail tapering to a blunt terminus bearing a single ventral mucro. Male tail curved about 180° when relaxed, bearing the

usual three pairs of ventrosubmedian papillae. Spicula of the usual type in leaf and bud nemas.

Aphelenchoides subtenuis is distinctive because of the following combined morphological characters: rather large size; four lines in lateral field; expanded lip region; position of excretory pore; long posterior uterine branch; single mucro on the blunt, rounded tail.

Habitat: Described by Cobb from narcissus bulbs. At one time the nema was frequently encountered in the Pacific Northwest. The above description is largely from Allen and is based on specimens from England. Steiner and Buhrer demonstrated that this species was the causal agent of brown ring symptoms similar to those produced by *Ditylenchus dipsaci*. At no time has the species been known to assume economic importance as a parasite of narcissi.

Genus *Rhadinaphelenchus* J. B. Goodey, 1960

Diagnosis: Aphelenchoidinae. Very slender nemas. Cephalic framework composed of strong sclerotized arches which are much more prominent than those of other members of the family. Spear bearing well-developed knobs which may be obscure, especially on immature specimens. Median bulb about twice as long as wide, with valve posterior to center. Ovary outstretched. Oviduct forming a spermatheca. Uterus a thick-walled, compact organ, as illustrated. Vulva with wide, overlapping flap. Vagina a curved tube from which the anterior gonad leads forward, while the terminal portion bends back to join the posterior uterine branch. This rudimentary, pouchlike organ extends about three-fourths the distance to the anal region and serves as a spermatheca. Female tail elongated to a small, rounded terminus. Male tail strongly arcuate, bearing four pairs of ventrosubmedian papillae and a sclerotized, spadelike terminal portion similar to that of *Bursaphelenchus*. Spicula slightly arcuate, with prominent rostrum. Ventral element of spiculum extended back over posterior portion, an arrangement which differs from that found in any other genus of the family.

Rhadinaphelenchus is distinctive because of the very slender body, massive sclerotization of the labial arches, elongated median bulb, wide vulvar flap, unusual curved vagina, spiculum form, and sclerotized spadelike extension of male tail. No other genus of the superfamily has such outstanding diagnostic characters.

Type species: *Rhadinaphelenchus cocophilus* (Cobb, 1919) J. B. Goodey, 1960

Synonyms: *Aphelenchus cocophilus* (Cobb); *Aphelenchus (Chitinoaphelenchus) cocophilus* (Cobb) Micoletzky, 1922; *Aphelenchoides cocophilus* (Cobb) T. Goodey, 1933; *Chitinoaphelenchus cocophilus* (Cobb) Corbbett, 1959

Coconut nema, *Rhadinaphelenchus cocophilus* (Cobb)

Morphology: ♀: 1.2 mm; a = 69; b = 8.4; c = 12; V = $^{35}65^{20}$
  ♂: 1.0 mm; a = 65; b = 7.8; c = 19; T = 42

Characters of the genus. Lateral fields, deirids, and phasmids not seen. Lip region set off by slight narrowing of body contour. Spear with strong basal knobs and conspicuous protrudor muscles. Nerve ring about half as wide as body. Excretory pore about two body widths behind bulb. Lobes of esophageal glands extending back a distance equal to five or six times body width. Hemizonid about one-half body width behind excretory pore. Oöcytes arranged in single file. Male tail often bent into a complete circle in fixed specimens. Four pairs of obscure ventrosubmedian papillae present, arranged as illustrated. Sclerotized terminal flange almost as wide as body when seen from a dorsal view. Copulatory muscles a prominent feature of the tail.

Historical: Association of red ring disease of coconuts with nemas was first reported by Nowell (1919) on the island of Grenada, British West Indies. According to Nowell, other workers had reported similar symptoms as early as 1905 but had failed to determine the causal agent. Cobb (1919) studied specimens submitted by Nowell and described the species as *Aphelenchus cocophilus*. Nowell (1920) demonstrated pathogenicity of the nemas and made further observations of the symptoms (1923). Ashby (1924) gave a review of previous work and included data from his own experiments. Once the nature of the disease was discovered, there were numerous reports of its presence in different localities during the ensuing years. Little information has since been added to that contained

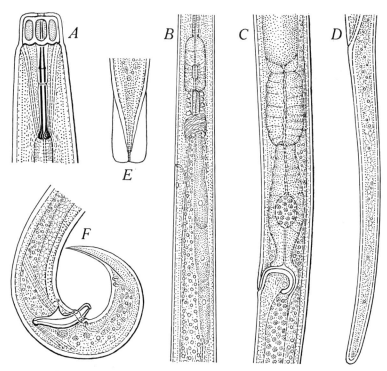

Fig. 15-13. *Rhadinaphelenchus cocophilus. A*—Head. *B*—Region of esophageal glands. *C*—Vulva and uterine region. *D*—Female tail. *E*—Ventral view of male tail. *F*—Posterior portion of male.

in these early papers. The disease remains a constant threat to the industry, even though heavy investments have been made in efforts to devise control methods.

Symptoms: External symptoms associated with the nemas are not specific, since certain other palm diseases have similar manifestations. However, the following usually indicate that nemas are present: Yellowing and browning of the leaves begin at the base of the tree and progress upward until the leaves die, break, and hang down. Withering and death of the growing point and inflorescence follow, and then the tree dies. Leaves split lengthwise and exhibit yellow to dull red streaks and mottling along a branch for a distance of 6 inches to 2 feet from the tree. Often this condition is succeeded by a soft brown rot of secondary origin. Occasionally trees may harbor considerable infestation without showing external symptoms.

Internal symptoms are more definite. A cross section exhibits a dull red ring 1 to 2 inches wide and about 2 inches in from the periphery. The condition may extend from the base up the trunk to a height of 4 feet or more, then break into red streaks and scattered red dots reaching to the growing point. Apparently the ring originates at the base of the trunk or extends down to that point soon after infestation occurs. Nemas may be found in tissues adjacent to the ring.

Red ring is typically a disease of adolescent trees four to ten years old. Very young and older trees are rarely attacked. Trees just before or entering the bearing stage are especially susceptible. Bearing trees may first drop nuts in various stages of growth. Withering of the inflorescences follows, and then leaf symptoms develop.

Roots are infested to varying degrees and exhibit discolored tissues between the hard cortex and internal strand. There appears to be no conclusive evidence that the nemas pass from the roots up through the bole into the trunk or from the trunk down into the roots. As roots become severely damaged, the nemas probably move out into the soil in search of uninfested roots.

Cobb (1922a) reported that in searching for a carrier of *Rhadinaphelenchus cocophilus* he had found:

> . . . A large palm weevil, common wherever coconuts are grown, feeds on the tissue and lays its eggs in the trunk. An examination showed that 50 per cent of these beetles carried the nematode. Whenever a palm is cut the weevils assemble rapidly to feed, thereby gaining access to the diseased tissue which has an ethereal odor. When the hairy mouth parts of the weevil are thrust into the diseased tissue, the nematodes are transferred to the hairs and also get onto the hairs of the legs. The transfer of the nematode is, therefore, purely mechanical. The nematodes spread best in humid environments.

The weevil referred to was *Rhyncophorus palmarum*.

Since Cobb made these observations, extensive work has been done on the nemic associates of insects, especially bark beetles. From these investigations it appears that Cobb determined what is probably the most common method of transporting nemas from one tree to another. Weevils visiting the trees might easily leave nemas in their tunnels, in the leaf axils, or in the cracks which usually are present at the base of leaves.

Severe outbreaks of red ring have been reported a few weeks after periods of prolonged rainfall. These may indicate that when the tree is wet the nemas move from the soil up the trunk and into the leaf axils or other points, where they gain access to inner tissues. Fenwick found abundant larvae and numerous males and females in roots and soil, and it appears probable that they may be responsible for at least a portion of the infestations.

Infestation experiments: Nowell (1920) bored holes into areas with an auger and inserted pieces of infested tissue. After 60 days the trees were cut down and were found fully infested with nemas in the trunk, leaf stalks, and heart. Conspicuous rings extended from the base of the trunks to the bud.

In another series of experiments, fragments of infested material were placed in the crowns. Death followed in 2 to 2½ months, with typical red rings extending to the base of the trunks.

Green nuts were inoculated, and a red ring developed midway between rind and shell, with a darker ring near the shell. Nematodes were abundant in these areas.

Cabbage palms 8 to 10 feet tall were inoculated with pieces of tissue and in less than three weeks were completely infested. Grugru palms 30 feet tall were inoculated in the crowns, and in eight months the nemas had reached the base of the trees.

Distribution: Since its discovery in the Lesser Antilles, *Rhadinaphelenchus cocophilus* has been recognized at various points along the south and west shores of the Caribbean Sea. Infestations have been reported from Trinidad, British Guiana, Venezuela, Panama, Honduras, and British Honduras. A southern extension of the range of the nema reaches down the northeast coast of Brazil to San Salvador. Investigations will doubtless reveal its presence in many other areas of tropical America.

Genus *Bursaphelenchus* Fuchs, 1937

Synonym: *Aphelenchoides (Bursaphelenchus)* Rühm, 1956

Diagnosis: Aphelenchoidinae. Male tail with thin, sclerotized terminal extension, forming a spadelike clasping organ. Spicula usually with prominent rostrum. Female tail conoid to blunt, rounded terminus. Lateral fields rarely visible. Lip region set off by expansion with well-sclerotized framework. Spear plain or with very small basal thickenings. Median bulb ovate, with valve near center. Excretory pore opposite base of median bulb. Hemizonid about one body width posterior to excretory pore. Ovary outstretched, the oöcytes in single file. Spermatozoa often present in uterine tract. Posterior uterine branch an elongated pouch in which spermatozoa are often present. Two to four pairs of ventrosubmedian papillae usually a prominent feature of male tail.

Type species: *Bursaphelenchus piniperidae* Fuchs, 1937

The name *Bursaphelenchus* is somewhat misleading, because the thin, flat, sclerotized extension of the male tail is not homologous with the true bursa of tylenchs. The group is very distinct and merits full generic standing. Rühm erred in reducing it to subgeneric status. About twenty species are known, all of them associates of insects, especially bark beetles of various genera. The following species is representative of the genus:

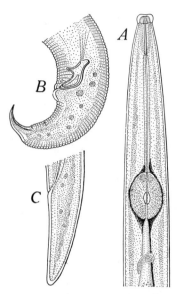

Fig. 15-14. *Bursaphelenchus talonus.* A—Anterior portion of body. B, C—Male and female tails. (*After Thorne. Courtesy of Nematology Section, U.S. Department of Agriculture.*)

Bursaphelenchus talonus (Thorne, 1935) Goodey, 1960a

Synonyms: *Aphelenchoides talonus* Thorne; *Aphelenchoides (Bursaphelenchus) talonus* Thorne, Rühm, 1956

Morphology: ♀: 0.8 mm; a = 37; b = 7.7; c = 20; V = $^{55}75^{15}$

♂: 0.8 mm; a = 39; b = 7.1; c = 18; T = 67

With characters of the genus. Lateral fields about one-eighth as wide as body, bordered by fine, bright lines, visible only on favorable specimens. Lip region caplike, with well-sclerotized framework. Spear about 15 μ long, without basal thickenings. Ovary sometimes reflexed a short distance. Esophageal gland lobes not greatly developed, obscure. Spermatozoa often present in uterus. Posterior uterine branch extending about two-thirds the distance to anal region. Male tail with talon-like terminus bearing the sclerotized, spadelike terminal process. Three pairs of ventrosubmedian papillae present, one about opposite middle of spicula and two near the base of the talonlike tail terminus. Spicula plump, short, and mitten-shaped.

Habitat: A frequent associate of the mountain pine beetle, *Dendroctonus monticolae,* and other related species in Utah. At least two other unidentified species are occasionally found associated with *Bursaphelenchus talonus.* Nothing is known of its life history, feeding habits, or how it is carried by beetles from tree to tree.

Genus *Anomyctus* Allen, 1940

Diagnosis: Aphelenchoidinae. Lateral field marked by three incisures. Lip region set off by constriction, bearing a shallow, bowl-shaped frontal disc. Spear linear, without basal swellings. Dorsal esophageal gland greatly developed, the two submedian ones small, obscure, and not extending far from the median

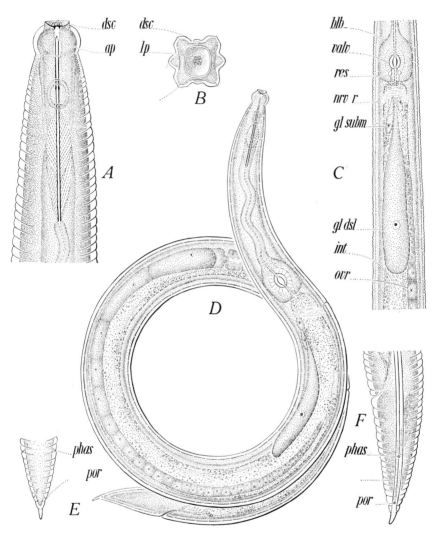

Fig. 15-15. *Anomyctus xenurus.* *A*—Head. *B*—Face view. *C*—Esophageal gland region. *D*—Female. *E*—Dorsal view of tail. *F*—Lateral view of tail. *(After Allen. Courtesy of Helminthological Society of Washington.)*

bulb. Intestine very broad, as it attaches to median bulb. Ovary single, out-stretched. Posterior uterine branch rudimentary, pouchlike, serving as a sper-matheca.

Type species: *Anomyctus xenurus* Allen, 1940

Morphology: ♀: 0.68 mm; a = 28; b = 5.9; c = 23; V = [48]76[6]
Characters of the genus as outlined above. Head nearly half as wide as neck base. Body practically cylindroid from base of neck to anal opening. Annules adjacent to lips about 0.3 μ wide, then increasing in width until 1.6 μ at base of spear and 1.8 μ near vulva. Six prominent lips are visible from a face view. An inner circlet of six tiny liplets surrounding the oral opening in the heavily sclerotized, bowl-like frontal disc. Amphid apertures located on outer margins of lateral lips. One papilla visible on each submedian lip. Ovary extending forward to near nerve ring, the oöcytes arranged in single file. Tail convex-conoid to a pointed terminus. Phasmids near middle of tail, and caudal pores near its terminus.

Habitat: Soil about desert plants west of Utah Lake, Utah, and culti-vated fields of the San Joaquin Valley, California.

Genus *Seineura* Fuchs, 1931

Diagnosis emended: Aphelenchoidinae. Tails of both sexes elongate-conoid or filiform to acute terminus. Lateral fields often obscure, marked by two to four incisures, visible only on favorable specimens. Deirids and phasmids not recorded. Lip region without refractive oral armature like that of *Aphelen-choides*. Cephalic framework generally obscure. Spear plain, with broad lumen, occasionally with small basal thickenings. Median esophageal bulb generally longer than wide, the anterior portion a hyaline storage chamber for dorsal salivary gland secretions. Intestine broad where it joins the median bulb. Nerve ring usually not more than one body width posterior to bulb. Hemizonid posterior to excretory pore a distance which may vary from one-half to two body widths. Ovary outstretched, with oöcytes in single file or multiple rows. Posterior uterine branch usually an elongate pouch in bisexual species, short and collapsed in monosexual forms. Male tail arcuate, with two to four pairs of ventrosubmedian papillae which frequently are difficult to see. Spicula with prominent ventral rostrum.

Type species: *Seineura mali* Fuchs, 1931

Seineuras are immediately recognized among other aphelenchs by their tapering, pointed tails, absence of refractive oral armature, cylin-droid spear with relatively wide lumen, widely separated excretory pore and hemizonid, and prominent ventral rostrum of the spiculum. Cer-tain pairs of male submedian papillae were probably overlooked by Fuchs and other workers.

Unfortunately, *Seineura* has not been accepted as a valid genus by most nematologists and has been relegated to a synonym of *Aphelen-choides*. Fuchs's diagnosis was brief but accurate and his sketches de-lineate important diagnostic characters. The above emendation of the diagnosis gives sufficient evidence to justify full generic rank.

Seineuras as predators: Linford and Oliveira (1937) made the important and interesting discovery that seineuras are predators on other nemas. By building up large colonies of *Aphelenchus avenae* and *Aphelenchoides parietinus* on agar plates, they were able to introduce seineuras and increase them to large numbers. *Seineura tenuicaudatus* and an undescribed species were especially responsive and proved to be highly specialized predators. In no instance were they observed to feed on mycelia of fungi. They readily attacked nemas larger than themselves, compensating for their small size by paralyzing their prey almost instantly when the spear was inserted. In one instance a *Seineura* only one hour old pierced an *Aphelenchus avenae* twice its own length. The prey was moving rapidly at the time and broke loose from the predator but advanced only half its length before ceasing movement, and it was then fed upon by another predator. Paralysis doubtless results from secretions of the dorsal esophageal gland which are injected at the time of attack. While actual injection was not observed, Linford and Oliveira did see the secretions flowing forward from the gland to the anterior portion of the median bulb. During feeding the secretions could be seen flowing forward toward the prey and back to the intestine as food was drawn in through the median bulb.

Christie received specimens of the species with which Linford and Oliveira were working and later (1939) reported on their identification. In this work he included a key to the nine species described at that time. The number has since been increased to about fifteen. All species probably are predators, but information is not available on most of them. In soil the writer has found them only in limited numbers, often associated with decaying organic matter, where they doubtless feed on the numerous saprophagous nemas present.

Seineura linfordi (Christie, 1939) J. B. Goodey, 1960a

Synonym: *Aphelenchoides linfordi* Christie

Morphology: ♀: 0.5–0.6 mm; a = 24–27; b = 8.5; c = 8–11; V = 71–75
Striae unusually coarse for a *Seineura*. Lateral fields usually visible, marked by four incisures. Lip region continuous with head contour, the lips distinctly separated. Spear 14 or 15 μ long, extending about one-third the distance to median bulb. Base of spear with small, thickened knobs. Excretory pore about one body width behind median bulb. Hemizonid about eight annules posterior to pore. Esophageal gland lobes three or four times as long as body width. Ovary outstretched, the oöcytes arranged in single file. Posterior uterine branch about as long as body width. Males unknown.

Seineura linfordi is distinctive because of the coarse striae, relatively prominent lateral fields, continuous lip region, short esophageal gland lobes, and a very short posterior uterine branch.

Habitat: Soil, island of Oahu, Hawaii.

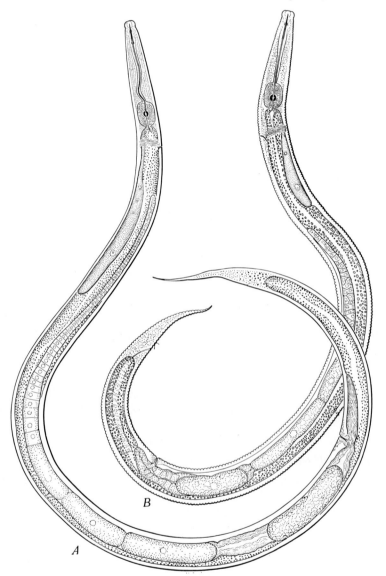

Fig. 15-16. *A—Seineura oahuensis. B—Seineura linfordi. (After Christie. Courtesy of Helminthological Society of Washington.)*

Seineura oahuensis (Christie, 1939) J. B. Goodey, 1960a

Synonym: *Aphelenchoides oahuensis* Christie

Morphology: ♀: 0.76–0.86 mm; a = 35–40; b = 9.6–11.9; c = 13–15; V = 69–75
Lateral field not seen. Framework of lip region with conspicuous arches and basal plate. Pharyngeal armature also more conspicuous than is usual in a *Seineura*. Spear 14 to 15 μ long, with small basal knobs. Excretory pore about one body width behind median bulb. Hemizonid one body width posterior to excretory pore. Lobes of esophageal glands about five times as long as body width. Ovary sometimes reaching almost to hemizonid, the oöcytes arranged in single file. Posterior uterine branch about two body widths long, ending in several cells which probably represent a rudimentary ovary. Tail with a slight constriction near the middle (Fig. 15-16).

Seineura oahuensis is distinctive because of the archlike construction of the labial framework, long lobes of the esophageal glands, slender extended ovary, posterior rudimentary uterine branch with its attached cells, and constriction near middle of tail.
Habitat: Soil, island of Oahu, Hawaii.

Genus *Laimaphelenchus* Fuchs, 1937

Diagnosis: Aphelenchoidinae. Tails of both sexes bearing three or four prominent tubercules extending radially from the terminus. Vulva with wide, overlapping flap. Ovary outstretched to region of esophageal glands, the oöcytes arranged in single file. Posterior uterine branch an elongated pouch in bisexual forms, short and collapsed in monosexual species. Spear plain or with small basal knobs. Excretory pore one to two body widths behind median bulb. Hemizonid far behind excretory pore, sometimes more than one body width. Lateral fields a plain band bordered by fine bright lines.

Type species: *Laimaphelenchus moro* Fuchs, 1937
Laimaphelenchus is distinctive because of the caudal tubercules and wide vulval flap. Fuchs states that three tubercules are present on *L. moro,* but all other known species have four. The first species described was *Aphelenchus penardi* Steiner, 1914, = *L. penardi* (Steiner) Filipjev and Schuurmans Stekhoven, 1941. Descriptions of this species and of *L. moro* are inadequate; emended descriptions from specimens collected in the type localities are desirable. Until such descriptions are available, the following description of specimens thought to be *L. penardi* is substituted.

Laimaphelenchus penardi (Steiner, 1914) J. B. Goodey, 1960a

Synonyms: *Aphelenchus penardi* Steiner; *Aphelenchoides penardi* (Steiner) McBeth, 1937; *Aphelenchus parietinus* T. Goodey, 1928

Morphology: ♀: 0.8 mm; a = 28; b = 11; c = 12; V = $^{42}65^{12}$
     ♂: 0.7 mm; a = 29; b = 11; c = 12; T = 54
With above characters of the genus. Occasionally a faint median line is observed in the lateral field, which is about one-fifth the body width. Spear 18 μ long, with distinct basal knobs. Median esophageal bulb ovate, with valve in

center. Excretory pore more than one body width behind median bulb. Hemizonid about one body width behind excretory pore. Esophageal glands extending back about six times the body width, two-thirds of this distance representing the slender ducts leading to the median bulb. Both uterus and posterior uterine branch often filled with large, granular spermatozoa which are one-fourth to one-third as wide as the body. Female tail dorsally convex-conoid to a broad terminus, ending in a cuticular stub from which four tubercules radiate. Each tubercule appears to end in an expanded, fringed, suckerlike disc. These probably secrete an adhesive exudate, since they frequently are covered with minute particles of debris which are difficult to dislodge. Male tail semicircular, with four tubercules and three pairs of ventrosubmedian papillae. Spicula massive, arcuate, with low rostrum. The male described by Fuchs did not belong in this genus.

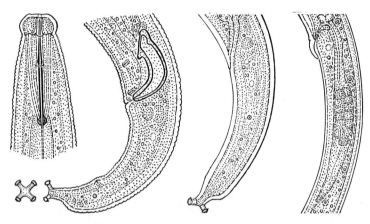

Fig. 15-17. *Laimaphelenchus penardi.*

Habitat: Described from soil, Switzerland. The above description based on specimens from frass of a beetle, *Ips confusus* (Leconte), living under the bark of piñon pine, *Pinus edulis* Engelm., collected near Tabiona, Utah. Two other species were found in similar habitats in Utah.

McBeth observed *Laimaphelenchus penardi* feeding on larvae of *Parasitorhabditis obtusa*. During feeding the nema was active and dragged its victim about. Doubtless the suckerlike tubercules act as anchors while it is struggling with its prey.

Genus *Tylaphelenchus* Rühm, 1956

Diagnosis: Nemas less than 0.5 mm long. Terminus peglike, with three tiny mucrones. Six conspicuous lips set off by deep constriction. Spear 10 μ long, with strongly developed basal knobs. Median bulb almost spherical, with small central valve. Dorsal esophageal gland less than three times as long as body width. Submedian glands lying separately in ventral portion of body cavity.

Type species: *Tylaphelenchus lichenicola* Rühm, 1956

Biology: Inhabitants of moss and lichens on tree trunks. Occasionally found in tunnels of bark beetles, Ipidae, Curculionidae, Cerambycidae. Females more numerous than males, oviviparous.

Habitat: Trees, Nuremberg and vicinity, West Germany.

Genus *Cryptaphelenchus* (Fuchs, 1915) Rühm, 1956

Synonym: *Parasitaphelenchus* (*Cryptaphelenchus*) Fuchs, 1915

Diagnosis: Robust, ventrally arcuate nemas less than 0.5 mm long. Lip region low, rounded. Lateral field a plain band or marked by incisures. Spear less than 10 μ long, with well-developed knobs. Posterior uterine branch absent, intestine ending in a blind sac, the rectum and anus being rudimentary or absent. Spicula with prominent rostrum.

Type species: *Cryptaphelenchus macrogaster* (Fuchs) Rühm, 1956
Synonyms: Synonomy extensive; see Rühm
Biology: Associates of beetles inhabiting conifers.

Cryptaphelenchus latus (Thorne, 1935) Rühm, 1956

Synonym: *Aphelenchoides latus* Thorne, 1935

Morphology: ♀: 0.5 mm; a = 18; b = 5.2; c = 13.5; V = $^{40}80$
♂: 0.5 mm; a = 20; b = 4.7; c = 13; T = 40
Cuticle with easily visible striae. Lateral field marked by four incisures. Tails of both sexes bluntly pointed. Lip region set off by slight depression.

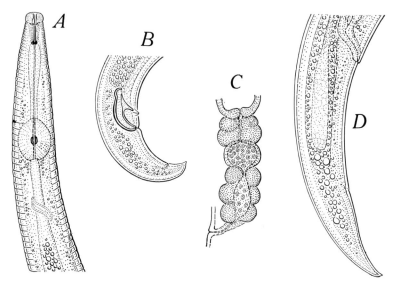

Fig. 15-18. *Cryptaphelenchus latus.* *A*—Anterior portion of female. *B*—Male tail. *C*—Uterine tract. *D*—Posterior portion of female. (*After Thorne. Courtesy of Nematology Section, U.S. Department of Agriculture.*)

Esophageal gland lobes sometimes extending back a distance equal to six or eight times the body width; their slender ducts account for about two-thirds of this distance. Excretory pore about two body widths posterior to bulb. Hemizonid two or three annules behind pore. Ovary outstretched, sometimes extending to nerve ring. Uterus made up of a few relatively large cells. A spheroid spermatheca present. Posterior uterine branch absent. Intestinal blind sac extending one-third to one-half the distance to the terminus. The writer (1935) erred in illustrating this as the posterior uterine branch. Rarely is any trace of the rectum or anus visible.

Habitat: Small numbers from frass of mountain pine bettle, *Dendroctonus monticolae* Hopk., collected from lodgepole pine, *Pinus contorta* Loudon, Summit County, Utah. Also collected by C. L. Massey in Talladega National Forest, Alabama.

Genus *Schistonchus* (Cobb, 1927) Fuchs, 1937

Synonym: *Aphelenchus (Schistonchus)* Cobb, 1927
Type species: *Schistonchus caprifici* (Gasparrini, 1864) Cobb, 1927
Synonyms: *Anguillola caprifici* Gasparrini; *Aphelenchus (Schistonchus) caprifici* Cobb, 1927; *Aphelenchoidea (Schistonchus) caprifici* Filipjev, 1934; *Pathoaphelenchus (Schistonchus) caprifici* Steiner, 1931

Morphology: ♀: 0.6 mm; a = 26; b = 5.3; c = 16; V = $^{35}72^{2.5}$
  ♂: 0.5 mm; a = 25; b = 5.1; c = 14; T = 46

Lateral fields one-sixth to one-eighth as wide as body, bordered by bright lines with sometimes two faint lines between them. Deirids and phasmids not observed. Lip region distinctly set off. A face view reveals one papilla on each submedian lip and tiny porelike amphid apertures on the lateral lips. Cephalic framework symmetrically hexaradiate. Spear 21–24 μ long with strong knobs. Anterior two-thirds of spear surrounded by a fusiform capsule. Hemizonid about one body width posterior to pore. Vulva leading in and forward to a short cellular uterus. Spermatheca spheroid. Ovary outstretched or with double flexure. Male tail strongly arcuate with ventrosubmedian cuticular ridges extending from the terminus forward around the arcuate portion. Three pairs of submedian copulatory papillae present. Spicula rostrate, arcuate. Terminus with narrow sclerotized membrane. Gubernaculum triangular with an extension extending back along the spicula. Testis outstretched or reflexed. Spermatozoa flagellate.

Schistonchus caprifici is an associate of *Blastophaga psenes* (L.), an insect which pollinates the Smyrna fig, *Ficus carica* L. The above emended description from specimens collected near Izmur, Turkey. Outstanding characteristics are the strongly developed spear, presence of a gubernaculum, and flagellate spermatozoa. Perhaps the most closely related species known is *Aphelenchoides megadorus*. Male tail somewhat like that of *Bursaphelenchus*.

Skrjabin et al. (1954) placed 10 species of *Parasitaphelenchus* in *Schistonchus,* a very questionable procedure. Extensive collecting and study are essential to establish relationships with other members of Aphelenchoidea.

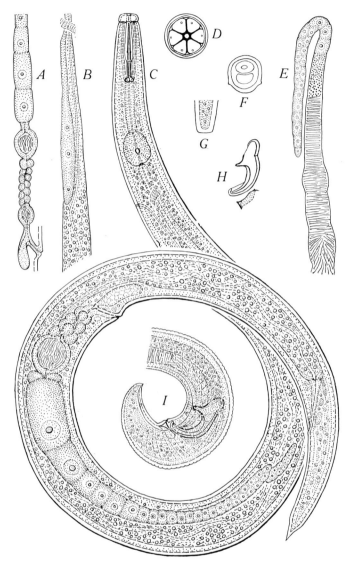

Fig. 15-19. *Schistonchus caprifici.* *A*—Reproductive tract of recently matured and fertilized female. *B*—Esophageal gland region. *C*—Female with double flexure in ovary. *D*—Face view. *E*—Testis with flexure. *F*—Cross section just anterior to spicula. *G*—Ventral view of male terminus. *H*—Spiculum and gubernaculum. *I*—Male tail. (*Specimens courtesy of Tekin Diker, Turkish Sugar Refineries.*)

Subgenus *Aphelenchus* (*Chitinoaphelenchus*) Micoletzky, 1922

Micoletzky established this subgenus for the foliar nematodes and listed *Aphelenchus* (*Chitinoaphelenchus*) *ormerodis* as first in order. Chitwood (1935) raised the subgenus to generic rank and designated *C. ormerodis* as type. The true identity of *C. ormerodis* is unknown and therefore it and the genus *Chitinoaphelenchus* must be regarded as in status *inquirenda*.

Subfamily PARASITAPHELENCHINAE Rühm, 1956

Rühm placed *Parasitaphelenchus*, *Ektaphelenchus*, *Entaphelenchus*, and *Peraphelenchus* in this subfamily. These four genera are associates of insects, and the reader is referred to Rühm's paper for details on their morphology, biology, and distribution.

Chapter 16

Order Rhabditida Chitwood, 1933

Diagnosis: Non-spear-bearing Secernentea with esophagus divided into corpus, isthmus, and bulbar regions. These three regions may be found only in the larval stages of certain animal parasitic forms.

Type superfamily: Rhabditoidea (Örley, 1880) Travassos, 1930
Rhabditida includes a diverse group of nemas with a wide range of habitat. Species most interesting to the nematologist are those of the Superfamily Rhabditoidea, which inhabit soil, decaying organic matter, and tunnels of insects. Often they follow endoparasitic nemas into plant tissues and occasionally make their way into healthy tissues without aid from other organisms. Many species of the Diplogasteridae are predators and feed on various microorganisms, including other nemas. The order includes one other superfamily, Drilonematoidea, which inhabits the body cavities of earthworms.

Superfamily Rhabditoidea (Örley) Travassos, 1930

Diagnosis: Rhabditida. Stoma typically consisting of a shallow cheilostom, elongated prostom, and a glottoid apparatus. In certain genera the cheilostom and glottoid apparatus may be greatly reduced or even absent.

Type family: Rhabditidae Örley

Key to families of Rhabditoidea

1. Lip region armed with strong mandibles................Chambersiellidae
   Lip region not armed with mandibles................................ 2
2. Stoma armed with one or more large onchia..............Diplogasteridae
   Stoma not armed with large onchia.................................. 3
3. Stoma occupying about one-fourth neck length.........Cylindrocorporidae
   Stoma less than one-eighth neck length............................. 4
4. Stoma an elongated chamber, with short glottoid apparatus.....Rhabditidae
   Stoma rarely longer than width of lip region, with well-delineated, tripartite glottoid apparatus.......................................Cephalobidae

Historical: Dujardin (1845) established the genus *Rhabditis* and described four species which he had observed. Bastian (1865) mentioned

443

a like number in his monograph. Schneider (1866) found ten species, and his extensive studies made an important contribution to our knowledge of their anatomy and biology. Bütschli (1873) listed eleven species, for which he prepared some of the finest illustrations that have ever been made of representatives of this genus. His morphological studies of the nervous and excretory systems still stand among the outstanding contributions on these subjects. Maupas (1900) demonstrated that members of the genus were easily reared in the laboratory and made extensive investigations of their reproduction. He found that both males and females were present in certain species, while in others hermaphroditism was prevalent.

Biology: Efforts of these pioneer workers in nematology proved that *Rhabditis* feed on the products of decomposition of a wide variety of decaying organic material and on artificial media. As a result of this work, these nemas have become favorite subjects for studies by several workers, including Reiter (1928), Chitwood (1930), Dougherty and Nigon (1949), and Dougherty (1954). Marked variations in size are exhibited in populations produced on media with high and low nutrient values. Ludwig (1938) observed that, when *Rhabditis teres,* = *Pelodera* (*Pelodera*) *teres,* were produced on media with different nutrient values, the means and standard deviations of several measurements were altered. Similar variations in size are often found in collections from the field, where food sources probably vary. Even in single collections, differences of 25 to 50 per cent are not unusual.

Field populations of rhabditids in temperate climates vary greatly with the seasons and the amount of organic material in the soil. Soils high in humus, especially barnyard or green manure, have enormous numbers during the early part of the season, when decomposition is taking place. With cessation of decomposition and the advent of hot weather populations decline rapidly and sometimes almost disappear. Renewed activity and a moderate increase in numbers are sometimes found during the autumn months. Most of the population usually is found in the first 4 to 8 inches of soil.

Insect associates: Many species of rhabditids are associates of dung beetles and other insects inhabiting the decomposing organic material in which they live. Larval forms frequently attach themselves to the insect body by a cementlike secretion from the mouth. Thus they are carried from place to place as the beetles fly about. Cobb (1922) observed that larvae from dung beetles were able to crawl across dry surfaces by producing an oily substance from the mouth. These larvae did not become wet with water when immersed. Cobb also found that they were apogeotropic, a habit which took them to the top of the dung heap, where they had an opportunity to reach the beetles and attach themselves to their bodies. Bovien (1937) recounts how larvae of *Rhabditis dubia,* = *R.* (*Choriorhabditis*) *dubia,* arranged themselves in the intersegmental furrows about the bodies of Psychodidae sp. They were obscured by the hairs of the insect and might very easily be overlooked or mistaken for endoparasites if the abdomen were torn apart with dissecting needles. Larvae from the beetle developed into adults in a few days when placed in dung.

Economic importance: Rhabditids are of economic importance because of their role as secondary organisms in breaking down organic material into humus and thus influencing fertility and tilth of the soil. They feed upon microorganisms which are primarily responsible for the production of humus and aid in distributing them. It is probable that they also feed on slimes, juices, and similar products yielded by organic matter during decomposition.

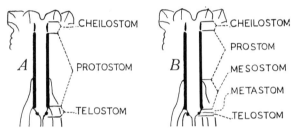

Fig. 16-1. Arrangement of rhabdions in rhabditids. *A.* According to Steiner. *B.* According to Sachs.

Nomenclature of the rhabditoid stoma: Maupas (1900) recognized that the stomatal walls of *Cephalobus lentus,* = *Chiloplacus lentus,* were divided into five segments. The writer (1925) recognized the importance of Maupas' observation and illustrated the five-segment arrangement of the stomatal plates of Acrobelinae.

Steiner (1933) determined the homologous relationship of the five segments in Cephalobidae and Diplogasteridae. For these five segments he proposed the names cheilorhabdions, prorhabdions, mesorhabdions, metarhabdions, and telorhabdions. The corresponding portions of the stoma were designated as cheilostom, prostom, mesostom, metastom, and telostom. For the assembly of meso-, meta-, and telostoms he applied the name "glottoid apparatus," which is equivalent to *Übergangstelle,* used by Sachs and Osche.

But in adjusting this nomenclature to the stoma of *Rhabditis,* Steiner designated only three sections—cheilostom, protostom, and telostom. The cheilostom was homologous to that of Cephalobidae and Diplogasteridae. However, the elongated, cylindroid portion of the stoma was considered an assembly of the pro-, meso-, and metastoms which he named the protostom. Thus only the telostom remained as the glottoid apparatus. This system of nomenclature was followed by Chitwood (1950), Goodey (1951), and Hyman (1951).

Sachs (1950) modified the terminology of the protostom to include only the prostom and mesostom. The line of demarcation between the two was assumed to be the point at which the esophageal musculature is attached to the protostom, or collar, sleeve, or manchette. According to Chitwood this is the point of separation during moulting. Osche (1953) and Dougherty (1955) followed the terminology suggested by Sachs; however, the writer has not observed this in hundreds of moulting larvae.

If one follows the reduction in length of the glottoid apparatus from *Eucephalobus* through *Panagrolaimus* to *Rhabditis,* it is apparent that all workers have overlooked the fact that this structure in *Rhabditis* is homologous with those of the other genera. It consists of sclerotized metarhabdions suspended between the meso- and telorhabdions. Thus we have a mobile masticatory apparatus bearing verrucae, denticles, or teeth, operated by strong muscles which always are easily observed. Figures 3-7 and 16-1 set forth the Steiner and Sachs theories of the rhabdion arrangements and those of the writer. After studying ample collections of rhabditids, cephalobs, and diplogasterids the reader is free to take his choice.

Taxonomy: Upward of 200 names have been recorded under the genus *Rhabditis,* of which about 150 probably are valid species. The remainder are largely in a status *inquirendum* because of inadequate diagnoses. Several instances of synonymy are also probably involved. Identification of species is complicated by the fact that no specimens have been preserved, even during recent years. Hermaphroditic females are difficult to place because in many instances generic diagnoses are dependent upon male characteristics. Spicula may be paired or fused distally. Bursae may be peloderan (surrounding the terminus) or leptoderan (terminus extending past bursa). Number and arrangement of bursal rays are always important characters. Without these guides, identification of hermaphrodites, or of females unaccompanied by males, is difficult, if not impossible.

Micoletzky (1922) assembled measurements and brief descriptions in a key which included fifty-five species. In addition he listed about twenty synonyms and other unidentifiable forms. He also reported work on producing populations for laboratory, life-cycle, and ecology studies. Reiter (1928) gave excellent descriptions and illustrations of seventeen species, several of which are included herein. Schneider (1939) gave brief descriptions of forty-three species, reproduced many of the original illustrations, and included a key to species.

A complete rearrangement of *Rhabditis* was made by Osche (1952). In this comprehensive work he assembled 150 species, which he divided into seven subgenera and nine groups. Unfortunately Osche gave meager diagnostic characters of each subgenus, group, and species and illustrations of only six species. Thus his paper was largely an index to species in their new categories, and the reader must search through scores of literature citations if he wishes to become informed on the detailed morphology of the many forms.

Osche based much of his taxonomy on the form and armature of the glottoid apparatus. He determined that the metarhabdions usually bore a certain number of minute projections which varied in form from tiny verrucae (wartlike excrescences) to slender, sharp teeth. In certain species verrucae are arranged in lines or in an arc. Denticles or teeth usually are located in a triangle of three or in lines of two or three. These characteristic arrangements are of considerable value in determining in which group a species should be placed. However, the system has a serious fault in that the numbers and arrangements of these organs are rarely seen on whole specimens. Consequently it is necessary to crush the specimen until the stoma is extruded in order to achieve identification. Even after performing this rather difficult technique the results are frequently far from satisfactory. Only fresh specimens are suitable for this operation, after which they are lost to science because they cannot be recovered and preserved. This method practically precludes the use of fixed or permanently mounted specimens. Face views sometimes show the glottoid armature, provided that the stoma is clear of detritus or other obscuring material.

Osche was too conservative in his appraisals of the groups he established and failed to give them the rank they merited. Dougherty (1953, 1955) followed with a revision of the Family Rhabditinae, in which he raised the subgenera of Osche to generic rank and his groups to subgenera. Dougherty recognized 140 species, which he distributed to fourteen genera and subgenera, and made certain alterations necessary to meet requirements of the International Rules of Zoological Nomenclature.

Status of the subgenera is questionable until more adequate diagnoses are presented. Detailed morphological studies of actual specimens may reveal sufficient diagnostic characters to justify generic standing and avoid the use of clumsy trinomials. But this result cannot be achieved until thousands of permanently mounted specimens from all parts of the world are available for comparative analysis. Placement of species on the basis of their present inadequate diagnoses is too often a matter of guesswork. Needless to say, someone must eventually assume the thankless task of monographing the group in detail before even an accomplished nematologist can attempt correctly to identify the species at hand.

The writer has been unable to formulate a satisfactory key to subfamilies and genera because of inadequate diagnostic information. Organization of the family is shown in the outline on page 448, which follows Dougherty (1955) except in the placement of *Parasitorhabditis* and *Cruznema*.

Outline of Family Rhabditidae Örley, 1880

Family	Subfamily	Genus and subgenus
Rhabditidae	Rhabditinae	*Rhabditis:* *Rhabditis* *Pellioditis* *Choriorhabditis* *Rhabditella* *Cephaloboides* *Pelodera:* *Pelodera* *Coarctadera* *Cylindrodera* *Caenorhabditis* *Cruznema* *Mesorhabditis* *Parasitorhabditis* *Teratorhabditis* *Rhabditoides* *Rhabditonema* *Pterygorhabditis*
	Protorhabditinae	{ *Protorhabditis* *Neorhabditis*
	Poikilolaiminae	{ *Poikilolaimus* *Brevibucca*
	Diploscapterinae	*Diploscapter*
	Bunonematinae	*Bunonema*

Family RHABDITIDAE Örley, 1880

Diagnosis: Rhabditoidea. Generally plump nemas, with six distinct or three duplex lips. Lateral fields usually marked by obscure incisures. Stoma composed of a shallow cheilostom, an elongated prostom, and a short, basal glottoid apparatus. The glottoid apparatus is composed of sclerotized metastoms armed with verrucae, minute teeth, or spinelike denticles. The mesostoms and telostoms form hinges which join the metastoms to the prostom and esophagus, respectively. Corpus of esophagus usually with a basal expansion. Basal bulb with sclerotized valve. Females usually with paired reflexed ovaries, occasionally with a single, prodelphic ovary, which also is reflexed. Testis single, reflexed. Males with costate (ribbed) bursae. Spicula straight to slightly arcuate, paired or fused distally. (The writer's interpretation of the glottoid apparatus is used in the above diagnosis.)

Type subfamily: RHABDITINAE Micoletzky, 1922

Diagnosis: Rhabditidae. Lip region plain, without elaborate cephalic appendages. Prostom cylindroid, strongly sclerotized. Glottoid apparatus reduced but distinct, except in *Parasitorhabditis*.

Type genus: *Rhabditis* Dujardin, 1845

Nemas of this genus represent five rather distinct groups which have been given subgeneric standing. Bisexual species are readily placed in their proper categories, but monosexual females are difficult to classify.

IDENTIFICATION OF RHABDITIDAE

Diagnostic characters: Determinations of species usually are based on certain combinations of the following morphological characters: form of lip region—rounded and continuous with body contour, or set off by expansion or contraction; cephalic papillae—obscure or setose; female tail—blunt, spicate, conoid, or filiform; male tail—peloderan or leptoderan; arrangement of bursal rays; spicula—paired or fused distally; ovaries—one or two; vulva—near mid-body or back at 80 per cent or more; relative length and width of prostom; structure of glottoid apparatus—tripartite or reduced; armature of metarhabdions—verrucae, denticles, or spicate teeth, and their arrangement.

The long-established use of the term "bursal rays" is continued herein. Actually these organs are structures enclosing the nerve fibers of copulatory papillae, as Chitwood has pointed out. The cuticular nature of the bursa is ample for its own support, and reinforcing "rays," or "ribs" as they have sometimes been named, are unnecessary.

Arrangement of bursal rays is conveniently expressed by means of mathematical formulas, as suggested by Cobb (1920a), e.g., 1-2()2-3-3. This indicates that eleven pairs of rays are present, arranged in five groups. The parentheses indicate the position of the cloacal opening.

A male specimen must be mounted in ventral view to determine if spicula are paired or fused. Permanent slides may be prepared by the following technique: Melt a tiny piece of hard glycerin jelly on the slide, and spread it thin. Heat a dissecting needle, touch the jelly with it, and immediately insert the specimen, orienting it with ventral side up. When the specimen is set, add a small drop of desiccated glycerin, apply a cold cover glass, and ring in the usual manner.

Subfamily RHABDITINAE Micoletzky, 1922

The following section presents some of the best-known generic and subgeneric groups established by Osche (1952) and Dougherty (1953, 1955). Descriptions and illustrations of type or representative species are included when available. Many groups are so poorly defined that the writer has been unable to compose a satisfactory key to subfamilies, genera, and subgenera. Admittedly, this brief outline is little more than a hunting license for the reader while attempting to identify the genus to which a species may belong.

Genus *Rhabditis* Dujardin, 1845

Subgenus *Rhabditis* (*Rhabditis*) (Dujardin, 1845) Osche, 1952

Diagnosis: Lips low, rounded, obscure. Metarhabdions with four or five minute, rounded verrucae. Tails of both sexes elongate convex-conoid to acute terminus. Bursa leptoderan, with only a short, spicate terminus extending past its margin. Spicula paired.

Type species: *Rhabditis* (*Rhabditis*) *terricola* Dujardin, 1845
Synonym: *Rhabditis aspera* Butschli, 1873

Morphology: ♀: 1.1 mm; a = 17; b = 5.1; c = 22; V = $^{30}5^{7}$28
         ♂: 1.2 mm; a = 21; b = 6.0; c = 22; T = 72

Characters of the subgenus. Lateral field marked by a single obscure, bright line. Female tail concave-conoid to an elongate spicate terminus, with phasmid at end of anterior fourth. Male tail with a short spicate terminus extending past the leptoderan bursa. Spicula paired, cephalated. Gubernaculum with

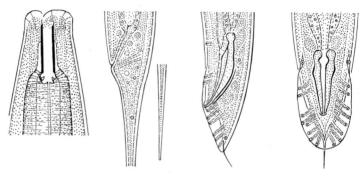

Fig. 16-2. *Rhabditis* (*Rhabditis*) *terricola*. (*Specimens courtesy of Ella Mae Noffsinger*.)

obtuse distal end. Bursal rays eight or nine, rather uniformly spaced, but sometimes in a 1-2()3-3 series. Two circlets of six and ten papillae visible on the low, rounded lips. Amphid apertures minutely ellipsoid. Ovaries reflexed, sometimes with ends overlapping.

A cosmopolitan species which is most readily recognized by the low, rounded lips and forms of the tails.

Members of the genus *Rhabditis* and its four subgenera all have paired spicula and leptoderan bursae.

Subgenus *Rhabditis* (*Pellioditis*) Dougherty, 1955

Diagnosis: Lips low, rounded. Stoma relatively shallow. Three short, spine-like denticles on each metarhabdion. Vulva near mid-body. Female tail convex-conoid in anterior half, then slender, conoid to filiform terminus. Male tail leptoderan, with only a slender, spicate terminus extending past the bursa. Spicula paired.

Type species: *Rhabditis* (*Pellioditis*) *pellio* (Schneider, 1866) Bütschli, 1873

Morphology: ♀: 1.1–2.0 mm; a = 14; b = 8; c = 11; V = 21483[30]
  ♂: 1.2–1.8 mm; a = 17; b = 7; c = 34; T = 70

Characters of the subgenus. Lateral field about 5 μ wide, with four incisures. Lips with the usual circlets of six and four papillae easily visible. Prostom only about 10 μ long and 3 μ wide. Denticles of metarhabdions small and difficult to observe. Corpus of esophagus unusually massive, almost filling the neck cavity with distinctly expanded base. Glottoid apparatus conspicuous. Nerve ring near middle of isthmus. Excretory pore opposite anterior end of bulb. Hemizonid just anterior to pore. Several eggs often present in uterus, some of them containing well-developed larvae, especially in older specimens, which may become distended and misshapen. Phasmid near end of anterior third of tail.

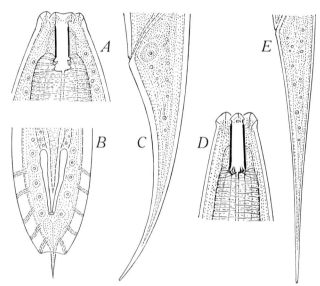

Fig. 16-3. *A–C—Rhabditis* (*Pelloides*) *pellio. D, E—Caenorhabditis elegans.* (*Specimens courtesy of E. C. Dougherty.*)

Male tail with five to eight rays; when there are five only, they are rather uniformly spaced. Bütschli illustrates the rays as arranged in a 1-1()1-3-2 series. Spicate terminus so slender and transparent that it may easily be overlooked.

A cosmopolitan species. The above description from specimens grown on *Escherichia coli* by E. C. Dougherty.

Subgenus *Rhabditis* (*Choriorhabditis*) Osche, 1952

Diagnosis: Lip region continuous with head contour, the lips conoid and prominent. Metarhabdions each with three or five small verrucae. Tails of both sexes elongated to a fine-pointed terminus. Male leptoderan, the spicate terminus extending past the bursa a distance about equal to the total length of the bursa. Spicula paired. Vulva near middle of body.

Type species: *Rhabditis* (*Choriorhabditis*) *longicaudatus* (Bastian, 1865) Osche, 1952

Morphology: ♀: 1.1–1.6 mm; a = 15–21; b = 4.9–6.5; c = 4.6–6.8;
V = 47–51
♂: 0.9–1.4 mm; a = 17–20; b = 4.6–5.5; c = 8.7–14.5

Lips with an apical circlet of subsetose papillae. Stoma almost one-third as wide as head. Glottoid apparatus very short, each metarhabdion with five tiny verrucae. Corpus of esophagus with moderately developed basal bulb. Basal bulb with strong, refractive valvular apparatus. Cardia hemispheroid. Ovaries long, slender, reflexed until ends overlap. Spermatozoa in uterus near vulva. Female tail slightly concave, then uniformly elongate-conoid to filiform terminus.

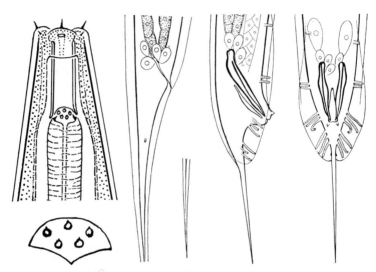

Fig. 16-4. _Rhabditis (Choriorhabditis) longicaudatus. (After Reiter.)_

Rhabditis (Cephaloboides) Rahm, 1928

Synonyms: _Cuticularia_ van der Linde, 1938; _Curviditis_ Dougherty, 1953

Diagnosis: Cuticle abnormally thick. Tails blunt, with spicate termini. Lips low, rounded. Two strong teeth on each metarhabdion. Ovaries paired, reflexed to vulvar region. Bursa leptoderan. Spicula paired.

Type species: _Rhabditis (Cephaloboides) oxycerca_ deMan, 1895

Morphology: ♀: 0.97 mm; a = 15–21; b = 4; c = 35–45; V = near mid-body
♂: 0.97 mm; a = 16–18; b = 4.3; c = 23–27

Characters of the genus. Six labial and four submedian cephalic papillae present. Amphid apertures tiny, ellipsoid, located on outer contour of lateral lips. Stoma almost one-third as wide as head. Teeth on the metarhabdions unusually strong, slightly arcuate. Muscles of the glottoid apparatus a prominent feature of the region. Apparently the teeth are used for shredding food particles of considerable consistency; hence the strong radial muscles of the rhabdions. Corpus with a slightly enlarged basal bulb. Sucking bulb with refractive valvular apparatus. Spicula slightly arcuate, cephalated. Gubernaculum plain, with flat, rounded terminus. Bursa with five pairs of rays arranged in a 1-1()3 series. At least three pairs of conical submedian papillae lie within the bursa.

The above measurements from deMan. Specimens from Wisconsin range from 0.5 to 0.8 mm long and differ somewhat in the a, b, c measurements. Probably they represent a geographical race of the type species.

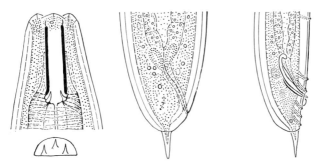

Fig. 16-5. *Rhabditis (Cephaloboides) oxycerca.*

Genus *Caenorhabditis* (Osche, 1952) Dougherty, 1953

Synonym: *Rhabditis (Caenorhabditis)* Osche

Diagnosis: Head continuous with body contour, the lips low and rounded. Two short, spinelike denticles on each metarhabdion. Vulva near mid-body. Ovaries reflexed until the ends overlap. Bursa peloderan. Female tail concave-conoid, then slender conoid to filiform terminus.

Type species: *Caenorhabditis elegans* (Maupas, 1900) Dougherty
Synonym: *Rhabditis elegans* Maupas

Morphology: ♀: 1.8 mm; a = 21; b = 6.4; c = 6.4–8; V = $^{25}52^{24}$
Characters of the genus. Lateral fields marked by four fine incisures. Lips bearing the usual circlets of six and four papillae. Prostom 15 μ long, 4 μ wide; denticles on metarhabdions often very difficult to observe from a lateral view. Corpus of esophagus with prominent basal swelling. Nerve ring near middle of isthmus. Excretory pore opposite anterior end of bulb. Hemizonid anterior to pore a distance equal to about one-fourth the neck width. Spermatozoa not seen in genital tract. Phasmids located at one-fourth to one-third the tail length. Terminus so exceedingly fine that frequently a part of it is broken off (Fig. 16-3).

The above description from hermaphroditic females grown on *Escherichia coli* by E. C. Dougherty. Nigon and Dougherty (1949) found that hermaphroditic females of *Caenorhabditis elegans* and *C. briggsae* occasionally produced males. They endeavored to make reciprocal crosses between these males and females, but in no instance did they succeed.

Genus *Pelodera* Schneider, 1866

Synonym: *Epimenides* Gutierrez, 1944

Subgenus *Pelodera* (*Pelodera*) (Schneider) Dougherty, 1953

Diagnosis: Lip region expanded, the prominent lips bearing two circlets of six and four papillae. Lateral lips smaller than submedian. Lip axils refractive, sclerotized. Stoma about one-third as wide as head. Metarhabdions each bearing three spinelike teeth. Vulva near mid-body. Female tail conoid to a short, spicate terminus. Male tail peloderan. Spicula fused distally.

Type species: *Pelodera* (*Pelodera*) *strongyloides* (Schneider) Dougherty

Morphology: ♀: 1.2–1.6 mm; a = 13–17; b = 5.2–6.5; c = 24–30; V = $^{30}5 6^{28}$
                 ♂: 1.0–1.4 mm; a = 19; b = 6; c = 22; T = 60

Characters of the subgenus. Cheilostom with refractive triquetrous wall. Prostom cylindroid with massive walls, the ventral side slightly longer than the

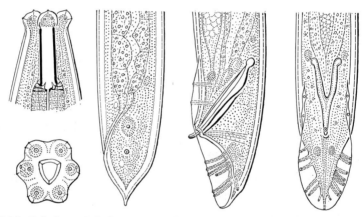

Fig. 16-6. *Pelodera* (*Pelodera*) *strongyloides*. (*Specimens courtesy of Ella Mae Noffsinger.*)

dorsal. Corpus with expanded base. Bulb with a rather obscure valve, not strongly ribbed and refractive. Ovaries reflexed until ends overlap. Female tails from convex to concave-conoid, ending in a spicate terminus. Phasmids near middle of tail. Bursa with 10 or 11 rays, usually distributed in a 2()5-4 series, but considerable variations in arrangement may occur. Reiter shows the spicula as fused through two-thirds their length, and specimens from Wisconsin are practically identical. Gubernaculum obtuse distally.

A cosmopolitan species which is distinctive because of the form of lip region and tails. The above description from a colony growing on *Escherichia coli*. Colonies from soil and decaying plant material usually show greater variations in body length.

Pelodera and its subgenera are distinctive because of their fused spicula and peloderan bursae.

Subgenus *Pelodera* (*Cylindrodera*) Dougherty, 1953

Diagnosis: Body cylindroid through most of its length. Lip region expanded with conspicuous lips. Stoma broad, slightly expanded at base. Metarhabdions each with two strong, forward-pointing onchia. Vulva near 60 per cent. Ovaries reflexed to near vulva, sometimes past it. Female tail hemispheroid. Male tail peloderan, bursa almost circular when seen from a ventral view, the type species bearing 10 pairs of rays. Spicula slender, apparently fused near the distal ends.

Type species: *Pelodera* (*Cylindrodera*) *cylindricum* (Cobb, 1898) Dougherty
Synonym: *Rhabditis cylindricum* Cobb

Morphology: ♀: 1.0 mm; a = 14; b = 5; c = 52; V = $^{32}64^{26}$
♂: 1.0 mm; a = 20; b = 5; c = 27; T = 60

Characters of the subgenus. Striae excessively fine. Lateral fields not observed. Lips with the usual two circlets of 6 and 10 papillae. Amphid apertures

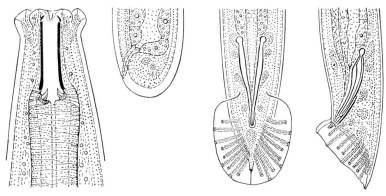

Fig. 16-7. *Pelodera* (*Cylindrodera*) *cylindrica.*

high on the outer contour of lateral lips. Cheilostom very shallow. Stoma almost one-third as wide as head. Glottoid apparatus more highly developed than that of any other rhabditid. Corpus of esophagus with well-developed basal swelling. Isthmus about as long as corpus. Excretory pore about opposite basal bulb. Valve of bulb refractive, conspicuous. Cardia discoid. Anterior ovary always about one-fourth longer than posterior. Female rectum with broad, overlapping flap. Gubernaculum tapering to a broad, spadelike distal end which forms a trough in which the spicula glide.

Pelodera (*Cylindrodera*) *cylindricum* is an outstanding form wherever it is seen. It is cosmopolitan in distribution. An inhabitant of decaying organic material and soil rich in humus. The above data are from specimens collected in a date garden at Indio, California. Reiter reported specimens 1.5 mm long.

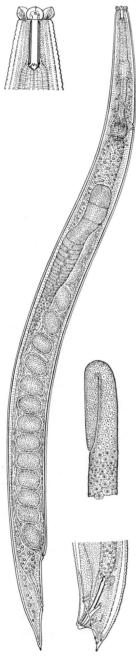

Genus *Cruznema* Artigas, 1927

Synonym: *Pelodera* (*Cruznema*) (Artigas, 1927) Dougherty, 1953

Diagnosis: Lip region expanded. Sclerotized axils between lips. Metarhabdions each with three spinelike teeth. Vulva far posterior. Ovary reaching to near esophagus, then reflexed. Posterior uterine branch absent. Female tail conoid to acute terminus. Male tail shorter than anal body diameter. Spicula almost straight, paired, cephalated.

Type species: *Cruznema cruznema* Artigas, 1927

This distinctive genus contains several related forms of which some are no doubt distinct species. Since the description of the type species is inadequate, that of *Cruznema lambdiensis* is substituted.

Cruznema lambdiensis (Maupas, 1900) n. comb.

Synonym: *Rhabditis lambdiensis* Maupas, 1900

Morphology: $\female$: 0.5 mm; a = 16; b = 4.2;
c = 22; V = $^{56}85$
$\male$: 1.2 mm; a = 20; b = 5.2;
c = 33; T = 66

Characters of the subgenus. Lateral fields marked by four bright lines except toward the extremities, where they are reduced to two. The coarse annules of the cuticle are marked in various patterns by excessively fine longitudinal lines, sculptured patterns, or punctations. Lip region set off by constriction and abrupt expansion. Each of the six lips has a papilla located near its apex and another on the outer contour. In addition the submedian lips have a third papilla, making a total of 16. This is the only species of *Rhabditis* observed by the writer on which the full complement of papillae is easily seen. Amphid apertures appear as minute crescentic markings on outer contour of lateral lips. Stoma cylindroid, slightly longer than width of lip region. Glottoid apparatus strongly developed, each metarhabdion bearing three spinelike denticles. Deirid in latitude of nerve ring. Hemizonid anteriorly adjacent to excretory pore. As many as 15 eggs may

Fig. 16-8. *Cruznema lambdiensis.* Female, head, anterior end of testis, and male tail.

be present in the uterus at one time. Females frequently viviparous. Male peloderan, the bursal rays arranged in a 2()-3 series.

Chitwood (1933a) considered *Cruznema lambdiensis* a synonym of *C. cruznema*. However, the writer believes it best to regard them as distinct species and accepts the emended diagnosis of *C. lambdiensis* as outlined by Steiner (1933).

Steiner (1933) found *Cruznema lambdiensis* in mushroom beds near Leeds, Missouri. The nemas were feeding on *Bacterium tolaasi,* for which they apparently acted as carriers. Nemas were found in small, decaying pits in the caps of mushrooms. Progress of the disease was

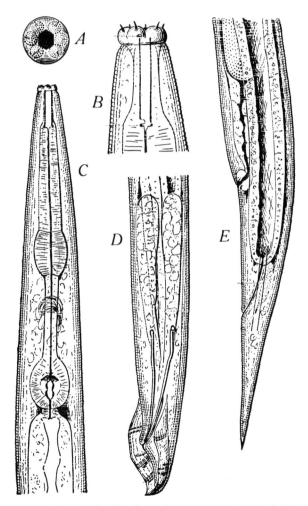

Fig. 16-9. *Mesorhabditis spiculigeria. A, B*—Face view and head. *C*—Neck region. *D, E*—Posterior portions of male and female. *(After Steiner. Courtesy of Helminthological Society of Washington.)*

marked by increase in size of pits until the mushrooms were destroyed by decay. In certain instances the entire beds in some cellars were destroyed.

Genus *Mesorhabditis* (Osche, 1952) Dougherty, 1953

Synonym: *Rhabditis (Mesorhabditis)* Osche, 1952

Diagnosis: Lips prominent, set off by constriction. Stoma cylindroid, with short glottoid apparatus. Metarhabdions each with two, sometimes three, slender denticles. Vulva far posteriad. Ovary extending forward, then reflexed. Bursa peloderan. Spicula about three times as long as anal body diameter, with distal ends amalgamated for a short distance.

Type species: *Mesorhabditis spiculigeria* (Steiner, 1936a) Dougherty

Morphology: ♀: 0.6 mm; a = 22; b = 4.7; c = 11.6; V = 82
$\qquad\qquad$ ♂: 0.55 mm; a = 19.1; b = 4.5; c = 9.5

Lateral fields marked by four prominent incisures. Female tail about as long as vulva-anus distance, the terminus varying from filiform to somewhat spicate in different collections. Male tail peloderan, the bursal rays in a 2()3-3 series. A single circlet of setose cephalic papillae. Cheilorhabdions obscure or absent. Stoma about one-third as wide as head. When seen in profile, the glottoid denticles extend in and upward with a graceful curve. Corpus of esophagus with a distinct bulb. Basal bulb with strongly sclerotized valve. Excretory pore opposite bulb. Hemizonid anteriorly adjacent to pore. Cardia discoid, four times as wide as thick. Oöcytes generally in single file. Eggs about twice as long as body diameter. Phasmid near region of anus.

Specimens from soil collected in New Jersey, Louisiana, and Wisconsin. Slight variations occur between individuals from various localities.

Genus *Parasitorhabditis* (Fuchs, 1937) Chitwood, 1950

Diagnosis: Body cylindroid. Lip region continuous with head contour. Stoma expanded at base. Glottoid apparatus absent, the stoma base consisting of a triquetrous opening with three opposed sclerotized plates which probably masticate food passing between them. Female prodelphic. Vulva far posterior. Ovary reflexed. Male with peloderan bursa. Spicula fused in distal eighth.

Type species: *Parasitorhabditis obtusa* (Fuchs, 1915) Dougherty, 1953
Synonym: *Rhabditis obtusa* Fuchs, 1915

Morphology: ♀: 0.8–1.1 mm; a = 25; b = 5; c = 56; V = [64]95
$\qquad\qquad$ ♂: 0.6–0.8 mm; a = 29; b = 4.5; c = 26; T = 60

Characters of the genus. Striae about 1 μ apart at mid-body. Lateral fields marked by two fine lines about 2 μ apart. Six labial papillae visible. Amphid apertures on outer contour of lateral lips. Corpus of esophagus with slight expansion. Isthmus same length as corpus. Nerve ring near middle of isthmus. Excretory pore slightly posterior to ring. Cardia hemispheroid. Ovary reflexed one-half to three-fourths its length. Posterior uterine branch absent. Female terminus variable, hemispheroid to elongate-conoid. Male tail with peloderan bursa, with nine rays usually arranged in a 2()3-1-1-2 series, but considerable variation occurs.

Parasitorhabditis obtusus frequently is found associated with bark beetles of different species. Slight variations occur in the various populations; yet all have a general similarity by which they are easily recognized. Fuchs names sixteen forms corresponding with the species of beetles with which they were associated. However, Rühm (1952) considered each form a distinct species, advanced nine of those described by Fuchs to specific rank, and described five new species. The writer believes that the course followed by Fuchs is preferable. The above description and figures from specimens collected in a lodgepole pine,

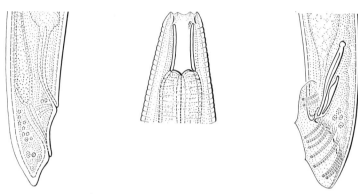

Fig. 16-10. *Parasitorhabditis obtusa.*

Pinus contorta, which had developed "sour sap" following beetle infestation. This collection and several others were made at various points in forests in Utah.

Dougherty (1955) placed *Parasitorhabditis* in the Subfamily Protorhabditinae because a tripartite glottoid apparatus is not present. However, in all other respects the genus is a typical member of Rhabditinae, and is retained in that group. True the meso-, meta-, and telorhabdions are well amalgamated, but low denticular processes are sometimes visible on the remnants of the metarhabdions. In fact, certain specimens appear to have an elongate, spinelike tooth extending up one-fourth to one-half the length of the prostom. This is best seen from a face view since it is located in a ventral recess of the stoma.

Subfamily DIPLOSCAPTERINAE Micoletzky, 1922

Diagnosis: Rhabditidae. Plump nemas less than 1.0 mm long. Dorsal and ventral lips modified into hooklike fossores (diggers). Stoma rhabditoid, with reduced glottoid apparatus.

Type genus: *Diploscapter* Cobb, 1913, a single genus

Diagnosis: With characters of the subfamily. Female tail elongate-conoid. Male tail short, arcuate, with peloderan bursa. Bursa with four to seven pairs of supporting rays. Ovaries one or two.

Type species: _Diploscapter coronata_ (Cobb, 1893) Cobb
Synonym: _Rhabditis coronata_ Cobb, 1893

Morphology: ♀: 0.5 mm; a = 16; b = 4.2; c = 7–9; V = $^{16.5}54^{13}$
    ♂: 0.5 mm; a = 16; b = 4.3; c = 19; T = 40–50

Characters of the genus. Lateral field about one-fifth body width, bordered by two bright lines. Dorsal and ventral lips mobile, enabling the nemas to dig with their sclerotized hooks. Lateral lips modified into fringed sclerotized projections. Glottoid apparatus so reduced that the identities of the meso-, meta-, and telorhabdions are lost. Excretory pore opposite anterior end of bulb. Intestine with broad, straight lumen and very narrow walls. Ovaries composed of only about a dozen developing oöcytes with very obscure nuclei. Flexed portion of ovary less than half the body width. Uterus about as long as ovary. Posterior uterus with an attached pouchlike spermatheca in which the spermatozoa are stored until they make their way out to meet developing ova. Eggs echinulate, but the spines are difficult to observe before deposition. Female tail conoid to an exceedingly fine terminus, which frequently may be broken off. Male tail with four to six pairs of bursal rays. Spicula yellow, refractive, arcuate, cephalated. Gubernaculum also yellow. Testis reflexed.

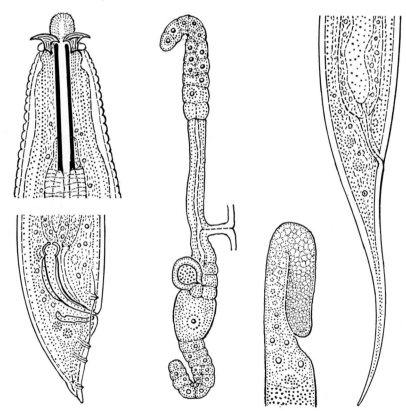

Fig. 16-11. _Diploscapter coronata._

Habitat: *Diploscapter coronata* is a cosmopolitan species. Cobb found the first specimens in decaying banana roots in Fiji. Peters collected them from the film of a sewage bed at Brent, Middlesex, England. The writer found occasional specimens inhabiting the cysts of the sugar beet nematode. Numerous other collections have been made from soil and decaying plant material.

The above description from specimens originating in a potato field near Antigo, Wisconsin. The nemas appear to correspond closely to those described by Cobb. Slight morphological variations occur in colonies from various geographical areas. Usually such variations are confined to length of female tail and number of bursal rays. Detailed studies may reveal that more than one species have been involved. Half a dozen species have been described.

Subfamily BUNONEMATINAE (Micoletzky, 1922) Chitwood, 1935

Synonym: Bunoneminae Micoletzky

Diagnosis: Length under 0.4 mm. Body plump, a = 8–16 in female, 15–25 in male. A series of wartlike tubercules extends along the left side of the body, an unusual asymmetry being thus produced. Labial prongs and lines of cuticular growths are also prominent features. Stoma cylindroid, with excessively small denticles on the obscure metarhabdions. Corpus of esophagus broad, with elongate valvular apparatus in basal portion. Spicula and gubernaculum slender, slightly arcuate. Bursa leptoderan, with supporting rays.

Type genus: *Bunonema* Jaegerskiold, 1905
Bunonemas are among the most bizarre terrestrial forms. About twenty-five species are known. Sachs (1949) divided the genus into six subgenera: *Bunonema* (*Bunonema*); *B.* (*Rhodolaimus*); *B.* (*Stammeri*); *B.* (*Aspidonema*); and *B.* (*Craspodedonema*). The advisability of six subgenera for only twenty-five species is questionable.

Habitat: Species of *Bunonema* inhabit moss, forest duff, decaying wood, and frass of bark beetles.

Family CEPHALOBIDAE, Chitwood and McIntosh, 1934

Historical: Our first record of Cephalobidae is that of Bastian (1865), who described the type species, *Cephalobus persegnis* and *C. striatus,* = *Eucephalobus striatus.* During the following years various workers added numerous species which represented several distinct types. Von Linstow (1877) established the genus *Acrobeles,* but deMan (1884) reduced it to a synonym of *Cephalobus. Acrobeles* was reestablished by the writer (1925) with an emended diagnosis and a complete review of related species published up to that time. *Acrobeles* is distinctive because of its labial processes (probolae), and the writer included in the genus all species which possessed any type of labial development. Seven previously described and thirty new species were presented in this paper.

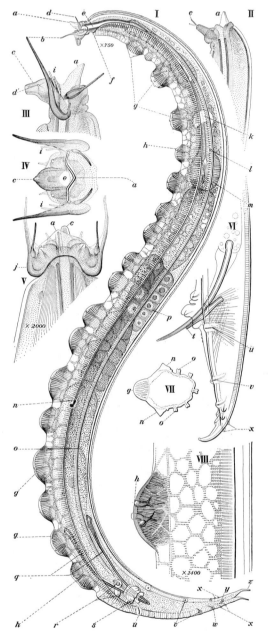

a—forward projecting membrane half encircling the mouth opening on the right side of the front of the head

b—dextral sub-median cephalic seta

c—labial tubercle

d—one of the two left-hand sub-median cephalic setae

e—pharynx

f—anterior border of the dextral cuticular armament

g—members of the dextral series of tubercles

h—one of the subtubercles

i—repetitive elements connected with the large median cephalic setae

j—saccate base of one of the largest setae

k—nerve ring

l—excretory pore

m—cardiac bulb

n—border of the dextral cuticular armament

o—median wing

p—reflexed blind end of single testes

q—spicula

r—anterior pairs of male papillae

s—right hand member of the second pair of male papillae

t—accessory piece

u—right hand member of the third pair of male papillae

v—fourth pair of male papillae

w—right hand member of the fifth pair of male papillae

x—sixth and seventh pairs of male papillae, dorsally submedian

y—hindermost pair of male papillae, subventral

z—terminus, from which the posterior end of the cuticular armament is separated by a furcation

Fig. 16-12. *Bunonema inaequale.* (*After Cobb. Courtesy of Section of Nematology, U.S. Department of Agriculture.*)

462

During the decade following the publishing of the *Acrobeles* paper, eight additional genera of Cephalobidae were established. The writer (1937) made a complete review of the family and added five additional genera. *Macrolaimus* and *Chambersiella* were transferred into the family at that time. Goodey (1943) established the Subfamily Turbactricinae and (1951) made it a member of Cephalobidae. The present composition of the family is outlined below.

Biology: Cephalobs are typically inhabitants of soil and decaying plant residues. Here they apparently feed on the products of decomposition including associated bacteria and perhaps other microorganisms. They are sometimes found in living tissues of succulent young crowns and leaves of wheat and other plants. Here they probably lead a true parasitic life but rarely, if ever, produce primary lesions. More frequently they follow plant parasitic species into plant tissues and congregate in decaying lesions. Occasionally they are found proceeding into uninjured healthy tissues.

Key to subfamilies and genera of Cephalobidae

1. Stoma much reduced, only cheilorhabdions developed. Basal esophageal bulb without valvular apparatus......Subfamily Daubaylinae, genus *Daubaylia*
   Stoma not reduced. Basal esophageal bulb with valves................. 2
2. Pharyngeal armature cephaloboid. Double flexure in ovary posterior to vulva (except in occasional aberrant specimens). Spermatheca present at anterior flexure of ovary. Annules about 2 μ or more wide..................... 3
   Pharyngeal armature panagrolaimoid. Ovary never with double flexure posterior to vulva. No spermatheca present at anterior flexure of ovary. Annules fine, much less than 2 μ...................Subfamily Panagrolaiminae 4
3. Lip region bearing three labial and frequently six cephalic probolae
                                   Subfamily Acrobelinae 13
   Lip region without probolae................Subfamily Cephalobinae 12
4. Circlet of six setose cephalic papillae present...............*Macrolaimus*
   Cephalic papillae not setose....................................... 5
5. Postcorpus of esophagus bulbar, separated by a distinct break in the corporeal lining...*Tricephalobus*
   Postcorpus of esophagus not bulbar................................ 6
6. Isthmus about as long as corpus; platelike denticles frequently, perhaps always, present in pharynx..............................*Panagrodontus*
   Isthmus much shorter than corpus; platelike denticles absent in pharynx.. 7
7. Ovary lying entirely anterior to vulva......................*Plectonchus*
   Ovary extending caudad past vulva................................ 8
8. Cheilostom hexagonal, the rhabdions conspicuous..........*Procephalobus*
   Cheilostom triquetrous, the rhabdions obscure........................ 9
9. Lips modified, flaplike, arched over stoma.................*Panagroboles*
   Lips rounded or papillate, not modified............................ 10
10. Cheilostom elongated, prostom greatly reduced...............*Panagrellus*
    Cheilostom shallow, prostom much longer........................... 11

11. Male with ventromedian preanal papilla.................*Neocephalobus*

     Male without ventromedian preanal papilla..............*Panagrolaimus*

12. Lateral fields extending to terminus, female tails blunt and rounded

                                                    Cephalobus

     Lateral fields extending only to phasmids, female tails attenuated

                                                   Eucephalobus

13. Labial probolae massive, low-rounded or furcate plates................ 14

     Labial probolae slender, furcate or elaborately fringed................. 18

14. Female tail ventrally arcuate, acute or subacute...................... 15

     Female tail blunt (except *Acrobeloides apiculatus*).................... 16

15. Female tail length less than twice anal body diameter..............*Zeldia*

     Female tail length four times anal body diameter...........*Pseudacrobeles*

16. Labial probolae, at least the dorsal one, furcate, the submedian ones usually asymmetrical..*Chiloplacus*

     Labial probolae low, rounded, not furcate........................... 17

17. Esophagus well developed, with enlarged postcorpus, cuticle near head with simple annules...*Acrobeloides*

     Corpus of esophagus slender throughout, cuticle near head divided into plates...*Placodira*

18. Labial probolae elaborately fringed..........................*Acrobeles*

     Labial probolae slender, furcate, rarely with a few branches............ 19

19. Cuticle with transverse striae only.........................*Cervidellus*

     Cuticle with both longitudinal and transverse striae.............*Stegelleta*

Outline of Family Cephalobidae Chitwood and McIntosh, 1934

Family	Subfamily	Genera
	Cephalobinae	*Cephalobus* *Eucephalobus*
	Acrobelinae	*Acrobeles* *Pseudacrobeles* *Acrobeloides* *Chiloplacus* *Stegellata* *Placodira* *Zeldia* *Cervidellus*
Cephalobidae	Panagrolaiminae	*Panagrolaimus* *Panagrodontus* *Plectonchus* *Neocephalobus* *Procephalobus* *Tricephalobus* *Panagrellus* *Panagrobeles* *Macrolaimus*
	Turbatricinae	*Turbatrix*

Diagnosis: Rhabditoidea: Armature of stoma divided into five distinct sections. Corpus of esophagus without basal swelling. Female gonad single, extending forward, then reflexed past vulva. Bursa absent. Submedian male caudal papillae present.

Type subfamily: CEPHALOBINAE Filipjev, 1934

Diagnosis: Cephalobidae. Cheilostom a broad chamber. Pro-, meso-, meta-, and telorhabdions forming an elongated, narrow, triquetrous glottoid apparatus. Ovary with double flexure in distal portion. Spermatheca present at anterior flexure of gonad. Nerve ring surrounding base of corpus.

Type genus: *Cephalobus* Bastian, 1865

Diagnosis: Cephalobinae. Tails of both sexes blunt, rounded. Lateral fields extending to terminus.

Type species: *Cephalobus persegnis* Bastian, 1865

Morphology: $\female$: 0.7–1.0 mm; a = 18–23; b = 4–4.5; c = 13–15; V = 60–63
$\qquad\qquad$ $\male$: 0.6–0.8 mm; a = 22; b = 4.3; c = 15; T = 55
Characters of the subfamily and genus. Lips low, rounded, obscurely duplex, the submedian slightly asymmetrical. Esophagus almost cylindroid except in basal fifth, where it tapers to join the isthmus. Female tail usually uniformly conoid to blunt terminus, occasionally slightly clavate. Male tail more tapering, arcuate.

Habitat: An infrequent species from soil in both Europe and America.

Genus *Eucephalobus* Steiner, 1936b

Synonym: *Cephalobus* (*Eucephalobus*) Rühm, 1956

Diagnosis: Cephalobinae. Tails of both sexes ventrally arcuate, pointed, except *Eucephalobus striatus*. Lateral fields extending only to phasmids. Nerve ring well up on base of corpus. Excretory pore about opposite nerve ring. Hemizonid posteriorly adjacent to excretory pore. Rühm erred in reducing *Eucephalobus* to a subgenus of Cephalobus.

Type species: *Eucephalobus oxyuroides* (deMan, 1876) Steiner, 1936b

Morphology: $\female$: 0.65 mm; a = 19; b = 3.9; c = 8.3; V = $^{14}60^{14}$
$\qquad\qquad$ $\male$: 0.55 mm; a = 21; b = 3.5; c = 11.6; T = 65
Characters of the genus. Lateral fields marked by three incisures. Lips conoid, pointed, with papillae well down on their outer contour. Amphid apertures slightly dorsal to median line. Cheilostom hexagonal from a face view. Prorhabdions slightly constricted near middle. Meso-, meta-, and telorhabdions of about equal length, forming an elongate glottoid apparatus. Dorsal metarhabdion somewhat dentate, a fact indicating that the apparatus functions in a masticatory manner. Corpus of esophagus slender, cylindroid, with nerve ring surrounding its base. Basal bulb with strongly sclerotized valve. Cardia conoid. Gonad with spermatheca at first flexure and double flexure in distal portion. Female tail uniformly conoid to acute terminus, usually ventrally bent in posterior third. The tail may be slightly longer or shorter than that figured. Male tail dorsally convex-conoid, ending in a ventrally bent terminus.

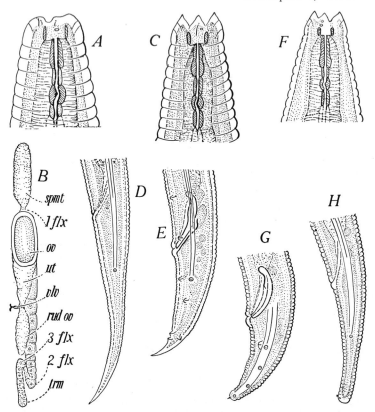

Fig. 16-13. *A, B—Cephalobus persegnis,* head and reproductive system. *C–E— Eucephalobus oxyuroides. F–H—Eucephalobus striatus.*

Six pairs of ventrosubmedian and one pair of dorsosubmedian papillae are present. Phasmid at terminus of lateral lines. Spicula cephalated, proximally arcuate, distally straight. Gubernaculum a thin, simple trough (Fig. 16-13).

Habitat: *Eucephalobus oxyuroides* is a cosmopolitan species found in soil. It does not appear to thrive in the presence of large amounts of decaying organic material. Numerous specimens were found in cysts of sugar beet nematodes in the western United States (Thorne, 1928).

Eucephalobus striatus (Bastian, 1865) Thorne, 1937

Morphology: ♀: 0.55 mm; a = 20; b = 4.1; c = 9; V = [19]61[21]
   ♂: 0.5 mm; a = 19; b = 3.9; c = 12.5; T = 70

Ventrosubmedian lips frequently smaller than the others. Only one circlet of papillae observed, and that well down on outer contour of lips. All elements of stoma well developed, the dorsal metarhabdion somewhat denticulate. Corpus of esophagus almost cylindrical to near base, then tapering to an obscure junction with isthmus. Nerve ring encircling base of corpus. Isthmus length slightly greater than neck width. Excretory pore about opposite nerve ring. Hemizonid posteriorly adjacent to pore. Female tail conoid, then cylindroid in terminal third. Terminus rounded, frequently bearing a ventrad mucro. Phasmids near middle of tail. Male tail arcuate to a mucronate terminus. Four pairs of ventrosubmedian papillae present. Phasmids near end of anterior third of tail (Fig. 16-14).

Habitat: A cosmopolitan species from cultivated and virgin soil.

Subfamily Acrobelinae Thorne, 1937

Members of this subfamily usually are found in soil associated with decaying organic material. They are typically plump nemas, with strongly annulated cuticle, and are conspicuous because of their specialized lip structures known as probolae. These vary from simple, sclerotized plates to elaborate, fringed structures. Little is known of the functions of the probolae, but doubtless they have some bearing on the feeding habits of the nemas.

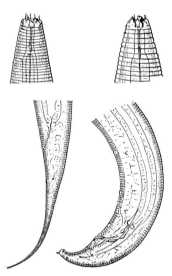

Diagnosis: Head bearing three labial and six cephalic probolae. Stoma cephaloboid, with the usual five sets of rhabdions. Female gonad extending forward, then reflexed beyond the vulva region, where a double flexure occurs. Spermatheca present at anterior flexure. Gubernaculum lineate.

Type genus: *Acrobeles* von Linstow, 1877

Genera comprising Acrobelinae form a rather uniform series of related types between the Family Cephalobidae and the genus *Acrobeles*. Therefore, they are presented in accordance with their probable relationships, beginning with the relatively simple forms of *Acrobeloides* and terminating in the highly developed *Acrobeles*. The aberrant genus *Pseudacrobeles* is presented first because of its obvious relationship with *Eucephalobus*.

Fig. 16-14. *Pseudacrobeles variabilis.* Head, dorsal and lateral views. Female and male tails. (*After Steiner. Courtesy of Helminthological Society of Washington.*)

Genus *Pseudacrobeles* Steiner, 1938

Diagnosis: Nemas closely resembling those of the genus *Eucephalobus* in general body form. Lip region armed with an inner circlet of three low, rounded probolae and an outer circlet of six spinelike processes. Stoma with five sets of rhabdions which are only slightly sclerotized. A circlet of six labial papillae present on outer contour of lips. Amphid apertures appear as minute oval markings on the lateral lips. Female tail ventrally arcuate, conoid to a filiform terminus. Male tail ventrally arcuate to a small, rounded terminus bearing a mucro. Seven pairs of submedian papillae are present as illustrated.

Type species: *Pseudacrobeles variabilis* (Steiner, 1936) Steiner, 1938
Synonym: *Acrobeles variabilis* Steiner, 1936

Morphology: ♀: 0.66 mm; a = 17; b = 4; c = 7.5; V = 60
    ♂: 0.66 mm; a = 18; b = 4.4; c = 19

Characters of the genus as outlined above. This is a most interesting form, combining characters of *Eucephalobus* and *Acrobeloides*, and has no immediate known relatives.

Genus *Acrobeloides* (Cobb, 1924) Steiner & Buhrer, 1933b

Diagnosis: Acrobelinae. Labial probolae not furcate. Cephalic axils low, rounded or extended in simple plates, sometimes apiculate. Tails convex-conoid (except *clavicaudatus*), with 9 to 12 annules. Stoma cephaloboid. Corpus of esophagus broadly expanded in comparison with that of other genera.

Type species: *Acrobeloides buetschlii* (deMan, 1884) Steiner & Buhrer, 1933b

Synonyms: *Cephalobus buetschlii* deMan, 1884; *Cephalobus persegnis* Bütschli, 1873; *Acrobeles* (*Acrobeloides*) *buetschlii* (deMan) Thorne, 1925

Morphology: ♀: 0.35–0.5 mm; a = 12–16; b = 5; c = 16–20; V = $^{20}66^{16}$

Characters of the genus. Lateral fields marked by three fine incisures which disappear on full-grown females. Cephalic axils rounded, without cuticular processes. Labial probolae conoid, varying in height among populations from different areas, rarely with bristlelike terminus. Cheilostom triquetrous. Prostom and glottoid apparatus forming a narrow triquetrous tube. Metarhabdions only about half as long as meso- and telorhabdions, the dorsal segment somewhat dentate. Basal half of corpus forming an elongated, spindleshaped swelling. Isthmus about as long as neck width. Nerve ring encircling isthmus near middle. Excretory pore opposite nerve ring. Hemizonid anteriorly adjacent to pore. Basal bulb strongly developed, with refractive, sclerotized valvular apparatus. Cardia conoid. Intestine thin-walled, with scattered, variable-sized granules. Nuclei of intestinal cells often conspicuous. Gonad typical, with short double flexure in terminal portion. Eggs completely fill body cavity and are twice as long as body width. Tail bluntly conoid, to rounded terminus, with 19 to 14 annules.

Habitat: *Acrobeloides buetschlii* is a cosmopolitan species usually found associated with decomposing organic material in soil. Often found in cysts of *Heterodera schachtii,* where they probably were feeding on the remnants of the internal organs.

Species of *Acrobeloides* are plump nemas under 0.7 mm long, except *A. maximus,* which attains a length of 1.2 mm. Form of labial probolae and tails are the diagnostic characters most frequently used. Illustrated with *A. buetschlii* are heads of *A. tricornis* and *A. minor* and tails of *A. clavicaudatus* and *A. apiculatus.* The male of *A. minor* is the only male of *Acrobeloides* the writer has seen. Three females in the same collection apparently did not contain spermatozoa; so this aberrant speci-

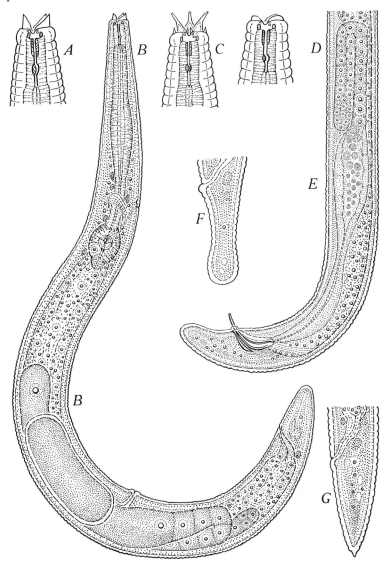

Fig. 16-15. *A, B—Acrobeloides buetschli* head and female. *C—Acrobeloides tricornis.* *D, E—Acrobeloides minor* head and posterior portion of male. *F— Acrobeloides clavicaudatus. G—Acrobeloides apiticus.*

men may not have been functional. Measurements were as follows: 0.36 mm; a = 14; b = 3.5; c = 18; T = 44. The testis was reflexed a distance equal to two times the body width.

Genus *Chiloplacus* Thorne, 1937

Diagnosis: Acrobelinae. Amphid apertures ovoid, located near base of the lateral lips. Labial probolae platelike; the dorsal one furcate, the submedian usually asymmetrical, sometimes rounded. Cephalic axils varying from rounded to flaplike, furcate, forward-pointing processes. Corpus of esophagus slender, cylindroid, except in the tapering posterior fourth, which is set off from the isthmus by only a break in musculature. Female tail slightly convex-conoid or subcylindroid to bluntly rounded terminus, generally with 15 or more annules. Male tail ventrally arcuate to small, rounded terminus. Several pairs of submedian papillae present.

Type species: *Chiloplacus symmetricus* Thorne, 1937
Synonym: *Acrobeles symmetricus* Thorne, 1925

Morphology: ♀: 0.6–0.9 mm; a = 16–20; b = 4–5; c = 17–20; V = $^{19}67^{16}$
♂: 0.5–0.8 mm; a = 19–25; b = 4–5; c = 18–21; T = 40

With characters of the genus. Body symmetrical, not ventrally contracted in vulvar region. Cephalic axils rounded, not forming probolae. Dorsal labial probolae symmetrically furcate, the submedian ones asymmetrical in varying degrees. From a face view the cheilostom is triquetrous, and the prorhabdions each bear three minute denticles about the entrance to the prostom. Dorsal metarhabdion denticulate. Nerve ring surrounding anterior portion of isthmus. Excretory pore slightly behind region of nerve ring. Hemizonid slightly posterior to excretory pore. Bulb with strongly sclerotized valvular apparatus. Cardia conoid. Gonad typical, with spermatheca at anterior flexure and double flexure in posterior portion. Female tail conoid to broad, rounded terminus. Male tail arcuate, with six pairs of ventrosubmedian and one pair of dorsosubmedian papillae. Phasmids of both sexes near middle of tail.

Habitat: *Chiloplacus symmetricus* is a widespread species throughout the United States in both cultivated and virgin soil. Specimens are practically identical to the type collected by T. Goodey in England.

Chiloplacus propinquus (deMan, 1921) Thorne, 1937

Synonyms: *Cephalobus buetschlii* deMan, 1885; *Cephalobus propinquus* deMan, 1921; *Acrobeles propinquus* (deMan, 1921) Thorne, 1935

Morphology: ♀: 0.7–1.0 mm; a = 19; b = 4.3; c = 20; V = $^{25}65^{19}$

Ventral narrowing of the body at the vulva is a prominent feature of this species. Lateral field marked by two bright lines. Cephalic axils rounded. Dorsal labial probolae symmetrically furcate, the submedian asymmetrical, of about the same length as those of *Chiloplacus symmetricus*. Esophagus, intestine, and gonad as illustrated. A sphincter muscle about the intestine midway between vulva and rectum is an unusual structure observed only in this species. DeMan illustrated a very small egg in his specimen, less than half as long as body diameter. Developing oöcytes in the same specimen indicate that normal eggs would be similar to those of specimens collected in Utah and Colorado which

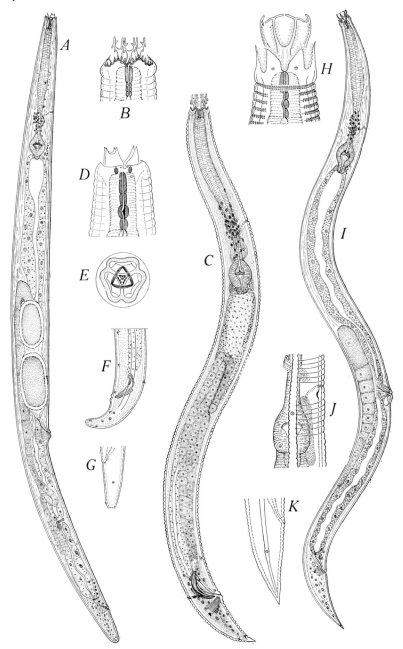

Fig. 16-16. *A—Chiloplacus propinquus. B, C—Cervidellus cervus. D—G—Chiloplacus symmetricus,* head, face view, posterior portion of male and female tail. *H—K—Acrobeles elaboratus.* Head, female, region of deirid and hemizonid, and female tail.

the writer (1925) described as *Acrobeles contractus*. This was the reason for the above synonomy (Fig. 16-16).

Habitat: An infrequent species in decaying sugar beets and alfalfa crowns in Utah and Colorado. Collected in the Netherlands by deMan.

Genus *Cervidellus* Thorne, 1937

Diagnosis: Acrobelinae. Lip region expanded, about half as wide as mid-body. Cephalic probolae thin, flaplike, inward-pointing, with plain or serrate sclerotized margins. Labial probolae slender, furcate, with simple or compound branches. Tails of both sexes conoid, acute. Small species generally less than 0.5 mm long.

Type species: *Cervidellus cervus* (Thorne, 1925) Thorne, 1937
Synonym: *Acrobeles cervus,* Thorne, 1925

Morphology: ♀ : 0.38 mm; a = 12.5; b = 2.9; c = 11; V = $^{21}64^{14}$
♂ : 0.38 mm; a = 15; b = 3.4; c = 11.6; T = 42

Characters of the genus. Lateral fields about one-tenth body width, bordered by two fine lines. Cephalic probolae forming a serrate, refractive fringe about the head, indented by the axils. Labial probolae bifurcate one-half their length, the prongs each bearing three branches. Two branches project backward, one inward. Stomatal rhabdions well delineated, the meso-, meta-, and telorhabdions equal in combined length to that of the prorhabdions. Corpus of esophagus slender, cylindroid. Isthmus slightly longer than body width. Female gonad extending forward three-fourths the distance to esophagus, then reflexed to midway between vulva and rectum. Tails convex-conoid, acute, with phasmids near middle. Male with one preanal and two postanal submedian papillae and one subdorsal near terminus. Spicula slender, arcuate, slightly cephalated (Fig. 16-16).

Habitat: Soil about foothill vegetation near Citrus Experiment Station, Riverside, California. As the name implies, the head of this tiny nema resembles the antlers of a deer.

Genus *Acrobeles* von Linstow, 1877

Diagnosis: Acrobelinae. Lip region narrowed until only about one-third as wide as mid-body. Cephalic probolae thin, forward-pointing, with elaborate fringes of almost transparent membranes which may be difficult to resolve. Labial probolae deeply furcate, with terminal branches and lateral membranes. Lateral fields with a central ridge and crenate borders. Tails of both sexes acute.

Type species: *Acrobeles ciliatus* von Linstow, 1877
Synonym: *Cephalobus ciliatus* (von Linstow) deMan, 1884

Acrobeles complexus Thorne, 1925

Morphology: ♀ : 0.7–0.9 mm; a = 12; b = 4.2; c = 12; V = $^{21}58^{19}$
♂ : 0.7–0.85 mm; a = 15; b = 4.5; c = 11; T = 48

Membranes of cephalic and labial probolae less developed than those of *Acrobeles ciliatus.* Terminal branches of labial probolae relatively short and strong compared with those of other species. However, in nemas with such elaborately developed organs there may be considerable variation between specimens from different collections, especially those from widely separated areas. Strong, bifurcate sclerotized plates lie in the axils between the cephalic and labial probolae. Prorhabdions and glottoid apparatus well developed, the metarhabdion somewhat dentate. Nerve ring near middle of isthmus. Excretory pore slightly posterior to latitude of nerve ring. Hemizonid indistinct, anteriorly adjacent to excretory pore. Gonad of usual form, with a large, pouchlike spermatheca at anterior flexure. Posterior rudimentary uterine branch about one-third as long as body width, not serving as a spermatheca. Tails of both sexes conoid to a pointed terminus. Phasmids slightly anterior to middle of tail. Male with six pairs of ventrosubmedian papillae.

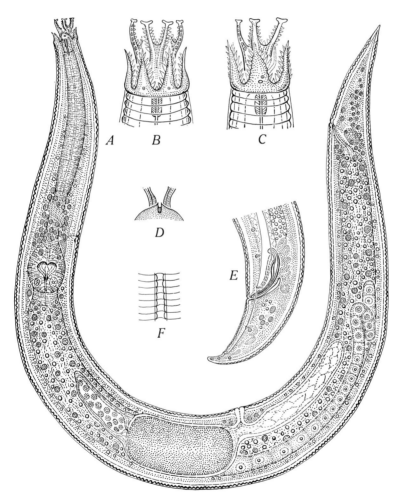

Fig. 16-17. *Acrobeles complexus.* *A*—Female. *B, C*—Head, dorsal and lateral views showing only three of the six probolar prongs. *D*—Axial structure at base of labial probolae. *E*—Posterior portion of male. *F*—Lateral field.

Habitat: A common inhabitant of both cultivated and virgin soil throughout the United States.

Subfamily PANAGROLAIMINAE Thorne, 1937

Diagnosis: Cephalobidae. Cheilostom and prostom forming a broad open chamber. Meso-, meta-, and telostoms forming a narrow glottoid apparatus. Female gonad extending forward, then reflexed straight back without flexures posterior to vulvar region. Anterior portions of uterus function as a seminal receptacle. A very short posterior uterine branch sometimes present. Annules fine, often obscure, never more than 2 μ wide. Gubernaculum appearing in longitudinal section as an irregular polygon (except *Panagrodontus*).

Sachs (1950) made Panagrolaiminae a synonym of Anguillulinae Micoletzky, 1922. This action is questionable and not recognized herein.

Type genus: *Panagrolaimus* Fuchs, 1930

Diagnosis: Panagrolaminae. Lips generally duplex, rarely amalgamated, the submedian usually asymmetrical. Inner circlet of labial papillae frequently located on outer contour of lips. Outer circlet never setose. Cheilostom and prostom combined are usually about twice as long as glottoid apparatus. Corpus of esophagus cylindroid or spindle-shaped. Isthmus one-half to two-thirds length of corpus. Nerve ring surrounding isthmus near middle.

Type species: *Panagrolaimus detritophagus* Fuchs, 1930

Because of the inadequate diagnosis of the type species, the cosmopolitan species *Panagrolaimus subelongatus* is herein described as a representative form.

Panagrolaimus subelongatus (Cobb, 1914) Thorne, 1937

Synonym: *Cephalobus subelongatus* Cobb, 1914

Morphology: $\female$: 0.7–1.2 mm; a = 20; b = 4.3–6; c = 18–22; V = $^{20}6^{27}$
$\qquad\qquad$ $\male$: 0.6–1.0 mm; a = 25; b = 4–4.6; c = 20; T = 65

Height of lips varying considerably in populations from widely separated areas. Lateral lips usually somewhat smaller than submedian. Cheilorhabdions lightly sclerotized. Prorhabdions massive, with basal expansions. Prostom triquetrous. Glottoid apparatus thinly sclerotized, the three sectors usually visible. Corpus of esophagus cylindroid to slightly fusiform. Nerve ring near middle of isthmus. Excretory pore opposite nerve ring. Hemizonid anteriorly adjacent to pore. Anterior portion of uterus forming a spermatheca. Ovary reflexed straight back, sometimes reaching almost to rectal region. Rudimentary posterior uterine branch about half as long as body width, not serving as a spermatheca. Female tail conoid to acute terminus, its length variable in different populations. In certain instances the tail may be irregularly conoid. Male tail conoid to a spicate terminus. Three or four pairs of ventrosubmedian and one or two pairs of dorsosubmedian papillae. Phasmids near beginning of terminal fourth of tail. Spicula arcuate, cephalated. Gubernaculum an elongated polygon in longitudinal section.

Habitat: A cosmopolitan species inhabiting soil and decaying organic material. Very frequently an associate of the alfalfa stem nematode in

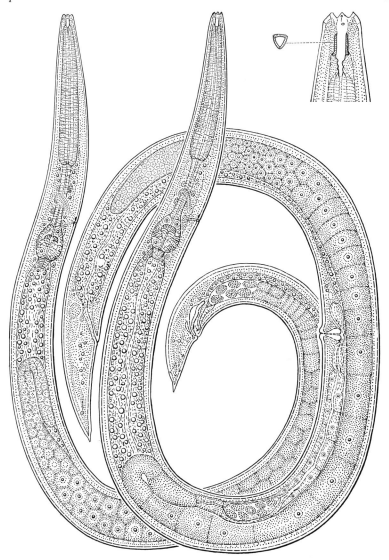

Fig. 16-18. *Panagrolaimus subelongatus,* male and female.

the western United States. Generally present in collections from high mountains. It is possible that several closely related species occur.

Panagrolaimus rigidus (A. Schneider, 1866) Thorne, 1937

Synonyms: *Leptodera rigida* A. Schneider; *Anguillula rigida* (A. Schneider) Bütschli, 1876; *Cephalobus rigida* (A. Schneider) Örley, 1880; *Rhabditis aquatica* Micoletzky, 1913

Morphology: ♀: 1.0–1.3 mm; a = 23; b = 5.9; c = 15; V = $2^{9}5^{5}9^{18}$

♂: 0.7–1.0 mm; a = 28; b = 5.5; c = 18; T = 65

Species closely resembling *Panagrolaimus subelongatus*, but with broader head, generally lower lips, shallower stoma, and more acute tails. Cheilorhabdions only slightly sclerotized. Prorhabdions strongly refractive. Glottoid apparatus about half length of prostom, with lightly sclerotized walls. Corpus of esophagus strongly developed. Isthmus equal to or slightly longer than neck width, the nerve ring surrounding it near middle. Excretory pore opposite or behind nerve ring. Basal bulb spheroid, with refractive valvular apparatus. Anterior portion of uterus forming a spermatheca. Terminus of ovary midway be-

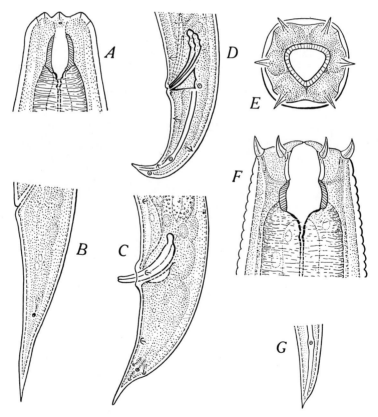

Fig. 16-19. *A–C—Panagrolaimus rigidus. D–G—Macrolaimus taurus.*

tween vulvar region and rectum, the oöcytes in multiple rows. Posterior uterine branch about half as long as body width. Male tail with four pairs of ventro-submedian and two pairs of dorsosubmedian papillae. Phasmids near beginning of posterior third of tails.

Habitat: A cosmopolitan species from soil and decaying organic material.

Genus *Macrolaimus* Maupas, 1900

Diagnosis: Panagrolaiminae? Lip region bearing a circlet of six horn-shaped, setose papillae. Head broad, with three lips arched over a wide stoma. Cheilostom as deep as or deeper than prostom. Other characters similar to those of *Panagrolaimus.*

Type species: *Macrolaimus crucis* Maupas, 1900
Representative species: *Macrolaimus taurus* Thorne, 1937

Morphology: ♀: 1.3 mm; a = 20; b = 5.9; c = 18; V = $^{15}60^{20}$
♂: 1.1 mm; a = 31; b = 5.8; c = 21; T = 57
Annules about 1.3 μ wide. Lateral fields marked by two elevations. Six forward-curved, hornlike papillae on margin of head. Details of stoma as illustrated. Corpus of esophagus cylindroid, abruptly narrowing to isthmus, which is about twice as long as neck width. Nerve ring near middle of isthmus. Excretory pore opposite anterior end of basal bulb. Deirid slightly posterior to latitude of nerve ring. Female tail tapering to an abruptly conoid terminus. Male tail arcuate, with seven pairs of papillae arranged as illustrated. Phasmids near beginning of posterior third of tail. Spicula slightly arcuate, cephalated. Gubernaculum triangular (Fig. 16-19).

Habitat: Frass of *Ips confusus* LeConte in piñon pine, *Pinus edulis,* collected near Tabiona, Utah.
The position of *Macrolaimus* is questionable. Most species have a hooked terminus reminiscent of *Chambersiella.* Perhaps the genera belong together. Both species observed by the writer were strong swimmers.

Family CHAMBERSIELLIDAE (Thorne, 1937) Sanwal, 1957a

Diagnosis: Rhabditoidea. Lip region bearing six filamentose cirri, a circlet of six setose papillae, and four low submedian papillae. Cheilorhabdions modified into six sclerotized mandibles. Stoma and esophagus panagrolaimoid. Amphid apertures ellipsoid, about one head width posterior to lip region. Ovaries one or two. Testis reflexed. Terminus hooked. Two known species, both under 1.5 mm long.

Type genus: *Chambersiella* Cobb, 1920

Diagnosis: Characters of the family. Ovary single, panagrolaimoid, or double and reflexed until the ends overlap. Male tail with about six preanal and an equal number of postanal submedian papillae. Spicula paired, panagrolaimoid, resting on a simple lineate gubernaculum.

Type species: *Chambersiella rodens* Cobb, 1920

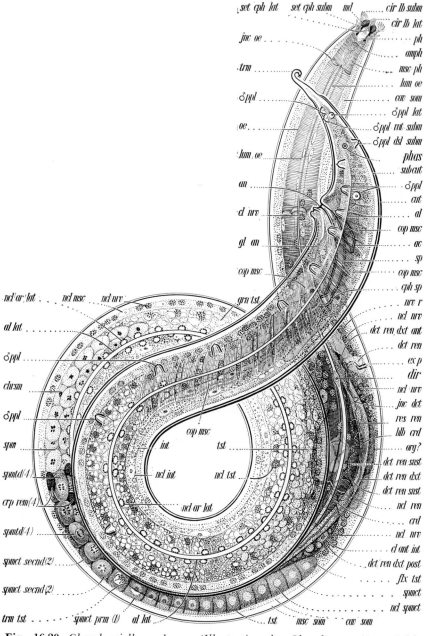

Fig. 16-20. *Chambersiella rodens.* (*Illustration by Chambers. After Cobb. Courtesy of Section of Nematology, U.S. Department of Agriculture.*)

One other described species, *Chambersiella bakeri*, has two ovaries, while *C. rodens* has only one. This genus is probably most closely related to *Macrolaimus*.

The ellipsoid, posteriorly located amphid apertures of *Chambersiella* are unique among Secernentea.

The accompanying illustration should be studied in detail, from the standpoints both of morphology and of methods of delineating the many features. This is perhaps the finest work of the master artist, W. E. Chambers.

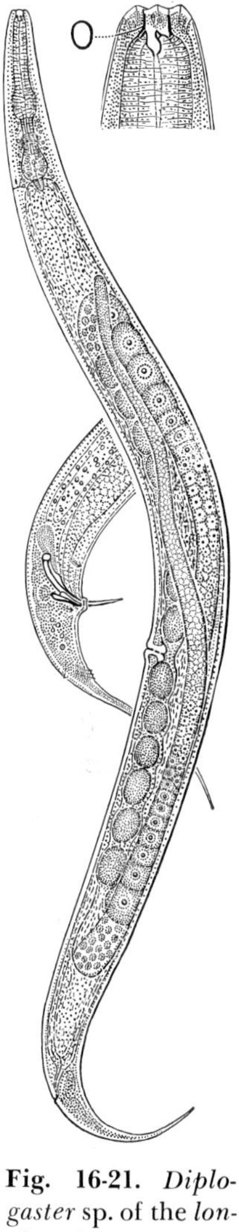

Family DIPLOGASTERIDAE Steiner, 1919

Diagnosis: Stoma usually armed with one or more strong teeth formed from modified rhabdions. Corpus of esophagus forming a muscular bulb in posterior portion. Basal bulb of esophagus without sclerotized valvular apparatus. Female gonads usually paired, reflexed, rarely single. Male gonad reflexed. Male with numerous submedian copulatory papillae. Spicula paired, generally slender, elongated. Gubernaculum in longitudinal section appearing as an irregular polygon. Tails of both sexes usually filiform.

Biology: Diplogasters are most frequently found associated with decaying plant material, often occurring in great numbers. They are common inhabitants of barnyard manure and are carried into fields when it is transported. Many species are associated with frass of bark beetles living in dead trees. Bovien (1937) observed that larvae of *Diplogaster stercorarius* and *D. magnibucca* were carried under the elytra of dung beetles, *Aphodius* spp. Many species were predators on other microorganisms, including nemas. Goodey and Triffitt (1927) and Bovien (1937) found leptomonad flagellates living in the intestines of certain species.

Taxonomy of the Diplogasteridae is in a chaotic condition, with upward of 150 species distributed through about twenty genera. Identification of species is complicated by the fact that many are inadequately described and must remain as species *inquirenda*. Generic monographs are necessary before the group can be properly evaluated. A species of the *Diplogaster longicaudatus* group is illustrated.

Fig. 16-21. *Diplogaster* sp. of the *longicaudatus* group.

Chapter 17

Class ADENOPHOREA (von Linstow, 1905) Chitwood, 1958

Synonym: Subclass APHASMIDIA Chitwood and Chitwood, 1933

Economically important plant parasitic nemas of Adenophorea are found only in the Superfamily Dorylaimoidea of the Order Dorylaimida. Original plans for this text included two chapters for this superfamily, based on the monographs of Thorne and Swanger (1936) and Thorne (1939). However, Andrassy (1959, 1960) revised the taxonomy of *Dorylaimus* and established seven new genera. He also made numerous synonyms, of which many are of doubtful validity. Meyl (1960) published a revision of the group which also contains numerous changes. As a result there remains but little semblance of the original taxonomic organization. It is deemed best to withhold publication of these two chapters on dorylaims until the situation is clarified. It is suggested that those possessing the two monographs delay making alterations in the nomenclature until the numerous transfers of species have been verified or corrected.

The plant parasitic genera *Longidorus*, *Xiphinema*, and *Trichodorus* are included in some detail because of their economic importance. A few other suspected plant parasites and associates are included, since they will frequently be encountered about plant roots.

Genus *Dorylaimus* Dujardin, 1845

Three very common soil-inhabiting species of *Dorylaimus* are described and illustrated herein. These will enable the beginner to become acquainted with the general morphological characteristics which designate this group. All three of these species were placed in new genera by Andrassy (1959), but the new nomenclatorial combinations are not used.

Dorylaimus obscurus Thorne and Swanger, 1936

Morphology: ♀: 2.0–3.0 mm; a = 30; b = 4.7; c = 50; V = $^{12}46^{12}$

♂: 3.3 mm; a = 30; b = 4.5; c = 67; T = 53

Lip region set off by a deep constriction, its width about one-third that of the neck base. Amphids duplex. Spear about as long as width of lip region, the aperture occupying one-half its length. Esophagus gradually expanded near

480

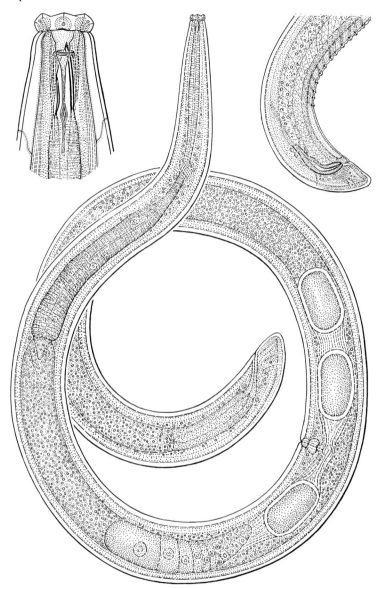

Fig. 17-1. *Dorylaimus obscurus.*

middle. Ovaries reflexed from one-half to all the distance back to the vulva. Eggs as long as body width, one-half as wide as long. Males very rare, only four found among several thousand specimens. Supplements 7 to 13, variable in arrangement, the series beginning about two tail lengths anterior to anus. Cardia flattish conoid, one-third the body width. Prerectum two to three times length of rectum. Body tapering posteriorly from a point about opposite the anterior end of the prerectum, the diminution being largely on the dorsal side. Cuticle of terminus radially striated. Lateral cord one-fifth the body width.

Habitat: A cosmopolitan species from cultivated fields and virgin soil. The most common species of *Dorylaimus* in the United States.

Dorylaimus monohystera deMan, 1880

Morphology: ♀: 1.2 mm; a = 30–40; b = 4.0–4.5; c = 30–40; V = 34[20]

Lip region one-third as deep as wide, set off by a depression. Spear one-sixth as wide as, and slightly longer than, lip-region width, the aperture occupying one-third its length. Posterior two-fifths of esophagus expanded until two-thirds the width of the neck. Rectum somewhat longer than anal body diameter. Prerectum one to two times length of rectum. Ovary single, reflexed more than halfway to vulva. Eggs more than twice as long and two-thirds as wide as body; tail convex-conoid to subdigitate terminus, the convexity greater on the dorsal side.

Habitat: A cosmopolitan species; specimens collected from many localities in the United States and Europe.

Dorylaimus bastiani Bütschli, 1873

Morphology: ♀: 1.4–2.0 mm; a = 40; b = 4.3; c = 12.5–25; V = 1655[14]
♂: 1.4 mm; a = 41; b = 5.2; c = 62.5; T = 60

Lips well amalgamated, set off by only a slight depression. Spear a little longer than width of lip region, the aperture occupying about one-third its length. Esophagus enlarged in posterior half until about three-fifths neck width. Cardia elongate-conoid, one-fourth body width. Female rectum length 1½ times anal body diameter. Prerectum twice length of rectum. Ovaries reflexed two-thirds back to vulva. Egg length about 1½ times body width. Lateral cord one-fifth body width. Supplements contiguous, 21 and 24 on two males examined; submedian papillae about eight pairs. Prerectum extending about one body width anterior to supplements. Lateral guiding pieces about one-third length of spicula (Fig. 17-2).

Habitat: A cosmopolitan species found especially in wet soils. Males rare.

Family BELONDIRIDAE

Axonchium amplicolle Cobb, 1920

Morphology: ♀: 1.5 mm; a = 35; b = 2.0–2.5; c = 71; V = 54[11]

Lip region one-fourth to one-fifth as wide as neck base. Lips conspicuous, set off by constriction. Spear length 1⅓ times the lip-region width, the aperture occupying one-third of its length. Esophagus enlarged in posterior two-thirds until about half as wide as neck. Cardia almost cylindrical, two-fifths as long as body width. Prerectum length equal to 4 to 6 times the body width. Vagina

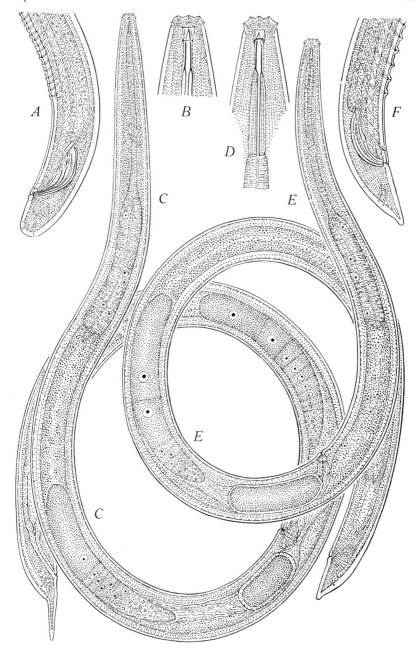

Fig. 17-2. A–C–Dorylaimus bastiani, male tail, head, and female. D–F–
Dorylaimus monohystera, head, female and male tail.

bent somewhat posteriad. Ovary reflexed about halfway to vulva, the length varying from 9 to 15 per cent of the body length. There are only slight traces of an anterior uterine branch. Distance from esophagus base to vulva varies from 6 to 13 per cent of the total body length.

The above description and measurements from Dr. Cobb's original balsam-preserved specimens in the collection of the Division of Nematology, U.S. Department of Agriculture. There were slight errors in the original measurements: length 2.2 mm; a = 32; b = 2.9; c = 83.
Habitat: Soil about roots in Luca de Persia, Brazil.

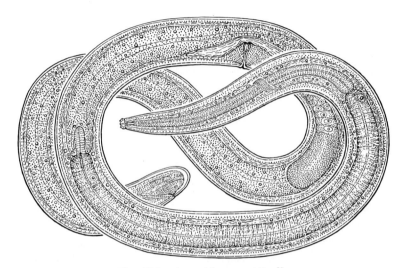

Fig. 17-3. *Axonchium amplicolle.*

Family LONGIDORIDAE (Thorne, 1935) Meyl, 1960

Synonym: Subfamily Longidorinae, Thorne, 1935

Diagnosis: Dorylaimoidea. Spear greatly attenuated, with long extensions which are plain (*Longidorus*) or flanged (*Xiphinema*). Anterior portion of esophagus a slender tube with little musculature, posterior portion reduced in length. Lateral series of pores in two lines. Tails of sexes similar where both are known.

Type genus: *Longidorus* Micoletzky, 1922
The general appearance and structure of nemas belonging to this family indicate a remote relationship with true dorylaims. Usually species of *Longidorus* are found in limited numbers, and for this reason they have been considered of doubtful economic importance. An exception to this rule was observed by Jensen and Horner (1957) in peppermint fields in Oregon. There *Longidorus sylphus* was determined to be the causal agent of mint decline in a field of several acres. Applications of standard nematicides increased yields three to sixteen times. Nemas were photographed while still attached to roots by their long spears.

Genus *Longidorus* Micoletzky, 1922

Diagnosis: Longidoridae. Body greatly attenuated. Lips bearing the usual two circlets of 6 and 10 papillae. Lateral cords comparatively broad, the series of lateral pores in two lines. Amphid apertures minute, slitlike, exceedingly difficult to observe. Amphids consisting of abnormally large pouches which practically encircle the head. They contain coiled fibrillar terminals and small refractive bodies which probably are nervous in function. The nerve tubes can easily be traced back to the sensillae. Spear greatly attenuated. Guiding ring located near lip region. Esophagus reduced to a slender, flexible tube with an elongated basal bulb. The dorsal and the anterior pair of submedian gland nuclei are easily visible, while the posterior submedian pair is rather small and obscure. Ovaries two in all known species, reflexed, very short compared with the total body length. Vulva transverse. Tails of sexes similar.

Type species: *Longidorus elongatus* (deMan, 1876) Thorne and Swanger, 1936

Longidorus is easily distinguished from its nearest relative, *Xiphinema*, by the forward position of the spear guiding ring and the absence of flanges on the spear extensions.

Because of the unusual size and slenderness of the species of *Longidorus* it is natural that considerable variation in length and body proportions occurs among individuals of the same species, especially those from different geographical sections.

Longidorus elongatus (deMan) Thorne and Swanger, 1936

Synonyms: *Dorylaimus elongatus* deMan, 1876; *Dorylaimus (Longidorus) elongatus* (deMan) Micoletzky, 1922; *Dorylaimus tenuis* von Linstow, 1879 as synonymized by deMan, 1884; *Trichodorus elongatus* (deMan) Filipjev, 1921

Morphology: deMan: ♀: 5.5 mm; a = 105; b = 12; c = 105; V = $^{8}52^{8}$
♂: 5.5 mm; a = 112; b = 12; c = 105
Turkey: ♀: 6.3 mm; a = 155; b = 15; c = 140; V = $^{5}51^{5}$
♂: 7.4 mm; a = 148; b = 18.5; c = 140; V = $^{3}46^{3}$

These measurements illustrate the great variability occurring within this species. Lip region set off by a uniform expansion. Amphid apertures slitlike, very difficult to see. Amphids abnormally large, almost encircling head. Lips with the usual two circlets of 16 distinct papillae. Spear length variable: 6.3 mm ♀ from Turkey, 84 μ; 6.3 ♂ from South Carolina, 105 μ; 3.7 mm ♂ from Florida, 68 μ. Spear extension averaging about two-thirds as long as spear. Esophagus beginning as a slender tube which rather suddenly expands to form the elongated basal bulb, which has a length equal to two to three times the neck width. Cardia bluntly conoid. Intestine about six cells in circumference. Ovaries two, short, reflexed. Female prerectum length about ten, male ten to thirteen, times body width. Spicula blunt, arcuate, with small, furcate lateral guiding pieces. Protractor muscle an unusually broad band. Supplements consisting of the adanal pair and ten to sixteen ventromedian ones, the series beginning within range of the spicula and being rather uniformly spaced. Oblique copulatory muscles a prominent feature.

Habitat: A cosmopolitan species frequently reported from Europe. About roots of fig trees, Smyrna, Turkey; in grass sod, Clemson, South Carolina; about roots of citrus trees, Eustis, Florida.

Longidorus sylphus Thorne, 1939

Morphology: ♀: 4.4 mm; a = 88; b = 12.3; c = 88; V = $^{10}48^{10}$

Body tapering anteriorly until the lip region is about one-fourth as wide as the neck base. Lip region practically continuous with body contour, bearing the usual 16 prominent papillae. Amphids much like those figured for *Longidorus*

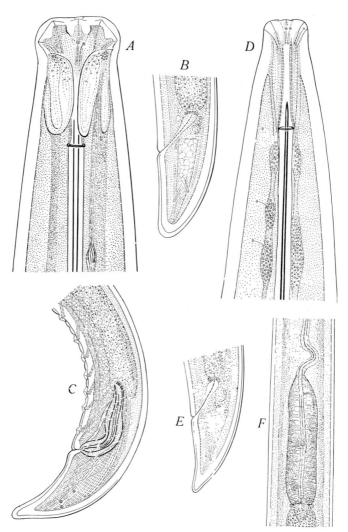

Fig. 17-4. *A–C—Longidorus elongatus. D–F—Longidorus sylphus. (After Thorne. Courtesy of Martinus Nijhoff.)*

elongatus, with exceedingly obscure, short, slitlike apertures. Lateral cords frequently exhibiting glandular bodies from which the lateral pores arise. On the anterior neck these pores are in a single line, but farther back they separate into two lines. Spear about 85 μ long, with extensions about 50 μ in length. Basal enlargement of the esophagus about twice as long as neck width. Cardia bluntly conoid. On young females, 3.5 mm, the vulva is near 35 per cent and the neck relatively longer, b = 8.7. Prerectum length six to twelve times body width. Tail dorsally convex-conoid to blunt terminus. Males unknown, and mature females contain no sperms (Fig. 17-4).

Genus *Xiphinema* Cobb, 1913a

Diagnosis: Longidoridae. Spear greatly attenuated, with long extensions bearing basal flanges. Guiding ring located near base of spear. Esophagus beginning as a slender, coiled tube which is straight only when the spear is extruded. This slender portion suddenly expands to form the elongate basal bulb, which usually is about three times as long as the neck width. Dorsal esophageal gland nucleus at extreme anterior end of bulb. Intestinal cells packed with coarse, refractive granules. Prerectum present. Vulva transverse. Ovaries one or two, reflexed. Spicula with lateral guiding pieces. Supplements consisting of an adanal pair and a ventromedian series. Testes two, dorylaimoid.

Type species: *Xiphinema americanum* Cobb, 1913a

Species of *Xiphinema* are immediately distinguished from those of *Longidorus* by the deep pharyngeal location of the spear guiding ring and well-developed, elongate flanges of the spear. Siddiqi (1959) described two new species, X. *brevicaudatum* and X. *citri,* which have the more anterior guiding ring and broad amphids of *Longidorus*. These appear to be intermediate forms between the two genera, and the writer considers them to belong in *Longidorus*. Obviously, they represent bridging species, which appear in all forms of animal and plant life and introduce complications into their taxonomy. Discovery of such forms should not be interpreted as justification for synonymizing otherwise valid genera like *Xiphinema* and *Longidorus*.

Luc (1958a) presented a very satisfactory key to species of *Xiphinema,* and the reader is referred to his work for general information on the taxonomy of the group. Siddiqi added three new species and reported the presence of X. *americanum* and X. *brevicaudatum* in India. Doubtless many species are of economic importance and merit attention when associated with crop plants. Only four species, X. *americanum,* X. *index,* X. *diversicaudatum,* and X. *chambersi,* have been determined as plant pathogenic. These are discussed in the following sections.

American dagger nematode, *Xiphinema americanum* Cobb, 1913a

Morphology: ♀: 1.5–2.0 mm; a = 35–50; b = 6–7; c = 50–60; V = $^{13}55^{18}$

        ♂: 1.6–2.0 mm; a = 52; b = 6.2; c = 47; T = 46

Body assuming an open spiral when relaxed by gentle heat. Lip region with the usual two circlets of 6 and 10 papillae. Amphid apertures slitlike, obscure. Lateral cords one-fourth body width, with pores arranged in two lines. Spear 120 to 140 μ long, the flanged portion occupying about two-fifths of the total length. Enlarged basal portion of esophagus two to three times as long as neck width. Cardia bluntly conoid. Intestinal cells often so densely packed that details of the cells are obscured. Vulva a transverse slit. Ovaries reflexed about halfway back to vulva. Eggs four or five times as long as body width. Males very rare, with the usual preanal pair of supplements and 4 to 10 ventromedian ones arranged rather regularly about half the body width apart. Tails of sexes similar, dorsally convex to a bluntly rounded terminus.

Comparison of specimens from many localities shows a remarkable similarity in body form and size and spear length. Slight differences occur in the length and tapering of the tails and in the arrangement of supplements, as might be expected. However, in no instance has sufficient variation been observed to justify separation of subforms or varieties.

Habitat: A cosmopolitan species from soil about the roots of many plants. A very common species throughout the United States. Also known in Hawaii, Europe, Israel, India, and Ceylon.

Historical: Cobb (1913a) described *Xiphinema americanum* and stated that the species was among those injurious to vegetation. He recorded it as occurring "About the roots of a variety of plants,—corn, grass, citrus trees, on the Atlantic and Pacific slopes of the United States." The writer frequently encountered it in soil samples from cultivated and virgin soil throughout the Western states. It was especially prevalent about the roots of declining apple and cherry orchards in Utah. Christie (1952) found *X. americanum* associated with extensive necrosis and destruction of feeder roots on laurel oak, *Quercus laurifolia,* in Florida. Later (1952a) he classed the species as one of the four major nematode pests of the Southeastern states.

Circumstantial evidence of the importance of the species continued to accumulate as it appeared in collections varying from unthrifty wheat

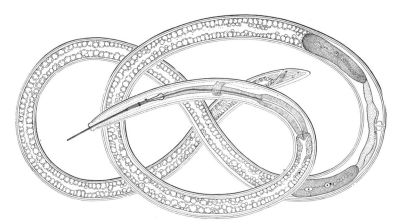

Fig. 17-5. *Xiphinema americanum.* (*After Cobb. Courtesy of Nematology Section, U.S. Department of Agriculture.*)

fields of the Great Plains, declining orchards and strawberries in many states, and in pine and maple forests of Wisconsin, where dieback was prevalent. Because of its great numbers, widespread distribution, and extensive host range the American dagger nematode may be the most destructive plant parasitic nematode in America.

Biology: Perry (1958) secured a fair demonstration of pathogenicity of *Xiphinema americanum* on strawberries, with some reduction of root systems and extreme black root. White (1959) demonstrated injury to cherry seedlings, and sectioned rootlets exhibited puncture injury. Difficulty is generally experienced in establishing colonies, since reproduction does not readily take place in captivity, perhaps because in temperate climates reproduction is apparently seasonal. During early spring months gravid females occur in great numbers, but in hot summer months they are rarely seen. Sometimes a second period of reproduction occurs in autumn.

Control: Applications of standard fumigants give good control of *Xiphinema americanum* on strawberries and other short-lived crops. On orchard trees, vineyards, and other perennials, fumigation will enable the plants to become well established, but slow decline and dieback can be expected to develop within 10 or 15 years, for the nemas frequently live several feet deep in the soil, where fumigants do not penetrate. Adams (1955) reported increased growth of young peach and apple trees on soil treated with benzene hexachloride. Information on host range is too meager to allow recommendation of crop rotations. The writer has observed that only small populations are found where row crops like sugar beets, beans, potatoes, and tomatoes are grown. In such fields the nemas were usually below the first foot of soil, a fact indicating that they did not thrive in the portion moved about by plows and cultivators.

Xiphinema index Thorne and Allen, 1950

Morphology: ♀: 3.4 mm; a = 58; b = 7.6; c = 76; V = $^{15}38^{16}$
                 ♂: 4.6 mm; a = 63; b = 7.3; c = 88; T = 49

Lip region continuous with the neck contour, bearing the usual two circlets of 6 and 10 papillae. Amphids almost as broad as head, with slender tubes leading back to the sensillae pouches. Minute fibrils are sometimes visible in the amphidial pouch. Lateral fields very narrow on the neck, but gradually becoming broader until they are about one-fourth as wide as the neck. A series of lateral pores is present, appearing in a single line on the neck, then branching into two lines. Dorsal and ventral pores present near the head. Four pairs of caudal pores present on both males and females. Caudal cuticle radially striated.

Spear typical of the genus, with the usual extensions and flanges, its total length averaging about 190 μ. Esophagus beginning as a slender tube which is reflexed when the spear is retracted. Just anterior to the nerve ring, a tiny spear can usually be seen in the esophageal tissues which marks the location of the cell from which the spear originated. Just before a moult, the fully developed spear occupies almost the entire length of the slender anterior portion of the esophagus. Frequently the basal portion of the esophagus is shifted in

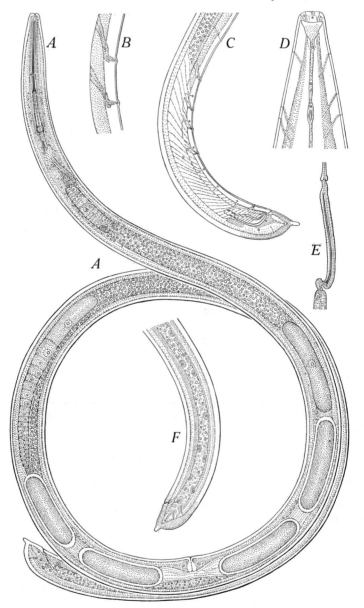

Fig. 17-6. *Xiphinema index.* *A*—Female. *B*—Supplements. *C*—Posterior portion of male. *D*—Head showing amphid in detail. *E*—Spear developing in esophageal tissues. *F*—Posterior portion of female. (*After Thorne and Allen. Courtesy of Helminthological Society of Washington.*)

position until the conspicuous dorsal gland may appear in a lateral or ventral position. The anterior pair of submedian gland nuclei generally is easily visible, but the posterior pair frequently is very obscure. Cardia conoid. Intestine about eight cells in circumference. Female prerectum eight to ten times as long as body diameter. Ovaries approximately symmetrical, reflexed, but varying greatly in location because of the large eggs, which crowd them out of position. Usually the anterior ovary lies on the right, the posterior on the left side of the body. Details of the development of the ova are as illustrated.

Male tail bearing the usual adanal pair of supplements, a ventromedian series of four, and an innervated organ anterior to the supplement series. There also is a ventrosubmedian series of seven pairs of innervated papillae. Musculature of the posterior portion of the male is a prominent feature. Spicula strong, arcuate, with small lateral guiding pieces.

Most closely related to *Xiphinema diversicaudatum* (Micoletzky, 1927) Thorne, 1939, from which it is distinguished by the more anterior position of the vulva, 38 to 47.7 per cent; four pairs of male caudal pores, compared with six for *diversicaudatum;* greater width of female, $a = 58–72$; and greater length of neck, $b = 7.6–10.1$. *Xiphinema index* is slightly smaller, 3.4 to 4.0 mm, but this difference can scarcely be considered as a character of specific importance.

Habitat: Hundreds of females and two males from soil about the roots of fig, *Ficus carica,* collected near Planada, California.

Xiphinema index as a vector of fanleaf virus of grapevine

Investigations revealed that *Xiphinema index* was widely distributed in California. Hewett, Raski, and Goheen (1958) made the very important discovery that this species was the vector of soil-borne fanleaf virus of grapevines. This discovery opened up an entirely new field in nematology and gave added weight to the importance of nematodes in their relation to plant diseases. Especially interesting was the fact that from 10 nematodes these investigators built up populations as high as 39,960.

Xiphinema diversicaudatum (Micoletzky, 1927) Thorne, 1939

Synonyms: *Dorylaimus* (*Longidorus*) *diversicaudatus* Micoletzky; *Dorylaimus* (*Longidorus*) *elongatus* deMan of Micoletzky, 1923; not *Dorylaimus elongatus* deMan, 1876

Morphology: ♀: 3.8–4.5 mm; $a = 66–74$; $b = 9–11$; $c = 96$; $V = {}^{15}45^{17}$
♂: 3.7–4.5 mm; $a = 72–77$; $b = 9–10$; $c = 96$; $T = 49$

Body tapering anteriorly until the female lip region is one-fifth, and that of the male one-fourth, as wide as the neck base. Tails of sexes similar, subdigitate, with radially striated cuticle. Lip region set off by a short cylindrical section. Amphids three-fourths as wide as head, stirrup-shaped. Spear averaging 130 μ long, with flanged extensions 65 μ in length. Esophagus enlarged near middle by a rather sudden expansion, the basal portion being 2 to 3 times as long as width of neck. Intestinal cells packed with hyaline granules. Vulva transverse. Vagina extending halfway across the body to join a broad, crescentic uterine chamber which is 1½ times as long as the body width. Ovaries symmetrical. Eggs three-fourths as wide as body and 5 times as long as wide. Near the middle of the elongated uterine tube is the spermatheca, a chamber about 3 times as long as the body width. Anterior to this is a thick-walled chamber in which a few spermatozoa await the eggs, and here the shell is deposited on the fertilized egg. Ovary composed of about 20 developing oöcytes, flexed about one-fifth the distance back to vulva. Prerectum length about 12 times body diameter. Ventromedian supplements three or four, the series beginning two spicula lengths anterior to the adanal pair.

Xiphinema diversicaudatum resembles *X. index* but is consistently much longer, males are more numerous, and number and arrangement of caudal pores are distinctly different.

Micoletzky described *Xiphinema diversicaudatum* from specimens found in soil in Austria. The writer (1939) emended the description from specimens collected in Utah, with illustrations by Chambers from specimens found in soil, Arlington Farm, Virginia.

Schindler (1954) frequently found this species associated with roots of roses exhibiting reduced vigor, chlorists, and galled root-tips. Later (1954a) he made the first demonstrations of pathogenicity by *Xiphinema* when he proved that this species was responsible for the symptoms observed in roses. Later (1957) he demonstrated that 200 nemas placed about cuttings of the rose Better Times built up to 22,000 and 27,000 in 39 months. Injury was characterized by an enlargement of the terminus and curling of the ends of the roots, a condition designated as "curly tip." Similar galling of peanut roots was produced. Roots of fig were severely reduced when 2,600 nemas were added to the pots in which they were growing. Supernatant water from infested pots affected plant growth in a manner similar to the effect produced by low populations of nemas. Concerning this observation Schindler stated, "These effects

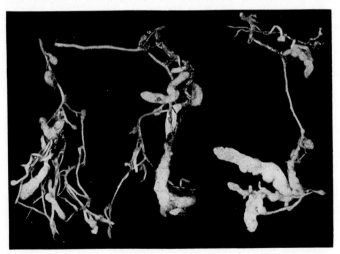

Fig. 17-7. Galls on roots of Better Times rose, produced by *Xiphinema diversicaudatum.* *(After Schindler, Nematologica. Courtesy of E. J. Brill.)*

may have been due to the action of fungi, bacteria or viruses, alone or in combination; or they may have been due to the action of a chemical growth inhibitor secreted by the nematodes while in the supernatant water." Demonstrations of pathogenicity on strawberries were made by Schindler and Braun (1957).

Xiphinema chambersi Thorne, 1939

Morphology: ♀: 2.5 mm; a = 54–63; b = 6.3; c = 22; V = 24⁹

         ♂: 2.5 mm; a = 55; b = 6; c = 20; T = 47

Cuticle with strong radial striae, especially on tails. Spear 100 μ, extension 69 μ long. Enlarged basal portion of esophagus three to four times as long as neck width, the five gland nuclei usually visible. Cardia bluntly conoid. Vulva far forward, three to five body widths posterior to esophagus. Anterior uterine branch absent. Posterior ovary reflexed about one-third distance back to vulva. Female prerectum length equal to ten to fourteen times body width. Rectum twice as long as anal body diameter. Supplements an adanal pair and three ventrosubmedian ones. Tail of sexes similar, uniformly elongate-conoid, with terminus frequently subcylindroid or slightly clavate.

Perry (1958) demonstrated that this species is definitely pathogenic to strawberry roots and associated with common black root of that plant.

Family LEPTONCHIDAE Thorne, 1935

Diagnosis: Dorylaimoidea. Meromyarian. Esophagus a slender tube with a short basal expansion. Spear with or without basal extensions. Lateral series of pores in two lines. Prerectum present. Testes two, dorylaimoid. Adanal pair of supplements present.

Type genus: *Leptonchus* Cobb, 1920

Diagnosis: Body cylindroid. Outer cuticle smooth or marked by excessively minute, crisscross lines. Subcuticle striated. Lateral cords broad, with coarse pores in two lines. Guiding ring a strongly sclerotized, truncated cone. Spear very slender, with arcuate, strong extensions. Esophagus a slender tube until it expands to the pyriform basal bulb, which contains a straight lumen and three large gland nuclei. Intestinal cells frequently densely granular. Prerectum obscurely differentiated from intestine, with a more transparent terminal portion. Caudal pores almost terminal, unusually large and conspicuous. Ovaries reflexed. Testes, spicula, and supplements dorylaimoid. Spicula with lateral guiding pieces. Tails of sexes similar.

Type species: *Leptonchus granulosus* Cobb, 1920

Leptonchus granulosus Cobb, 1920

Morphology: ♀: 1.2 mm; a = 30; b = 5.5; c = 92; V = ¹⁷60¹⁵

         ♂: 1.2 mm; a = 30; b = 5.6; c = 50; T = 70

Cuticle smooth. Subcuticle coarsely striated, in fixed specimens almost invariably separated from the outer layers and distorted. Lateral cords occupying a third of the body width, the coarse pores lying in two widely separated lines. Amphids almost as wide as head. Lip region caplike, amalgamated, set off by deep constriction. Guiding ring a truncated cone, appearing archlike in longi-

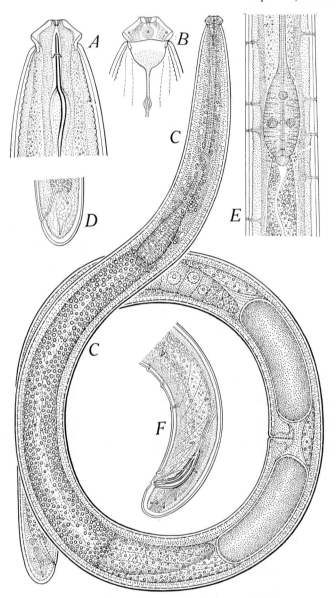

Fig. 17-8. *Leptonchus granulosus.* *A*—Sagittal section through head. *B*—Head showing details of cephalic papillae and amphid. *C*—Female; note that prerectum extends anterior to vulva. *D*—Female tail. *E*—Dorsal view of esophageal bulb region; note lateral pores. *F*—Posterior portion of male.

tudinal section. Spear slender, slightly longer than width of lip region. Spear extensions arcuate, about as long as spear. Esophagus a slender, nonmuscular tube until it expands to form the pyriform basal bulb. This bulb is about as long as the neck width and contains three prominent esophageal gland nuclei. An obscure excretory pore lies opposite the nerve ring. Cardia flatly conoid. Intestine two cells in circumference, the cells containing coarse, dark brown granules. The intestine length is only about six times the body width; then it joins the abnormally long prerectum, which extends anteriad to the front ovary. Ovaries nearly symmetrical, sometimes reflexed past the vulva. Eggs average 35 by 85 μ, almost twice as long as body width. Spicula slender, arcuate, with lateral guiding pieces. Supplements consisting of an adanal pair and five ventromedian ones, the series beginning well in front of the spicula and rather uniformly spaced about half the body width apart. Female tail hemispheroid; male tail similar but dorsally arcuate. Only three males observed among several hundred females.

Habitat: Described by Cobb from soil about roots of willow trees, Arlington Farm, Virginia. Collected by the writer from date gardens, Indio, California, and cultivated fields near St. George, Salem, and Salt Lake City, Utah; also Greeley, Idaho, and Fallon, Nevada. Generally distributed in seedling pine nurseries, Wellston, Michigan, and Wisconsin Rapids, Wisconsin. The writer suspects that this species is involved in disease complexes occurring in these nurseries and that it merits investigation. Widely distributed in forest soils, central Wisconsin.

Genus *Tylencholaimellus* M. V. Cobb, 1915

Diagnosis: Leptonchinae. Spear with an extra dorsal stiffening piece and three strongly knobbed extensions. Esophagus a slender tube with a short basal bulb set off by a distinct constriction. Vulva far forward. Anterior female sexual branch absent or very rudimentary; posterior branch normal. Prerectum present. Spicula frail where known, dorylaimoid, with lateral guiding pieces. No gubernaculum present. Supplements an adanal pair and a single ventromedian one. Tails of sexes similar where both are known, hemispheroid to bluntly conoid.

Type species: *Tylencholaimellus diplodorus* M. V. Cobb, 1915
Tylencholaimellus is distinctive because of the extra stiffening piece on the spear, which immediately differentiates it from *Doryllium*, its closest relative. Because of their powerful oral armature these species doubtless feed on roots and merit investigation as possible plant pathogens.

Tylencholaimellus affinis (Brakenhoff, 1914) Thorne, 1949

Synonym: *Tylencholaimus affinis* Brakenhoff, 1914

Morphology: ♀: 1.2 mm; a = 23; b = 7.0; c = 57; V = $^{73}0^{30}$
  ♂: 1.2 mm; a = 22; b = 6.5; c = 40–50; T = 70
Body obese, cylindroid; tapering near head until lip region is about one-third as wide as the base of the short neck. Cuticle with easily visible, transverse striae. Lip region set off by slight depression. Lips low, conical, rising but

little above the head contour. Spear length 1½ times lip-region width, with a strong dorsal stiffening piece. Spear extensions strongly knobbed, almost half as long as spear. Esophagus a slender tube until it reaches the basal bulb, which is set off by a definite constriction. Vulva transverse, far forward. Anterior female sexual branch a rudimentary pouch slightly longer than the body width; posterior branch very long, the ovary reflexed two-thirds the distance back to vulva. Prerectum length about twice body diameter. Spicula slender, frail, slightly arcuate, with lateral guiding pieces. Supplements an adanal pair and a ventromedian one. Female tail somewhat variable in form, hemispheroid to bluntly conoid.

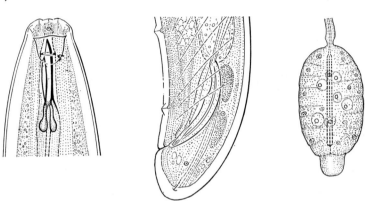

Fig. 17-9. *Tylencholaimellus affinis.* (*After Thorne. Courtesy of Martinus Nijhoff.*)

Tylencholaimellus affinis is most closely related to *T. diplodorus,* from which it differs in its much shorter spear and the more posteriad location of the single ventromedian supplement. It is also usually distinguished because of its larger size, some females reaching a length of 1.7 mm, and in these the vulva may be as far forward as 24 per cent. Males from Virginia and Utah sometimes have a much more conoid tail.

Habitat: Moist soil, Bremen, Germany; canyons near Salt Lake City, Utah; Broad Run, Virginia, and Fort Meyer, Florida.

Family DIPHTHEROPHORIDAE Thorne, 1935

Diagnosis: Dorylaimoidea? Meromyarian. Length of known species not over 2.0 mm. Anatomical details generally obscured by many granular bodies located throughout the body cavity. Lateral series of pores absent. Amphid apertures ellipsoid. Sensillae separated from the elongate amphids by only a short tube, their elements slender and very numerous. Pharynx armed with toothlike spear, generally of complicated structure, of which only the distal end is shed in moulting. Allen (1957) classes the spear of Diphtherophoridae as a dorsal onchiostyle. Esophagus a simple tube with a pyriform to elongate-conoid basal bulb. Prerectum absent. Testis one. Gubernaculum present. Supplements ventromedian, an adanal pair absent.

Type subfamily: Diphtherophorinae Micoletzky, 1922

The position of the Family Diphtherophoridae is questionable. Probably it belongs in an unknown order.

Subfamily DIPHTHEROPHORINAE Micoletzky, 1922

Diagnosis: Diphtherophoridae. Spear with basal knobs and distally of complicated, archlike construction in the anterior portion of its dorsal sector. Ventral sector not fused to dorsal in its distal portion. Guiding apparatus of spear a complex structure of sclerotized plates and rods. Supplements reduced or vestigial. Gubernaculum present.

Type genus: *Diphtherophora* deMan, 1880

Diagnosis: Diphtherophorinae. All known species less than 1.0 mm long. Cuticle sometimes loosely fitting, forming membranelike folds and shifting from side to side as the body bends. Spear cephalated, of archlike structure in its distal third or less, with strong basal knobs. Only the anterior end of spear shed in moulting. Ventral sector of spear not fused distally, diverging to the ventral wall of the globular pharynx. Spear guide a complicated structure of sclerotized rods and plates. Esophagus a simple tube with a plain pyriform or elongate-conoid (subcylindroid in *Diptherophora vanoyei*) basal bulb. Vulva transverse. Vagina small, joined near the middle of the elongated uterine sac. Ovaries two, reflexed. Testis single. Spicula simple, slightly arcuate. Supplements reduced or vestigial, the adanal pair absent. Gubernaculum present. Excretory pore present.

Type species: *Diphtherophora communis* deMan, 1880

Nothing is known of the feeding habits of *Diphtherophora*. The strong spear indicates that these nemas probably feed on roots. *Diphtherophora perplexans* was usually found about the roots of peach trees infected with Western X disease in eastern Utah and western Colorado.

Diphtherophora communis deMan, 1880

Morphology: ♀: 0.6 mm; a = 20; b = 4.9; c = 13; V = $^{13}5_{6}15$
♂: 0.54 mm; a = 22; b = 4.1; c = 1; T = 50

Cuticle thick, flexible, forming membranelike folds when the body is bent. Lip region about half as wide as neck base. Inner circlet of 6 papillae arranged near entrance to vestibule. Outer circlet of 10 papillae located on slightly elevated conical elevations. Amphid apertures ellipsoid, almost half as wide as head. Body details often obscured by large numbers of dense, granular bodies. Stoma bearing a complicated system of plates and rods which serve as a guiding ring for the massive, cephalated spear. Spear with archlike anterior portion attached to a massive shaft bearing strongly developed knobs. Ventral sector of spear not fused distally, diverging to ventral wall of globular stoma, its knobs much smaller than those of the dorsal sector. Esophageal bulb pyriform, with three prominent gland nuclei. Excretory pore conspicuous, located opposite nerve ring. Cardia about 5 μ long, bluntly conoid. Intestine with coarse, refractive granules. Ovaries with only five or six oöcytes arranged in single file. Eggs about three times as long as wide. Testis single, outstretched. Spicula slightly arcuate, not cephalated, resting on a thin, trough-shaped gubernaculum. The thick cuticle forms a shallow depression about the anal opening, often giving the appearance of a narrow bursa. A single ventromedian supplement present.

Diphtherophora communis is distinctive because of the elongated, dorsad-curved tail and flexible membranous cuticle.

Habitat: Fresh or brackish wet pasture lands, Netherlands, Germany, and France. The above description from specimens collected in a sugar beet field near Ballycayune, Ireland.

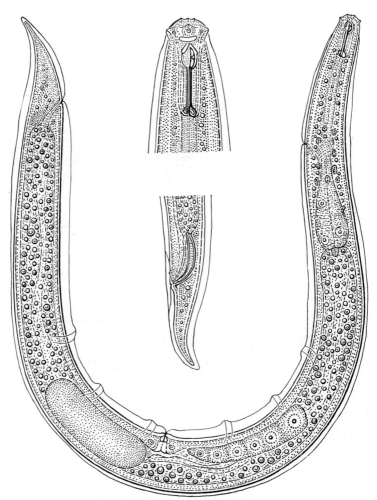

Fig. 17-10. *Diphtherophora communis.*

Genus *Triplonchium* Cobb, 1920

Diagnosis: Diptherophorinae. Body contents very dense, frequently obscuring details. Spear of complicated, archlike structure in its dorsal sector. Ventral sector of spear not fused distally, joining the ventral side of the pharynx. Spear guiding apparatus a compound structure of plates and rods. Amphid apertures ellipsoid. Sensillae separated from the elongate amphids by only a short tube.

Basal esophageal enlargement pyriform. Vulva transverse. Vagina connected near the middle of the elongated uterine sac, which sometimes is as much as eight times as long as the body width. Ovaries two, reflexed. Spicula semicircular, with conspicuous spiral protrudor muscles. Supplements vestigial.

Type species: *Triplonchium cylindricum* Cobb, 1920

Triplonchium cylindricum Cobb, 1920

Morphology: ♀ : 1.6–2.1 mm; a = 30; b = 8.0–12.0; c = 30–40;
$V = {}^{22}53^{23}$

♂ : 1.5–2.0 mm; a = 32; b = 11; c = 30; T = 65

Body tissues very dense, completely obscuring details in some specimens. Much of this density is due to hundreds of granular bodies, variable in size and form, which are distributed throughout the nema. Lip region continuous with neck contour. Six minute papillae around oral opening. Outer circlet of 10 papillae on low, conical elevations. Amphid apertures one-third as wide as head, the amphids extending deep into the tissues. Sensillae opposite spear base. A complicated cuticularized, tubular structure surrounds the vestibule, serving as the spear guide. Spear in two knobbed sections as in *Diphtherophora;* the dorsal sector is of archlike construction, the ventral one a simple rod with the anterior end joined to the ventral side of the pharynx. Esophagus a slender tube to the pyriform to elongate-conoid basal bulb which contains upward of 50 granular bodies. Intestinal cells dense and generally undefinable. Vulva a transverse slit. Vagina extending halfway across body to join the elongate, pouchlike uterine sac which extends approximately four body widths anteriad and posteriad from the vagina. Ovaries reflexed about halfway to vulva. Intestine extending a short distance into the caudal cavity. Female rectum length one-fifth anal body diameter. Testis single, outstretched. Spicula almost semicircular, with conspicuous musculature. Gubernaculum a thin trough

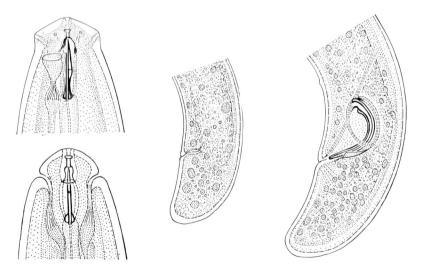

Fig. 17-11. *Triplonchium cylindricum.* (*After Thorne. Courtesy of Martinus Nijhoff.*)

in which the spicula glide. An obscure ventromedian elevation occurs just anterior to the spicula, the only trace of supplementary organs seen.

Habitat: Described by Cobb from Arlington, Virginia. A rather common species in the Wasatch Mountains, Utah, and in forest soil from central and northern Wisconsin. Pathogenicity tests are desirable.

Subfamily Trichodorinae Thorne, 1935

Diagnosis: Diphtherophoridae? Spear lineate, without basal knobs, tripartite in its middle sector. Vestibule elongated, tubular, serving as a guide for the slender spear. An obscure guiding ring is present at the base of the muscular pharynx. Amphids, esophagus, and reproductive systems as typical for the family. Supplements ventromedian, well developed.

Type genus: *Trichodorus* Cobb, 1913a

The position of Trichodorinae is questionable. Global collecting of forms related to Diphtherophoridae will probably reveal a group which will merit the rank of order. In this order the diphtherophorids and trichodorids will have superfamily status. But until the missing links are described it appears best to retain them in their present status.

The first recorded species of *Trichodorus* was described by deMan (1876) under the name *Dorylaimus primitivus*. Other species were not reported until Cobb (1913a) established the genus *Trichodorus* with *T. obtusus* as type. Micoletzky (1922) named deMan's species *T. primitivus* and made *T. obtusus* a synonym. The writer (1939) emended the diagnosis of *Trichodorus* from specimens collected in Cobb's type locality, Arlington, Virginia. Allen (1957) compared specimens from the Netherlands with those in the writer's collection from Virginia and found that they were not the same species. He then began a very detailed systematic study of the many specimens in collections made by nematologists in the Western states and found a total of ten new species. He also received collections of *T. primitivus* from Maryland and Pennsylvania which corresponded with the description and illustrations of Cobb and with the Netherlands specimens. On this evidence he validated Micoletzky's synonymy of the two species, leaving *T. primitivus* as type of the genus. He then renamed the writer's species *T. obscurus,* which is included later in this section. Allen's work on *Trichodorus* is, without doubt, the most outstanding example of careful, accurate taxonomy which has been published on free-living and plant parasitic nemas.

Genus *Trichodorus* Cobb, 1913a

Diagnosis: Trichodorinae. Plump nemas with blunt, rounded tails and thick cuticle. Spear, or onchiostyle, dorsally arcuate, slender, tripartite in its middle sector. Amphids elongate, pocketlike, with ellipsoid apertures. Sensillae arranged in fiberlike bundles almost adjacent to amphids. Esophagus with a pyriform basal bulb containing three large and two very small gland nuclei. Ovaries two except in *Trichodorus monohystera,* reflexed when two are present. Testis single, outstretched. Supplements ventromedian, an anal pair not present.

Males of certain species with bursae, the only instance in which this organ is known among the Dorylaimoidea. Gubernaculum present.

Type species: *Trichodorus primitivus* (deMan, 1876) Micoletzky, 1922
Synonym: *Dorylaimus primitivus* deMan; *Trichodorus obtusus* Cobb

Morphology: ♀: 0.75 mm; a = 25; b = 5.2; c = 0; V = $^{21}5_{6}^{22}$
♂: 0.78 mm; a = 24; b = 5.6; c = 58; T = 59

Onchiostyle of female 40 to 50 μ, of male 47 μ. Female with excretory pore at level of nerve ring. Three lateral pores as illustrated. Spermatheca present. Caudal pores subterminal, more ventrally located than in other species.

Male with excretory pore just anterior to expanded portion of esophagus. Three ventromedian papillae anterior to excretory pore as illustrated. Supplements three, located anterior to spicula. Paired postanal and caudal pores present. Spicula somewhat arcuate. Gubernaculum with slightly enlarged distal end.

Males of *Trichodorus primitivus* are distinguished by the presence of three or four esophageal papillae and the arrangements of supplements. Females are recognized by position of the excretory pore, location of lateral hypodermal pores, form of the sclerotized vulvar pieces, and more ventrad caudal pores.

Habitat: Soil from meadow, Netherlands; sugar beet field, Ballyculane, Ireland; soil, College Park, Maryland; and about roots of boxwood, Philadelphia, Pennsylvania.

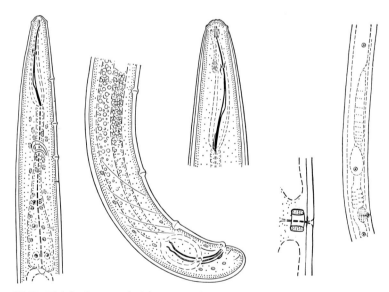

Fig. 17-12. *Trichodorus primitivus.* Neck, posterior portion of male, head, vulvar region, and anterior reproductive organ. Note lateral body pores. (*After Allen, Nematologica. Courtesy of E. J. Brill.*)

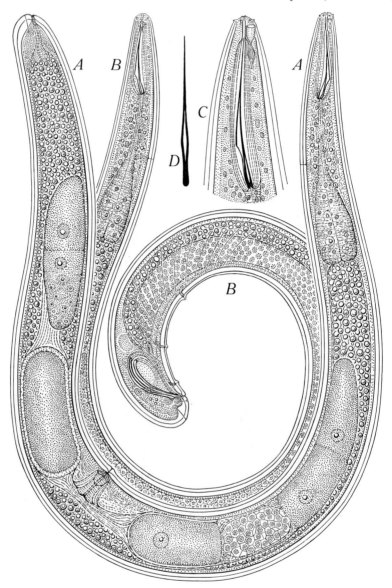

Fig. 17-13. *Trichodorus obscurus.* *A*—Female. *B*—Male. *C*—Head. *D*—Spear, ventral view.

Trichodorus obscurus Allen, 1957

Synonym: *Trichodorus primitivus* Thorne, 1939

Morphology: ♀: 0.7–1.2 mm; a = 16–24; b = 4.5–6.3; c = 0; V = $^{27}56^{27}$
♂: 0.7–1.0 mm; a = 14–22; b = 4.2–5.7; c = 55–69; T = 61–70

The general morphology of this species is shown in the accompanying illustration. Identification is based largely on male characters: Absence of ventromedian papillae anterior to excretory pore, which is about opposite anterior end of esophageal bulb. One lateral hypodermal pore just anterior to latitude of excretory pore. Three supplements, the first near the anus, the second opposite the proximal ends of the spicula, and the third about one body width anterior to the second. One pair of caudal pores near anus, another pair almost terminal. According to Allen, the females cannot be distinguished from those of *Trichodorus californicus*.

Trichodorus californicus Allen, 1957

Morphology: ♀: 0.8–1.3 mm; a = 15–20; b = 4.4–6.2; c = 0; V = $^{23}59^{20}$
♂: 0.8–1.1 mm; a = 15–21; b = 4.2–6.6; c = 44–58; T = 60–75

Male onchiostyle 82 μ long. Excretory pore at level of beginning of esophageal bulb. A single ventromedian papilla slightly anterior to pore, and a pair of lateral hypodermal pores at same level. Supplements three, equally spaced as illustrated. A pair of postanal, ventrosubmedian pores present. Caudal pores almost terminal. Female onchiostyle 79 μ long. One pair of lateral hypodermal pores slightly posterior to latitude of vulva. Spermatheca present. Anal opening and caudal pores almost terminal.

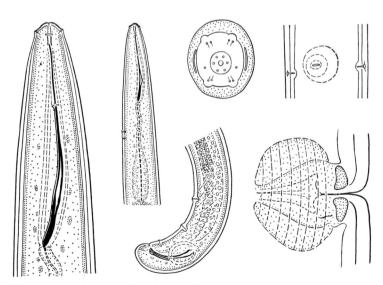

Fig. 17-14. *Trichodorus californicus.* Head, neck, posterior portion of male, face view, vulva from ventral and lateral views. (*After Allen, Nematologica. Courtesy of E. J. Brill.*)

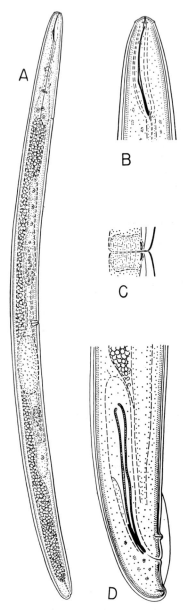

Fig. 17-15. *Trichodorus christiei.*
Female, head, vulvar region, and
posterior portion of male. (*After
Allen, Nematologica. Courtesy
of E. J. Brill.*)

Habitat: Soil about roots of *Pinus attenuata,* Moraga Ridge, Contra Costa County, and several other localities in California. Associated with *Xiphinema americanum* in thirty-year-old jack pine plantings in Wisconsin destroyed by slow decline and dieback.

Stubby-root nematode, *Trichodorus christiei* Allen, 1957

Morphology: ♀ : 0.46–0.7 mm;
                      a = 15–20; b = 4.6–6;
                      c = 110–140;
                      V = $^{20}53^{20}$
                 ♂ : 0.6 mm;
                      a = 16–20; b = 5.0–6.5;
                      c = 30–37; T = 50–67
Body cylindroid except near extremities. Onchiostyle about 36 μ long. Excretory pore near base of esophagus. Esophagus slightly overlapping anterior end of intestine on ventral side. Lateral hypodermal pores and ventral esophageal papillae absent. Spermatheca not observed. Bursa well developed, not enveloping terminus. Spicula almost straight, 63 μ long. Gubernaculum 19 μ. Sclerotized pieces about vagina small, inconspicuous.

Habitat: A common inhabitant of soil about the roots of many plants in the southeastern United States. Also reported by Allen from Maryland, Michigan, California, and Hawaii.

Trichodorus christiei as a plant parasite

Vegetable growers of Florida had for many years sustained heavy losses from an undetermined causal agent. Nemas were suspected and numerous plant and soil samples examined during a period of two years before a species of *Trichodorus* was discovered to be responsible, as reported by Christie and Perry (1951). This species had been observed in many instances but had not been suspected because of the relatively small numbers

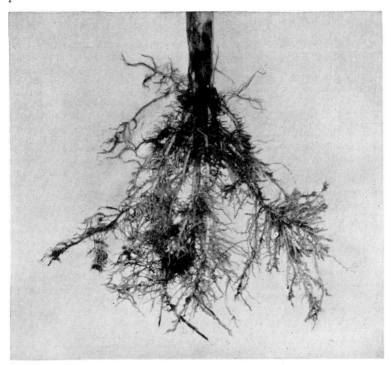

Fig. 17-16. Stubby root of corn produced by *Trichodorus christiei*. (*Courtesy of J. R. Christie*.)

present (Christie, personal communication). Discovery of the extreme phytotoxicity of the salivary secretions of *Trichodorus* gave a new concept to the importance of ectoparasitic nemas.

Hosts: Rohde and Jenkins (1957) reported extensive host tests with a *Trichodorus* sp. which probably was *T. christiei*. In the absence of plant roots of any kind the nemas did not survive after 60 days. A tenfold increase in population occurred on oat, tall fescue, cabbage, turnip, mustard, winter vetch, white and red clover, tomato, and lettuce. Less favorable hosts on which populations were maintained included field and sweet corn, several species of grass, beet, onion, bean, and alfalfa. Poor hosts were orchard grass, rye, spinach, radish, strawberry, pea, and tobacco. Nonhosts were asparagus, showy Crotalaria, poinsettia, and Jimson weed. Raski and Radewald (1958) failed to maintain colonies on roots of Thompson seedless grape. These results indicate an exceedingly wide host range which will enable the nemas to maintain populations in almost any field.

Symptoms: Feeding is confined to root-tips, and little necrosis occurs during early stages of attack. Growth is immediately checked, resulting in short, stunted roots, from which the name "stubby root" was derived.

Corn and certain other plants rarely show necrosis at any time. Rohde and Jenkins studied roots in section and found a loss of meristematic tissue. No definite root-cap or region of elongation remained, and the region of mitosis was much smaller than usual. Protoxylem thickenings developed almost to the apex of the root. Necrosis developed on roots of some crops during later stages of infestation.

Control: The wide host range of *Trichodorus christiei* probably makes crop rotation impractical. Soil fumigation gave good temporary results according to Perry (1953a), but within a few months populations returned and built up to greater numbers than had existed before. The reason for this sudden increase has not been determined. Probably the thick-shelled eggs escaped the fumigant, which killed adults and associated organisms. Among these associates may have been predatory nemas, which normally prevent development of high populations.

Family ALAIMIDAE

Alaimus primitivus deMan, 1880

Morphology: ♀: 1.2 mm; a = 41; b = 4.3; c = 9.0; V = 39^{20}
♂: 1.0 mm; a = 55; b = 4.0; c = 12

Body tapering uniformly both ways from near the middle. Lip region rounded, the papillae visible only under the most favorable conditions. From a face view the vestibule is found to be triradiate, probably allowing for considerable expansion while feeding. Sensillae located near the end of the first third of neck. Amphidial apertures exceedingly minute and obscure. Esophagus a uniform tube in the anterior two-thirds, then slowly expanding to form an elongate basal swelling. Vulva a transverse slit. Ovary reflexed about halfway to vulva. Eggs five to six times as long as body width. Body tapering uniformly to the elongate-conoid, arcuate tail. Male tail, according to deMan, shorter and less tapering than that of female. Spicula about as long as anal body diameter, with a slight ventral angle. Supplements four, appearing as low, rounded elevations.

Females of this species are frequently collected, but males rarely have been observed.

Habitat: A rather common species in Europe and the United States.

Family MONONCHIDAE

Mononchus papillatus Bastian, 1865

Morphology: ♀: 1.3–1.8 mm; a = 25; b = 38; c = 16; V = $10^{5}8^{10}$
♂: 1.5 mm; a = 27; b = 29; c = 17; T = 42

Morphological details of the females of this species are well delineated in the accompanying illustration. Males rare. Tail similar to that of female. Supplements mammiform, 2 to 14, uniformly spaced about one-half body width apart. A conspicuous constriction occurs in the intestine and other body tissues opposite the anterior supplements. Spicula arcuate, about as long as tail. Gubernaculum a simple trough about one-third as long as spicula. It is doubtful if males are functional.

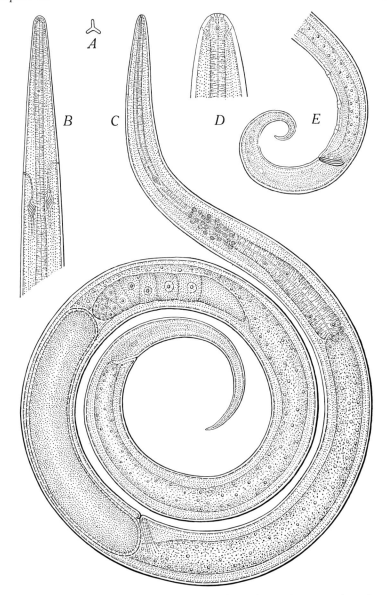

Fig. 17-17. *Alaimus primitivus.* *A*—Stoma from face view. *B*—Anterior end showing excretory pore and amphids. *C*—Female. *D*—Head in detail. *E*—Male tail.

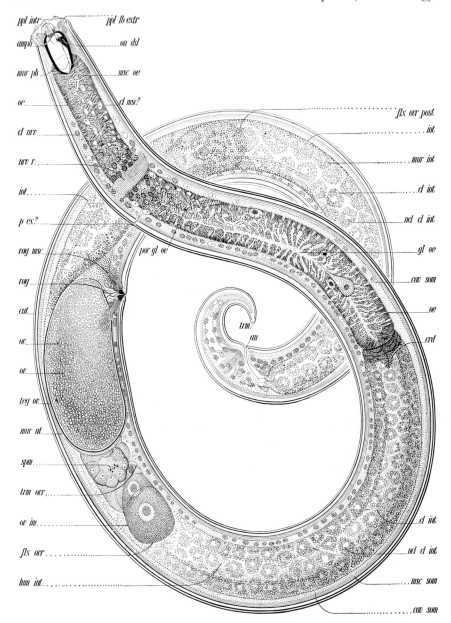

Fig. 17-18. *Mononchus papillatus.* (*After Cobb.   Courtesy of Nematology Section, U.S. Department of Agriculture.*)

Mononchus papillatus is a voracious predator feeding on nemas and other microorganisms.

Habitat: A cosmopolitan species found in cultivated and virgin soils and in aquatic to desert habitats.

The writer (1927) studied the ecology of *Mononchus papillatus* in sugar beet fields in Utah. Gravid females were numerous in April and May, but none was observed during summer months. Two gravid females were found in September.

Populations practically disappeared from fields without any apparent cause.

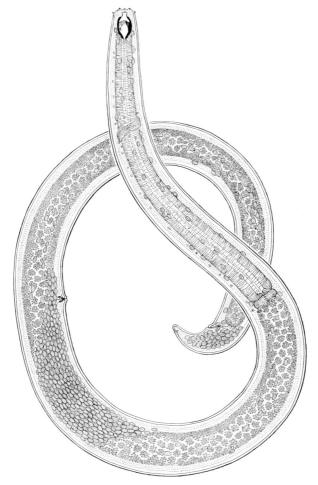

Fig. 17-19. *Mylonchulus parabrachyurus* infested with sporozoan parasites. *(After Thorne. Courtesy of U.S. Department of Agriculture.)*

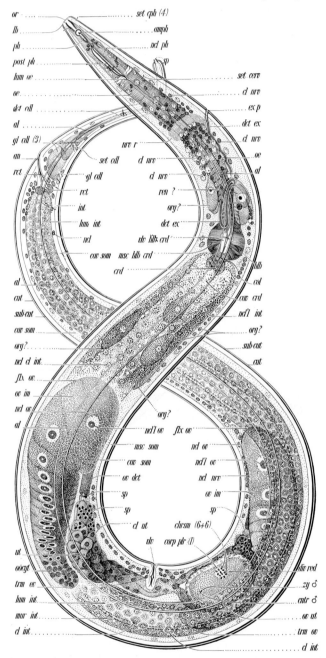

Fig. 17-20. *Plectus cirratus.* (*After Cobb. Courtesy of Nematology Section, U.S. Department of Agriculture.*)

Mylonchulus parabrachyurus

Synonym: *Monochus parabrachyurus* Thorne, 1924

Morphology: ♀: 1.5 mm; a = 29; b = 3.9; c = 25; V = $^{10}62^{10}$

♂: 1.6 mm; a = 33; b = 3.8; c = 25; T = 42

Amphid apertures appearing as narrow, oval slits about opposite apex of dorsal tooth. Pharynx armed with a strong, arcuate dorsal tooth, two small submedian teeth, and six rows of transverse denticles. General female morphology is shown in the accompanying illustration. Females syngonic, but rare males do occur, as recorded by the writer (1924). Supplements 10 to 14, mammiform, the anterior 3 or 4 usually somewhat rudimentary. Anterior to the supplements are about 10 small ventromedian papillae. Spicula plain, arcuate, slightly shorter than tail. Gubernaculum about half as long as spicula. Spinneret on dorsal side of tail, slightly anterior to terminus.

Mylonchulus parabrachyurus usually feeds on rotifers, protozoans, and other microorganisms. Rarely were nemas devoured. Ecological studies by the writer (1924) revealed that populations may be practically eradicated by sporozoans. An infected female is shown in the accompanying illustration.

Habitat: A frequent inhabitant of cultivated and virgin soils in the United States.

Family PLECTIDAE

Plectus cirratus Bastian, 1865

Morphology: ♀: 1.0–1.4 mm; a = 22–26; b = 3.5–4.0; c = 11–15; V = 52

Cobb and Chambers joined in making the accompanying illustration one of the finest that has ever been produced. The beginner should study the detailed anatomy very carefully. *Plectus cirratus* is another syngonic form, and details of the reproductive system are carefully delineated. A complete explanation is included in Cobb (1918).

Bibliography

Adam, W. 1932. Note sur *Heterodera schachtii* Schm. parasite des cactus. Bull. musée roy. hist. nat. Belg. 8: 1–10.

Adams, R. E. 1955. Evidence of injury to deciduous fruit trees by an ecto-parasitic nematode, *Xiphinema* sp. and a promising control measure. Phyto-pathology 45(9): 477–479.

Allen, M. W. 1940. *Anomyctus xenurus,* a new genus and species of Tylen-choidea (Nematoda). Proc. Helminth. Soc. Wash. 7(2): 96–98.

———. 1941. *Aphelenchoides megadorus,* a new species of Tylenchoidea (Nema-toda). Proc. Helminth. Soc. Wash. 8(1): 21–23.

———. 1952. Observations on the genus *Meloidogyne* Goeldi, 1887. Proc. Helminth. Soc. Wash. 19(1): 44–51.

———. 1952a. Taxonomic status of the bud and leaf nematodes related to *Aphelenchoides fragariae* (Ritzema-Bos, 1891). Proc. Helminth. Soc. Wash. 19(2): 108–120.

———. 1955. A review of the nematode genus *Tylenchorhynchus.* Univ. Calif. Publ. Zool. 61(3): 129–166.

———. 1957. A review of the nematode genus *Trichodorus* with descriptions of ten new species. Nematologica 2(1): 32–62.

———. 1957a. A new species of the genus *Dolichodorus* from California (Nema-toda: Tylenchida). Proc. Helminth. Soc. Wash. 24(2): 95–98.

——— and H. J. Jensen. 1950. *Cacopaurus epacris,* new species (Nematoda: Criconematidae) a nematode parasite of California black walnut roots. Proc. Helminth. Soc. Wash. 17(1): 10–14.

——— and ———. 1951. *Pratylenchus vulnus* n. sp. (Nematoda: Pratylenchinae), a parasite of trees and vines in California. Proc. Helminth. Soc. Wash. 18(1): 47–50.

——— and D. J. Raski. 1952. Soil fumigation to control root-lesion nematode, *Pratylenchus* sp., in tuberous begonia. Plant Dis. Reptr. 36(5): 201, 202.

Allison, J. L. 1956. Stem nematode of perennial forage legumes. (Abs.) Phyto-pathology 46(1): 6.

———. 1957. Nematodes and grassland farming. Plant Dis. Reptr. 39(5): 343–344.

Andrassy, I. 1954. Über einige von Daday beschriebene Nematoden-Arten. Zool. Anz. 152: 138–144.

———. 1958. *Hoplolaimus tylenchiformis* Daday, 1905 (Syn. *H. coronatus* Cobb, 1923) und die Gattungen der Unterfamilie Hoplolaiminae Filipjev, 1936. Nematologica 3(1): 44–56.

———. 1959. Taxonomische Übersicht der Dorylaimen (Nematoda), I. Acta Zool. Acad. Sci. Hungaricae 5(¾): 191–240.

———. 1960. Taxonomische Übersicht der Dorylaimen (Nematoda), II. Acta Zool. Acad. Sci. Hungaricae 6(½): 1–28.

Anonymous. 1958. Problems and progress in banana disease research. Department of Research, United Fruit Company. Fiftieth anniversary meetings, American Phytopathological Society.

Ark, P. A., and H. E. Thomas, 1936. *Anguillulina pratensis* in relation to root injury of apple and other fruit trees. Phytopathology 26(12): 1128–1134.

Artigas, P. 1927. Nematodeos de invertebrados. Bol. biol. fac. med. São Paulo 10: 209, 210.

Ashby, S. F. 1924. Red ring disease of the coconut. Proc. Ninth W.I. Agr. Conf. Jamaica, pp. 164–172.

Atanasoff, D. 1925. The *Dilophosphora* disease of cereals. Phytopathology 15(1): 1–40.

Atkins, J. G., and E. H. Todd. 1959. White tip disease of rice, III, Yield tests and varietal resistance. Phytopathology 49(4): 189–191.

Atkinson, G. F. 1889. A preliminary report upon the life-history and metamorphoses of a root-gall nematode, *Heterodera radicicola* (Greef) Müller, and the injuries caused by it upon the roots of various plants. Ala. Agr. Expt. Sta. Bull. n.s. 9.

Baermann, G. 1917. Eine einfache Methode zur Auffindung von Anklyostomum (Nematoden) Larven in Erdproben. Geneesk. Tijdschr. Nederl. Indië 57: 131–137.

Baines, R. C. 1950. Nematodes on citrus. Calif. Agr. 4(8): 7.

———, O. F. Clark, and W. P. Bitters. 1948. Susceptibility of some citrus and other plants to the citrus-root nematode, *Tylenchus semipenetrans*. (Abs.) Phytopathology 38(11): 912.

———, F. J. Foote, and J. P. Martin. 1957. Fumigate soil before replanting citrus for control of citrus nematode. Calif. Agr. Expt. Sta. Leaflet 91.

Baker, A. D. 1946. The potato-rot nematode, *Ditylenchus destructor* Thorne, 1945, attacking potatoes in Prince Edward Island. Sci. Agr. 26(3): 138, 139.

———. 1948. Some notes on experimental infestation of potato tubers with the potato-rot nematode, *Ditylenchus destructor* Thorne, 1945. Ann. Rept. Ent. Soc. Ontario 78: 32–39.

———. 1953. Rapid method for mounting nematodes in glycerin. Canad. Ent. 85: 32–38.

———, G. L. Brown, and A. B. James. 1954. Relationships of fungi, mites and the potato-rot nematode. Science 119(3081): 92, 93.

Ball, E., C. E. T. Mann, and L. N. Stanalind. 1927. Strawberry investigations at Long Ashton, II. Jour. Minst. Agr. 34: 627–641.

Bally, W., and G. A. Reydon. 1931. De tegenwoordige Stand van het Vraagstuk van de wortelaaltjes in die Koffiecultuur. Arch. Koffiecult. Nederl. Indië 5: 23–216.

Bastian, H. C. 1865. Monograph on the Anguillulidae. Linn. Soc. Lond. Trans. 25: 73–184.

Bauer, F. 1823. Microscopical observations of the suspension of muscular motions of *Vibrio tritici*. Philos. Trans. Roy. Soc. 113(8): 1–6.

Baunacke, W. 1922. Untersuchungen zur Biologie and Bekämpfung des Rübennematoden, *Heterodera schachtii* Schmidt. Arb. Biol. Reichanst. Land-u. Forstw. 11(3): 185–288.

Baylis, H. A., and R. Daubney. 1926. A synopsis of the families and genera of Nematoda. London.

Bazan de Segura, C. 1952. The golden nematode in Peru. Plant Dis. Reptr. 36: 253.

Beijerinck, M. W. 1883. De oorzak der kroefziekte van de jonge ajuinplanten. Maanblad uitgegeven van wege de Hollandsche maatschappij van Landbouw, V.

Benedict, W. G., and W. B. Mountain. 1956. Studies on the etiology of a root rot of winter wheat in southern Ontario. Canad. Jour. Bot. 34: 159–174.

Berkeley, M. J. 1855. Vibrio forming excrescences on the roots of cucumber plants. Gard. Chron. (14): 220.

Bessey, E. A. 1911. Root-knot and its control. U.S. Dept. Agr. Bull. 217. 89 pp.

Bingefors, S. 1957. Studies on breeding red clover for resistance to stem nematodes. Plant husbandry. Roy. Agr. College Sweden Publ. 8.

Blodgett, E. C. 1943. Stem nematode on potato; a new disease in Idaho. Plant Dis. Reptr. 27(24): 658, 659.

Boquet de la Gyre. 1899. La régénération des plantations de caféiers dans les Antilles. Bull. séances soc. nat. agr. France 59: 683–687.

Borellus, P. 1656. Historiarum, et observationum medicophysicarum. Centuriae quattuor. 384 pp.

Bory de Saint Vincent, G. J. B. M. 1824. Vibrion, Vibrio. Encyclopédie méthodique, Paris, Vol. 2, pp. 773–780.

Bosher, J. E. 1953. Potato rot caused by the iris bulb nematode in British Columbia. Plant Dis. Reptr. 37(4): 201, 202.

―――― and W. E. McKeen. 1954. Lyophilization and low temperature studies with the bulb and stem nematode, *Ditylenchus dipsaci* (Kühn, 1857) Filipjev. Proc. Helminth. Soc. Wash. 21(2): 113–117.

Bovien, P. 1937. Some types of association between nematodes and insects. Saertryk af Videnskabelige Medd. Fra Dansk. Naturhist. Forenig 101: 1–114.

―――. 1955. Host specificity and resistance in plant nematodes. Ann. Appl. Biol. 42: 382–390.

Breda de Haan, J. van. 1902. Een aaltjesziekte der rijst, omo mentek of omo banbang. Meded. uit's Lands Planten. 53: 1–65.

Brierly, P., F. F. Smith, and F. P. McWhorter. 1947. Symptoms and controls for diseases of Easter lilies. Florists' Rev., Sept. 4.

Brooks, A. N. 1931. Crimp—a nematode disease of strawberry. Fla. Agr. Expt. Sta. Tech. Bull. 235.

Brown, E. B. 1956. A seed-borne attack of chrysanthemum eelworm (*Aphelenchoides ritzema-bosi*) on the annual aster (*Callistephus chinensis*). Jour. Helminth. 30(⅔): 145–148.

Brown, Georgiana L. 1959. Three new species of the genus *Paratylenchus* from Canada (Nematoda: Criconematidae). Proc. Helminth. Soc. Wash. 26(1): 1–8.

Buhrer, Edna M. 1954. Common names of some important plant pathogenic nematodes. Plant Dis. Reptr. 38(8): 535–544.

―――, Corrine Cooper, and G. Steiner, 1933. A list of plants attacked by the root-knot nematode *Heterodera marioni*. Plant Dis. Reptr. 17(1): 64–69.

Burkart, A. 1937. Le seleccion de alfalfa al nematode del tallo *Anguillulina dipsaci*. Rev. Argentina agron. 4(3): 171–196.

Butler, E. J. 1913. An eelworm disease of rice. Agr. Res. Inst. Pusa, India, Bull. 34.

Butler, E. J. 1919. The rice worm (*Tylenchus angustus*) and its control. Mem. Dept. Agr. India 10(1):1–37.

Bütschli, O. 1873. Beiträge zur Kenntnis der freilebenden Nematoden. Nova Acta Acad. Leop. Carol. 36(5): 1–124, pls. 17–27.

Byars, L. P. 1914. Phytopathological notes: *Tylenchus dipsaci* in the United States. Phytopathology 4(2):118.

——. 1914a. Preliminary notes on the cultivation of the plant parasitic nematode, *Heterodera radicicola*. Phytopathology 4(4): 323–326.

——. 1920. A nematode disease of red clover and strawberry in the Pacific Northwest. Phytopathology 10(2): 91–95.

——. 1920a. The nematode disease of wheat caused by *Tylenchus tritici*. U.S. Dept. Agr. Bull. 842.

Camp, A. F. 1954. Introduction to Symposium on spreading decline of citrus. Fla. Citrus Expt. Sta., Lake Alfred. Mimeographed report no. 536.

Cannon, O. S. 1941. Potato nematode disease. Nassau County Farm and Home Bur. News 27(8): 3.

Carroll, J., and E. McMahon. 1935. Potato eelworm (*Heterodera schachtii*) investigations. Jour. Helminth. 13(2): 77–90.

Carter, H. J. 1959. On *Dracunculus* and microscopic Filaridae in the island of Bombay. Ann. Nat. Hist. 3.s. 4(19): 28–44; (20): 98–116.

Carter, W. 1943. A promising new soil amendment and disinfectant. Science 97(2521): 383–384.

Carvalho, R. de Sousa. 1942. O nematoide das raizes das plantas citricas, *Tylenchulus semipenetrans* Cobb, e sus possival relacao com a doenca "Podriadao das radicelas." Rev. agr. Piracicaba 17: 423–434.

Caveness, F. E. 1958. A study of nematodes associated with sugar beet production in selected northwest and north central states. Beet Sugar Development Foundation, Fort Collins, Colo. (Mimeographed.)

—— and H. J. Jensen. 1955. Modification of the centrifugal flotation technique for the isolation and concentration of nematodes and their eggs from soil and plant tissue. Proc. Helminth Soc. Wash. 22(2): 87–89.

Certes, A. 1889. Mission scientifique du Cap Horn 1882, 1883. Appendix, T. VI, Zoologie, Protozoaires, pp. 45–50.

Chandler, A. C. 1938. *Diploscapter coronata* as a facultative parasite of man, with a general review of vertebrate parasitism by rhabditoid worms. Parasitology 30(1): 44–55.

Chatin, J. 1884. Recherches sur l'anguillule de l'oignon. Paris.

Cheo, C. C. 1946. A note on the relation of nematodes (*Tylenchus tritici*) to the development of the bacterial disease of wheat caused by *Bacterium tritici*. Ann. Appl. Biol. 33(4): 446–449.

Chitwood, B. G. 1930. Studies on some physiological functions and morphological characters of *Rhabditis* (Rhabditidae, Nematoda). Jour. Morph. 49(1): 251–275.

——. 1933. Notes on nematode systematics and nomenclature. Jour. Parasit. 19(3): 242, 243.

——. 1933a. A note on the systematic position of *Cruznema cruznema* Artigas, 1927. Jour. Parasit. 19(3): 253.

——. 1933b. On some nematodes of the superfamily Rhabditoidea and their status as parasites of reptiles and amphibians. Jour. Wash. Acad. Sci. 23(12): 508–520.

——. 1935. Nomenclatorial notes, I. Proc. Helminth. Soc. Wash. 2(1): 51–54.

Chitwood, B. G. 1936. Observations on the chemical nature of the cuticle of *Ascaris lumbricoides* var. *suis*. Proc. Helminth. Soc. Wash. 3(2): 39–40.

——. 1938. Further studies on nemic skeletoids and their significance in chemical control of nemic pests. Proc. Helminth. Soc. Wash. 5(2):68–75.

——. 1949. Ring nematodes (Criconematinae). A possible factor in decline and replanting peach orchards. Proc. Helminth. Soc. Wash. 16(1): 6, 7.

——. 1949a. Root-knot nematodes, Part I. A revision of the genus *Meloidogyne* Goeldi, 1887. Proc. Helminth. Soc. Wash. 16(2): 90–104.

——. 1951. The golden nematode of potatoes. U.S. Dept. Agr. Cir. 875.

——. 1952. Nematocidal action of halogenated hydrocarbons. Advances in Chemistry Ser. 7: 91–99.

——. 1957. Two new species of the genus *Criconema* Hofmänner and Menzel, 1914. Proc. Helminth. Soc. Wash. 24(1): 57–61.

——. 1958. The classification of plant-parasitic nemas and related forms. Fifteenth International Congress of Zoology, Sect. VIII, Paper 28.

—— and W. Birchfield. 1957. A new genus, *Hemicriconemoides* (Criconematidae: Tylenchida). Proc. Helminth. Soc. Wash. 24(2): 80–86.

—— and Edna M. Buhrer. 1946. The life history of the golden nematode of potatoes, *Heterodera rostochiensis,* Wollenweber, under Long Island, New York, conditions. Phytopathology 36(3): 180–189.

—— and Mabel B. Chitwood. 1934. *Daubaylia potomaca,* n. sp., a nematode parasite of snails with a note on other nemas associated wih molluscs. Proc. Helminth. Soc. Wash. 1(1): 8, 9.

—— and ——. 1937. An introduction to nematology. 213 pp.

—— and ——. 1950. An introduction to nematology. (Rev. ed.)

——, C. I. Hannon, and R. P. Esser. 1956. A new nematode genus, *Meloidera,* linking the genera *Heterodera* and *Meloidogyne*. Phytopathology 46(5): 264–266.

——, F. A. Hassis, and F. S. Blanton. 1941. Hot-water–formalin treatment (at 110°–111°F.) of field grown and of forced narcissus bulbs, infected with the bulb or stem nematode, *Ditylenchus dipsaci*. Proc. Helminth. Soc. Wash. 8(2): 44–50.

——, A. G. Newhall, and R. L. Clement. 1940. Onion bloat or eelworm rot, a disease caused by the bulb or stem nematode, *Ditylenchus dipsaci* (Kühn) Filipjev. Proc. Helminth. Soc. Wash. 7(1): 44–51.

——, A. W. Specht, and L. Havis. 1952. Root-knot nematodes, III. Effects of *Meloidogyne incognita* and *M. javanica* on some peach rootstocks. Plant and Soil 4(1): 77–95.

—— and A. C. Tarjan. 1957. A redescription of *Atylenchus decalineatus* Cobb, 1913 (Nematoda: Tylenchinae). Proc. Helminth. Soc. Wash. 24(1): 48–52.

—— and E. E. Wehr. 1934. The value of cephalic structures as characters in nematode classification, with special reference to the superfamily Spiruroidea. Zeitschr. Parasit. 7(3): 273–335.

Christie, J. R. 1936. The development of root-knot nematode galls. Phytopathology 26(1): 1–22.

——. 1938. Two distinct strains of the nematode, *Aphelenchoides fragariae* occurring on strawberry plants in the United States. Jour. Agr. Res. 57(1): 73–80.

——. 1938a. Pathogenicity of culture-reared specimens of the bud-and-leaf nematode and the susceptibility of different strawberry varieties. Phytopathology 28(8): 587–591.

Christie, J. R. 1939. Predaceous nematodes of the genus *Aphelenchoides* from Hawaii. Jour. Wash. Acad. Sci. 29(4): 161–171.

——. 1942. A description of *Aphelenchoides besseyi*, n. sp. the summer dwarf nematode of strawberries, with comments on the identity of *Aphelenchoides subtenuis* (Cobb, 1926) and *Aphelenchoides hodsoni* Goodey, 1935. Proc. Helminth. Soc. Wash. 9(2): 82–84.

——. 1942a. The influence of chrysanthemum propagating methods on dissemination of the foliar nematode. Proc. Helminth. Soc. Wash. 9(2): 1–4.

——. 1946. Host-parasite relationships of the root-knot nematode, *Heterodera marioni*, II. Some effects of the host on the parasite. Phytopathology 36(5): 340–352.

——. 1949. Host parasite relationships of the root-knot nematodes, *Meloidogyne* spp., III. The nature of resistance in plants to root knot. Proc. Helminth. Soc. Wash. 16(2): 104–108.

——. 1951. The feeding habits of plant parasitic nematodes. Fla. State Hort. Soc. 64: 120–122.

——. 1952. Some new nematodes of critical importance to Florida growers. Proc. Soil Sci. Soc. Fla. 30–39.

——. 1952a. Ectoparasitic nematodes of plants. (Abs.) Phytopathology 42(9): 483, 484.

——. 1953. Ectoparasitic nematodes of plants. Phytopathology 43(6): 295–297.

——. 1957. The yellows disease of pepper (*Piper*) and spreading decline of citrus. Plant Dis. Reptr. 41(4): 267, 268.

——. 1959. Plant nematodes, their bionomics and control. Florida Agricultural Experiment Station, 256 pp.

—— and F. E. Albin. 1944. Host-parasite relationships of the root-knot nematode, *Heterodera marioni*, I. The question of races. Proc. Helminth. Soc. Wash. 1(1): 31–37.

—— and R. C. Arndt. 1936. Feeding habits of the nematodes, *Aphelenchoides parietinus* and *Aphelenchus avenae*. Phytopathology 26(7): 698–701.

—— and W. Birchfield. 1958. Scribner's lesion nematode, a destructive pest of amaryllis. Plant Dis. Reptr. 42(7): 873–875.

——, A. N. Brooks, and V. G. Perry. 1952. The sting nematode, *Belonlaimus gracilis*, a parasite of major importance on strawberries, celery and sweet corn in Florida. Phytopathology 42(4): 173–176.

—— and Grace S. Cobb. 1941. Notes on the life history of the root-knot nematode, *Heterodera marioni*. Proc. Helminth. Soc. Wash. 8(1): 23–26.

—— and Louise Crossman. 1935. Water temperatures lethal to begonia, chrysanthemum, and strawberry "strains" of the nematode *Aphelenchoides fragariae*. Proc. Helminth. Soc. Wash. 2(2): 98–103.

—— and ——. 1936. Notes on the strawberry strains of the bud and leaf nematode, *Aphelenchoides fragariae*, I. Proc. Helminth. Soc. Wash. 3(2): 69–72.

—— and L. Havis. 1948. Relative susceptibility of certain peach stocks to races of the root-knot nematode. Plant Dis. Reptr. 31(4): 153–154.

—— and V. G. Perry. 1951. A root disease of plants caused by a nematode of the genus *Trichodorus*. Science 113(2937): 491–493.

—— and ——. 1951a. Removing nematodes from soil. Proc. Helminth. Soc. Wash. 18:106–108.

—— and Neil Stevens. 1933. Strawberry dwarf. U. S. Dept. Agr. Cir. 297.

Clayton, C. N. 1947. Roots of Shalil peach seedlings are not resistant to all races of the root-knot nematode. Plant Dis. Reptr. 32(12): 510–514.

Clayton, E. E., K. L. Shaw, T. E. Smith, J. G. Gaines, and T. W. Graham. 1944. Tobacco disease control by crop rotation. Phytopathology 34(1): 870–883.

Cobb, Grace S., G. Steiner, and F. S. Blanton. 1934. Observations on the significance of weeds as carriers of the bulb or stem nematode in narcissus plantings. Plant Dis. Reptr. 18(10): 127–129.

——— and A. L. Taylor. 1953. *Heterodera leptonepia* n. sp., a cyst-forming nematode found in soil with stored potatoes. Proc. Helminth. Soc. Wash. 20(1): 13–15.

Cobb, N. A. 1890. *Tylenchus* and root-gall. Agr. Gaz. N.S. Wales 1(2): 213, 214.

———. 1891. Strawberry bunch. Agr. Gaz. N.S. Wales 2: 390–401.

———. 1893. Nematodes, mostly Australian and Fijian. Dept. Agr. N.S. Wales Misc. Publ. 13.

———. 1898. Extract from ms report on the parasites of stock. Agr. Gaz. N.S. Wales 9: 296–321; 419–454.

———. 1906. Free-living nematodes inhabiting the soil about the roots of cane, and their relation to root diseases. (Fungus maladies of the sugar cane.) Hawaiian Sugar Planters' Assoc., Div. Path. and Physiol., Bull. 5:163–195.

———. 1913. Notes on *Mononchus* and *Tylenchulus.* Jour. Wash. Acad. Sci. 3(12): 288, 289.

———. 1913a. New nematode genera found inhabiting fresh water and non-brackish soils. Jour. Wash. Acad. Sci. 3(16): 432–444.

———. 1914. North American free-living fresh-water nematodes. Amer. Micr. Soc. Trans. 33(2): 69–134.

———. 1914a. Nematodes and their relationships. U.S. Dept. Agr. Yearbook, 1914, pp. 457–490.

———. 1914b. Citrus-root nematode. Jour. Agr. Res. 2(3): 217–230.

———. 1915. *Tylenchus similis,* the cause of a root disease of sugar cane and banana. Jour. Agr. Res. 4(6): 561–568.

———. 1917. A new parasitic nema found infesting cotton and potatoes. Jour. Agr. Res. 11(1): 27–33.

———. 1917a. The mononchs. Soil Sci. 3(5): 1–124.

———. 1918. Estimating the nema population of soil. U.S. Dept. Agr., Bur. Plant Ind., Agr. Tech. Cir. 1: 1–48.

———. 1918a. Nematodes of the slow-sand filter beds of American cities. Contr. Sci. Nematol. 7: 189–212.

———. 1919. A new nema, *Tylenchus musicola,* n. sp. said to cause a serious affection on the Bluggoe banana in Grenada, British West Indies. W.I. Bull. 17: 179–182.

———. 1919a. A newly discovered nematode, *Aphelenchus cocophilus* n. sp., connected with a serious disease of the coconut palm. W.I. Bull. 17(4): 203–210.

———. 1920. One hundred new nemas. Contr. Sci. Nematol. 9: 217–343.

———. 1920a. Bursal formula for *Rhabditis.* Jour. Parasit. 6(4): 198.

———. 1922. Two tree infesting nemas of the genus *Tylenchus.* Ann. zool. appl. (Chile) 9: 27–35.

———. 1922a. Notes on the coconut nema of Panama. Jour. Parasit. 9: 44–45.

———. 1923. An amendation of *Hoplolaimus* Daday 1905 nec. auctores. Contr. Sci. Nematol. 13: 363–370.

Cobb, N. A. 1923a. Notes on *Paratylenchus* a genus of nemas. Contr. Sci. Nematol. 14; reprinted Jour. Wash. Acad. Sci. 13(12): 254–257.

———. 1923b. Observations on nemas. Salivary glands of the nemic genera *Tylenchus* and *Aphelenchus*. Jour. Parasit. 9: 236–238.

———. 1924. Notes on nemas. Proc. Helminth. Soc. Wash.; Jour. Parasit. 11: 102, 103.

———. 1925. Biological relationships of the mathematical series 1, 2, 4, etc. Contr. Sci. Nematol. 15: 371–374.

———. 1927. Notes in Proc. Helminth. Soc. Wash.; Jour. Parasit. 14:54–72.

———. 1929. Observations on the morphology and physiology of nemas including notes on new species. Jour. Wash. Acad. Sci. 19(10): 283–286.

———. 1932. The English word "nema." Jour. Amer. Med. Assoc. 98: 75, 76.

———. 1932a. Nematosis of a grass of the genus *Cynodon* caused by a new nema of the genus *Tylenchus* Bastian. Jour. Wash. Acad. Sci. 22(9): 243–245.

———. 1933. New nemic genera and species, with taxonomic notes. Jour. Parasit. 20(2): 81–94.

Cobbold, T. S. 1884. New parasites from the horse and ass. Veterinarian, Lond. 57(⅓₀): 4–7.

Colbran, R. C. 1953. Problems in tree replacement, 1. The root lesion nematode, *Pratylenchus coffeae* Zimmerman as a factor in the growth and replant trees in apple orchards. Australian Jour. Agr. Res. 4(4): 384–389.

———. 1954. Problems in tree replacement, 2. The effect of certain methods of management on the nematode fauna of an orchard soil. Australian Jour. Agr. Sci. 20: 234–237.

Cooper, B. A. 1955. A preliminary key to British species of *Heterodera* for use in soil examination. Proc. Univ. Nottingham Second Easter School Agr. Sci. Soil Zool., pp. 269–280.

Corbbett, M. K. 1959. Diseases of the coconut palm. Fla. Agr. Expt. Sta. Jour. Ser. 846; reprint from Principes, Jour. Palm Soc., July.

Corder, Margaret N., Edna M. Buhrer, and G. Thorne. 1936. A list of plants attacked by the sugar beet nematode *Heterodera schachtii*. Plant Dis. Reptr. 20(3): 38–47.

Cornu, M. 1879. Études sur le *Phylloxera vastatrix*. Mém. prés. acad. sci. Paris 26: 164–174.

Courtney, W. D. 1936. An apparent natural transfer of the bulb and stem nematode from clover to the strawberry plant. Phytopathology 26(6): 607–609.

———. 1945. Nematode infection of Croft Easter lilies. Phytopathology 35(7): 572.

———. 1952. The teasel nematode, *Ditylenchus dipsaci* (Kühn, 1857) Filipjev, 1936. Jour. Wash. Acad. Sci. 42(9): 303–309.

———. 1953. Nematodes in bulbs. U.S. Dept. Agr. Yearbook, 1953, pp. 621–624.

——— and H. B. Howell. 1952. Investigations on the bent grass nematode, *Anguina agrostis* (Steinbuch, 1799) Filipjev, 1936. Plant Dis. Reptr. 36(3): 75–83.

Cralley, E. M. 1949. White tip of rice. (Abs.) Phytopathology 39(1): 5.

———. 1957. The effect of seeding methods on the severity of white tip of rice. (Abs.) Phytopathology 47(1): 7.

Crosse, J. E., and R. S. Pitcher. 1952. Studies on the relationship of eelworms and bacteria to certain plant diseases. 1. The etiology of strawberry cauliflower disease. Ann. Appl. Biol. 39(4): 475–484.

Crossman, Louise, and J. R. Christie. 1936. A list of plants attacked by the leaf nematode, *Aphelenchoides fragariae*. Plant Dis. Reptr. 20(10): 155–165.

Daday, E. von. 1905. Untersuchungen über die Süsswasser-Mikrofauna Paraguaya. Zoologica, Stuttgart (1844). 374 pp.

Dallimore, C. E. 1955. Methods of increasing the efficacy of soil fumigation in experimental fields. Plant Dis. Reptr. 39(6): 511–514.

—— and G. Thorne. 1951. Infection of sugar beets by *Ditylenchus destructor* Thorne, the potato rot nematode. Phytopathology 41(10): 872–874.

Darling, H. M., L. R. Faulkner, and P. Wallendal. 1957. Culturing the potato rot nematode. (Abs.) Phytopathology 47(1): 7.

Dastur, J. F. 1936. A nematode disease of rice in the central provinces. Proc. Indian Acad. Sci. 4(2): 108–122.

Davaine, C. 1857. Recherches sur l'anguillule du blé niellé considérée au point de vue de l'histoire naturelle et de l'agriculture. 88 pp. Paris.

Day, L. H., and W. P. Tufts. 1939. Further notes on nematode resistant root stocks for deciduous trees. Proc. Amer. Soc. Hort. Sci. 37: 327–329.

Diesing, C. M. 1851. Systema helminthum, Vol. 2.

Dimock, A. W. 1953. Control of three ills of chrysanthemum. U.S. Dept. Agr. Yearbook, pp. 592–595.

—— and C. H. Ford. 1949. Parathion controls leaf nematode disease of chrysanthemums. N.Y. State Floral Growers Bull. 50: 8.

—— and ——. 1950. Control of foliar nematode of chrysanthemum with parathion sprays. (Abs.). Phytopathology 40(1): 7.

Dougherty, E. C. 1953. The genera of the subfamily Rhabditidae Micoletzky, 1922 (Nematoda). Thapar Commemoration Volume, pp. 69–76.

——. 1955. The genera and species of the subfamily Rhabditinae Micoletzky, 1922 (Nematoda): a nomenclatorial analysis—including an addendum on the composition of the family Rhabditidae Örley, 1880. Jour. Helminth. 29(3): 105–152.

—— and V. Nigon. 1949. A new species of the free living nematode genus *Rhabditis* of interest in comparative physiology and genetics. Jour. Parasit. 35(6, Sect. 2): 11.

Drechsler, C. 1941. Some hyphomycetes parasitic on free living terricolus nematodes. Phytopathology 31(9): 733–801.

Dropkin, V. H. 1953. Studies on the variability of the anal plate patterns in pure lines of *Meloidogyne* spp., the root-knot nematode. Proc. Helminth. Soc. Wash. 20(1): 32–39.

DuCharme, E. P., and W. Birchfield. 1956. Physiologic races of the burrowing nematode. Phytopathology 46(11): 615, 616.

Dujardin, F. 1845. Histoire naturelle des helminths. Paris.

Eberth, C. J. 1863. Untersuchungen über Nematoden. Leipzig.

Edwards, E. T. 1932. Stem nematode disease of lucerne. Agr. Gaz. N.S. Wales 43(4/5): 531–544.

Ellenby, C. 1954. Susceptibility of South American tuber-forming *Solanum* to the potato root eelworm, *Heterodera rostochiensis* Wollenweber. Empire Jour. Expt. Agr. 13: 158–168.

Fassuliotis, G., and J. Feldmesser. 1952. An attempt to concentrate golden nematode-stimulatory elements from potato leachings. Phytopathology 42(9): 466. (Abs.)

—— and ——. 1954. Infection of eggplant, *Solanum melongena*, by the golden nematode, *Heterodera rostochiensis*. Plant Dis. Reptr. 38(11): 791, 792.

Fawcett, S. G. M. 1938. A disease of the Australian grass *Microlaena stipoides* R., Br. caused by the nematode *Anguillulina microlaenae* n. sp. Jour. Helminth. 16(1): 17–32.

Feder, W. A., et al. 1958. Citrus varieties, species and relatives susceptible to attack and damage by the burrowing nematode, *Radopholus similis*. Plant Dis. Reptr. 42(8): 934–940.

Feldmesser, J., R. V. Rebois, and A. L. Taylor. 1959. Progress report on growth responses of burrowing nematode infected citrus following chemical treatments under greenhouse conditions. Plant Dis. Reptr. 43(2): 261–263.

Fenwick, D. W. 1940. Methods for the recovery and counting of cysts of *Heterodera schachtii* from soil. Jour. Helminth. 18(4): 155–172.

———. 1943. A refinement of Gemmell's single cyst technique. Jour. Helminth. 21(1): 33–36.

———. 1952. The bio-assay of potato root diffusate. Ann. Appl. Biol. 39: 457–467.

———. 1957. Red ring disease of coconuts in Trinidad and Tobago. Colonial Office Report.

——— and Mary T. Franklin. 1942. Identification of *Heterodera* species by larval length, technique for estimating the constants determining the length and variations within a given species. Jour. Helminth. 20(¾): 67–114.

Ferris, Virginia R., and B. M. Siegel. 1957. Electron microscopy of golden nematode cyst wall. Nematologica 2(1): 16–18.

Fielding, M. J. 1951. Observations on the length of dormancy in certain plant infecting nematodes. Proc. Helminth. Soc. Wash. 18(2): 110–112.

Filipjev, I. N. 1934. The classification of the free living nematodes and their relation to the parasitic nematodes. Smithsonian Misc. Coll. (3216) 89(6): 1–63.

———. 1936. On the classification of the Tylenchinae. Proc. Helminth. Soc. Wash. 3(2): 80–82.

——— and J. H. Schuurmans-Stekhoven, Jr. 1941. A manual of agricultural helminthology. E. J. Brill, Leiden. 878 pp.

Fischer, M. 1894. Über eine Clematis-Krankheit. Ber. physiol. Lab. Univ. Halle 3: 1–11.

Franklin, Mary T. 1938. On the occurrence of *Heterodera* cysts in various soils on the roots of *Agrostis stolonifera* L. Jour. Helminth. 16(1): 5, 6.

———. 1938a. Experiments with the cysts of the potato eelworm, *Heterodera schachtii*, of different ages. Jour. Helminth. 16(2): 67–76.

———. 1939. On the structure of the cyst wall of *Heterodera schachtii* Schmidt. Jour. Helminth. 17(3): 127–134.

———. 1940. On the specific status of the so-called biological strains of *Heterodera schachtii*. Jour. Helminth. 18(4): 193–208.

———. 1945. On *Heterodera cruciferae* n. sp. of brassicas and on a *Heterodera* strain infecting clover and dock. Jour. Helminth. 21(⅔): 71–84.

———. 1950. Two species of *Aphelenchoides* associated with strawberry bud disease in Britain. Ann. Appl. Biol. 37(1): 1–8.

———. 1951. The cyst-forming species of *Heterodera*. Imp. Bur. Agr. Parasit. 147 pp.

———. 1952. A disease of *Scabiosa caucasica* caused by the nematode *Aphelenchoides blastophorus* n. sp. Ann. Appl. Biol. 39(1): 56–60.

Franklin, Mary T. 1955. A redescription of *Aphelenchoides parientinus* (Bastian, 1865) Steiner, 1932. Jour. Helminth. 29(½): 65–76.

———. 1957. *Aphelenchoides composticola* n. sp. and *A. saprophilus* n. sp. from mushroom compost and rotting plant tissues. Nematologica 2(4): 306–313.

——— and J. B. Goodey. 1949. A cotton-blue lactophenol technique for mounting plant parasitic nematodes. Jour. Helminth. 23(¾): 175–178.

Fuchs, A. G. 1930. Neue an Borkenkäfer und Rüsselkäfer gebundene Nematoden, halbparasitische und Wohnungeseinmiether. Zool. Jahrb. Syst. 59: 505–696.

———. 1931. *Seineura* gen. nov. Zool. Anz. 98: 37.

———. 1937. Neue parasitische und halbparasitische Nematoden bei Borkenkäfern und einige andere Nematoden. Zool. Jahrb. 70(⅚): 291–380.

———. 1938. Neue parasitische und halbparasitische Nematoden bei Borkenkäfern und einige andere Nematoden. Zool. Jahrb. Syst. 71: 123–190.

Fuchs, O. 1911. Beiträge zur Biologie der Rübennematoden, *Heterodera schachtii*. Zeitschr. Landwirts. Versuch. Österreich 14:923–949.

Gadd, C. H., and C. A. Loos. 1941a. Observations on the life history of *Anguillulina pratensis*. Ann. Appl. Biol. 28: 39–51.

——— and ———. 1941b. Host specialization of *Anguillulina pratensis*, I. Attractiveness of roots. Ann. Appl. Biol. 28: 373–381.

——— and ———. 1941c. Host specialization of *Anguillulina pratensis*, II. Behavior of the parasite within the roots. Ann. Appl. Biol. 28: 382–388.

Gemmell, A. R. 1943. The resistance of potato varieties to *Heterodera schachtii* Schmidt, the potato-root eelworm. Ann. Appl. Biol. 30: 67–70.

Gervais, P., and P. J. van Beneden. 1859. Zoologie médicale, Vol. 2.

Godfrey, G. H. 1923. The eelworm: A menace to alfalfa in America. U.S. Dept. Agr. Cir. 297.

———. 1924. Dissemination of stem and bulb-infesting nematode, *Tylenchus dipsaci*, in seeds of certain composites. Jour. Agr. Res. 28(5): 473–478.

———. 1929. A destructive root disease of pineapple and other plants due to *Tylenchus brachyurus* n. sp. Phytopathology 19(7): 611–629.

———. 1931. The host plants of the "burrowing nematode," *Tylenchus similis*. Phytopathology 21(3): 315–322.

——— and M. B. McKay. 1924. The stem nematode, *Tylenchus dipsaci*, on wild hosts in the Northwest. U.S. Dept. Agr. Bull. 1229.

——— and J. M. Oliveira. 1932. The development of root-knot nematode in relation to root tissues of pineapple and cowpea. Phytopathology 22(4): 325–348.

———, ———, and H. M. Hoshino. 1934. Increased efficiency of chloropicrin for nematode control. Phytopathology 24(12): 1332–1346.

——— and C. E. Scott. 1935. New economic hosts of the stem and bulb infesting nematode. Phytopathology 25(11): 1003–1010.

———. 1943. Effect of summer plowing on root knot. Texas Agr. Expt. Sta. Progress Rept. No. 837.

Goeldi, E. A. 1887. Relatorio sobre a molestia do cafeeiro na provincia do Rio de Janeiro. Apparently an advanced separate of Arch. mus. nac. Rio de Janeiro 8: 7–121, 1892.

Goffart, H. 1928. Zur Systematik und Biologie von *Aphelenchus ritzemabosi* Schwartz (Nemat.). Zool. Anz. 76: 242–271.

———. 1929. Beobachtungen über *Anguillulina pratensis* deMan. Zeitschr. Parasitenk. 2(1): 97–120.

Goffart, H. 1930. Die Aphelenchen der Kulturpflanzen. Monographien zum Pflanzenschutz 4.

———. 1930a. Rassenstudien an *Heterodera schachtii* Schm. Arb. biol. Reichsanst. Land- u. Forstw. 18(1): 83–100.

———. 1932. Untersuchungen am Hafernematoden, *Heterodera schachtii* Schm. Unter besonderer Berücksichtigung der schleswig-holsteinischen Verhältnisse, I. Arb. biol. Reichsanst. Land- u. Forstw. 20(1): 1–26.

———. 1936. *Heterodera schachtii* Schmidt an gemeiner Hanfnessel (*Galeopsis tetrahit* L.) und an Kakteen. Zeitschr. Parasitenk. 8(5): 528–532.

———. 1941. Der Göttinger Erbsennematode (*Heterodera goettingiana*), ein Rückblick auf eine 50 jährige Entwicklung. Zbl. Bakt., Abt. 2, 104(¼): 81–86.

———. 1942. *Anguina klebahni* n. sp. (Tylenchidae), ein Nematode in Blüten von *Primula florindae* Ward. Zool. Anz. 138: 174–179.

———. 1951. Nematoden der Kulturpflanzen Europas. Verl. für Landw. Gartenb. und Forstw. Berlin.

Golden, A. M. 1956. Taxonomy of the spiral nematodes (*Rotylenchus* and *Helicotylenchus*), and the developmental stages and host-parasite relationships of *R. buxophilus*, n. sp. attacking boxwood. Univ. Md. Agr. Exp. Sta. Bull. A-85: 1–28.

———. 1957. Occurrence of *Radopholus gracilis* (Nematoda: Tylenchidae) in the United States. Plant Dis. Reptr. 41(2): 91.

———. 1958. *Dolichodorus similis* (Dolichodorinae), a new species of plant nematode. Proc. Helminth. Soc. Wash. 25(1): 17–20.

Good, J. M., W. K. Robertson, and L. G. Thompson, Jr. 1954. Effect of crop rotations on the populations of the meadow nematode, *Pratylenchus leiocephalus*, in Norfolk sandy loam. Plant Dis. Reptr. 38(2): 178–180.

Goodey, J. B. 1948. The galls caused by *Anguillulina balsamophila* (Thorne) on the leaves of *Wyethia amplexicaulis* Nutt. and *Balsamorhiza sagittata* Nutt. Jour. Helminth. 22(2): 109–116.

———. 1951. The potato tuber nematode, *Ditylenchus destructor*, Thorne, 1945; the cause of eelworm disease in bulbous iris. Ann. Appl. Biol. 38(1): 79–90.

———. 1951a. A new species of hyphomycete attacking the stem eelworm, *Ditylenchus dipsaci*. Trans. British Myco. Soc. 34(3): 270–272.

———. 1952. Investigations into the host range of *Ditylenchus destructor* and *D. dipsaci*. Ann. Appl. Biol 39(2): 221–228.

———. 1952a. The influence of the host on the dimensions of the plant parasitic nematode, *Ditylenchus destructor*. Ann. Appl. Biol. 39(4): 468–474.

———. 1957. Laboratory methods for work with plant and soil nematodes. Tech. Bull. Minist. Agr. Lond. 2. (3d ed.)

———. 1957a. *Hoplolaimus proporicus* n. sp. (Hoplolaiminae: Tylenchida). Nematologica 2(2): 108–113.

———. 1958. *Paraphelenchus myceliophthorus* n. sp. (Nematode: Aphelenchidae). Nematologica 3(1): 1–5.

———. 1958a. *Sphaeronema minutissimum* n. sp. (Sphaeronematinae: Tylenchulidae). Nematologica 3(3): 168–172.

———. 1960. *Rhadinaphelenchus cocophilus* (Cobb, 1919) n. comb., the nematode associated with "Red Ring" disease of coconuts. Nematologica 5(2): 98–102.

Goodey, T. 1923. A review of the plant parasitic members of the genus *Aphelenchus*. Jour. Helminth. 1(4): 143–156.

———. 1925. *Tylenchus hordei* Schøyen, a nematode parasite causing galls on the roots of barley and other Graminae. Jour. Helminth. 3(5): 193–202.

———. 1926. *Hexatylus viviparus* gen. et sp. nov., a nematode found in a diseased potato tuber. Jour. Helminth. 4(1): 27–30.

———. 1928. The species of the genus *Aphelenchus*. Jour. Helminth. 6: 121–160.

———. 1929. Some details of comparative anatomy in *Aphelenchus*, *Tylenchus* and *Heterodera*. Jour. Helminth. 7(4): 223–230.

———. 1930. On *Tylenchus agrostis* (Steinbuch, 1799). Jour. Helminth. 8(4): 197–210.

———. 1932. On the nomenclature of root-gall nematodes. Jour. Helminth. 9(1): 21–28.

———. 1932a. Some observations on the biology of the root-gall nematode, *Anguillulina radicicola* Greeff (1872). Jour. Helminth. 10(1): 33–44.

———. 1932b. The genus *Anguillulina* Gerv. & v. Ben., 1859, vel *Tylenchus* Bastian, 1865. Jour. Helminth. 10(⅔): 75–180.

———. 1933. Plant parasitic nematodes and the diseases they cause. 306 pp.

———. 1933a. *Anguillulina graminophila* n. sp., a nematode causing galls on the leaves of fine bent-grass. Jour. Helminth. 11(1): 45, 46.

———. 1934. *Anguillulina cecidoplastes* n. sp., a nematode causing galls on the grass, *Andropogon pertusus* Willd. Jour. Helminth. 12(1): 225–236.

———. 1934a. Observations of *Paratylenchus macrophallus* (deMan, 1880). Jour. Helminth. 12(2): 79–88.

———. 1935. *Aphelenchoides hodsoni* n. sp., a nematode affecting narcissus bulbs and leaves. Jour. Helminth. 13(3): 167–172.

———. 1935a. Observations on a nematode disease of yams. Jour. Helminth. 13(3): 173–190.

———. 1936. On *Anguillulina oryzae* (v. Breda de Haan, 1902) Goodey, 1932, a nematode parasite of the roots of rice, *Oryza sativa* L. Jour. Helminth. 14(2): 107–112.

———. 1936a. Some applied biological aspects of problems relating to plant parasitic nematodes. Ann. Appl. Biol. 23(2): 203–230.

———. 1937. Two methods for staining nematodes in plant tissues. Jour. Helminth. 15(3): 137–144.

———. 1937a. Observations on the susceptibility of certain varieties of oats to "tulip root" caused by the stem eelworm, *Anguillulina dipsaci*. Jour. Helminth. 15(4): 203–214.

———. 1938. Observations on the destruction of the stem eelworm, *Anguillulina dipsaci*, by the fungus *Arthrobotrys oligospora* Fres. Jour. Helminth. 16(3): 159–164.

———. 1943. *Anguillulina dipsaci* in the inflorescence of onions and in samples of onion seed. Jour. Helminth. 21(1): 22–30.

———. 1945. *Anguillulina dipsaci* on onion seed and its control by fumigation with methyl bromide. Jour. Helminth. 21(⅔): 45–59.

———. 1945a. *Anguillulina brenani* n. sp. a nematode causing galls on the moss, *Pottia bryoides*. Mitt. Jour. Helminth. 21(⅔): 105–110.

———. 1951. Soil and freshwater nematodes.

——— and J. B. Goodey. 1949. Tuber-rot eelworm of potato and its weed hosts. Jour. Helminth. 23(1): 89.

Goodey, T., and Marjorie J. Triffitt. 1927. On the presence of flagellates in the intestine of the nematode *Diplogaster longicaudata*. Protozoology (Suppl. to Jour. Helminth.) 3: 47–58.

Goto, K., and R. Fukatsu. 1956. Studies on the white tip of rice plant. Inst. Agri. Sci. (Japan) Ser. C, No. 6.

Goto, S., and J. W. Gibler. 1951. A leaf gall forming nematode on *Calmagrostis canadensis* (Michx.) Beauv. Plant Dis. Reptr. 35(4): 215, 216.

Gould, C. J. 1950. Diseases of bulbous iris. Wash. State College Ext. Bull. 424.

Graham, T. W. 1951. Nematode root rot of tobacco and other plants. S.C. Agr. Expt. Sta. Bull. 390.

———. 1954. The tobacco stunt nematode in North Carolina. (Abs.) Phytopathology 46(1): 12–13.

———. 1955. Pathogenicity of *Rotylenchus brachyurus* and *Criconemoides* sp. on tobacco and peanuts. (Abs.) Phytopathology 6: 347.

——— and Q. L. Holdeman. 1953. The sting nematode, *Belonolaimus gracilis* Steiner, a parasite of cotton and other crops in South Carolina. Phytopathology 43(8): 443–449.

Granek, I. 1955. Additional morphological differences between the cysts of *Heterodera rostochiensis* and *H. tabacum*. Plant Dis. Reptr. 39(10): 716–718.

Greeff, R. 1872. Ueber nematoden in Wurtzelanschwellungen (Gallen) verschiedener Pflanzen. Sitzber. Ges. Naturw. Marburg 169–174.

Gutierrez, R. O. 1947. El nematode de las raicillas de los citrus *Tylenchulus semipenetrans* en la Republica Argentina. Rev. invest. agr., Buenos Aires 1: 119–146.

Hague, D. W. 1954. Concentration of potato-root diffusate by vacuum distillation. Nature, Lond. 174: 1018.

Halsted, B. D. 1891. Nematodes as enemies of plants. Ann. Rept. N.J. Agr. Exp. Sta. Bull., pp. 366–370.

Hardy, J. 1850. On the effects produced by some insects, etc., on plants. Ann. Mag. Nat. Hist., Vol. VI, 2d Ser., pp. 182–183.

Hastings, R. J. 1939. The biology of the meadow nematode. Canad. Jour. Res. (Sect. D) 17: 39–44.

——— and J. E. Bosher. 1938. A study of the pathogenicity of the meadow nematode and associated fungus, *Cylindrocarpon radicicola* Wr. Canad. Jour. Res. (Sect. C) 16: 225–229.

——— and ———. 1952. The discovery of nematodes belonging to the genus *Heterodera* in British Columbia and their host relationships. Sci. Agr. 32: 507–510.

Havertz, D. S. 1957. Nematode pathogenicity to crested wheat grass, *Agropyron cristatum* (L.) Gaertn, at U.S. Forest Service Experiment Station, Benmore, Utah. University of Utah. (Unpublished thesis.)

Hegemeyer, Joyce W. 1951. A new stage in the life cycle of the golden nematode *Heterodera rostochiensis* Wollenweber. Proc. Helminth. Soc. Wash. 18(2): 112–114.

Henderson, V. E. 1951. Some host relationships of the potato-rot nematode, *Ditylenchus destructor* Thorne, 1945. Nature 167: 952, 953.

Henslow, J. S. 1841. Report on the diseases of wheat. Jour. Roy. Agr. Soc. England 2: 1–25.

Hewett, W. B., D. J. Raski, and A. C. Goheen. 1958. Nematode vector of soil-borne fanleaf virus of grapevines. Phytopathology 48(11): 586–595.

Hijner, J. A., M. Oostenbrink, and H. den Ouden. 1953. Morfologische verschillen tussen de belangrijkste *Heterodera*-soorten in Nederland. Tijdschr. Plantenziekten 59: 245–251.

Hildebrand, A. A., and L. W. Koch. 1936. A microscopical study of infestation of the roots of strawberry and tobacco seedlings by microorganisms of the soil. Canad. Jour. Res. (Sect. C) 19: 183–198.

Hirschmann, Hedwig. 1954. Unerwarteter Wiederfund tropischer Nematoden [*Radopholus oryzae* (V. Breda deHann, 1902) Thorne 1949, *Panagrolaimus hygrophilus* Bassen, 1940, *Atylenchus decalineatus* Cobb, 1913] an heimischen Sumpfpflanzen. Zeitschr. Pflanzenkrank. u. Pflanzensch. 61(7): 352–357.

———. 1955. *Radopholus gracilis* (deMan, 1880) n. comb. [synonym—*Tylenchorhynchus gracilis* (deMan, 1880) Filipjev, 1936]. Proc. Helminth. Soc. Wash. 22(2): 57–63.

———. 1956. Comparative morphological studies on the soybean cyst nematode, *Heterodera glycines*, and the clover cyst nematode, *H. trifolii* (Nematoda: Heteroderidae). Proc. Helminth. Soc. Wash. 23(2): 140–151.

———. 1959. Histological studies on the anterior region of *Heterodera glycines* and *Hoplolaimus tylenchiformis* (Nematoda: Tylenchida). Proc. Helminth. Soc. Wash. 26(2): 73–90.

——— and J. N. Sasser. 1955. On the occurrence of an intersexual form in *Ditylenchus triformis* n. sp. (Nematoda: Tylenchida). Proc. Helminth. Soc. Wash. 22(2):115–123.

Hofmanner, B. 1913. Contribution a l'étude des nématodes libres du lac Leman. Rev. suisse zool. 21(16): 589–658.

——— and R. Menzel. 1914. Neue Arten freilebender Nematoden aus der Schweiz. Zool. Anz. 44: 80–91.

Holdeman, Q. L. 1954. Nematodes as possible members of disease complexes involving other plant pathogens. Plant Dis. Reptr. (Suppl.) 227: 77–79.

———. 1955. The present known distribution of the sting nematode, *Belonolaimus gracilis*, in the coastal plain of the southeastern United States. Plant Dis. Reptr. 39(1): 5–8.

———. 1956. The effect of the tobacco stunt nematode on the incidence of *Fusarium* wilt in flue cured tobacco. Phytopathology 46(2): 129.

——— and T. W. Graham. 1953. The effect of different crop species on the population trends of the sting nematode. Plant Dis. Reptr. 37(10): 497–500.

Hyman, L. H. 1951. Aconthocephala, Aschelminthes, and Entoprocta. The pseudocoelomate Bilateria. The Invertebrates, Vol. III. 572 pp.

Ichinohe, M. 1952. On the soybean nematode, *Heterodera glycines*, n. sp. from Japan. Mag. Appl. Zool. 17: 1–4.

Imamura, S. 1931. Nematodes in the paddy field. Jour. Agr. Imp. Univ. Tokyo 11(2): 198–240.

Jaegerskiold, L. A. 1905. *Bunonema richtersi*, n. g. n. sp., ein Eigentümlicher neuer Landnematode aus dem Schwarzwald von Kerguelen und Possession-Island (Crozet-Inseln). Zool. Anz. 28: 557–561.

Jenkins, W. R. 1956. Nematology. *Paratylenchus projectus* new species (Nematoda: Criconematidae) with a key to species of *Paratylenchus*. Jour. Wash. Acad. Sci. 46(9): 296–298.

——— and D. P. Taylor. 1956. *Paratylenchus dianthus* new species (Nematoda: Criconematidae), a parasite of carnations. Proc. Helminth. Soc. Wash. 23(2): 124–127.

Jensen, H. J. 1950. The biology and morphology of the root lesion nematode parasitic on walnuts in California. (Unpublished Ph.D. dissertation.) University of California Library.

——. 1953. Experimental greenhouse host range studies of two root-lesion nematodes, *Pratylenchus vulnus* and *P. penetrans*. Plant Dis. Reptr. 37(7): 384–387.

—— and F. E. Caveness. 1954. Hot water and systox for control of foliar nematodes in Bellingham hybrid lilies. Plant Dis. Reptr. 38(3): 181–184.

—— and C. E. Horner. 1957. Peppermint decline caused by *Longidorus sylphus* can be controlled by soil fumigation. (Abs.) Phytopathology 47(1): 18.

Johnson, E. C. 1909. Notes on a nematode in wheat. Science (n.s.) 30: 576.

Johnson, M. O., and G. H. Godfrey. 1932. Chloropicrin for nematode control. Ind. Eng. Chem. 24: 311–313.

Jones, F. G. W. 1950. Observations on the beet eelworm and other cyst-forming species of *Heterodera*. Ann. Appl. Biol. 37: 407–440.

——. 1956. Soil populations of beet eelworm, *Heterodera schachtii* Schm. in relation to cropping, II. Microplot and field plot results. Ann. Appl. Biol. 44(1): 25–56.

——. 1957. Resistance breaking biotypes of potato root eelworm (*Heterodera rostochiensis* Woll.). Nematologica 2(3): 185–192.

Jordon, N. E. 1935. Improving rice varieties. La. Rice Expt. Sta. Biennial Rept., 1933–1934, pp. 15–18.

Junges, W. 1938. Systematik und Variabilität der pflanzenparasitischen Aphelenchen sowie deren Verbreitung an verschiedenen Wirtspflanzen. Zeitschr. Parasitenk. 10: 559–607.

Kamrodt. 1867. Zeitschr. Landwirts. Vereins Rhein-Preussen. 6: 251–378.

Kemner, N. A. 1930. Några iakttagelser över Kornnematoden, *Tylenchus hordei* Schøyen, i Sverge. Medd. Cent. Anst. försökv. Jordbr. Stockh. 63: 1–26.

Kirjanova, Ekaterina S. 1951. Variability in phytopathogenic nematodes caused by their food specificity. Akad. Nauk S.S.S.R. Trudy Zool. Inst. 9(2): 378–404.

——. 1954. The fig root eelworm. Trans. Problematic Thematic Conf., Vol. III, Collected works on nematodes of agricultural plants. (In Russian. Translated title and citation.)

Kofoid, C. A., and W. A. White. 1919. A new nematode infection of man. Jour. Amer. Med. Assoc. 72: 567–569.

Kostoff, D., and J. Kendall. 1929. Studies on the structure and development of certain Cynipid galls. Biol. Bull. Woods Hole 56(6): 402–458.

Krueger, H. J., and M. B. Linford. 1957. Sex differences in the cephalic region of *Hoplolaimus coronatus* (Nematoda: Tylenchida). Proc. Helminth. Soc. Wash. 24(1): 20–23.

Krusberg, L. R., and J. N. Sasser. 1956. Host-parasite relationships of the lance nematode in cotton roots. Phytopathology 46(9): 505–510.

Kühn, J. 1857. Über das Vorkommen von *Anguillula* an erkrankten Blühtenköpfen von *Dipsacus fullonum* L. Zeitschr. wiss. Zool. 9: 129–137.

——. 1874. Über das Vorkommen von Ruben-Nematoden an den Wurzeln der Halmfruchte. Landwirts. Jahrb. 3: 47–50.

——. 1881. Die Ergebnisse der Versuche zur Ermittelung der Ursache der Rübenmüdigkeit und zur Erforschung der Natur der Nematoden. Ber. Physiol. Lab. Univ. Halle 3: 1–153.

Kühn, J. 1890. Neue Erfahrungen auf dem Gebiete der Zuckerrübenkultur. Jahrb. deut. Landwirts. Ges. für 1889 4: 93, 94.

Kuiper, K., and E. Drijfhout. 1957. Bestrijding van het worterlaaltje *Hoplolaimus uniformis* Thorne, 1949, bij de Teelt van peen. Overdruck uit Meded. Landbouwhogesch. Opzoekingsst. Staat Gent 22(3): 419–426.

Lambert, E. B., G. Steiner, and C. Drechsler. 1933. The "*Cephalothecium* disease" of cultured mushrooms caused by a nematode (*Ditylenchus* sp.) evidenced by surface development of oredacious fungi. Plant Dis. Reptr. 33(6): 252, 253.

Lane, M. C., and M. W. Stone. 1954. Wireworms and their control on irrigated lands. U.S. Dept. Agr. Farmers' Bull. 1866.

LaPage, G. 1937. Nematodes parasitic in animals. Methuen & Co., Ltd., London. 172 pp.

Lavergne, G. 1901. L'anguillule du Chili (*Anguillula viale*). Rev. viticult. 16: 445–452.

Leidy, J. 1851. Helminthological Contr. 2. Jour. Acad. Nat. Sci. Philadelphia 5: 224–227.

Leuckart, T. 1891. Über einen als *Aphodius fimentarius* sich verpuppenden freilebende Rundwurm, *Rhabditis coarctata* n. sp. Verh. deut. Zool. Ges. 1: 54–56.

Leukel, R. W. 1924. Investigations on the nematode disease of cereals caused by *Tylenchus tritici*. Jour. Agr. Res. 27(12): 925–955.

Liebscher, G. 1892. Beobachtungen über das Auftreten eines Nematoden an Erbsen. Jour. Landwirts. 40: 357–368.

Limber, D. P. 1938. Notes on the hot water treatment of *Anguina tritici* galls on wheat. Proc. Helminth. Soc. Wash. 5(1): 20–23.

Linde, W. J. van der. 1938. A contribution to the study of nematodes. Entomol. Mem. Dept. Agr. Forest, Un. S. Africa 2: 1–40.

Linford, M. B. 1937. The feeding of root-knot nematodes in root tissue and nutrient solution. Phytopathology 27(8): 824–835.

———. 1937a. The feeding of some hollow-stylet nematodes. Proc. Helminth. Soc. Wash. 4(2): 41–46.

———. 1937b. Notes on the feeding of *Ditylenchus dipsaci*. Nematoda: Tylenchidae. Proc. Helminth. Soc. Wash. 4(1): 46–47.

———. 1939. Attractiveness of roots and excised shoot tissues to certain nematodes. Proc. Helminth. Soc. Wash. 6(1): 11–18.

———. 1941. Parasitism of root-knot nematode in leaves and stems. Phytopathology 31(7): 634–648.

———. 1942. The transient feeding of root-knot larvae. Phytopathology 32(7): 580–589.

———. 1942a. Methods of observing soil flora and fauna associated with roots. Soil Sci. 53: 93–103.

——— and Juliette M. Oliveira. 1937. The feeding of hollow-spear nematodes on other nematodes. Science 85(2203): 295–297.

——— and ———. 1940. *Rotylenchulus reniformis* nov. gen. n. sp., a nematode parasite of roots. Proc. Helminth. Soc. Wash. 7(1): 35–42.

———, ———, and M. Ishii. 1949. *Paratylenchus minutus* n. sp., a nematode parasitic on roots. Pacific Sci. 3(2): 111–119.

——— and F. Yap. 1940. Some host plants of the reniform nematode in Hawaii. Proc. Helminth. Soc. Wash. 7(1): 42–44.

———, ———, and Juliette M. Oliveira. 1938. Reduction of soil populations of the root-knot nematode during decomposition of organic matter. Soil Sci. 45: 127–141.

Linnaeus, C. 1768. Systema naturae, Vol. 1. Holmiae. (10th ed.)

Loof, P. A. A. 1956. *Trophurus*, a new tylenchid genus (Nematode). Versl. Planzen ziekten Dienst. Waginingen 129: 191–195.

———. 1957. Was ist *Aphelenchus neglectus* Rensch? Nematologica (Suppl.) 2: 348.

———. 1958. Some remarks on the status of the subfamily Dolichodorinae, with description of *Macrotrophurus arbusticola* n. g., n. sp. (Nematoda: Tylenchidae). Nematologica 3(4): 301–307.

—— and M. Oostenbrink. 1958. Die Identität von *Tylenchus robustus* deMan. Nematologica 3(1): 34–43.

Loos, C. A. 1948. Notes on free-living and plant parasitic nematodes of Ceylon 3. Ceylon Jour. Sci. (B)23: 119–124.

———. 1953. *Meloidogyne brevicauda* n. sp. a cause of root-knot of mature tea in Ceylon. Proc. Helminth. Soc. Wash. 20(2): 85–91.

———. 1957. Plant parasitic nematodes and their association with bananas. United Fruit Company Res. Dept. Res. Ext. Letter 4(4): 8–16.

Lordello, L. G. E. 1956. *Meloidogyne inornata* sp. n., a serious pest of soybean in the state of São Paulo, Brazil. Rev. Brazil. Biol. 16(1): 65–70.

—— and A. P. L. Zamith. 1954. Constatacoa da molestia do "anel vermelho" do conqueiro no Estado do Rio de Janeiro. Redescricao do agente causador —*Aphelenchoides cocophilus* (Cobb, 1919) Goodey, 1933 (Nematoda: Aphelenchidae).

—— and ———. 1958. A note on nematodes attacking coffee trees in Brazil. Plant Dis. Reptr. 42(2): 199.

Lorenzetti, J. B. 1913. La alfalfa en la Argentina. Buenos Aires. 360 pp.

Löw, F. 1874. *Tylenchus millefolii* n. sp., eine neue gallenerzeugende Anguillulidae. Abhdl. zool. bot. Ges. 24: 17–24.

Lownsberry, B. F., and Joyce W. Lownsberry. 1954. *Heterodera tabacum* new species, a parasite of solanaceous plants in Connecticut. Proc. Helminth. Soc. Wash. 21(1): 42–47.

———, E. M. Stoddard, and Joyce W. Lownsberry. 1952. *Paratylenchus hamatus* pathogenic to celery. Phytopathology 42(12): 651–655.

Luc, M. 1957. *Radopholus lavabri* n. sp. (Nematoda: Tylenchidae) parasite du riz au Cameroun Français. Nematologica 2(2): 144–148.

———. 1957a. *Tylenchulus magenoti* n. sp. (Nematoda: Tylenchulidae). Nematologica 2(4): 329–334.

———. 1958. Trois nouvelles espèces Africaines du genera *Hemicycliophora* deMan, 1921 (Nematoda: Criconematidae). Nematologica 3(1): 15–23.

———. 1958a *Xiphinema* de l'Ouest Africain description de cinq nouvelles espèces (Nematoda: Dorylaimidae). Nematologica 3(1): 57–72.

Lucas, G. B., J. N. Sasser, and A. Kelman. 1955. The relationship of root-knot nematodes to Granville wilt resistance in tobacco. Phytopathology 45(10): 537–540.

Ludwig, H. 1938. Die Variabilität von *Rhabditis teres* (A. Schn.) unter veränderten Ernährungsbedingungen. Zeitschr. wiss. Zool. 151(3): 291–336.

Macher, J. H. 1953. *Criconemoides* sp., a ring nematode associated with peanut yellows. Plant Dis. Reptr. 37(3): 156.

Man, J. G. de. 1876. Onderzoekingen over vrij in de aarde levende Nematoden. Tijds. Nederland. Dierk. Vereen. 2: 78–196.

Man, J. G. de. 1880. Die einheimischen, frei in der reinen Erde und im süssen-Wasser lebenden Nematoden. Tijds. Nederland. Dierk. Vereen. 5(½): 1–104.

———. 1884. Die frei in der reinen Erde und im süssen-Wasser lebenden Nematoden der niederländischen Fauna. 206 pp.

———. 1892. Ueber eine neue, in Gallen einer meereslage lebende Art der Gattung *Tylenchus* Bastian. Festschr. zum siebensigsten Geburst. Rudolf Leuchart, pp. 121–125.

———. 1895. Description of three species of Anguillulidae observed in diseased pseudo-bulbs of tropical orchids. Proc. Trans. Liverpool Biol. Soc. 9: 76–94.

———. 1921. Nouvelles recherches sur les nématodes libres terricoles de la Hollande. Capita Zoologica. 's Gravenhage. 1(1): 3–62.

Mankau, G. R., and M. B. Linford. 1956. Soybean varieties tested as hosts of the clover cyst nematode. Plant Dis. Reptr. 40(1): 39–42.

Marcinowski, Kati. 1909. Parasitische und semiparasitische an pflanzen lebenden Nematoden. Arb. kaiserlichen biol. Anstalt Land- u. Forst., Berlin 7(1): 1–192.

Martin, G. C. 1955. Plant and soil nematodes of the Federation of Rhodesia and Nyasaland. Jour. Rhod. Agr. (52): 346–351.

Massee, G. 1913. Nematodes or eelworms. Kew Bull. 9.

Mathews, Mrs. J. D. 1919. Report on the work of the W. B. Randall research assistant. Nurs. and Mark. Gard. Ind. Dev. Coc. Exp. and Res. Sta. Chechunt, Herts. Ann. Rept. 5: 18–21; 1920, 6: 45–51.

Maupas, E. 1900. Modes et formes de reproduction des nématodes. Arch. zool. expt. gén. (Ser. 3) 8: 463–624.

———. 1919. Essais de hybridation chez des nématodes. Bull. biol. 52: 466–498.

May, J. N. 1888. Club roots. Amer. Florist 3: 649.

McBeth, C. W. 1937. Observations on a predaceous nematode. Proc. Helminth. Soc. Wash. 4(1): 18.

———. 1938. White clover as a host of the sugar-beet nematode. Proc. Helminth. Soc. Wash. 5(1): 27, 28.

———. 1945. Tests on the susceptibility and resistance of several southern grasses to the root-knot nematode, *Heterodera marioni*. Proc. Helminth. Soc. Wash. 12(2): 41–44.

———, A. L. Taylor, and A. L. Smith. 1941. Note on staining nematodes in root tissue. Proc. Helminth. Soc. Wash. 8(1): 26.

McCubbin, W. A., et al. 1946. The potato rot nematode, *Ditylenchus destructor* Thorne. Unnumbered circular, Plant Protection Branch, U.S. Department of Agriculture.

McKay, M. B. 1921. A serious disease of strawberry and clover in Oregon. Ore. Agr. College Crop Pest and Hort. Rept. 1915–1920: 139–144.

McWhorter, F. P. 1945. The diseases of *Lilium longiflorum* in the Pacific northwest. Plant Dis. Reptr. 29(2): 40–44.

———, S. L. Emsweller, and P. Brierly. 1944. Suggestions for growing Easter lily bulbs in the Pacific northwest. Ore. Agr. Expt. Sta. Circ. Inf. 339: 12.

Menzel, R. 1917. Zur Kenntnis der freilebenden Nematodengattung *Hoplolaimus* v. Daday. Rev. suisse zool. 25: 153–162.

Merzheevska, O. I. 1951. New species of nematodes. Akad. Nauk B.S.S.R., Minsk. Inst. Biol. Sbornik Nauchnykh Trudov. 2: 112–120.

Meyl, A. H. 1960. Freilebende Nematoden. In Die Tierwelt Mitteleuropas, Vol. 1.

Micoletzky, H. 1915. Neue Süsswasser-Nematoden aus der Bukowina. Mitt. naturw. Ver. Steiermark. 51: 445–454.

——. 1922. Die freilebenden Erd-Nematoden. Arch. Naturgesch. Berlin (1921) 87, Abt. A (⁹⁄₁₀): 1–650.

——. 1925. Die freilebenden Süsswasser- und Moornematoden Dänemarks. K. Danske Vidensk. Selsk. Skr., Naturw. math. (Afd. 8) 10(2): 57–103. (1–256.)

Millikan, C. R. 1938. Eelworm (*Heterodera schachtii* Schmidt) disease of cereals. Jour. Dept. Agr. Victoria 36: 452–468, 509–520.

Minz, G. 1956. How the potato root nematode was discovered in Israel. Plant Dis. Reptr. 40(8): 688–699.

Molz, E. 1909. Ueber *Aphelenchus olesistus* Ritz Bos. und die durch ihn hervorgerufene Aelchenkrankheit der Chrysanthemum. Zbl. Bakt. (Abt. II) 23: 656–671.

——. 1930. Ueber die Bekämpfung des Rübennematoden (*Heterodera schachtii*) mit reizphysiologisch wirkenden Stoffen. Zbl. Bakt. (Abt. 2) 81(7): 92–103.

Moreton, B. D., M. E. John, and J. B. Goodey. 1956. *Aphelenchoides* sp. destroying mushroom mycelium. Nature, Lond. 177: 795.

Morgan, D. O. 1925. Investigations on eelworm in potatoes in South Lincolnshire. Jour. Helminth. 3: 185–192.

Mortensen, M. L., S. Rostrup, and K. Ravn. 1908. Oversigt over Landbrugsplanternes Sygdomme i 1907. Tidsskr. Bandbr. Planteavl. 15: 145–158.

Mountain, W. B. 1954. Studies of nematodes in relation to brown rot of tobacco in Ontario. Canad. Jour. Bot. 32: 737–759.

——. 1955. A method of culturing plant parasitic nematodes under sterile conditions. Proc. Helminth. Soc. Wash. 22(1): 49–52.

Müller, C. 1880. Einige Bemerkungen über die von Anguillulen auf *Achillea* erzeugten Gallen. Bot. Centrbl. 1: 187, 188.

——. 1884. Mitteilungen über die unseren Kulturpflanzen schädlichen das Geschlecht *Heteroderea* bildenden Würmer. Landwirts. Jahrb. 13: 1–42.

Muller, O. F. 1786. Animalcula infusoria fluviatilla et marina, etc. Havniae.

Mulvey, R. H. 1957. Taxonomic value of the cone top and the underbridge in the cyst-forming nematodes *Heterodera schachtii, H. schachtii* var. *trifolii*, and *H. avenae* (Nematoda: Heteroderidae). Canad. Jour. Zool. 35: 421–423.

——. 1957a. Chromosome number in the sugar-beet nematode, *Heterodera schachtii* Schmidt. Nature 180: 1212, 1213.

——. 1959. Investigations on the clover cyst nematode, *Heterodera trifolii* (Nematoda: Heteroderidae). Nematologica 4(2): 147–156.

Neal, J. C. 1889. The root-knot disease of peach, orange, and other plants in Florida, due to the work of *Anguillula*. U.S. Dept. Agr. Div. Ent. Bull. 20.

Needham, T. 1743. A letter concerning certain chalky tubulous concretions called malm; with some microscopical observations on the farina of the red lily, and of worms discovered in smutty corn. Philos. Trans. Roy. Soc. 42: 173, 174, 634–641.

Nelson, R. R. 1956. Resistance to the stunt nematode in corn. Plant Dis. Reptr. 40(7): 635–639.

Newhall, A. G. 1943. Pathogenesis of *Ditylenchus dipsaci* in seedlings of *Allium cepa*. Phytopathology 33(1): 61–69.

Newhall, A. G., and B. G. Chitwood. 1940. Onion eelworm rot or bloat caused by the stem or bulb nematode, *Ditylenchus dipsaci.* Phytopathology 30(5): 390–400.

Nigon, V., and E. C. Dougherty. 1949. Reproductive patterns and attempts in reciprocal crossing of *Rhabditis elegans* Maupas, 1900 and *Rhabditis briggsae* n. sp. Jour. Expt. Zool. 112(3): 485–503.

Nilsson-Ehle, H. 1920. Ueber Resisstenz gegen *H. schachtii* bei gewissen Gerstensorten, ihre Vererbungsweise und Bedeutung für die Praxis. Hereditas 1: 1–34.

Nishizawa, T., and K. Iwatomi. 1955. *Neotylenchus acris* Thorne, as a parasitic nematode of strawberry plant. Japanese Jour. Appl. Zool. 20(½): 47–55.

Nowell, W. 1919. The red ring or "root" disease of coconut palms. W.I. Bull. 17(4): 189–202.

———. 1920. The red ring disease of coconut palms. Infection experiments. W.I. Bull. 18(½): 74–76.

———. 1923. Diseases of coconut. Diseases of crop plants of the Lesser Antilles, Chapter 18, pp. 177–186. London.

Nusbaum, C. J. 1955. Variable effects of nematocides on parasitic nematode populations in row-fumigated tobacco plots. (Abs.) Phytopathology 45(6): 349.

Nypels, P. 1898. Maladies de plantes cultivées, I. Maladie vermiculaire des *Phlox.* Ann. soc. belge micr. 23: 1–32.

O'Brien, D. G., and E. G. Prentice. 1930. An eelworm disease of potatoes caused by *Heterodera schachtii.* Scottish Jour. Agr. 13(4): 415–444.

Oostenbrink, M. 1950. Het Aardappelaaltje (*Heterodera rostochiensis* Wollenweber) een gevaarlijke paraseit voor de eenzijdige aardappel cultuur. Versl. Meded. Plantenziekten. Dienst. No. 115.

———. 1951. Het erwtencystenaaltje, *Heterodera göttingiana* Liebscher, in Nederland. Tijds. Plantenziekten 57: 52–64.

———. 1953. A note on *Paratylenchus* in the Netherlands with the description of *P. goodeyi* n. sp. (Nematoda: Criconematidae). Tijds. Plantenziekten 59: 207–216.

———. 1954. Een doelmatige methode voor het toetsen van aaltjesbestrijdingsmiddelen in grond met *Hoplolaimus uniformis* als proefdier. Meded. Landbouwhogesch. Opzoekingsst. Staat Gent 19: 377–408.

———. 1954a. Over de betekenis van vrijlevende wortelaaltjes in land-en tuinbow. Versl. Meded. Plantenziekten. Dienst. No. 124: 196–233.

———. 1955. Over de waardplanten van het bietencystenaaltje. Versl. Meded. Plantenziekten, Vol. 127, Jaarboek 1954–1955, pp. 186–193.

———. 1956. Over de invloed van verschillende dewassen op de vermeerdering van en de schade door *Pratylenchus pratensis* en de *Pratylenchus penetrans* (Vermes: Nematoda). Tijds. Plantenziekten 62: 189–203.

———. 1957. An inoculation trial with *Pratylenchus penetrans* in potatoes. Nematologica 3(1): 30–33.

———, J. J. s'Jacob, and K. Kuiper. 1957. Over de waardplanten van *Pratylenchus penetrans.* Tijds. Plantenziekten 63: 345–360.

———, M. K. Kuiper, and J. J. s'Jacob. 1957a. *Tagetes* als Feindpflanzen von *Pratylenchus* Arten. Nematologica (Suppl.) 2: 424–433.

Oostenbrink, M., and H. den Ouden. 1954. De structuur van den kegeltop als taxonomisch kenmerk bij *Heterodera*-soorten met citroenvormige cysten. Tijds. Plantenziekten. 60: 146–151.

Örley, L. 1880. Az anguillulidak maganrajza. Monographie der Anguilluliden. Budapest. (Hungarian and German texts.) 165 pp.

———. 1886. Die Rhabditen und ihre medizinische Bedeutung. Berlin.

Orton, W. A. 1902. The wilt disease of cowpea and its control. U.S. Dept. Agr. Bur. Plant Ind. Bull. 17: 9–22.

Osche, G. 1952. Systematik und Phylogenie der Gattung *Rhabditis* (Nematoda). Zool. Jahrb. 81(3): 190–280.

Ouden, H. den. 1956. The influence of hosts and non-susceptible hatching plants on populations of *Heterodera schachtii*. Nematologica 1(2): 138–144.

Owens, J. V. 1951. The pathological effects of *Belonolaimus gracilis* on peanuts in Virginia. (Abs.) Phytopathology 41(1): 29.

Paetzold, D. 1958. Beobachtungen zur Stachellosigkeit der Männchen von *Helicycliophora typica* deMan, 1921 (Criconematinae). Nematologica 3(2): 140–142.

Paramanov, A. A. 1953. Review of the superfamily Aphelenchoidea Fuchs, 1937. (In Skrijabin's seventy-fifth birthday volume, pp. 488–496.

Peacock, F. C. 1956. The reniform nematode in the Gold Coast. Nematologica 1(4): 307–310.

Pearse, A. S. 1936. Zoological names. A list of Phyla, Classes, and Orders. Sect. F, American Association for the Advancement of Science, Duke University Press, Durham, North Carolina, pp. 1–24.

Perry, V. G. 1953. The awl nematode, *Dolichodorus heterocephalus*, a devastating plant parasite. Proc. Helminth. Soc. Wash. 20(1): 21–27.

———. 1953a. Return of nematodes following fumigation of Florida soils. Proc. Fla. State Hort. Soc. 66: 112–114.

———. 1958. Parasitism of two species of dagger nematodes (*Xiphinema americanum* and *X. chambersi*) to strawberry. Phytopathology 48(8): 420–423.

———. 1959. A note on digonic hermaphroditism in spiral nematodes (*Helicotylenchus* spp.). Nematologica 4(1): 87, 88.

———, H. M. Darling, and G. Thorne. 1959. Anatomy, taxonomy and control of certain spiral nematodes attacking blue grass in Wisconsin. Univ. Wis. Res. Bull. 207: 1–24.

Peters, B. G. 1927. On the nomenclature of the vinegar eelworm. Jour. Helminth. 5(3): 133–142.

Plakidas, A. G. 1928. Strawberry dwarf. Phytopathology 18(5): 439–444.

Prillieux, E. 1881. La maladie vermiculaire des jacinthes. Jour. nat. soc. hort. 3(3): 253–260.

Putnam, D. F., and L. J. Chapman. 1935. Oat seedling diseases in Ontario, I. The oat nematode, *Heterodera schachtii*. Schm. Sci. Agr. 15(9): 633–651.

Quanjer, H. M. 1927. Een aaltjesziekte van de aardappelplant, de aantastingswijze en den herkomst van haar oorzaak, *Tylenchus dipsaci* Kühn. Tijds. Plantenziekten 33: 177–172.

Rahm, G. 1928. Alguns nematodes parasitas e semi-parasitas das plantas culturaes do Brasil. Arch. inst. biol. (def. agric. anim.) São Paulo 1:239–252.

Ramsbottom, J. K. 1918. Experiments on the control of the eelworm disease of narcissus. Jour. Roy. Hort. Soc. 43: 65–78.

Raski, D. J. 1950. The life history and morphology of the sugar-beet nematode, *Heterodera schachtii* Schmidt. Phytopathology 40(8): 135–152.

Raski, D. J. 1952. On the host range of the sugar-beet nematode in California. Plant Dis. Reptr. 36(1): 5–7.

———. 1952a. On the morphology of *Criconemoides* Taylor, 1936, with descriptions of six new species (Nematoda: Criconematidae). Proc. Helminth. Soc. Wash. 19(2): 85–99.

———. 1952b. The first record of the brassica-root nematode in the United States. Plant Dis. Reptr. 36(11): 438, 439.

———. 1956. *Sphaeronema arenarium,* n. sp. (Nematoda: Criconematidae), a nematode parasite of salt rush, *Juncus leseuri,* Boland. Proc. Helminth. Soc. Wash. 23(1): 75–77.

———. 1957. *Trophotylenchulus* and *Trophonema,* two new genera of Tylenchulidae n. fam. (Nematoda). Nematologica 2(1): 85–90.

———. 1958. Four new species of *Hemicycliophora* deMan, 1921 with further observations on *H. brevis* Thorne, 1955 (Nematoda: Criconematidae). Proc. Helminth. Soc. Wash. 25(2): 125–131.

———. 1958a. Nomenclatorial notes on the genus *Criconemoides* (Nematoda: Criconematidae) with a key to species. Proc. Helminth. Soc. Wash. 25(2): 139–142.

——— and M. W. Allen. 1948. Spring dwarf nematode. Calif. Agr., pp. 23, 24.

——— and W. H. Hart. 1953. Observations on the clover root nematode in California. Plant Dis. Reptr. 37(4): 197–200.

——— and J. D. Radewald. 1958. Reproduction and symptomology of certain ectoparasitic nematodes on roots of Thompson seedless grape. Plant Dis. Reptr. 42(8): 941–943.

——— and S. A. Sher. 1952. *Sphaeronema californicum,* nov. gen. nov. spec. (Criconematidae: Sphaeronematinae, nov. subfam.) an endoparasite of the roots of certain plants. Proc. Helminth. Soc. Wash. 19(2): 77–80.

———, ———, and F. N. Jensen. 1956. New host records of the citrus nematode in California. Plant Dis. Reptr. 40(12): 1047, 1048.

Rau, G. J. 1958. A new species of sting nematode. Proc. Helminth. Soc. Wash. 25(2): 95–98.

Reiter, M. 1928. Zur Systematik und Oekologie der zweigeschlechtlichen Rhabditiden. Arb. Zool. Inst. Univ. Innsbruck 3(4): 93–184.

Rensch, B. 1924. Eine neue Methode zur Bekämpfung der Rübennematode. Mitt. deut. Landwirts.-Ges. 38: 412–414.

———. 1924a. *Aphelenchus neglectus* n. sp., eine neue parasitäre Nematodonart. Zool. Anz. 59: 277–280.

Reynolds, H. W. 1949. Relative degree of infection of American-Egyptian cotton by three populations of root-knot nematode. Plant Dis. Reptr. 33: 306–309.

———. 1955. Varietal susceptiblity of alfalfa to two species of root-knot nematodes. Phytopathology 45(2): 70–72.

——— and M. M. Evans. 1953. The stylet nematode, *Tylenchorhynchus dubius,* a root parasite of economic importance in the southwest. Plant Dis. Reptr. 37(11): 540–544.

——— and J. H. O'Bannon. 1958. The citrus nematode and its control on living citrus in Arizona. Plant Dis. Reptr. 42(11): 1288–1292.

Rhoades, H. L., and M. B. Linford. 1959. Control of *Pythium* root rot by the nematode, *Aphelenchus avenae.* Plant Dis. Reptr. 43(3): 323–328.

Ritzema Bos, J. 1888. Untersuchungen über *Tylenchus devastatrix* Kühn. Biol. Centrbl. 7: 646–659, 8: 129–138, 164–178.

Ritzema Bos, J. 1888–1892. L'Anguillule de la tige (*Tylenchus devastatrix* Kühn), et les maladies des plantes dues a ce nématode. Arch. mus. Teyler (Ser. 2) 3: 161–348, 545–588.

———. 1890. De bloemkoolziekte der aardbeien, veroorzaakt door *Aphelenchus fragariae* nov. spec. Maandblad Natuurwetenschappen 16(7): 107–117.

———. 1891. Zwei neue Nematodenkrankheiten der Erdbeer pflanze. Zeitschr. Pflanzenkrank. 1: 1–16.

———. 1893. Neue Nematodenkrankheiten bei Topfpflanzen. Zeitschr. Pflanzenkrank. 3: 69–82.

———. 1899. Twee tot due onbekende ziekten in *Phlox decussata*. Tijds. Plantenziekten 5: 29–32.

———. 1926. Het stengelaaltje in iris. Tijds. Plantenziekten 32: 199.

Robertson, D. 1928. Observations on the disease of oats caused by the stem eelworm, *Anguillulina dipsaci* (Kühn, 1857). Ann. Appl. Biol. 15(3): 488–498.

Roffredi, D. M. 1775. Mémoire sur l'origine des petits vers on anguilles du blé rachitique. Observ. mém. phys. hist. nat. 5: 1–19.

Rohde, R. A., and W. R. Jenkins. 1957. Host range of a species of *Trichodorus* and its host-parasite relationships on tomato. Phytopathology 47(5): 295–298.

Rühm, W. 1956. Die Nematoden der Ipiden. Parasit. Schriftenreihe 6: 1–437.

Sachs, H. G. 1949. Revision der Bunonematinae (Anguillulidae Nematoda). Zool. Jahrb. 79: 209–272.

———. 1950. Die Nematodenfauna der Rinderexkremente. Zool. Jahrb. 79: 211–271.

Sanwal, K. C. 1957. The morphology of the nematode, *Radopholus gracilis* (deMan, 1880) Hirschmann, 1955, parasitic in roots of wild rice, *Zizania aquatica* L. Canad. Jour. Zool. 35: 75–92.

———. 1957a. Chambersiellidae n. fam. (Nematoda) with emended diagnosis of the genus *Chambersiella* Cobb, 1920. Canad. Jour. Zool. 35: 615–621.

Sasser, J. N. 1954. Identification and host-parasite relationships of certain root-knot nematodes (*Meloidogyne* spp.) Md. Agr. Expt. Sta. Bull. A-77.

———, G. B. Lucas, and H. R. Powers, Jr. 1955. The relationship of root-knot nematodes to black-shank resistance in tobacco. Phytopathology 45(8): 459–461.

Sauer, M. R. 1958. *Hoplolaimus gracilidens, Radopholus inaequalis* and *Radopholus neosimilis,* three new tylenchs native to Australia. Nematologica 3(2): 97–107.

——— and J. E. Giles. 1957. Effects of some field management systems on root-knot of tomato. Nematologica 2(2): 97–107.

Schacht, H. 1859. Ueber einige Feinde und Krankheiten der Zuckerrübe. Zeitschr. Ver. Rübenzucker-Ind. Zoolver. 9: 390.

Schindler, A. F. 1954. Nematodes associated with roses in a survey of commercial greeenhouses. Plant Dis. Reptr. 40(4): 277, 278.

———. 1954a. Root galling associated with dagger nematode, *Xiphinema diversicaudatum* (Micoletzky, 1927) Thorne, 1939. Phytopathology 44(9): 389.

———. 1957. Parasitism and pathogenicity of *Xiphinema diversicaudatum,* an ectoparasitic nematode. Nematologica 2(1): 25–31.

——— and A. J. Braun. 1957. Pathogenicity of an ectoparasitic nematode, *Xiphinema diversicaudatum,* on strawberries. Nematologica 2(1): 91–93.

Schmidt, A. 1871. Ueber den Rüben-Nematoden (*Heterodera schachtii*). Zeitschr. Ver. Rübenzucker-Ind. Zoolver. 22: 67–75.

Schmidt, O. 1930. Sind Rüben- und Hafer-Nematoden identisch? Arch. Pflanzenbau 3(3): 420–464.

Schneider, A. 1866. Monographie der Nematoden. Berlin.

Schneider, W. 1939. Freilebende und pflanzenparasitische Nematoden. Tierwelt Deutschlands 36: 1–260.

Schuurmans Stekhoven, J. H., Jr. 1954. *Neorhabditis,* a new name for *Pararhabditis* Schuurmans Stekhoven. Proc. Helminth. Soc. Wash. 21(1): 47.

Schwartz, M. 1911. Die Aphelenchen der Veilchengallen und Blattflecken an Farnen und Chrysanthemum. Arb. ksl. biol. Anst. Land- u. Forstw. 8(2): 303–334.

Scribner, F. L. 1889. Diseases of the Irish potato. Tenn. Agr. Expt. Sta. Bull. 2: 27–43.

Schøyen, W. M. 1885. By gallen (*Tylenchus hordei* n. sp.) en ny for Bygget skadelig Planteparasit blandt Rundormeme. Forh. Vidensk Sel. sk. Krist., pp. 1–16.

Schuster, M. L., and G. Thorne. 1956. Distribution, relation to weeds, and histology of sugar beet root galls caused by *Nacobbus batatiformis* Thorne and Schuster. Jour. Am. Soc. Sugar Beet Tech. 9(3): 193–197.

Schwertz. 1825. Anleitung zum praktischen Ackerbau. 2: 414.

Scopoli, J. A. 1777. Introductio ad historiam naturalem sistens genera lapidum, plantarum, et animalium. Prague.

Seinhorst, J. W. 1954. Een ziefte in erwten, veroorzaakt door het saltje *Hoplolaimus uniformis* Thorne. Tijds. Plantenziekten 60: 262–264.

———. 1956. Population studies on stem eelworms. Nematologica 1(2): 159–164.

———. 1956a. The quantitative extraction of nematodes from soil. Nematologica 1(3): 249–267.

——— and P. J. Bels. 1951. *Ditylenchus destructor* Thorne in mushrooms. Overd. Tijds. Plantenziekten 57: 167–169.

Sengbusch, R. von. 1927. Beitrag zur Biologie der Rübennematoden, *Heterodera schachtii.* Zeitschr. Pflanzenkrank. u. Pflanzensch. 37: 36–102.

Shamel, A. D., and W. W. Cobey. 1907. Tobacco breeding. U.S. Dept. Agr. Bur. Plant Ind. Bull. 86. 72 pp.

Shaw, H. B. 1915. The sugar beet nematode and its control. Sugar, Chicago 17: 2–9. (Reprint.) 55 pp.

Shaw, H. M., and O. H. Muth. 1949. Some types of forage poisoning in Oregon cattle and sheep. Jour. Amer. Vet. Med. Assoc. 114(866): 315–317.

Sher, S. A. 1954. Observations on plant parasitic nematodes in Hawaii. Plant Dis. Reptr. 38(9): 687, 688.

——— and M. W. Allen. 1953. Revision of the genus *Pratylenchus* (Nematoda: Tylenchidae). Univ. Calif. Publ. Zool. 57(6): 441–470.

——— and D. J. Raski. 1956. *Heterodera fici* Kirjanova, 1954 in California. Plant Dis. Reptr. 40(8): 700.

Sherbakoff, C. D., and W. W. Stanley. 1943. The more important diseases and insect pests of crops in Tennessee. Tenn. Agr. Expt. Sta. Bull. 186.

Siddiqi, M. R. 1959. Studies on *Xiphinema* spp. (Nematoda: Dorylaimoidea) from Aligarh (North India), with comments on the genus *Longidorus* Micoletzky, 1922. Proc. Helminth. Soc. Wash. 26(2): 151–163.

Skrabilovich, T. S. 1947. Revision of the systematics of the nematode family Anguillulinidae Baylis and Daubney, 1926. Comptes rendus acad. sci. U.R.S.S. 57(3): 307, 308.

Skrjabin, K. I., N. P. Shikhobalova, A. A. Sobolev, A. A. Paramonov, and V. E. Sudarikov. Camallanata, Rhabditata, Tylenchata, Trichocephalata and Dioctophymata and the distribution of parasitic nematode by hosts (Russian text). Izdatel'stvo Akad. Nauk U.R.S.S. 4, 927 pp. Moskva (Opredelitel paraz. nematod).

Slogteren, E. van. 1920. Bestrijding in de Bloembollstresk. Tijds. Plantenziekten 26: 126.

Slootweg, A. F. G. 1956. Rootrot of bulbs caused by *Pratylenchus* spp. and *Hoplolaimus* spp. Nematologica 1(3): 192–201.

Smart, G. C., Jr. 1959. *Ditylenchus destructor* from grass, dahlia and gladiolus infesting potato tubers. Plant Dis. Reptr. 43(11): 1212.

Smith, A. L., and A. L. Taylor. 1941. Nematode distribution in the 1940 regional cotton-wilt plots. Phytopathology 31(2): 771.

Smith, O. F. 1951. Biologic races of *Ditylenchus dipsaci* on alfalfa. Phytopathology 41: 189–190.

Southey, J. F. 1957. Observations on *Heterodera cacti* Filipjev and Stekhoven and *Meloidogyne* spp. on imported cactus plants with a list of new host records. Nematologica 2(1): 1–6.

Steinbuch, J. G. 1799. Das Grasälchen, *Vibrio agrostis*. Naturforscher 28: 233–259.

Steiner, G. 1914. Freilebende Nematoden aus der Schweiz. Arch. Hydrobiol. Planktonk. 9(2): 259–276, (3): 420–438.

———. 1925. The problem of host selection and host specialization of certain plant-infesting nemas and its application in the study of nemic pests. Phytopathology 15: 499–534.

———. 1927. *Tylenchus pratensis* and various other nemas attacking plants. Jour. Agr. Res. 35(11): 961–981.

———. 1931. On the status of the nemic genera *Aphelenchus* Bastian, *Pathoaphelenchus* Cobb, *Paraphelenchus* Micoletzky, *Parasitaphelenchus* Fuchs, *Isonchus* Cobb, and *Seineura* Fuchs. Jour. Wash. Acad. Sci. 21(18): 468–475.

———. 1931a. *Neotylenchus abulbosus* n. g., n. sp. (Tylenchidae: Nematoda) the causal agent of a new nematosis of various crop plants. Jour. Wash. Acad. Sci. 21(21): 536–538.

———. 1932. The successful transfer of *Aphelenchoides ritzema-bosi* from chrysanthemums to strawberry plants. Jour. Parasit. 19(1): 90.

———. 1932a. Annotations on the nomenclature of some plant parasitic nematodes. Jour. Wash. Acad. Sci. 22: 517–518.

———. 1933. The nematode *Cylindrogaster longistoma* (Stefanski) Goodey and its relationship. Jour. Parasit. 20: 66–68.

———. 1934. Observations on nematodes parasitic in tubers of the cinnamon-vine, *Dioscorea batatas*. Proc. Helminth. Soc. Wash. 1(1): 15–17.

———. 1935. *Anguillulina gallica* n. sp. living in the burls of an elm (*Ulmus* sp.) from France. Proc. Helminth. Soc. Wash. 2(1): 41–42.

———. 1936. *Anguillulina askenasyi* (Bütschli, 1873), a gall forming nematode parasite of the common fern moss, *Thuidium delicatulum* (L.) Hedw. Jour. Wash. Acad. Sci. 26(10): 410–414.

———. 1936a. Opuscula miscellanea nematologica, III. Proc. Helminth. Soc. Wash. 3(1): 16–21.

———. 1936b. Opuscula miscellanea nematologica, IV. Proc. Helminth. Soc. Wash. 3(2): 74–80.

Steiner, G. 1937. Opuscula miscellanea nematologica, V. Proc. Helminth. Soc. Wash. 4(1): 33–38.

———. 1940. Opuscula miscellanea nematologica, VIII. A new grass nematode, *Anguina australis* n. sp. Proc. Helminth. Soc. Wash. 7(1): 54–62.

———. 1941. Nematodes parasitic on and associated with roots of marigolds (*Tagetes* hybrids). Proc. Biol. Soc. Wash. 54: 31–34.

———. 1942. Opuscula miscellanea nematologica, IX. Proc. Helminth. Soc. Wash. 9(1): 32–38.

———. 1943. New nematodes associated with a disease of the papaya in Chile. Bol. dept. sanidad vegetal, Santiago 3(2): 95–116.

———. 1943a. *Pratylenchus scribneri* n. sp. In the more important diseases and insect pests of crops in Tennessee by C. D. Sherbakoff and W. W. Stanley. Tenn. Agr. Expt. Sta. Bull. 186, p. 69.

———. 1945. *Helicotylenchus*, a new genus of plant-parasitic nematodes and its relationship to *Rotylenchus* Filipjev. Proc. Helminth. Soc. Wash. 12(2): 24–38.

———. 1947. Some little known nematodes parasitic on roots. Phytopathology 37(6): 441.

———. 1949. Plant nematodes the grower should know. Proc. Soil Sci. Fla. (1942) 4-b: 72–117. Emended 1956 as Fla. State Dept. Agr. Bull. 131. 47 pp.

———. 1953. Changes in basic concepts of plant nematology. Plant Dis. Reptr. 37(4): 203–205.

———. 1953a. The problem of the taxon in the nematode genus *Ditylenchus* and its agricultural implications. Proc. Fourteenth Internat. Cong. Zool., Copenhagen.

——— and Edna M. Buhrer. 1932. A list of host plants attacked by *Tylenchus dipsaci*, the bulb or stem nema. Plant Dis. Reptr. 16(8): 76–85.

——— and ———. 1932a. The nonspecificity of the brown-ring symptoms in narcissus attacked by nematodes. Phytopathology 22(12): 927, 928.

——— and ———. 1933. The bulbous irises as hosts of *Tylenchus dipsaci*, the bulb or stem nema. Phytopathology 23(1): 103–105.

——— and ———. 1933a. The nematode *Tylenchus similis* Cobb, as a parasite of the tea plant (*Thea sinensis*, L.), its sexual dimorphism, and its nemic associates in the same host. Zeitschr. Parasitenk. 5(2): 412–420.

——— and ———. 1933b. Recent observations on diseases caused by nematodes. Plant Dis. Reptr. 17(14): 172–173.

——— and ———. 1934. *Aphelenchoides xylophilus* n. sp., a nematode associated with blue-stain and other fungi in timber. Jour. Agr. Res. 48(10): 949–951.

———, ———, and A. S. Rhodes. 1934. Giant galls caused by the root-knot nematode. Phytopathology 24(2): 161–163.

——— and B. O. Dodge. 1929. The bulb or stem nematode, *Tylenchus dipsaci* Kühn, as a pest of phlox. Jour. N.Y. Bot. Gard. 30: 177–184.

——— and Helen Heinley. 1922. The possibility of control of *Heterodera radicicola* and other plant-injurious nemas by means of predatory nemas, especially *Mononchus papillatus* Bastian. Jour. Wash. Acad. Sci. 12(16): 367–386.

——— and Rowena R. LeHew. 1933. *Hoplolaimus bradys* n. sp. (Tylenchidae: Nematoda) the cause of a disease of yams (*Dioscorea* sp.). Zool. Anz. 101(9/10): 259–264.

——— and C. E. Scott. 1935. A nematosis of *Amsinckia* caused by a new variety of *Anguillulina dipsaci*. Jour. Agr. Res. 49(12): 1087–1092.

Stewart, F. H. 1921. The anatomy and biology of the parasitic aphelenchi. Parasitology 13: 160–179.

Stift, A. 1912. Zur Geschichte der Rübennematoden. Öst.-ungar. Zeitschr. Zuckerind. u. Landwirts. 3: 417–498, Jahrg. 41.

Stiles, C. W., and A. Hassall. 1920. Index-catalog of medical and veterinary zoology. Roundworms. U.S. Public Health Service Hyg. Lab. Bull. 114. 886 pp.

Stone, G. E., and R. E. Smith. 1898. Nematode worms. Hatch. Expt. Sta., Mass. Agr. College, Bull. 65.

Strubell, A. 1888. Untersunchungen über den Bau und die Entwicklung des Rüben-Nematoden, *Heterodera schachtii* Schmidt. Bibliotheca Zool. 2: 1–52.

Suit, R. F., and H. W. Ford. 1950. Present status of spreading decline. Proc. Fla. State Hort. Soc. 63: 36–42.

——— and E. P. DuCharme. 1953. The burrowing nematode and other plant parasitic nematodes in relation to spreading decline of citrus. Plant Dis. Reptr. 37(7): 379–383.

Sylvén, N. 1936. Die natürliche Auslese im Dienste der Rotkleezüchtung. Züchter 8: 179–182.

Tarjan, A. C. 1952. The nematode genus *Hemicycliophora* deMan, 1921 (Criconematidae) with a description of a new plant parasitic species. Proc. Helminth. Soc. Wash. 19(2): 65–77.

———. 1953. Pathogenicity of some plant-parasitic nematodes from Florida soils, III. Growth of Chinese waterchestnut *Eleocharis dulcis* (Burm.) Henschel inoculated with *Dolichodorus heterocephalus* Cobb (Tylenchinae). Proc. Helminth. Soc. Wash. 20(2): 94–96.

———. 1957. An emended description of the marine nematode genus *Halenchus* Cobb, 1933 (Tylenchinae). Quart. Jour. Fla. Acad. Sci. 20(2): 121–125.

———. 1957a. Observations on *Ecphyadophora tenuissima* deMan, 1921. Nematologica 2(2): 152–158.

———. 1958. A new genus, *Pseudahalenchus* (Tylenchinae: Nematoda), with descriptions of two new species. Proc. Helminth. Soc. Wash. 25(1): 20–25.

———, B. F. Lownsberry, Jr., and W. O. Hawley. 1952. Pathogenicity of some plant-parasitic nematodes from Florida soils, I. The effect of *Dolichodorus heterocephalus* Cobb on celery. Phytopathology 42(3): 131, 132.

Taylor, A. L. 1935. A review of the fossil nematodes. Proc. Helminth. Soc. Wash. 2(1): 47–49.

———. 1936. The genera and species of the Criconematinae, a subfamily of the Anguillulinidae (Nematoda). Trans. Amer. Micr. Soc. 55(4): 391–421.

———. 1944. Root-knot on Shalil and Yunnan peach seedlings. Twenty-fourth Ann. Rept. Ga. Coastal Plains Expt. Sta. Bull. 40, p. 112.

———. 1957. Identification of cysts of the genus *Heterodera*. A manual of plant nematology for experiment station workers in the northeastern region. Cornell University, Ithaca, N.Y.

———, V. H. Dropkin, and G. C. Martin. 1955. Perineal patterns of root-knot nematodes. Phytopathology 45(1): 26–34.

——— and W. Q. Loegering. 1953. Nematodes associated with root lesions of Abaca. Turrialba 3: 8–15.

——— and C. W. McBeth. 1945. Tests on the susceptibility and resistance of several southern grasses to the root-knot nematode, *Heterodera marioni*. Proc. Helminth. Soc. Wash. 12(2): 41–44.

Taylor, A. L., et al. 1955. Root-knot nematode diseases. (Reactions of the accessions of the wild species of tomato to root-knot nematodes, *Meloidogyne* spp.) Ohio Agr. Expt. Sta. North Central Regional Publ. 51: 42–44.

Taylor, A. M. 1917. Black currant eelworm. Jour. Agr. Sci. 8: 927, 928.

Taylor, D. P., and W. R. Jenkins. 1957. Variation within the nematode genus *Pratylenchus*, with the description of *P. hexincixus*, n. sp. and *P. subpenetrans*, n. sp. Nematologica 2(2): 159–174.

Thomas, E. E. 1913. A preliminary report of a nematode observed on citrus roots and its possible relation with the mottled appearance of citrus trees. Calif. Agr. Expt. Sta. Cir. 85, pp. 1–14.

———. 1923. The citrus nematode, *Tylenchulus semipenetrans*. Univ. Calif. Agr. Expt. Sta. Tech. Paper 2.

Thorne, G. 1923. The length of the dormancy period of the sugarbeet nematode in Utah. U.S. Dept. Agr. Cir. 262.

———. 1924. Utah nemas of the genus *Mononchus*. Trans. Amer. Micr. Soc. 43(3): 157–171.

———. 1925. The genus *Acrobeles* von Linstow, 1877. Trans. Amer. Micr. Soc. 44(4): 171–210.

———. 1926. *Tylenchus balsamophilus*, a new plant parasitic nematode. Jour. Parasit. 12: 141–145.

———. 1927. The life history, habits and economic importance of some mononchs. Jour. Agr. Res. 34(3): 265–286.

———. 1928. Nematodes inhabiting the cysts of the sugarbeet nematode, *Heterodera schachtii* Schmidt. Jour. Agr. Res. 37: 571–575.

———. 1928a. *Heterodera punctata* n. sp., a nematode parasitic on wheat roots from Saskatchewan. Sci. Agr. 8(11): 707–710.

———. 1929. Nematodes from the summit of Longs Peak, Colorado. Trans. Amer. Micr. Soc. 48(2): 181–195.

———. 1930. Predaceous nemas of the genus *Nygolaimus* and a new genus, *Sectonema*. Jour. Agr. Res. 41(6): 445–466.

———. 1934. Some plant parasitic nemas, with descriptions of three new species. Jour. Agr. Res. 49(8): 755–769.

———. 1935. Nemic parasites and associates of the mountain pine beetle *(Dendroctonus monticolae)* in Utah. Jour. Agr. Res. 51(2): 131–144.

———. 1937. A revision of the nematode family Cephalobidae Chitwood and Chitwood, 1934. Proc. Helminth. Soc. Wash. 4(1): 1–16.

———. 1938. Notes on freeliving and plant-parasitic nematodes, IV. (1) *Panagrellus pycnus* n.g., n. sp. Proc. Helminth. Soc. Wash. 5(2): 64, 65.

———. 1939. A monograph of the nematodes of the superfamily Dorylaimoidea. Capita Zool. 8(5): 1–190.

———. 1941. Some nematodes of the family Tylenchidae which do not possess a valvular median esophageal bulb. Great Basin Naturalist 2(2): 37–85.

———. 1943. *Cacopaurus pestis* nov. gen. nov. spec. (Nematoda: Criconematinae), a destructive pest of the walnut, *Juglans regia* Linn. Proc. Helminth. Soc. Wash. 10(2): 78–83.

———. 1945. *Ditylenchus destructor* n. sp., the potato rot nematode, and *Ditylenchus dipsaci* (Kühn, 1857) Filipjev, 1936, the teasel nematode. Proc. Helminth. Soc. Wash. 12(2): 27–33.

———. 1948. Nematodes as a disturbance factor in greenhouse, plot and field experiments. Plant Dis. Reptr. 32(11): 473–475.

———. 1949. On the classification of the Tylenchida, new order (Nematoda: Phasmidia). Proc. Helminth. Soc. Wash. 16(2): 37–73.

Thorne, G. 1951. Diffusion patterns of soil fumigants. Proc. Helminth. Soc. Wash. 18(1): 18–24.

———. 1952. Control of the sugar beet nematode. U.S. Dept. Agr. Farmers' Bull. 2054.

———. 1955. Fifteen new species of the genus *Hemicycliophora* with an emended description of *H. typica* deMan (Tylenchida: Criconematidae). Proc. Helminth. Soc. Wash. 22(1): 1–16.

———. 1956. Effects of sugar beet root diffusates and extracts, and other substances, on the hatching of eggs from the cysts of the sugar beet nematode, *Heterodera schachtii* Schmidt. Jour. Amer. Soc. Sugar Beet Tech. 9(2): 139–145.

——— and M. W. Allen. 1944. *Nacobbus dorsalis* nov. gen. nov. spec. (Nematoda: Tylenchidae) producing galls on the roots of alfileria, *Erodium cicutarium* (L.) L'Her. Proc. Helminth. Soc. Wash. 11(1): 27–31.

——— and ———. 1950. *Paratylenchus hamatus* n. sp. and *Xiphinema index* n. sp. two nematodes associated with fig roots, with a note on *Paratylenchus anceps* Cobb. Proc. Helminth. Soc. Wash. 17(1): 27–35.

Thorne, G., and M. W. Allen. 1959. Variation in nematodes. Plant Pathology, Problems and Progress, pp. 412–418.

——— and M. L. Schuster. 1956. *Nacobbus batatiformis* n. sp. (Nematoda: Tylenchidae), producing galls on the roots of sugar beets and other plants. Proc. Helminth. Soc. Wash. 23(2): 128–134.

——— and Helen Heinley Swanger. 1936. A monograph of the nematode genera *Dorylaimus* Dujardin, *Aporcelaimus* n.g., *Dorylaimoides* n.g. and *Pungentus* n.g. Capita Zool. 6(4): 1–223.

Timm, R. W. 1955. The occurrence of *Aphelenchoides besseyi* Christie, 1942 in deep water paddy of East Pakistan. Pakistan Jour. Sci. 7(1): 47–49.

———. 1957. *Pterygorhabditis*, a remarkable new genus of soil nematodes. Nematologica 2(1): 68–71.

Todd, E. H., and J. G. Atkins. 1958. White tip disease of rice, I. Symptoms, laboratory culture of nematodes, and pathogenicity tests. Phytopathology 48(11): 632–637.

——— and ———. 1959. White tip disease of rice, II. Seed treatment studies. Phytopathology 49(4): 184–188.

Trail, J. W. H. 1881. Scottish galls. Scot. Nat. 6: 15–21.

Treub, M. 1885. Onderzoekingen ever sereh-zik Suikerreit. Meded. uit's Lands Plantentuin, 2: 1–39. Batavia, Java.

Triffitt, Marjorie J. 1929. Further observations on the morphology of *Heterodera schachtii*, with remarks on the bionomics of a strain attacking mangolds in Britain. Jour. Helminth. 7(3): 119–140.

———. 1930. On the bionomics of *Heterodera schachtii* on potatoes, with special reference to the influence of mustard on the escape of the larvae from the cysts. Jour. Helminth. 8(1): 19–48.

———. 1934. Experiments with the root excretions of grasses as a possible means of eliminating *Heterodera schachtii* from infected soil. Jour. Helminth. 12(1): 1–12.

Tyler, Jocelyn. 1933. Reproduction without males in aseptic root culture of the root-knot nematode. Hilgardia 7(10): 373–388.

———. 1941. Plants reported resistant or tolerant to root-knot nematode infestation. U.S. Dept. Agr. Misc. Publ. 406, 91 pp.

Van Gundy, S. D. 1957. The first report of a species of *Hemicycliophora* attacking citrus roots. Plant Dis. Reptr. 41(12): 1016–1018.

Van Gundy, S. D. 1958. The life history of the citrus nematode, *Tylenchulus semipenetrans*. Nematologica 3(4): 283–294.

———. 1959. The life history of *Hemicycliophora arenaria* Raski (Nematoda: Criconematidae). Proc. Helminth. Soc. Wash. 26(1): 67–72.

Van Weerdt, L. G. 1957. Studies on the biology of *Radopholus similis* (Cobb, 1893) Thorne, 1949, Part I. Plant Dis. Reptr. 41(10): 832–835.

———. 1958. Studies on the biology of *Radopholus similis* (Cobb, 1893) Thorne, 1949. Nematologica 3(3): 184–195.

Vecht, J. van der. 1950. Op planten parasiterende aaltjes. Reprint from De plagen van de cultuurgewassen in Indonesie, by L. G. E. Kalshoven.

———. 1953. The problem of the mentek disease of rice in Java. Landbouw (Djakarta, Java) 25(1–6): 45–130.

——— and B. H. H. Bergman. 1952. Studies on the nematode *Radopholus oryzae* (van Breda de Haan) Thorne and its influence on the growth of the rice plant. Contr. Gen. Agr. Res. Sta. Bogor, 131: 1–82.

Venkatarayn, S. V. 1932. "*Tylenchus* sp" forming galls on *Andropogon pertusus* Willd. Jour. Indian Bot. Soc. 11(3): 243–247.

Voigt, W. 1894. Neue Varietät des Rübennematoden, *Heterodera schachtii*. S. B. Niederrhein. Ges. Nat. u. Heilk., pp. 94–97.

Völk, J. 1950. Die Nematoden der Regenwürmer und aasbesuchunden Käfer. Zool. Jahrb. 79: 514–566.

Voss, W. 1930. Beiträge zur Kenntnis der Aelchenkrankheit der Chrysanthemum. Zeitschr. Parisitenk. 2(3): 310–356.

Wachek, F. 1955. Die entoparasitischen Tylenchiden. Parasit. Schriftenreihe 3: 1–119.

Wallace, H. R. 1955. Factors influencing the emergence of larvae from cysts of beet eelworm, *Heterodera schachtii* Schmidt. Jour. Helminth. 29(½): 3–16.

———. 1956. The emergence of larvae from the cysts of the beet eelworm, *Heterodera schachtii* Schmidt, in aqueous solutions of organic and inorganic substances. Ann. Appl. Biol. 44(2): 274–282.

———. 1959. Movement of eelworms, V. Observations on *Aphelenchoides ritzema-bosi* (Schwartz, 1912) Steiner, 1932 on florists' chrysanthemums. Ann. Appl. Biol. 47(2): 350–360.

Ware, M. W. 1925. A disease of wild white clover caused by the eelworm, *Tylenchus dipsaci*. Ann. Appl. Biol. 12: 113–119.

Watson, J. R., and H. E. Bratley, 1939. Root Knot Investigations. Agr. Expt. Sta. Univ. of Fla. Ann. Report, 94.

——— and C. C. Goff. 1937. Control of root-knot in Florida. Fla. Agr. Expt. Sta. Bull. 311.

Weber, H. J., and W. A. Orton. 1902. A cowpea resistant to root-knot (*Heterodera radicicola*). U.S. Dept. Agr. Bur. Plant Ind. Bull. 17(2): 23–38.

Weiss, H. B. 1923. The occurrence of the devastating nematode of Europe, *Tylenchus dipsaci* Kühn, in New Jersey. N.J. Dept. Agr. Bur. Stat. Inspect. Cir. 64.

Welsford, E. J. 1917. Investigations of the bulb rot of narcissus. Ann. Appl. Biol. 4: 36–46.

Whitehead, A. G. 1959. *Nothanguina cecidoplastes* n. com. syn. *Anguina cecidoplastes* (Goodey, 1934) Filipjev, 1936. (Nothotylenchinae: Tylenchida). Nematologica 4(1): 70–75.

Wieser, W. 1953. On the structure of the cyst wall in four species of *Heterodera*. Statens Växtskyddsanstalt, Meddelande 65: 1–15.

Wieser, W. 1956. The attractiveness of plants to larvae of root-knot nematodes, II. The effect of excised bean, eggplant, and soybean roots on *Meloidogyne hapla.* Proc. Helminth. Soc. Wash. 23(1): 59–64.

Wilson, C. 1948. Root-knot nematodes on peanuts in Alabama. U.S. Dept. Agr. Plant Dis. Reptr. 32: 443.

Wilson, G. F. 1930. Further investigations of the eelworm disease of phloxes. Jour. Roy. Hort. Soc. 45(1): 88–100.

Winslow, R. D. 1954. Provisional lists of host plants of some root eelworms (*Heterodera* spp.). Ann. Appl. Biol. 41(4): 591–605.

Winstead, N. N., C. B. Skotland, and J. N. Sasser. 1955. Soybean cyst nematode in North Carolina. Plant Dis. Reptr. 39(1): 9–11.

Woolenweber, H. 1923. Krankheiten und Beschädigungen der Kartoffel. Arb. Forsch. Inst. Kartoff. 7: 52.

———. 1924. Zur Kenntnis der Kartoffel-Heteroderen. Illustrierte Landwirtschaftliche Zeitung 12: 100, 101.

Yokoo, T. 1948. *Aphelenchoides oryzae* Yokoo n. sp., a nematode parasite of rice. Ann. Phytopath. Soc. Japan. 13: 40–43.

Yoshii, H. 1946. Studies on the rice nematode. Annual report on the rice diseases to the Ministry of Agriculture for the year 1945. Laboratory of Plant Pathology, Kyushu University.

Young, T. W. 1954. An incubation method for collecting migratory endoparasitic nematodes. Plant Dis. Reptr. 38(11): 794, 795.

Zimmermann, A. 1898. De nematoden der koffiewortels. Meded. pl. Tuin. Batavia 27(1): 16–41.

Zimmermann, H. 1914. Bericht der Haupstelle für Pflanzenschutz in Mecklenburg-Schwerin und Mecklenburg-Strelitz für das Jahr 1914. Mitt. Landw. Vers. Sta. Rostock, 73–75.

Zopf, W. 1888. Zur Kenntnis der Infektionskrankheiten niederer Thiere und Pflanzen. Nova Acta Acad. Leop. Carol. 42: 313–341.

Index

Numbers in **boldface** type refer to pages on which there are illustrations